Humankind Emerging

Humankind Emerging

Seventh Edition

BERNARD G. CAMPBELL

JAMES D. LOY
University of Rhode Island

HarperCollinsCollegePublishers

Senior Editor: Alan McClare
Developmental Editor: Michael Kimball
Project Editor: Marina Vaynshteyn
Text Designer/Design Manager: Alice Fernandes-Brown
Art Studio: Fineline Illustrations, inc.
Timeline Makeup: Paul Lacy
Cover Designer: Alice Fernandes-Brown
Cover Photo: Magdalenian cave painting (15,000 B.C.) from © Ronald
  Sheridan/Ancient Art & Architecture Collection
Photo Researcher: Mira Schachne
Electronic Production Manager: Alexandra Odulak
Manufacturing Manager: Willie Lane
Electronic Page Makeup: I.C.C. Utah
Printer and Binder: R R Donnelley & Sons Company
Cover Printer: The Lehigh Press, Inc.
Insert Printer: The Lehigh Press, Inc.

This volume has been adapted in part from materials published by Time-Life Books in two series: The
Emergence of Man *and* The LIFE Nature Library

*For permission to use copyrighted material, grateful acknowledgment is made to the copyright holders on pages
577–579, which are hereby made part of this copyright page.*

Humankind Emerging, Seventh Edition

Copyright © 1996 by HarperCollins College Publishers

Library of Congress Cataloging-in-Publication Data

Humankind Emerging / Bernard G. Campbell, James D. Loy,—7th ed.
  p. cm.
  "Adapted in part from materials published by Time-Life Books in two series:
    The emergence of man and The Life nature Library."
  Includes bibliographical references and index.
  ISBN 0-673-52364-0
  1. Human evolution. 2. Man, Prehistoric 3. Physical anthropology.
  I. Campbell, Bernard Grant II. Loy, James.
  GN281.h85 1995
  573.2—dc20   95-11686
                                                         CIP

96 97 98 9 8 7 6 5 4 3 2

Contents

Preface xiii
Introduction xv

PART I EVOLUTION

Chapter 1 The Search for Human Origins 2

Overview 3

Early Theories of Human Origins 3

Early Naturalists 5

*John Ray, Isaac de la Peyrère 5   J. F. Esper, John Frere, P. C. Schmerling 5
Jacques Boucher de Perthes 6   Problems of Early Investigators: J. MacEnery 6
Comte de Buffon 7   James Hutton 7   Georges Cuvier, Alexandre Brongniart,
William Smith 9   Charles Lyell 10   Lamarck 10   Charles Darwin 11*

Theory of Evolution 14

Modern Study of Human Origins 19

Paleoanthropology in Progress 21

*Scarcity of Human Fossils 21   Fossil Sites 22   Relative Dating Methods:
Earth and Fossils 23   Chronometric Dating Methods: Atomic Physics 25
Chronometric Dating Methods: Molecular Clocks 29   Modern Excavations 31*

Summary 32

Review Questions 33

Postscript 34

Chapter 2 Evolutionary Mechanisms: I. The Riddle of Heredity 35

Overview 36

Early Views on Heredity 36

Work of Gregor Mendel 37

*First Experiments 38   Experiments Using Many Characteristics 42
Principles of Segregation and Independent Assortment 43*

v

Mendel's Work Rediscovered 45
  De Vries's Work on the Evening Primrose 46
Mutation and Natural Selection 47
  The Case of Mimicry 47   Mathematical Evidence 48   Role of Mutations 49
Summary 50
Review Questions 50
Postscript 50

Chapter 3 Evolutionary Mechanisms: II. Genes and Populations 52

Overview 53
Units of Heredity 53
  *Chromosomes 53   Morgan's Work on Fruit Flies 55   Genes 57   Mutations 63
  Meiosis and Crossing-over 63*
Populations and Species 66
  *Genotype and Gene Pool 66   Gene Flow, Speciation, the Founder Effect,
  and Genetic Drift 66   Polymorphism and Genetic Load 73   Hardy-Weinberg
  Theorem 76   Sexual Selection 78   Measures of Fitness 80   Extinction 81*
Summary 82
Review Questions 82
Postscript 83

PART II   THE ORIGIN OF HUMANKIND

Chapter 4 Humans Among the Primates 86

Overview 87
Names and Classifications 87
The Primates 90
  Prosimians 93   Anthropoids 101   Changes in Anatomy 108
Human Characteristics 110
  *Bipedalism 110   Vision 113   Hands 115   The Brain 116   Language and
  Speech 118   Cultural Adaptation 119*
Summary 120
Review Questions 120
Postscript 121

Chapter 5 The Behavior of Living Primates 123

Overview 124
Studying Primates 124
  Early Work 125   Recent Studies 127
Basis of Social Organization 127
  *Learning in Childhood 128   The Dominance Hierarchy 132   Sex and Status 134
  Sexual Physiology and Behavior 136   Sexual Selection Among Primates 138
  Grooming and Social Interaction 139*

Territory and Ecology 141

Socioecology of East African Baboons 144   Primate Feeding Strategies 145

The Apes 146

*Asiatic Apes: Gibbons and the Orangutan 146   Gorillas: Research of Fossey 148
Goodall and the Gombe Chimpanzees 153   Nishida and the Mahale Mountain
Chimpanzees 154   The Chimpanzee as Hunter 156   The First Herbalists? 157
Tools and Weapons 158   Murder and War 160   Chimpanzee Politics 161
Bonobos: The Best Evolutionary Model for Early Hominids? 162
Speculations About Ape-Human Common Ancestors 165*

Summary 166

Review Questions 167

Postscript 167

Chapter 6 Apes and Other Ancestors: Prehominid Evolution   170

Overview 171

The Earliest Primates 171

Undoubted Primate Fossils 175

The First Higher Primates 176

*Oligocene Anthropoids 178   Evolution of the New World Monkeys 181
The Miocene: Apes at Last 182   Apes to Hominids: The Anatomical Criteria 187*

Summary 193

Review Questions 194

Postscript 194

Chapter 7 The Transvaal Hominids   197

Overview 198

Dart's Discovery of the Taung Skull (1924) 198

*The Evidence and Dart's Interpretation 200   Dart's Claims Dismissed 201
Dentition of Taung 203*

Discoveries of Robert Broom 205

*A Skull from Sterkfontein (1936) 205   Paranthropus robustus at Kromdraai 206
Age of Australopithecus africanus 209   Further Discoveries at
Sterkfontein (1947) 210   Assessing Australopithecus and Paranthropus 213*

Fossils and Artifacts 214

*Australopithecus at Makapansgat 214   Pebble Tools at Sterkfontein 215
New Finds at Swartkrans 217*

Summary 218

Review Questions 218

Postscript 218

Chapter 8 The Great Savanna   221

Overview 222

Discoveries at Olduvai 222

*Discovery of Paranthropus boisei (1959) 224   Age of P. boisei 226   Discovery
of Homo habilis (1960–1964) 227   Classifying Homo habilis 228   The
Question of Brain Size 229*

Omo, Turkana, Hadar, Laetoli, and Aramis   231

*Omo Hominids (1967–1974) 232   Robust Hominids at Koobi Fora (1969–1976) 233
A New Robust Australopithecine from West Turkana (1985) 236   Evidence of
Homo at Koobi Fora 237   Discoveries at Hadar (1973–1976) 240   Discoveries at
Laetoli (1974–1977) and the Awash (1981) 248   Oldest Hominid (?) Found at
Aramis, Ethiopia (1992–1993) 251   Early Stone-Tool Evidence 255*

Lifestyles of the Early Hominids   256

Evolutionary Relationships Among the Early Hominids   259

Summary   260

Review Questions   261

Postscript   261

Late-Breaking Discoveries (Summer 1995) 262

Chapter 9 The Evolution of Hominid Behavior   264

Overview   265

Hominid Locomotion   265

*From the Trees to the Ground 265   Tool Use and Bipedalism 266   Energy
Efficiency and Bipedalism 267   Body Temperature and Bipedalism 268
Reproduction and Bipedalism 269   The Relationship of Bipedalism to Other
Hominid Traits 271*

Early Technology   274

*Earliest Stone Industry: The Oldowan 275   Occupation Levels at Olduvai
Gorge 280*

Summary   284

Review Questions   285

Postscript   286

PART III   THE EVOLUTION OF HUMANKIND

Chapter 10 Discovering *Homo erectus*   290

Overview   291

Work of Eugene Dubois   292

*Nineteenth-Century Background 292   Dubois's Search for the Missing Link 293
Discovery of Pithecanthropus (1891) 296   Java Controversy 299*

Twentieth-Century Discoveries   301

*Search for Human Fossils in China 301   Sinanthropus Discovered (1927) 302
Intensive Work at Zhoukoudian 304   Assessment of Sinanthropus 306
Culture at Zhoukoudian 307   Relationship of Pithecanthropus
and Sinanthropus 308   Fate of the Java and Beijing Fossils 309*

***Homo erectus* Fossils from Africa and Europe   312**

The Anatomy of *Homo erectus*   314

Anatomical Evidence of Speech and Language 316

***Homo erectus* Migrations and New Dates from Java   318**

Summary   320

Review Questions   320

Postscript   321

Chapter 11 Environment and Technology of *Homo erectus*   324

Overview   325

***Homo erectus*: New Questions About an Old Species**   325

Stone Tools   328
    Core and Flake Tools 329

Shelter and Fire   336

Subsistence Patterns and Diet   339

Summary   341

Review Questions   343

Postscript   343

Chapter 12 Hunting, Gathering, and the Evolution of Society   347

Overview   348

Behavioral Speculations   348

The Archaeology of the Hunters   349
    Hunter's Diet 350   *Skin Adaptation* 350   *Hunting and Intelligence* 352

Beginnings of Hunting   352
    Persistence Hunting 353   *Stalking, Driving, and Ambush* 353

New Social Developments   355
    The Evolution of Male and Female Roles 355   *Families and Bands* 358
    Incest Taboo 359   *Exogamy* 360   *Home Base* 360

Intraspecies Aggression   361
    Theories of Aggression 361   *Aggression Among* **Homo erectus** 361

Summary   363

Review Questions   364

Postscript   364

Chapter 13 The Evolution of Language and the Brain   366

Overview   367

Ways of Communicating   367
    Early Theories on the Origins of Speech 367   *Communication Among Animals* 368
    Limbic and Nonlimbic Communication 372   *Nature of Language* 374

Ability to Speak   374
    Talking Apes? 374   *The Pharynx* 376   *Centers of Vocal Communication:*
    The Cerebral Cortex 378   *Limbic System* 378

Evolution of Speech   381
    Phonation: Lieberman and Crelin 382   *Articulation: Linda Duchin* 383
    Krantz: The Brain of **Homo erectus** 383   *The Importance of*
    Rudimentary Speech 384

The Brain   385
    Humans Among Mammals 385   *Brains, Minds, and Radiators* 388

Summary   392

Review Questions   393

Postscript 451

PART IV MODERN HUMANITY

Chapter 14 Discovery of Neandertals and Their Contemporaries 396

Overview 397

First View of Neandertals 397

First Discovery (1856) 398   Missing Links in the Chain of Being 398
Homo neanderthalensis? 399   Discoveries at Spy (1886) 401   La Chapelle-
aux-Saints (1908) and Other Finds 402   Boule's Reconstruction (1911–1913) 401

Discovery of Archaic *Homo sapiens* Beyond Europe 406

African Fossils 406   Asian Fossils 408   Discoveries from Israel 409
Pre-Neandertal Archaics from Europe: Swanscombe and Steinheim Skulls
(1933–1936) 411   Other European Archaics 412

An Assessment of Archaic *Homo sapiens* 413

*Species and Speciation 416   Species Model of Archaic **Homo sapiens** 418*

Summary 421

Review Questions 421

Postscript 421

Chapter 15 Archaic *Homo sapiens:* Culture and Environments 424

Overview 425

Range and Adaptations of Archaic *Homo sapiens* 425

Evidence of Adaptations 426   Stone Industries 426   Prepared Tortoise Core:
Levallois Technique 427

The Penultimate Pleistocene Glacial Cycle 428

Changes Around the World 429   Stimulus to Intelligence and Ingenuity 430
Neandertal Cranial Capacity and Intelligence 430

The Ice Sheets Return 431

Sunlight and Skin Color 433   Disk-Core Technique: The Mousterian Industry 435
Non-Mousterian Industries 437   Expansion and Adaptations 437

Rituals and Art 440

Hunting Rites and Magic 440   Bear Cult 441   Beginnings of Art? 442

Death and Burial 443

Evidence of Burial Customs 443   La Ferrassie (1912–1934) 444   Middle
Eastern and Asian Burials 445   The Old and the Handicapped 447   Evidence
of Violence 448   Evidence of Cannibalism? 448

Summary 450

Review Questions 451

Postscript 451

Chapter 16 The Final Transformation 454

Overview 455

First Modern People 455

Discovery in the Dordogne (1868) 455   Characteristics of Anatomically
Modern People 458

Fate of Archaic *Homo sapiens* 459

Sequence of Tools 459   Flakes and Blades 460   Aurignacian and Chatelperronian Industries 461   Fossil Record 462   Anatomical Comparison: Archaic and Modern People 463   The Regional-Continuity Model 464   The Rapid-Replacement Model 467

The Biological and Cultural Transition 472

Pilbeam's Hypothesis 473   The Appearance of the Chin 474   Transition Completed 475

A New Breed 475

Variability 475   Advantages of the Large Gene Pool 476

New Lands 477

The Americas 478   Australia 478   Diet and Hunting 480

Summary 482

Review Questions 483

Postscript 483

Chapter 17 Technology, Magic, and Art 486

Overview 487

An End to Wandering 487

A New Lifestyle 487   Mastery of Fire 488   Solutrean Laurel Leaves 490 Tool Specialization 491   Hunter Par Excellence 493   Spear Throwers and Points 494   Bow and Arrow 496   Fishing Gear 496   Sedentary Life and Sewn Clothing 497

Art and Ritual 498

Cave Art 498   Painting and Hunting Magic 499   Art and Fertility 502 Spectacular New Painted Cave Found in Southern France (1994) 505   Sculpture and Ceramics 506   Female Figurines 506   Burial Customs and Rites 509 Synthesizing Art, Ritual, and Religion in the Upper Paleolithic 511

Summary 512

Review Questions 512

Postscript 513

Chapter 18 The Human Condition 515

Overview 516

The Story of Humankind 516

Environmental History and Adaptation 517   Altruism and Bioaltruism 518 Cultural History 520   Domestication of Plants and Animals 521 Civilization 523

Human Variability 526

Anatomical Traits 526   Physiological Traits 530   Blood Groups 531 Blood Groups and Disease 534

The Question of Race 535

Biological Races 535   Ethnic and Other Social Groups 541

CONTENTS

Challenges for the Future   542
>   *Population and Evolutionary Success 542*   *Limits to Growth 543*   *Gaining Control over Our Evolution 545*

Summary   547

Review Questions   547

Postscript   547

Glossary   549
Selected Bibliography   567
Acknowledgments   577
Index   581

Preface

Humankind Emerging, first published in 1976, is one of the longest-running anthropology texts, and the time has come to give both the structure and the contents of the book a very thorough review. In preparing this seventh edition, I am fortunate in having found an excellent collaborator in James Loy, professor of anthropology at the University of Rhode Island. James Loy is a distinguished primatologist and, as such, has been able to add an extra dimension to the text. Perhaps more important, he is also an experienced teacher who has used the text in his classes for many years and is therefore in a strong position to bring about substantial improvements in the book.

As a result we have taken the book to pieces and put it back together again in a way that has made the first introductory chapters more logical in their layout. We have continued to do everything possible to maintain the book's value for introductory anthropology, physical anthropology, and human evolution courses. The book treats all the subdisciplines and relatives of physical anthropology, such as genetics, variation and adaptation, and the behavior of nonhuman primates. The main focus of the book, however, is on paleoanthropology, the science that fits together fossil and cultural evidence of human evolution into a coherent statement. Through the book's 18 chapters, the reader learns what we know of how, when, and where we came to exist. The investigation of our past is exciting, and *Humankind Emerging* conveys this excitement to students who are studying physical anthropology for the first time.

Outdated material has been removed and some sections have been simplified or reduced in length. This seventh edition has been thoroughly updated, and new research has been added. Important additions and changes include:

- Information on the newest hominid species, *Australopithecus (Ardipithecus?) ramidus* and *Australopithecus anamensis*

- An updated treatment of the geographic spread of *Homo erectus* taking into account the new dates from Java

- A revised treatment of diversity in modern humans that argues against race as a biological concept

- An expanded treatment of genetics, including updated information on the structure of DNA, protein synthesis, noncoding DNA sequences, meiosis, and genetic drift

- Updated information on primate behavior, including a new section on bonobos and speculations on the characteristics of ape–human common ancestors

♦ A fully revised chapter on prehominid evolution, including information on *Eosimias* and other recently discovered Chinese fossils, the oligopithecines from Egypt, and the distinction between "dental" and "locomotor" apes

♦ A discussion of the radiator theory of brain evolution

♦ A description of the 300,000-year-old Neandertals from Sima de los Huesos (Sierra de Atapuerca) in northern Spain

♦ An expanded discussion of the regional-continuity and rapid-replacement models of the evolution of anatomically modern humans

♦ New views on the production and meaning of Upper Paleolithic art and information on the newly discovered painted cave of La Grotte Chauvet (France)

As in previous editions, the extensive illustrations provide students with important visual supplements for learning physical anthropology. To this end, there are 70 new photos, figures, drawings, and tables.

The other pedagogical features have also been thoroughly revised and extended. There is now an Overview at the beginning of each chapter, describing the chapter contents and listing important topics and concepts. Concise data summaries and useful supplementary information are presented in boxes. Each chapter ends with review questions that will be useful as a study guide for students and as stimulation for classroom discussion. Finally, a Postscript follows each chapter and briefly touches on an interesting supplementary topic. There is also a running glossary, as well as an end-of-book glossary, that makes it easier for the reader to understand and remember technical terms. Finally, we have added two full-color photo essays to increase the book's appeal: one of the living apes and one of fossil hominids.

Humankind Emerging continues to benefit from material in Time-Life Books' *Emergence of Man* series and *The Life Nature Library*, from which the text and illustrations were originally developed. My thanks go to the authors, editors, and consultants who worked on this volume, especially copy editor Margaret Ritchie, as well as to many of the people on the HarperCollins staff, including Michael Kimball, Margaret Loftus, Jeffrey Allen, Arthur Pomponio, and Marina Vaynshteyn. Teachers and students who used the early editions have provided constructive suggestions for change. Many friends and colleagues were generous with their time and comments. Several anthropologists helped especially by sharing their thoughts in careful and detailed reviews. My special thanks to Professor Evelyn J. Bowers-Bienkowski; Professor Bruce La Brack, University of the Pacific; Professor Carol Lauer, Rollins College; Professor Lorena Madrigal, University of South Florida; Richard A. Nisbett, Iowa State University of Science and Technology; Professor Rene Peron, Santa Rosa Junior College; Professor Dennis O'Rourke, University of Utah; Professor Jeffrey H. Schwartz, University of Pittsburgh; Professor Liza Shapiro, University of Texas—Austin; and Professor B. Jill Smith, University of South Dakota.

Finally, I would like to thank Susan Campbell, whose companionship and love sustain me and whose help is indispensable; and Alan McClare, my editor at HarperCollins, for his continuing and enthusiastic support. I owe a great deal to the painstaking research and lively writing style of my collaborator James Loy. His contribution has made this new edition a landmark in the book's history.

Bernard G. Campbell

Introduction

Know then thyself, presume not God to scan;
The proper study of mankind is man.
Placed on this isthmus in a middle state,
A being darkly wise, and rudely great:
With too much knowledge for the sceptic side,
With too much weakness for the Stoic's pride,
He hangs between; in doubt to act or rest;
In doubt to deem himself a God, or beast;
In doubt his mind or body to prefer;
Born but to die; and reas'ning but to err;
Alike in ignorance, his reason such,
Whether he thinks too little or too much;
Chaos of Thought and Passion, all confused;
Still by himself abused, or disabused;
Created half to rise, and half to fall;
Great Lord of all things, yet a prey to all;
Sole judge of truth, in endless error hurled;
The glory, jest, and riddle of the world!

ALEXANDER POPE, 1688–1744.
Essay on Man, Ep. II, 1, 1–18.

These profound and brilliant lines by the English poet and satirist Alexander Pope describe the paradox of human nature. Throughout history, people have been puzzled and exasperated by humankind's strange duality—half animal, half angel—and much of religious and philosophical teaching has been an attempt to understand and integrate these two sides of our being. Neither priest nor philosopher has offered us an explanation that has proved either intellectually satisfactory or (in modern jargon) operationally effective. The writings of the wise throughout the ages have not enabled most of us to come to terms with our dual nature, however much we may have thought about these things or faced the moral dilemmas that are our inheritance. On the one hand, we carry the marks and needs of an animal, but on the other hand, we find ourselves alienated and unsure in the natural world and in the face of our own biology. In our imagination, we travel far beyond the bounds of our own environment and our biological nature, and yet we still feel rooted to it in a way that seems to constrict the highest reaches of our humanity. Our forces tend to be ranged opposite each other like the poles, and we find ourselves torn between them, caught in a conflict that has been cruelly sharpened by the demands of every culture in every age.

Humanity has, quite logically, looked to the past to explain the present and in so doing has developed mythological accounts of human origins. In the Judeo-Christian religions our duality is explained by a story about a stern God, who placed a perfect man and a perfect woman in paradise and then expelled them from it when they disobeyed His commands. This story of humankind's fall from perfection has been used to account for the darker side of human nature.

Today we have a different story to explain our duality. This story began to be written with the work of the Scottish geologist James Hutton, who demonstrated in 1795 that the world was vastly older than had previously been believed. As this remarkable scientific deduction became generally accepted, humanity's short past was stretched a thousandfold, and to the future, present, and immediate past of the historical period was added prehistory. Understanding this new dimension of human history has become a major requirement for understanding our present.

Humankind Emerging is about this new dimension. It recounts the extraordinary story of the discovery of, and the evidence for, humanity's long past. It reveals to us the nature of our distant ancestors, who began the long journey from the African forests to today's modern cities. It brings prehistory to bear upon present-day human nature and thus gives us an entirely new way of approaching and understanding ourselves. The evolutionary perspective, which we owe to the genius of Charles Darwin and Alfred Russel Wallace, throws light not only on the origin of our humanity but on the darker side of our nature. But that is not all: this perspective also shows us the integrated and dynamic evolution of both aspects and their essentially interlocking relationship. The evolutionary perspective gives us profound insights into human nature and shows us that its duality arises not from two warring halves but from two interdependent aspects of an integrated whole—or what should and could be an integrated whole if we saw ourselves as we truly are, instead of as we have mistakenly believed ourselves to be.

This new view of human nature is just one small part of the revolution in knowledge and understanding brought about by the work of Charles Darwin and his successors. Our past has created us and influences or determines every part of our lives. Our present condition is a consequence not just of our individual life histories, important though they may be, but of the whole history of the human species. We are, in this sense, a product both of our childhood and of our prehistory.

The theory of evolution by natural selection has now been developed over more than a century as a result of an enormous amount of painstaking research. The evidence that living organisms have evolved over many millions of years is today very strong and convincing. Science builds up such hypotheses or theories on the basis of a vast range of accumulated evidence derived from experiment and observation. Each new piece of evidence has corroborated the central theory. No evidence currently known either falsifies or undermines the theory of organic evolution by natural selection.

Creationism (misnamed "creation-science"), which posits the separate creation of every species, is based on *belief*—a system of belief developed without a scientific assessment of evidence. It is a modern version of traditional beliefs that is based on the Book of Genesis. It claims that the earth and the universe are only 6,000 to 10,000 years old; that the present physical form of the earth can be explained by "catastrophism," including a worldwide flood that covered the highest mountains; and that all living organisms, including humans, were created at one time, essentially in the form in which we find them today. To any person who has read widely, traveled, and observed the earth and its creatures, these ideas are incredible. More than 100 years of objective observation and research show them to have no foundation. Only by selecting a very limited range of evidence can any sort of case be made for creationism. It is therefore not a scientific theory but a statement of religious belief, which for support draws on the biblical texts and the work of a few biologists whose work can be manipulated to clothe the belief in pseudoscience.

The theory of evolution and a belief in special creation are not rival explanations of organic life that have comparable status as scientific hypotheses; they are quite distinct approaches to the problem of the origin of species.

Although it was seen in the past century as a devastating threat to fundamentalist religious belief, the theory of evolution does not in any way disprove the existence of God—nor is that its purpose. It merely describes the mode in which the production of living species occurred. We are beginning to understand the mechanics of this process of species production: it is no less miraculous, no less full of wonder. As Charles Darwin wrote on the last page of *On the Origin of Species:*

> There is a grandeur in this view of life, with its several powers, having been originally breathed into a few forms or into one; and that . . . from so simple a beginning endless forms most beautiful and most wonderful have been, and are being, evolved.

EVOLUTION

CHAPTER

1

The Search for Human Origins

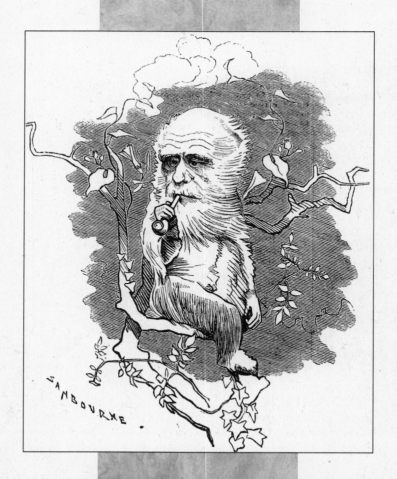

A nineteenth-century caricature of
Charles Darwin as a monkey.

I would not be ashamed to have a monkey for my ancestor, but I
would be ashamed to be connected with a man who used great gifts
to obscure the truth.
THOMAS HENRY HUXLEY, 1825–1895. *Defending Darwin's theory against
the attack of Bishop Samuel Wilberforce.*

OVERVIEW

Modern physical anthropologists pursue the search for human origins within the Western scientific tradition, and some knowledge of that tradition is necessary to understand current theories and conclusions. Therefore this chapter opens with a brief account of the beginnings of natural history, the concept of "deep time" within the discipline of geology, and evolutionary theory as developed by Charles Darwin and A. R. Wallace. As the concept of evolutionary development throughout a long earth history began to be accepted, the importance of fossils as evidence of extinct life forms came to be appreciated. Accordingly, for the past two centuries, investigators have searched for the fossils of humans' ancestors; this search continues to be the focal point of modern paleoanthropology. In anticipation of the fossil information to come, therefore, after the historical background we jump forward in time to describe how today's anthropologists work with a variety of specialists to locate and date fossils. The chapter ends with a discussion of the contribution of molecular studies to our understanding of human evolution. Important concepts in the chapter include catastrophism, uniformitarianism, deep time, fossilization, evolution, natural selection, paleoanthropology, absolute and relative dating techniques, and molecular clocks.

EARLY THEORIES OF HUMAN ORIGINS

Where did humans come from? The question of our origin has preoccupied human thought for thousands, conceivably for tens of thousands, of years. It is responsible for numerous myths found throughout the world among all human societies, from the smallest tribes to members of the great international religions. Each myth seems to be an explanation of the creation of the earth and its people, its plants, and its animals. Many of these explanations are exceedingly interesting and beautiful, but today much of their detail is no longer regarded as strictly factual. Instead, they are interpreted as reflections of a yearning to fathom mysteries not understood, and they are seen as poetic attempts to construct a kind of theological prehistory to satisfy people's curiosity and their need for meaning.

The two stories of creation told in the Bible (Genesis 1 and 2) are a good case in point (Figure 1–1). Although many Fundamentalists take them literally, most people do not—particularly if they have read extensively in science. Their sweeping concepts are interpreted today by most modern Christians and Jews as symbolic of the spirit and majesty of God. Today the evidence seems unavoidable that the world was not created in six days as the Bible says it was, and this discrepancy no longer troubles most devout people. Still, old ideas die hard; the belief in the *special creation* by God of the entire earth, its animals and plants, at the beginning

FIGURE 1–1 A woodcut from Schedel's *World Chronicle of 1493* depicting God's creation of woman from Adam's rib as told in Genesis.

of time, is still powerfully held by many people. There are men and women in the United States today who believe that the earth is flat.

Three hundred years ago most self-respecting citizens took the Bible literally. Hell was a fiery place beneath their feet; heaven was above them. In the year 1650, Archbishop James Ussher of Armagh, Ireland, making careful calculations based partly on biblical references, determined that the year of creation was 4004 B.C. Subsequently this date was inserted in the margins of authorized versions of the Bible, and before long it came to acquire the infallibility of Scripture itself. At about the same time, another cleric, James Lightfoot, Vice-chancellor of Cambridge University, working independently of Ussher, came up with the exact day and time: the moment of creation was 9 A.M. on October 23.

The Bible also dictated explanations of odd discoveries from within the earth. Along with the shells, petrified wood, and other ancient objects that people had been digging from the earth over the years were some curious things strangely resembling the bones of animals. Though a few authorities held that these objects had been molded into familiar forms by Satan to deceive humankind, the generally accepted notion was that these fossils had been formed by natural forces in chance imitation of life.

EARLY NATURALISTS

John Ray, Isaac de la Peyrère

The Reverend John Ray (1627–1705), a Cambridge University lecturer and a great naturalist, recognized that some of the fossilized shells he collected in the mountains were exactly like other shells he gathered on the seashore. The landlocked fossils were obviously the remains of fish and shellfish that must have lived in the ocean deeps. To account for the presence of marine fossils in the mountains, Ray resorted to ingenious interpretations of Old Testament earth history. He concluded after much study that the fossils had been washed up to their places of deposit when the Bible's 40 days and 40 nights of unceasing deluge filled the reservoirs of the world and caused the "Fountains of the Great Deep" to break forth. In the tremendous surge that overflowed the globe, he reasoned, the fish and other creatures of the sea had simply been swept up rivers and carried through underground streams, right into the high mountains.

In these early days of prehistoric studies, there was no body of tested scientific knowledge, and beyond a rare genius like Ray, Galileo, or Isaac Newton, there were few active scientists. The individuals who were interested in exploring for and collecting such things as stones and bones were usually antiquarians motivated by their own curiosity. In the seventeenth century one such person, a Frenchman named Isaac de la Peyrère (1594–1676), studied a large collection of oddly chipped stones gathered in the French countryside. He then had the courage to publish a book suggesting that these stones had been shaped by primitive people who had lived before the time of Adam. His book was burned publicly in 1655.

J. F. Esper, John Frere, P. C. Schmerling

But odd-shaped stones continued to turn up. So did strangely shaped bones. Gradually a few skeptical people began to realize that the earth had been inhabited at one time by a great number of creatures that no longer existed: huge mammoths, woolly rhinoceroses, saber-toothed tigers. More digging produced more puzzles. In 1771 human bones were found in association with the remains of extinct cave bears at a site in Germany; these bones suggested not only ancient animals but ancient people, too. Their finder, Johann Friedrich Esper (1732–1781), was flabbergasted. "Did they belong to a Druid, or to an Antediluvian, or to a Mortal Man of more recent times?" he wrote. He would not face the logical answer and concluded that the human and animal fragments must have come together by chance.

Others guessed rightly but could not get a hearing. In 1797 John Frere (1740–1807) found unfamiliar stone tools in the same beds with the remains of extinct animals at Hoxne, England. He recognized that they must have been made in "a very remote period indeed; even beyond that of the present world." Working in Belgian caves in 1830, P. C. Schmerling (1791–1836) found many stone artifacts associated with the bones of long-since-vanished rhinoceroses and mammoths, and in addition he uncovered two human skulls. He, too, recognized the contemporaneity of the human and animal bones. These astonishing finds went generally unnoticed.

Jacques Boucher de Perthes

It was difficult even to get anyone to pay serious attention to the idea that stone tools were indeed tools. The first person to attempt to prove systematically that certain chipped stones were human artifacts was a French customs official named Jacques Boucher de Perthes (1788–1868). Interested in archaeology, he began poking about in gravel banks near Abbeville in northern France and was perplexed by the number of flint objects that not only did not "belong" in the pits, because they were made of a different kind of stone, but also bore unmistakable signs of human workmanship. Many of them were carefully chipped around the edges and looked enough like axes to set even a less observant person than Boucher de Perthes thinking. He began collecting and organizing his finds, and some years later he had what he considered an overwhelmingly strong case for the existence of human beings far older than any previously known. In 1838 and 1839 his findings were laid before two French learned societies and rejected by both. He published them later in five volumes, but for many years they were ignored.

Problems of Early Investigators: J. MacEnery

These early investigators were laboring under two handicaps. The first was the lack of any scientific method in excavating, recording finds, or presenting results. This lack made it easier for critics to argue that tools and human and extinct animal bones had come together by accident (or even by the sinister design of the excavator) than for the excavator to prove that they had come to their final resting place by natural means. A Catholic priest, Father J. MacEnery (1796–1841), was to suffer from this first handicap. In 1829 he dug his way through an absolutely unbroken layer of stalagmite to find flint tools and ancient bones below a cave floor on the south coast of England. When he reported his discovery, other geologists, led by the Dean of Westminster, William Buckland (1784–1856), insisted that the tools belonged to ancient Britons who had dug ovens in the stalagmite floor of the cave and accidentally dropped some of their stone implements into the holes. Father MacEnery's earnest rebuttal that there were no such holes fell on deaf ears; his findings, to which he had devoted some fifteen years, were not published until after his death. Meanwhile, William Buckland was also excavating skeletal remains of great age (Figure 1–2) but entirely failed to understand their true significance.

A second and much more serious handicap was that scientists and the laity alike seemed almost instinctively suspicious of stone tools and fossils and, from our viewpoint, were severely limited in their thinking. Most people still had not the faintest notion of how old the earth actually was, nor did they have any way of accurately determining its age. The prevailing belief in a young earth (supported by Ussher's calculations of the date of creation) simply precluded notions of biological or cultural histories with any significant time depth.

FIGURE 1–2 Excavation of the cave called Goat Hole in Wales took William Buckland many years. Although a human skeleton that he found there has since been dated to about 25,000 years B.P. (before the present), Buckland insisted that the bones were no older than Roman times. He described his finds in his book *Reliquiae Diluvianae* (1823), from which this figure comes.

Comte de Buffon

Early geologists had made some progress, however. The great French naturalist Comte de Buffon (1707–1788) had published his three-volume *Natural History* in 1749 and included in it an account of the creation of the earth. The earth originally derived, he wrote, from the collision of a comet with the sun and had slowly and steadily developed over a very long time—not the six days outlined in Genesis. Such was the response that in 1753 he was forced by theologians to retract in print: the time for such ideas was not yet ripe. However, he was among the first to introduce the idea that the earth's mantle had been shaped over long eons by natural forces such as wind and water erosion, volcanic activity, and faulting.

James Hutton

This concept was taken up by a few scholars who were beginning to get some alarming ideas about the earth's long history. This they read in the "testimony of the rocks," the various layers of different kinds of sediments—river gravels, sands, and marine limestones—that they encountered, one layer beneath another, some of them dozens of feet thick, indicating that the layers, or *strata*, had been laid down over long periods of time. The antiquity of the earth (often referred to as *"deep time"*), however, was not effectively documented or demonstrated until the Scot James Hutton (1726–1797) developed it fully in his book *Theory of the Earth* (1795). He showed convincingly the immense period of time to which the earth

Deep time: the theory that the earth is billions of years old and thus has a long history of development and change.

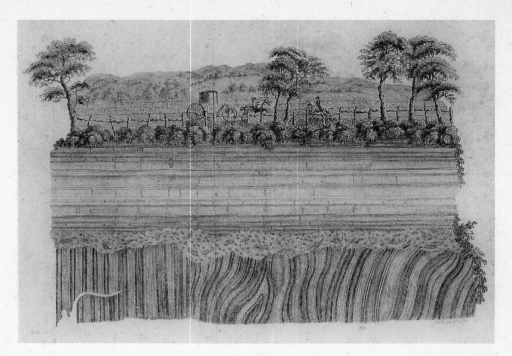

FIGURE 1–3 This engraving was published by James Hutton in 1795 in his book *Theory of the Earth*. It shows an unconformity—an ancient eroded surface—between the underlying vertical strata and the overlying horizontal strata of marine sediments at Jedburgh, Scotland. Since all these water-laid strata must have been deposited flat, it follows that the underlying sequence had arisen horizontally. Thus we know that the lower strata were uplifted and tilted through 90 degrees. The land so formed was then eroded and produced the horizontal surface of the unconformity itself. Later the land subsided (or the seas rose), and further marine strata were deposited. Finally, the land again rose (or the sea subsided), so that the strata formed a new land surface. Thus, from this single exposure of rock, Hutton was able to deduce that the land at this place had undergone two periods of marine deposition and two periods of uplift, the first very dramatic, and the second gentle. Hutton had the genius to recognize the breathtaking significance of the sight: the immense antiquity of the earth.

bore witness, and he made the remarkable claim that it carried "no vestige of a beginning—no prospect of an end" (see Figure 1–3).

Clearly, the passage of immense amounts of time can explain the presence of such diverse strata as exist in the earth's crust. The world is constantly remaking itself, and the only reason we are not aware of the continual reconstruction is that it happens so slowly. Watching a few pebbles fall from a crag, we are watching the disintegration of a mountain. Muddy water flowing down a river can eventually move billions of tons of material from the center of a continent to the bottom of the sea. This immense layer of mud may harden and may be covered in turn by other layers in a process extending over great amounts of time. All this, which seems so obvious now, was entirely new thinking at the end of the eighteenth century; it was a new and mechanistic interpretation of earth history and a new key to past and present. And to a society accustomed to believing that the earth was less than 6,000 years old, it was a heretical proposition, a staggering revelation.

Georges Cuvier, Alexandre Brongniart, William Smith

Much excitement was generated in 1796 when Georges Cuvier (1769–1832), professor of natural history at the Collège de France, discovered elephant bones in the underlying rocks of the Paris area itself. Soon Cuvier and other diggers were unearthing even stranger inhabitants of an unknown and unsuspected past: reptiles as big as whales, mammoths with long tusks, bears, wolves, and other creatures that bore only a superficial similarity to living forms. From a few of their bones, Cuvier put the animals back together with such startling realism that the novelist Honoré de Balzac marveled, "Is Cuvier not the greatest poet of our century? Our immortal naturalist has reconstructed worlds from blanched bones. He picks up a piece of gypsum and says to us 'See!' Suddenly stone turns into animals and another world unrolls before our eyes."

Like the living members of the animal kingdom, such collections of ancient animals did not come in a random assortment but could be grouped into species (collections of similar individuals) and genera (collections of similar species) following the principles established by the great Swedish classifier Linnaeus (1707–1778; see also Chapter 4). Cuvier counted 90 species, and some whole genera, that had entirely disappeared from the earth. What could have brought about such terrible decimation, he wondered, and how could the lost species have been succeeded by still others before the animals of the present day appeared?

To find the answers to such riddles, Cuvier set out to learn how the fossil creatures had been entombed and to find out all he could about the earth of their distant time. He enlisted the aid of Alexandre Brongniart (1770–1847), a professor of mineralogy and head of the famous Sèvres china factory. For years the two studied the Paris countryside in depth. They discovered that layer was piled upon layer: one stony bed filled with millions of seashells, and just below it a different formation with a scattering of freshwater or land shells. Other strata were studded with the bones of extinct giant mammals. Still others had no fossils at all.

Cuvier and Brongniart tried to interpret the puzzling succession of vanished worlds. At times, as they explained to rapt Parisian audiences, the seas had flooded into the Paris basin. At other times, the salt waters had receded, and the dry land had been dotted with freshwater lakes. Again the seas had returned, and again they had rolled back. In deposits laid down during the marine eras were the shells and bones of ocean life; in sediments marking the bottoms of the freshwater lakes lay freshwater shells and bones of land animals. There was no mixing of the freshwater and seawater deposits; one ended when the other began.

At about the same time as Cuvier was making his studies, an English surveyor named William Smith (1769–1839) was making similar observations in his own country and coming to similar conclusions. "Each stratum contains organized fossils peculiar to itself," he reported. In 1815 Smith published a painstaking geologic map of England, showing the strata that underlay the landscape and proving again that "the same species of fossils are found in the same stratum, even at wide distances."

Cuvier's conclusive proof of the extinction of species was an important contribution since it opened the way for fossils to be used as historical markers in the geologic record. But despite his extensive knowledge of fossils, Cuvier remained strongly opposed to evolutionary theories (then being proposed by his compatriot Lamarck), preferring to explain changes over time in plant and animal communities as the results of numerous large-scale catastrophes, such as Noah's flood. Under this theory, dubbed *catastrophism*, devastated areas were repopulated as

Catastrophism: Georges Cuvier's theory that vast floods and other disasters wiped out ancient life forms again and again throughout the earth's history.

organisms migrated in from unaffected regions or (as proposed by certain of Cuvier's followers) by the creation of new species by God.

Charles Lyell

By far the most influential nineteenth-century statement on the antiquity of the earth and the forces that have shaped the globe was produced by the Scottish geologist Charles Lyell (1797–1875). His three-volume work, *Principles of Geology,* synthesized the available evidence for deep time and, building on the earlier work of Hutton and others, established a theoretical position quickly named *uniformitarianism.* Although Lyell applied his uniformitarian tenets primarily to geology, the young Charles Darwin read the *Principles,* adopted Lyell's theoretical model, and later applied it to the organic world.

In the *Principles,* Lyell made four uniformitarian claims:

> **Uniformitarianism:** Charles Lyell's theory that the forces now affecting the earth— water and wind erosion, frost, volcanism—had acted in a similar way in the past, and that change is always gradual and nondirectional.

1. *Uniformity of law:* Through space and time, natural laws remain constant.
2. *Uniformity of process:* When possible, past phenomena should be explained as the results of processes now in operation.
3. *Uniformity of rate:* Change usually occurs slowly and steadily.
4. *Uniformity of state:* Change, although continuous, is nondirectional and nonprogressive.

Lyell's world was thus one of constant and gradual, but nonprogressive, change produced by processes that could be identified and understood. And although his uniformitarian model provided the vast time needed for organic evolution to produce the diversity of living species, Lyell rejected such notions. The idea of evolution was "in the air" during the early nineteenth century, however, primarily because of the efforts of a French scientist, Jean Baptist Lamarck.

Lamarck

The French naturalist Jean Baptiste de Monet, Chevalier de Lamarck (1744–1829), was a friend of Buffon and provided the first persuasive theory that could account for the process of organic evolution. In his *Système des Animaux* (1801) and later books, Lamarck developed his theory of the means by which animal species had been transformed. He recognized that animals and plants were finely adapted to their environments and that their relationship was dynamic, with environmental change generating biological change and adaptation. He suggested that in their daily lives animals recognized certain needs, and that, through altered behavior patterns and the action of "subtle fluids" within the body, forces were generated that stimulated the development and growth of organs, even completely novel ones. Thus the evolution of the species was a response to need, to use, or to disuse of organs, and the changes produced in each generation were inherited. This theory is sometimes described as that of the "inheritance of acquired characters."

Although Lamarck's ideas were to be discredited, they were extremely important in the early part of the nineteenth century and had a small place in evolutionary biology until recently. The theory, however, is generally discounted because it has not been possible to demonstrate conclusively that characters acquired during the lifetime of an individual are in fact passed on genetically to the succeeding generation.

Charles Darwin

Lyell's great work, *Principles of Geology*, was published between 1830 and 1833. Among its readers was a young man named Charles Darwin (1809–1882), who in another 26 years was to publish an even more revolutionary book. Darwin's student life at Cambridge was undistinguished except in one respect: he was passionately interested in natural history and in collecting birds, butterflies, spiders, flowers, and even rocks—there was nothing in nature that did not fascinate him. While a student he became a great friend of the Reverend J. S. Henslow, the professor of botany, who gave him much encouragement. When Darwin heard of the sailing of one of the navy's survey ships, HMS *Beagle*, he joined first as the captain's companion, later as the ship's naturalist, and sailed around the world observing and collecting for nearly five years. The *Beagle* left Devonport on December 27, 1831, and returned to Falmouth on October 2, 1836. Three-and-a-half years were spent surveying and collecting along the coasts of South America; five weeks were spent in the Galapagos Islands of Ecuador, and a year was spent returning home via Tahiti, New Zealand, Australia, and South Africa (Figure 1–4). This voyage offered Darwin a priceless opportunity to carry his observations to foreign lands, and it gave him a brilliant panorama of the variety of organic life.

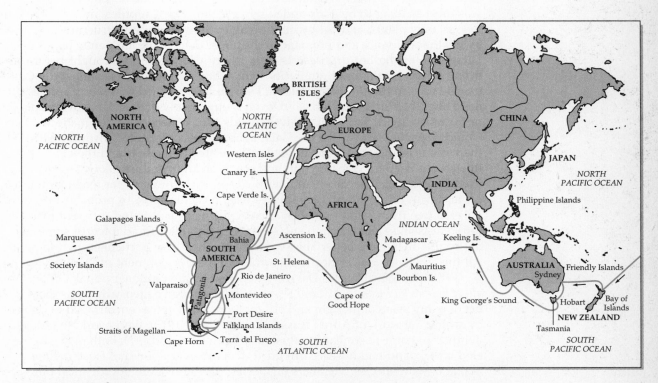

FIGURE 1–4 Charles Darwin left Devonport, England, in December 1831 and returned to Falmouth in October 1836. Out of the four-and-a-half years spent on the voyage in HMS *Beagle*, Darwin spent over three years in South America and its islands. The voyage was completed with visits to New Zealand, Australia, the Keeling (Cocos) Islands, the Cape of Good Hope, and St. Helena. Darwin's experience on this voyage was a rich and fertile source of observation and inspiration in the development of his ideas.

FIGURE 1–5 These four species of Galapagos finch show some of the variety of form into which the beak evolved. The left species is most powerfully equipped and is adapted to crack seeds and nuts. That on the right is adapted to feed from flowers and fruit. These species evolved in isolation on different islands, with little or no competition.

One of the most important parts of the voyage for the later development of Darwin's ideas was the visit to the Galapagos or Enchanted Islands 600 miles off the coast of Ecuador.

Soon after his arrival there, Darwin wrote in his journal, "Here, both in space and time, we seem to be brought somewhere near to that great fact—that mystery of mysteries—the first appearance of new beings on this earth." Later he wrote, "It was most striking to be surrounded by new birds, new reptiles, new shells, new insects, new plants, and yet by innumerable trifling details of structure, and even by the tones of voice and plumage of the birds, to have the temperate plains of . . . Patagonia, or the hot dry deserts of northern Chile, vividly brought before my eyes." Struck by the basic similarities yet subtle differences that linked the Galapagos fauna to that of the mainland, Darwin later learned that many species differed slightly from island to island, even though many of the islands were only 50 or 60 miles apart. From an analysis of his bird collections later made by John Gould, Darwin learned that the Galapagos finches constituted distinct species on the various islands but were all obviously related. On one island they had strong thick beaks used for cracking nuts and seeds; on another the beak was smaller and used for catching insects; on another the beak was elongated for feeding on flowers and fruit (Figure 1–5). One species used a cactus spine to probe grubs out of holes in tree trunks and branches. Clearly the birds had found different foods on different islands and through successive generations had adapted in some manner so that they were better able to survive in their own particular environments. All this evidence was critically important in the development of Darwin's ideas.

When, in 1859, Charles Darwin published his revolutionary book *On the Origin of Species by Means of Natural Selection,* he presented a theory that was the product of many years of thought and observation. Darwin was encouraged to publish by seeing the work of Alfred Russel Wallace (1823–1913), who, working independently, had come to similar conclusions (Figures 1–6 and 1–7). Both men had traveled widely and had observed in great detail the variation that exists within animal and plant species. Members of species, they noted, are not identical but vary in size, strength, health, fertility, longevity, behavior, and many other characteristics. Darwin realized that humans use this natural variation when they selectively breed plants and animals; a breeder selects to interbreed only particular individuals possessing the desired qualities.

Both Darwin and Wallace saw that a kind of *natural* selection was at work, and an understanding of the means by which selection operates in nature came to both

FIGURE 1–6 Charles Darwin as a young man. In his *Autobiography* he wrote, "In September 1858 I set to work by the strong advice of Lyell and Hooker to prepare a volume on the transmutation of species, but was often interrupted by ill-health. . . . [The book] cost me thirteen months and ten days hard labour." Darwin was an intermittent invalid for 40 years, but he found that invalidism had some advantages: "Even ill-health, though it annihilated several years of my life, has saved me from the distractions of society and amusement." He lived to the age of 73.

FIGURE 1–7 Alfred Russel Wallace was a complete contrast to Darwin in both background and character. Whereas Darwin did not need to work for a living, Wallace earned his way by collecting rare tropical plants and animals for private collectors and museums. As a result, he traveled far more widely than Darwin in both South America and Southeast Asia. Later in his life he wrote a number of books on evolution. Although of considerable interest, they do not have the originality and intellectual integrity of Darwin's writings.

from the same source. The first edition of *An Essay on the Principle of Population* by an English clergyman, T. R. Malthus (1766–1834), appeared in 1798. In his book Malthus showed that the reproductive potential of humankind far exceeds the natural resources available to nourish an expanding population. In a revised version of his essay, published in 1830, Malthus began, "In taking a view of animated nature, we cannot fail to be struck with the prodigious power of increase in plants and animals . . . their natural tendency must be to increase in a geometrical ratio—that is, by multiplication." He continued by pointing out that, in contrast, subsistence can increase only in an arithmetical ratio: "A slight acquaintance with numbers will shew the immensity of the first power in comparison of the second." And he had written in 1798, "By that law of our nature that makes food necessary to the life of man, the effects of these two unequal powers must be kept equal. This implies a strong and constantly operating check on population from the difficulty of subsistence." As a result, he argued, the size of human populations is limited by disease, famine, and war and that, in the absence of "moral restraint," such factors alone appear to check what would otherwise be a rapid growth in population.

Both Darwin and Wallace read Malthus's essay, and, remarkably, both men recorded in their diaries how they realized that in that book lay the key to understanding the evolutionary process. It was clear that what Malthus had discovered of human populations was true of populations of plants and animals: the reproductive potential vastly exceeds the rate necessary to maintain a constant population size. They realized that the individuals that do survive must be in some way better equipped to live in their environment that those that do not survive. It follows that, in a naturally interbreeding population, any variation that increased the organism's ability to produce fertile offspring would most likely be preserved and passed on to future generations, while the variations that decreased that ability would most likely be eliminated.

Darwin had carried these ideas for some years; he wrote a short sketch in 1842 and a more extended *Essay* in 1844 but was not prepared to publish either. He knew he would shock the public and his family; he could hardly face the implications of his thoughts. Wallace was held back by no such inhibitions, and early in 1858, after he read Malthus, the idea of natural selection occurred to him. He immediately sent a short paper on the subject to Darwin. Darwin received this paper on June 18. He was quite astounded and wrote in his diary, "I never saw a more striking coincidence; if Wallace had my MS sketch written out in 1842, he could not have made a better short abstract."

THEORY OF EVOLUTION

Natural selection: the principle mechanism of Darwinian evolutionary change, by which the individuals best adapted to the environment contribute more offspring to succeeding generations than others do. As more of such individuals' characteristics are incorporated into the gene pool, the characteristics of the population evolve.

As the Harvard zoologist Ernst Mayr has recently shown, Darwin's theory of evolution through *natural selection*, as presented in *On the Origin of Species*, is based on five facts and three inferences (Figure 1–8). From Malthus, Darwin took the elements of organisms' potential superfecundity (Fact 1) and the limitations placed on population expansion by limited environmental resources (Fact 3). He combined these elements with the observation that most natural populations tend to remain stable in size rather than to constantly expand (Fact 2). From these three facts, Darwin (following Malthus) inferred that individual organisms (especially members of the same species) are in strong competition with one another (Inference 1). Combining this inference with the observation that individuals (including

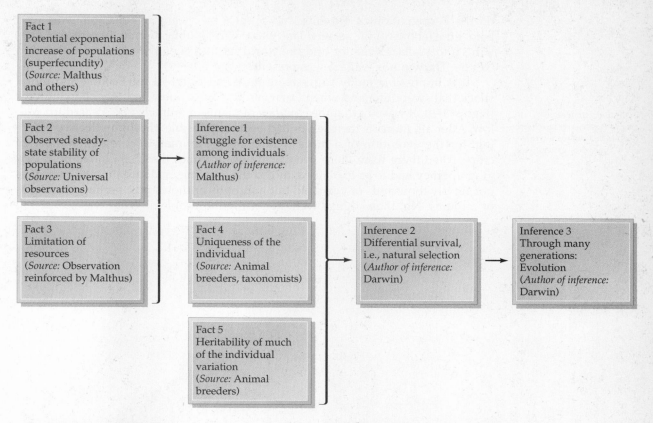

FIGURE 1–8   Zoologist Ernst Mayr has reduced Darwin's explanatory model of evolution through natural selection to 5 facts and 3 inferences.

conspecifics) show variations in physical and behavioral traits (Fact 4) and the observation that parents often pass their individual variations on to their offspring (Fact 5) allowed Darwin to reach a second inference, that organisms experience differential survival and reproduction based on the possession of traits that are adaptive in their particular environment (Inference 2; this is the statement that we recognize as natural selection). Finally, Darwin argued that through the action of natural selection over many generations a species could slowly, but surely, *evolve* (Inference 3).

Thus natural selection was presented as a process by which adaptive traits are preserved (through the survival and reproduction of their carriers) and maladaptive (or *less* adaptive) traits are winnowed out of species. This process occurs in both plants and animals, and true to Lyell's uniformitarian principles, Darwin described the evolutionary process as extremely slow and gradual. Such a process clearly could not have been responsible for species diversity on Bishop Ussher's 6,000-year-old earth, but fortunately, by the mid-nineteenth century, Hutton, Lyell, and others had provided ample evidence for deep time.

The first presentation of the Darwin/Wallace evolutionary model was made at the Linnaean Society in London over a year prior to the *Origin*'s publication. On July 1, 1858, a paper entitled "On the Tendency of Species to Form Varieties, and

Conspecifics: members of the same species.

on the Perpetuation of Varieties and Species by Means of Selection" was read before the fellows of the society. This was the first publication to the world of Darwin's and Wallace's theory, and the world has not been the same since that day. Neither Darwin nor Wallace was present.

It is impossible today to re-create the atmosphere of intellectual and moral shock that swept England when Darwin's book was published the following year (Figure 1–9). It was not that the *evolution* of plants or animals was so hard to swallow. After all, humans themselves had been responsible, through selective breeding, for the evolution of a number of domestic animals and a great variety of crops. Then there were those peculiar dinosaur bones that people had been digging up; they had to be explained, as did the growing evidence that the earth was not simply thousands of years old but hundreds of thousands, perhaps hundreds of millions. No, those things were not really the problem. What was so hard to

Evolution: cumulative changes in the average characteristics of a population that occur over many generations.

FIGURE 1–9 This 1861 *Punch* cartoon, which appeared two years after Darwin's publication of *On the Origin of Species*, typifies the contemporary reaction of shock to the idea that humans could be descended from apes.

accept was the implied suggestion that human beings were descended from a bunch of "repulsive, scratching, hairy apes and monkeys."

Those awful monkeys! As one Victorian lady is reported to have said, "My dear, let us hope that it is not true, but if it is, let us pray that it will not become generally known."

Darwin was an extremely cautious scientist, and the evidence he used to support his theory ranged among both plants and animals, but it did not include human beings. He mentioned the origin of humans only once in *On the Origin of Species,* permitting himself a single timid sentence in his conclusion: "Light will be thrown on the origin of man and his history." But the implication was plain, and nobody missed it.

In 1863 Thomas H. Huxley (1825–1895), a friend of Darwin and an ardent propagandist for his theory, published *Zoological Evidences as to Man's Place in Nature.* This was the first book to address itself in an orderly and scientific way to the problem of human origins. By making many telling anatomical comparisons between humans and the apes, Huxley established that, of all animals on earth, the African great apes—the chimpanzee and gorilla—are most closely related to humans (Figure 1–10). He further stated that the evolutionary development of apes and humans had taken place in much the same way and according to the same laws. From this it followed that, if prehuman fossils were ever found, older and older humanlike fossils would be found, leading eventually to types that would turn out to be ancestral to both apes and humans. And these common ancestors would probably be found in Africa.

Darwin, confronted by the same relationship of fossil species to living ones, saw that the latter were the modified descendants of the former. Carrying the case to its full conclusion in *The Descent of Man,* published in 1871, Darwin was forced to propound the theory of an unbroken chain of organisms that began with the first forms of life and evolved to humans. Here was a true scientific theory, a theory of evolution subject to proof. But where was the proof? Where were the bones

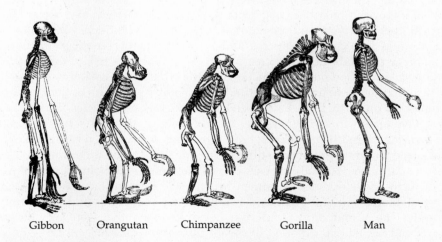

Gibbon   Orangutan   Chimpanzee   Gorilla   Man

FIGURE 1–10   In 1863, Thomas H. Huxley published this drawing of the skeletons of the four apes and a human to illustrate their extraordinary similarity. He wrote, "Whatever part of the animal fabric might be selected for comparison, the lower Apes (monkeys) and the Gorilla would differ more than the Gorilla and the Man." All drawings are to the same scale except the gibbon, which is drawn to twice the scale.

of this multitude of organisms? Surely many of them should have survived in the earth, yet the fossils found up to Darwin's day supplied only the most fragmentary evidence. Where were the missing links? It was a painful time for the evolutionists. Despite all the logic in Huxley's and Darwin's views, they were difficult to support, because in Africa, or indeed anywhere else, there was an embarrassing lack of fossils resembling human beings.

In all the ancient menageries that Georges Cuvier had dug out of the Parisian subsoil nearly a century earlier, there was not a trace of prehistoric humans. It seemed plain enough to the great paleontologist: "L'homme fossile n'existe pas" ("Fossil man does not exist"). This did not stop people from looking. Here and there, in this old cave and that old riverbed, excavators ran across chipped flints and polished axes, but the bones mixed in with such finds were those of animals and not humans. It never occurred to the finders that some of the pebble implements they had collected might actually be older than modern humans—that tools had been the making of humans as well as humans the makers of tools.

At this turning point in the history of human knowledge, there had emerged two great and related ideas about the origin of nature and of humankind: the earth is extremely ancient, long populated by many kinds of animals, some of which are no longer living, and humans themselves, mutable creatures like the animals, have their ancestors far back in time. But how far back and who those ancestors were nobody had even the slightest notion. Everything we know about our ancestry we have learned in the past one hundred years, most of it during the past four decades.

Darwin and Wallace had provided a rational and convincing explanation of the diversity and changing nature of species. If humans, too, were products of this process, humankind had to develop a completely new attitude toward the natural world and face an entirely novel view of human origins. This agonizing reappraisal was possible only for those who were philosophically flexible, free from the straitjacket of limitations of earlier ideas and prejudices. It would not be unreasonable to claim that Darwin's book is one of the most important books ever published, and that the changes it has brought about in our view of ourselves are only a part of its revolutionary impact. From it derives our modern and extraordinarily fruitful perspective on humankind and all nature: evolutionary biology.

Evolution is a creative process and, as the eminent geneticist Theodosius Dobzhansky pointed out, "Any creative process involves a risk of failure, which in biological evolution means extinction. On the other hand, creativity makes possible striking successes and discoveries." In the billions of years of the grand procession of life on earth, there have been both successes and failures. Thousands of forms have arisen to swim, wriggle, crawl, walk, or fly past some immutable reviewing stand and then collapse. Some creatures seemed merely bizarre experiments, and others were successful for varying lengths of time: the dinosaurs ruled the earth for 130 million years before they vanished. Some dropouts were crucial to the development of human beings. The human line can be traced to early vertebrates that first possessed a rudimentary backbone and the beginnings of a brain. The human body is full of traces of ancestors that were very different from us and led wholly different lives. For instance, we have a coccyx—the vestige of a tail—at the end of our spines, and as embryos (Figure 1–11) we carry ephemeral gill slits, which remind us that our ancestors were once marine creatures. This book is about one experiment in the creation of animal life, a process of variation and selection that began over 3 billion years ago and that in time led to modern humans and all other organisms.

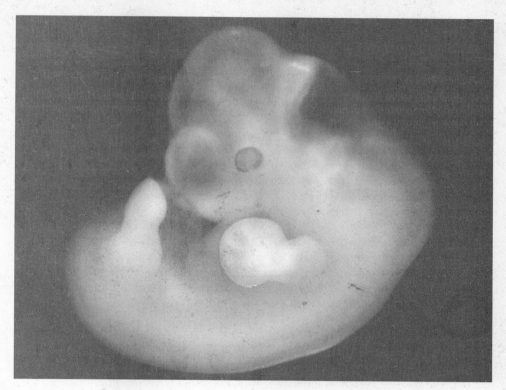

FIGURE 1–11   The human embryo grows in a salty solution called *amniotic fluid*, which is not greatly different in composition from the ocean. The embryo shows certain characteristics of ancestral forms, some of which are remnants of marine fish-like adaptations of 500 million years ago. At about 4 weeks, gill slits and a tail, which rapidly develop into other structures, can be seen.

MODERN STUDY OF HUMAN ORIGINS

Paleoanthropology is the branch of science dealing with the study of early humans. It involves connecting humans and nonhumans in an evolutionary network so long lost that the links we possess are often difficult to understand and arrange. For those engaged in this science, today is a time of extraordinary interest. Recent discoveries and analysis now begin to make it possible to lay out some of those links next to one another and to look at them closely in relation to one another.

In 1859, when Darwin propounded the theory of evolution, scientists knew of only two fossils that were relevant to the search for our origins: one of an extinct ape and another of the early type of *Homo sapiens* called *Neandertal*. Just a little more than a hundred years later, expeditions in East Africa unearthed more than six hundred near-human bones in a decade. The discovery and interpretation of such evidence of our ancestors involves many specialists (Table 1–1).

The knowledge and insights of other modern sciences also contribute to attempts to understand human evolution. Atomic physicists, for example, have determined that certain radioactive elements discharge energy at a constant rate, turning into certain other elements. This knowledge has provided paleontologists with new methods of establishing the age of fossils and of interpreting the stages in the evolution of life.

Paleoanthropology: the study of the fossil and cultural remains and other evidence of humans' extinct ancestors.

Table 1–1 Special Skills to Study Fossil Sites

In the Field

Paleoanthropologists	In charge of investigations from start to finish, they must pick the site, get permission to excavate, obtain financial support, hire the labor, and organize, plan, and supervise the work in progress. Finally, they must integrate the data collected by each of the specialists and publish their conclusions.
Geologists	Often assist in selecting the site. Their knowledge of the geologic history of the region is indispensable in determining the relative ages of fossils. Their study of the strata at the site determines the natural processes—deposition, volcanic action—that laid the strata down and the conditions under which fossilization took place.
Surveyors	Map the general region of the site and the site itself, plotting it in relation to natural landmarks and making a detailed record of its contours before they are obliterated by digging.
Draftspeople	Record the exact position of all fossils, tools, and other artifacts as excavated, marking their relationships to each other in both the horizontal and vertical planes.
Photographers	Document fossil remains and artifacts and their associations as they are uncovered, record work in progress and the use of special equipment, and provide overall views of the site as well as of personnel at work.

In the Laboratory

Petrologists	Identify and classify the rocks and minerals found around the site. They can determine the nature of rocks from which tools were made and identify stones that do not occur naturally in the area, which would indicate that the stones were imported by early humans.
Palynologists	Specialize in the study and identification of fossil plant pollen, which may shed light on early humankind's environment and diet and the climate at the time.
Pedologists	Experts on soils and their chemical composition, their findings round out the picture of the environment as it once was.
Geochemists	With geophysicists, conduct chemical and physical tests in the laboratory to determine the absolute age of material found at the site. They may also study the chemical composition of bones and artifacts.

In the Field and Laboratory

Preparators	At the site, preserve and protect fossils and artifacts with various hardening agents and make plaster casts for particularly fragile bones and other organic remains. In the laboratory, preparators clean and restore the specimens, making them ready for study by various specialists.
Paleontologists	Study the fossil animal remains found at the site. From the finds, they can learn much about the ecology and the eating habits of early humans.
Physical anthropologists[a]	Specialists in the comparative anatomy of apes and humans, they evaluate remains found at the site and the evolutionary status of fossil hominids who lived there.
Taphonomists	Study the condition and arrangement of the fossils in relation to the deposits which carry them, to determine the origin and formation of the fossil assemblage.
Archaeologists	Study humankind's past material culture: tools of stone, bone, and wood; living sites, settlement patterns, and food remains; art and ritual.

[a]Physical anthropology (sometimes called *biological anthropology*) is a biological part of anthropology and the branch of biology that deals with other aspects of humankind besides our prehistory. It includes the distribution and nature of modern human beings, their physical diversity, their adaptations, and their adaptability.

FIGURE 1–12 The more closely chimpanzees are studied, the more like them we appear to be, especially in the realm of individual relationships and nonverbal communication. Here, two chimpanzees reassure one another with a touch.

Equally valuable have been the contributions of modern biochemistry. In the past decades biochemists have deciphered the code found in the substance DNA (see Chapter 3) by which instructions for building new cells and new organisms are passed from one generation to the next. Knowledge of this code provides insights into how members of a species reproduce themselves, generation after generation, virtually unchanged; how, on the other hand, minute variations do occur in offspring; and how these variations may accumulate in time. Knowledge of how these variations create differences in the structures of proteins can be used to determine the affinity between different types of organisms. Some scientists believe that these differences accumulate at a more-or-less steady rate over time, so that this biochemical knowledge can provide yet another method of dating and thus be used to determine when existing species of animals first emerged.

Other clues to the past are coming from studies of a very different kind, involving living animals: the science of animal behavior, called *ethology*. It is a relatively new discipline, but a flourishing one. Studies of the behavior of living animals (for example, the chimpanzees shown in Figure 1–12) have been used to help explain the basis of some human behaviors and to suggest how ancestral humans may have acted and why. We will see the usefulness of animal behavior studies when we discuss the possible social organization of our ancestors (Chapter 9).

Ethology: study of the social behavior of animal species in their natural environment.

PALEOANTHROPOLOGY IN PROGRESS

Scarcity of Human Fossils

Fossils are traces of organisms that are preserved in rock. Most often the hard parts, shells or bones, are preserved as their original molecules are replaced by minerals. Unfortunately humans are a maddeningly poor source of fossils. In 1956 the late paleontologist G. H. R. von Koenigswald calculated that, if all the then-known fragments of human beings older than the Neandertal people were gathered together, they could be comfortably displayed on a medium-sized table. Although many more fossils of early hominids have been found since then, discoveries are still rare.

Why are human fossils so scarce? Why can one go to good fossil sites almost anywhere in the world and find millions of shell remains or thousands of bones of extinct reptiles and mammals, while peoples earlier than Neandertal are known from only a handful of sites at which investigators, working through tons of deposits, pile up other finds by the bushel basket before recovering a single human tooth?

There are many reasons. First, the commonness of marine fossils is a direct reflection of the abundance of these creatures when they were alive. It also reflects the tremendous span of time during which they abounded. Many of them swarmed through the waters of the earth for hundreds of millions of years. When they died, they sank and were covered by sediments. Their way of life—their life in the water—preserved them, as did their extremely durable shells, the only parts of them that now remain. Humans, by contrast, have never been as numerous as oysters and clams. They existed in small numbers, reproduced slowly and in small numbers, and lived a relatively long time. They were more intelligent than, for example, dinosaurs and were perhaps less apt to get mired in bogs, marshes, or quicksands. Most important, their way of life was different. They were not sea creatures or exclusively riverside browsers, but lively, wide-ranging food-gatherers and hunters. They often lived and died in the open, where their bones were gnawed by scavengers, were trampled on, and were bleached and decomposed by the sun and rain. In hot climates, particularly in tropical forests and woodlands, the soil is likely to be markedly acid. Bones dissolve in such soils, and early humans who lived and died in such an environment had a very poor chance of leaving remains that would last until today. Finally, human ancestors have been on earth only a few million years. There simply has not been as much time for them to leave their bones as there has been for some of the more ancient species of animals.

Fossil Sites

To find remnants of a clever, elusive, uncommon animal like an early human, we need a quiet cave where a corpse can be gently covered by blown-in dust or washed-in soil, or even sand and mud from the rising water level of a river. Or the cave might be a large one with a deep rock fissure at the back serving as a garbage dump in which the dead were once placed along with the bones of game animals, just to get them out of the way. Finally, the cave may simply be one that was occupied steadily for a long time. The dirt and debris of mere living would gradually build up the floor so that it became deeper and deeper, and if people lived in it long enough, their story would be revealed—from recent times to increasingly primitive ones—just by a careful digging downward from one layer to another.

Not all fossil sites are caves; the earliest known certain cave occupations are little more than half a million years old. From earlier times we find sites that were in the open, often by a stream or on a lake shore. In these circumstances, evidence is more difficult to come by, but seasonal flooding sometimes left deposits of mud and clay on the bones of animals and early humans. In other places, fossils of human ancestors have been found scattered among animal bones without any clear archaeological context; these are the rarest occurrences. Indeed, as we go backward in time, the fossil record becomes dimmer, and the specimens become scarcer, as might be expected. But where animal bones are found preserved (most commonly near an ancient lake shore or river) and where human artifacts are present, there we can reasonably expect to find fossils of early humans, if the geographical area, climate, age, and environment are appropriate.

The gradual revealing of the story of human evolution can be compared to the cleaning of an old tapestry that has been covered with mud and dirt. Let us suppose modern humanity is at the top of the tapestry, and that our most primitive ancestors are woven into it near the bottom. The whole tapestry is fragile, increasingly so the nearer one gets to the bottom. It must be cleaned with great care so that it will not be destroyed. There is no assurance that the spot one picks to clean will have a meaningful picture on it. It may be bare. It may have a hole in it. It may reveal only a fragment of one of the figures in the design, a fragment so small and mysterious as to be of little value. It may reveal an entire figure, but a totally unexpected one whose presence cannot be explained until further parts are cleaned. But the position of every piece of design on the tapestry—exactly where it is located with respect to all other pieces—is enormously important. In paleontology, deductions can be made about specific fossils and their relationship only when they are evaluated in the light of all other available evidence and knowledge.

Relative Dating Methods: Earth and Fossils

To begin to understand our ancestors' fossil remains, we must know how old these bits and pieces are. Strange shapes and sizes may suggest all sorts of intriguing ideas and hypotheses about who descended from whom. But these hypotheses can be nailed down tightly only by reliable dating.

The problem of determining the age of fossils is handled in several ways. The first is through *geology*, the study of the earth itself. This branch of science is concerned with the location, size, and nature of the various layers of clay, silt, sand, lava, limestone, and other kinds of rock that constitute the earth's surface, and with their relationship to one another. It examines certain processes, such as continental drift, erosion, the accumulation of layers of silt at the bottom of the sea, and their compaction into rock again by heat and pressure; it notes that these processes take place now at measurable rates and assumes that the same processes took place at comparable rates in the past, just as Lyell suggested. Analysis of these layers, or strata—a scientific discipline known as *stratigraphy*—permits the working out of a rough picture of past earth history (Figures 1–3, 1–13). From this information the fossils found in different rock structures can be arranged in order of age. The deepest strata are the oldest, and the more recent levels are laid down above them. Thus fossils in the upper strata are relatively younger than those in the lower strata. These data, however, do not give us the absolute age of the fossils in years.

The second way to determine relative age is by studying the fossils themselves. Fossil types are usually not the same in different layers. Animals evolved through time, and since all species have finite lifetimes (ultimately go extinct), their fossils provide clues of their own, particularly if the time sequence can be worked out. The evolution of the horse, for example, is very well known through fossils. Over a period of about 60 million years, the creature developed from an animal the size of a dog with four toes on each foot to the modern large animal with one toe per foot; the numerous intermediate fossil stages located in various

Geology: study of the earth's physical formation, its nature, and its continuing development.

Stratigraphy: the sequence of geologic strata, or layers, formed by materials deposited by water or wind; also, the study of this sequence.

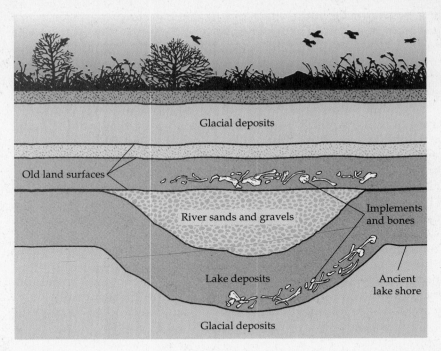

FIGURE 1–13 Fossils are found in deposits formed by the action of glaciers and rivers or laid down in ancient riverbeds, lakes, estuaries, and seas. Some deposits are windblown and may contain volcanic ash. Fossils are laid down in more-or-less horizontal beds, or strata, as shown here. Stratigraphy is the science that attempts to understand stratigraphic deposition—its form, its sequence, and its age.

geological strata tell this story with great clarity. Fossils of ancestral horses become tools for dating, because any other animal or plant fossil that occurs in the same layer as one of the ancestral horses can be considered of the same age. Once relative ages are established, one fossil can help date another. This method is called dating by *faunal correlation.*

Faunal correlation: dating a site by the similarity of its animal fossils to those of another site that may carry a reliable absolute date.

One problem paleontologists have had to face is establishing contemporaneity when fossils from the same site are said to be associated but their association is questioned. This problem is now less serious than in earlier days, for two reasons. First, today we can check claims of contemporaneity and association by chemically analyzing the bone: bones of roughly the same age should have roughly the same chemical analyses. The chemicals usually assayed are nitrogen (which occurs in bone in the form of the protein collagen and is lost slowly during fossilization) and uranium and fluorine (both of which frequently enter bone from the surrounding groundwater and increase in concentration over a long period). Such analyses can be very valuable in establishing contemporaneity at a site: they are especially valuable if it is suspected that a skeleton has been buried within a deposit that is substantially older than the skeleton itself.

The second reason that contemporaneity can be more clearly established today is that more careful records of excavations are now being kept. Early investigators usually failed to realize the importance of carefully analyzing fossil sites and the position of fossils. Too often they dug with reckless abandon, recovering only the largest bones and major pieces of worked stone. They did not appreciate the information they could get from the position of things relative to one another—and from the surrounding earth itself. Many questions will occur to the curious and well-trained observer. Is there evidence of fire? If so, was it natural or controlled by humans? Do certain kinds of animal bones predominate at one level and decrease at another, indicating a change of diet or climate? Do the deposits preserve snails, or perhaps pollen grains, which are more sensitive clues to vegetation, and hence climate, than the mineral deposits themselves? With their careful plotting of finds and sites, paleontologists can come closer to answering these questions.

Chronometric Dating Methods: Atomic Physics

Through the constant cross-checking and fitting together of enormous amounts of both rock and fossil evidence, geologists were able to fit together quite a detailed succession of rock formations and fossils from the present back to the distant Cambrian period (Figure 6–1). But this succession provided only the *relative dating* of the fossils; the *absolute,* or *chronometric dating,* of the fossils was lacking.

Today, atomic physics provides us with some very valuable techniques for obtaining chronometric dates of geological formations (and, in some cases, bones), which have revolutionized our study of human evolution. We know that certain radioactive elements discharge energy at a constant rate, known as the *decay rate.* Radium, for example, turns slowly but steadily into lead. Once this steady decay rate is known, it is only a matter of using laboratory technique to determine how old a piece of radium is by measuring how much of it is still radium and how much is lead.

One long-lasting radioactive substance used for chronometric dating is potassium 40. This material breaks down into the gas argon at the relatively slow rate of one half of the original potassium every 1,250 million years (this is known as potassium 40's *half-life*). Because potassium 40 is found in volcanic ash and lava, *potassium-argon* (abbreviated K/Ar) dating can be used to date fossils located in volcanic rock or ash or sandwiched between two layers of volcanic matter. The "clock" starts as the lava or ash cools (argon produced previously escaped while the lava was heated in the volcano), and it continues to run steadily with the breakdown of potassium 40. The age of the rock can therefore be calculated with remarkable precision by determining the ratio of argon gas to potassium 40. Problems arise when the rock sample containing the potassium also contains air (which itself contains small quantities of argon), or if the rock has been reheated by later volcanic eruptions, which may have driven off the argon already produced by radioactive decay. The other, more general difficulty is that the method can be used to date fossils only from areas where volcanic eruptions occurred at about the same time as the fossils were deposited. Fortunately, many of the most important fossil sites in East Africa are in an area where volcanic activity was widespread (see Chapter 8), but in much of Asia, the Americas, and Europe, this method cannot be used.

An important development that supports this technique involves recognizing ash layers that have been deposited over wide areas. It has been shown by Frank Brown of the University of Utah that each ash layer (or *tuff* as such a layer is often called) can be recognized by a unique analysis of its mineral components; that is, each tuff has its own "chemical signature." Because of this characteristic, dated tuffs can be recognized over very great distances; their spread may be thousands of miles in extent. Thus it is possible to correlate tuffs from sites as far apart as

Relative dating: estimating the age of geologic deposits (and the fossils in them) by determining their stratigraphic level in relation to that of other deposits whose relative or absolute age is known.

Absolute dating: determining the actual age of geologic deposits (and the fossils in them) by examining the chemical composition of rock fragments and organic remains containing radioactive substances such as uranium 238, potassium 40, and carbon 14, which decay at a known rate. Also known as *chronometric dating.*

Kenya, Ethiopia, and the Indian Ocean, where they can be recognized in deep-sea cores. In this way, dated tuffs may be widely mapped, and their K/Ar dates in one area checked against their K/Ar dating in another.

A derivation from K/Ar dating is the Ar^{40}/Ar^{39} procedure. In this test, previously irradiated crystals are melted with a laser beam in order to release argon. The procedure has the advantage of being extremely precise even when very small mineral samples are tested. Together, the K/Ar and Ar^{40}/Ar^{39} procedures can date rocks over a wide span of time, from only a few tens of thousands to many millions of years B.P. (before the present). As discussed in a later chapter, new Ar^{40}/Ar^{39} dates from Java have greatly extended the period of known human occupancy in that part of the world.

Another useful radioactive element is carbon 14, which reverts to atmospheric nitrogen (Figure 1–14). Physicist Willard Libby showed that carbon 14 is present in the atmosphere as carbon dioxide (CO_2) and is incorporated into all plant material. In the plant, the proportion of carbon 14 to the stable atom carbon 12 is the

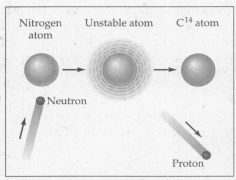

1. Nitrogen atom becomes C^{14} atom in the atmosphere.

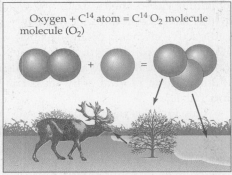

2. C^{14} and oxygen enter live organisms.

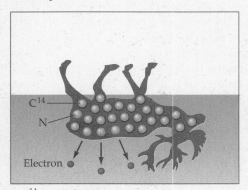

3. C^{14} atoms disintegrate.

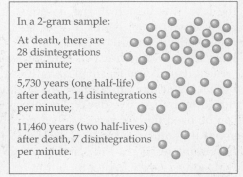

In a 2-gram sample:

At death, there are 28 disintegrations per minute;

5,730 years (one half-life) after death, 14 disintegrations per minute;

11,460 years (two half-lives) after death, 7 disintegrations per minute.

4. C^{14} continues to disintegrate at an orderly, predictable rate.

FIGURE 1–14   Carbon 14, or C^{14}, is an unstable form of carbon (the stable form is carbon 12). A certain proportion of C^{14} exists in the atmosphere and as carbon dioxide (CO_2) is absorbed and incorporated by plants into their bodies in the form of carbohydrates. Animals absorb C^{14} by eating the plants. Thereafter the C^{14} disintegrates at a known rate (the half-life), and the extent of this disintegration can be measured and related to the amount of C^{14} remaining, and so too the age of the organic material.

same as the proportion of the two in the atmosphere. The clock starts when the CO_2 is taken into the plant (which animals may feed on) and is buried as either fiber or wood, or as the collagen in bone, or as charcoal left by a fire (which is found in many archaeological sites). After an organism's death, the carbon 14 it contains breaks down, and the proportion of carbon 12 increases. The laboratory technique measures the ratio of carbon 14 to carbon 12 in these prehistoric samples. Carbon 14 has a half-life of only 5,730 years and therefore measurements of the age of carbon compounds cover a relatively short period. The method is most useful between 500 and 40,000 years B.P., although its range can be extended somewhat further into the past.

Errors in this method arise from a number of factors. It was originally supposed that the carbon 14 level in the atmosphere was constant, but we now know that it is not. Volcanoes produce CO_2 without carbon 14, which causes local reductions in the level of carbon 14 in the atmosphere. A more serious variation is in the atmospheric level itself, which alters according to variations in the chemical reactions in the upper atmosphere that create the carbon 14 in the first place. Samples may also become contaminated by modern organic compounds (such as the inks with which the fossils are labeled) or by modern CO_2 from the atmosphere. Although these factors somewhat limit the value of carbon 14 dating, the method has proved of great value to paleoanthropologists when it is carefully used.

Another dating method that depends in a different way on radioactive decay is the *fission-track* method. The rare radioactive element uranium 238 splits spontaneously to create a minute region of crystal disruption in a mineral. The disruption is called a *track*. In the laboratory, microscopic examination can determine track densities in mineral crystals containing uranium 238, in proportion to total uranium content. Since the rate of spontaneous fission is known, the age of the crystal can be calculated. The clock is started with the eruption of volcanoes, and so this method has the same geographic limitations as the potassium-argon method.

The main value of the fission-track method at present is as a cross-check on the potassium-argon method. The same volcanic samples can often be used, and the comparison aids in the detection of errors. The fission-track method itself has other problems. With low uranium content and rather recently formed minerals, the track density will be low. Heating eliminates tracks (as we have seen, heating also causes problems in potassium-argon dating). Fission-track dating, however, has proved of great value in dating samples from the beginning of the earth to about 300,000 years B.P. It is now being used quite widely in dating early periods of human evolution in volcanically active regions.

A final method of dating that depends on radioactivity is the measurement of *thermoluminescence* (TL). Over a period of time, electrons become trapped in the crystal structure of buried substances irradiated by naturally occuring uranium, thorium, and potassium 40. When these irradiated substances are heated, the electrons are released with a quantity of light proportional to the number of electrons trapped. If the rate of electron accumulation can be established, the amount of light emitted can be used to measure the time elapsed since the substance was last heated. The method works best with pottery, but it can also be used on burnt flints and other materials heated in fire by early humans. There are major problems associated with this method (such as estimating the rate of electron entrapment), but it does have potential and has been recently used to establish some important dates. The other point in its favor is that its range of usefulness overlaps those of the carbon 14 and K/Ar methods.

The value of radioactive dating methods has been greatly increased by their use to date changes that we now know to have occurred in the earth's magnetic field. It appears that the north-south magnetic field of the earth has reversed in direction many times during the earth's history. (On such an occasion, a compass needle would point south instead of north.) The direction of the prehistoric magnetic field can be detected by measuring the "fossilized" direction of the magnetic field in a rock sample in the laboratory and comparing it with the north-south orientation that the sample had at the site. Such measurements of the so-called *fossil magnetism,* or *paleomagnetism,* of dated rocks have enabled geophysicists to prepare a chart (Figure 1–15) that indicates past ages of normal and reversed magnetism. The data help to tell us the age of sites for which potassium-argon or fission-track dates are not available. Fossil magnetism can also be used to cross-check potassium-argon and fission-track dates at better known sites. In Figure 1-15, the chart of normal and reversed polarity is matched with the stratigraphic sequence of the important and well-studied site of Olduvai Gorge, Tanzania (see also Table 9–1).

Paleomagnetism: magnetism preserved in rock originally generated by the earth's magnetic field. Past fluctuations in the intensity and direction of this field allow correlation between strata; a form of relative dating that can be used for absolute dating because the historic pattern of magnetic fluctuations and reversals is known and dated.

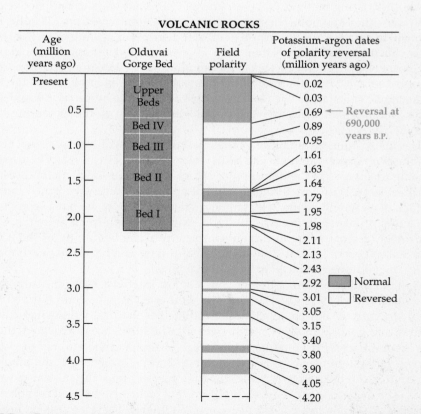

FIGURE 1–15 This time scale shows known reversals in world magnetic polarity during the past 4.5 million years. The evidence is obtained by measuring the polarity of volcanic lavas, which can also be potassium-argon–dated. Deposits that are only roughly dated by relative methods can often be more accurately dated by the measurement of their magnetic polarity and referral to this chart.

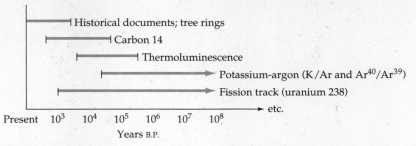

FIGURE 1–16 Approximate ranges of time in which dates can be established by the methods discussed in this chapter. Dates at the limits of any method are less reliable than those toward the center. The time scale is logarithmic.

Figure 1–16 summarizes the effective time spans of several chronometric dating methods based on radioactive decay.

Chronometric Dating Methods: Molecular Clocks

Finally, the dates for some of the key events in human evolution have been calculated from biochemical differences existing between living primate species. As we will see in Chapter 3, an integral part of the evolutionary process is change at the biochemical level in every species. Of particular importance, there is some evidence that amino acid sequences in certain proteins change over time at a roughly constant rate. Therefore, if we can measure the protein differences between related species, and if we know how fast those proteins change, we can use accumulated change to determine the date when the lineages leading to different living species diverged from their common ancestor (Figure 1–17). Such calculations produce scales known as *molecular clocks* (Table 1–2).

Molecular clocks: a variety of molecular measures for estimating the time of divergence of living species from their common ancestor.

Table 1–2 ESTIMATED TIMES OF EVOLUTIONARY DIVERGENCE AMONG HIGHER PRIMATES (IN MILLIONS OF YEARS AGO)

Species	Time of Divergence Based on Molecular Clock	Time of Divergence Estimated from Fossil Evidence
Humans and *Panidae*[a]	4.6 ± 0.7[b]	5–7
Humans and gibbons	12 ± 3[b]	12–21
Humans and Old World monkeys	20 ± 2[b]	26–35
Humans and New World monkeys	33.1[c]	38–45

[a]Chimpanzees, bonobos, and gorillas.
[b]Dates from J. E. Cronin, 1986, *South African Journal of Science* 82:83–85.
[c]Dates from V. Sarich, 1992, in *The Cambridge Encyclopedia of Human Evolution* (S. Jones, R. Martin, and D. Pilbeam, eds.), Cambridge, Cambridge University Press, pp. 303–306.

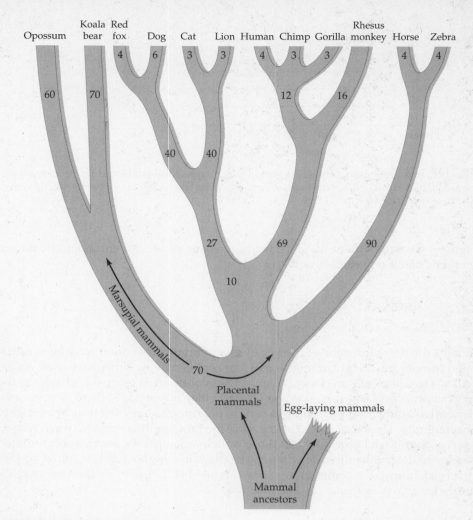

FIGURE 1–17 The protein molecules of all animals are made up of the same building blocks: 20 amino acids that link to form long chains. It is how the acids are arranged on the chains that determines which animal is which. The more alike the sequences of acids are, the more closely related the animals are; the more different the sequences are, the more distant the relationship, and the longer ago they evolved in different ways. This "family tree" devised by Vincent Sarich and Allan Wilson shows how differences in the proteins of species reflect their evolution since they split from a common ancestor. For instance, analysis shows 6 differences in one protein (serum albumin) between chimpanzees and gorillas, meaning that they evolved differently in relatively recent times (see the small fork at the top of the diagram). Humans show 7 differences from both chimpanzees and gorillas. Since the latter are already credited with 3 differences each, the remaining 4 go to humans, and their fork can be plotted at about the same point on the tree as the chimp-gorilla fork. Rhesus monkeys, which have about 31 serum albumin differences from humans, chimpanzees, and gorillas, must have split from the others earlier, so the fork is lower on the diagram. Only half the differences go to the rhesus monkeys; the other half are assigned to the apes (for the chimps and gorillas 12 + 3 = 15; for humans 12 + 4 = 16). The forks for the other animals shown are similarly derived.

Table 1-3 RELATIONSHIPS BETWEEN HUMANS AND OTHER PRIMATES USING BIOCHEMICAL MARKERS

Biochemical Marker	Chimpanzee	Gorilla	Gibbon	Old World Monkey	New World Monkey	Prosimian	Source
Protein immunology	8	8	18	40	70	140	V. M. Sarich and J. E. Cronin (1976)
DNA hybridization	2.3	2.4	6.4	9	15	—	R. E. Beneviste and G. J. Todaro (1976)
Amino acid sequencing	0.3	0.6	2.4	3.8	7.5	11.3	M. Goodman (1975)

Note: The figures in this table indicate the distance of humankind from other primates using various biochemical markers. Protein immunology (Line 1) uses several different classes of blood protein and gives a broad indication of immunological distance. The results are roughly comparable to those shown in Figure 1–17 based on a single protein. DNA hybridization results (Line 2) are claimed to signify the approximate number of major changes in DNA sequencing that have occurred since the two species separated in evolution. Each change in sequencing represents approximately 17,000 protein substitutions. Amino-acid-sequencing work on a number of different proteins shows percentage differences in amino acids between the same pairs of primates (Line 3). All these data contrast clearly the close biochemical relationship between humans and the great apes of Africa with the more distant relationships of humans with monkeys and prosimians.

All molecular clocks are based on certain working assumptions, particularly about the rate of biochemical change. While these clocks are becoming increasingly accurate, many paleontologists still feel that only fossils can give us conclusive evidence of the times when major lineages diverged.

Researchers have studied numerous biochemical systems, including amino acid sequences of blood serum proteins, hemoglobins, fibrinopeptides, and transferrins (the nonbinding proteins from serum). Also, DNA (discussed in Chapter 3) has been studied for the degree of chemical differences between different but related species. All this evidence points to an extremely close relationship between humankind and the African great apes (Table 1–3).

Modern Excavations

The excavation of sites occupied by early humans is time-consuming and demanding. The tools of today's field-worker are not so much picks and shovels as surveyor's transits, dental instruments, and small camel's hair brushes. With such tools, it may take two weeks to excavate properly a few square yards. Every scrap of bone that is gently and patiently worked free must be mapped both horizontally and vertically—everything recorded, everything labeled. When this kind of study in three dimensions is done, the information compiled from one occupation site can be compared with data gained from another site. There may well be an overlap, permitting the matching up of several layers from each of the two sites and a better understanding of both than was possible with one alone. Work of this sort is made still more precise when stone tools are brought into the picture, for different cultural phases are characterized by different kinds of tools and different techniques for making them.

Thus the full development of an important site may take many years and may require many specialists to analyze the findings in different ways, as well as substantial amounts of money. But the scientist does not select a site haphazardly. Something—bones or tools—must first be exposed by the erosional forces in nature to suggest that a site is worth investigating. Then a series of test trenches are opened to expose the layered deposits and to pinpoint concentrations of interesting materials. In these ways paleoanthropologists vastly improve their chances of significant discoveries; otherwise they might dig out an entire hillside, using up much time and large sums of research money, and find nothing at all.

Does this difficulty in finding sites mean that the great, exciting days of paleoanthropology are over? Not at all. It is true that the basic concepts have been established and there can no longer be quite the sense of absolute astonishment that greeted Hutton's concept of geological time and Darwin's theory of evolution, or even the amazed disbelief that greeted the discovery of Java man (see Chapter 10). Nevertheless, these are stirring times for paleoanthropologists. Not only is the body of evidence growing almost faster than it can be analyzed, but there are still surprises in store and problems unsolved. Each fact, each new bit of evidence that is found, speeds up the overall process of coming to an understanding of the story of human evolution. It also poses new and fascinating problems.

SUMMARY

Humans have always been keenly interested in their origins. Although in Europe early scientific inquiries into the subject were constrained by the Biblical story of creation and the belief that the world was very young, these obstacles began to fall away in the eighteenth and nineteenth centuries as evidence was amassed of an ancient earth (deep time) and the Darwin-Wallace evolutionary model was developed. Within a few years of the publication of *On the Origin of Species* in 1859, scientists began to apply Darwinian evolutionary theory to humans (Darwin himself did so in 1871). The likelihood that humans have had a long biological and cultural history opened the way for a true understanding of the stone artifacts that had been accumulating in European collections for 200 years.

Investigations into human origins have accelerated dramatically since the evolutionary breakthrough. Today teams of specialists work together to gather and interpret human fossils and artifacts, most of which can be quite accurately dated thanks to the development of new and sophisticated techniques. Further, numerous biochemical studies have proved the close evolutionary relationship of humans to the nonhuman primates (particularly the African apes) and have allowed reasonable estimates of evolutionary divergence dates.

In the chapters that follow, the full story of human evolution will be told. In order to understand that story, we will first explore the mechanisms of evolution and the biological and behavioral differences (and similarities) between humans and the other primates. The stage will then be set for a review of the fossil record from our ape ancestors through the apelike australopithecines and on to the genus *Homo* and modern people (Figure 1–18).

FIGURE 1–18 (Top) All versions (there are several, as discussed in later chapters) of humans' complete evolutionary tree show a "bushy" structure with lots of branches, including some dead ends. (Bottom) Streamlining the evolutionary tree down to those creatures thought to be direct ancestors of modern humans produces the familiar "march of progress." While such reconstructions provide some information about the sequence of our forebears, they often suggest far more knowledge of anatomy than we actually possess. In particular, information on degree of hairiness and skin color is lacking.

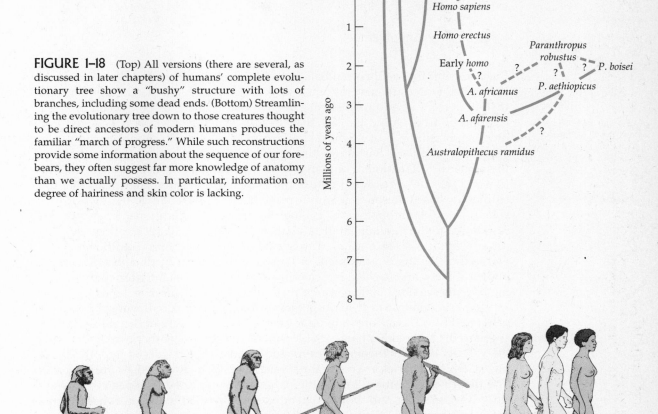

Australopithecus   Early *Homo*   *Homo erectus*   Archaic *Homo sapiens*   Early modern human   Modern humans

REVIEW QUESTIONS

1. Describe the effects of Christian beliefs and teachings on the development of evolutionary theory and the science of prehistory.

2. Discuss the development of *deep time* within European science. What were the ramifications of this development for evolutionary theory? Compare the ways Cuvier and Lyell read the record of geologic and organic change through time.

3. Compare *relative dating* and *absolute dating*. Give one or two examples of each sort of dating procedure.

4. Explain how *competition* and *natural selection* are related in Darwin's evolutionary model.

POSTSCRIPT

Creationism: the belief that humans and all life forms were specially created by God or some other divine force.

Fundamental Judeo-Christian beliefs and biblical literalism are alive and well in the United States and several other parts of the world. A 1993 Gallup poll found that 49 percent of adult Americans believe that humans are the result of special creation by God within the last 10,000 years. While *creationism* is believed in by only a tiny minority of scientists, its acceptance by a substantial portion of the American populace has important implications. Creationists argue that their Bible-based explanation of human origins is as valid as the evolutionary explanation and thus deserves equal time in public school curricula. They insist that their studies are based on sound scientific principles and even refer to their work as *creation science.* Anthropologists, geologists, and other traditional scientists have responded to the Fundamentalists' challenge by arguing that "creation science" is a sham and no science at all. The argument goes like this: Traditional science works through the development of *theories* (broad sets of principles that explain bodies of facts) and *hypotheses.* Scientific theories are constantly tested by generating hypotheses (falsifiable research predictions), which are then tested by laboratory experimentation or field observations. If most of the predictions (hypotheses) generated by a theory prove to be correct, then the validity of the entire theory is supported. On the other hand, if one's hypotheses consistently prove to be wrong, the validity of one's theory is destroyed. Based on the results of hypothesis testing, scientific theories are maintained unchanged, are modified, or are discarded. The theory of evolution, for example, has been subjected to repeated tests ever since Darwin's day, and though extended and modified in places, it has survived essentially intact.

Scientists argue that the problem with creation science is that the Fundamentalists' basic theory—that God created the world and its inhabitants recently and in a short time span—is not really open to falsification. Creationists may formulate hypotheses and gather data, but since their theory is truly an article of faith, there is no possibility of changing or discarding it, regardless of their results.

Creationists continue to press local school boards and textbook publishers to include their views. And traditional scientists continue to argue that, while material on creationism may be included legitimately in Bible courses or studies of comparative religion, it does not belong in the science classroom. What do you think? Your stand on this question could well affect your children's future public education.

Evolutionary Mechanisms
I. The Riddle of Heredity

*Variety's the very spice of life,
That gives it all its flavour.*

WILLIAM COWPER, 1731–1800. *The Task*,
BOOK 2

OVERVIEW

Darwin worked out his theory of evolution without a clear understanding of the mechanisms of heredity. These mechanisms were greatly clarified during the nineteenth and early twentieth centuries by several workers, including Mendel, De Vries, Fisher, and Wright. This chapter tells the story of the beginnings of the science of genetics, the discovery of the hereditary units (genes), and the debate over the relative contributions of mutation and natural selection to evolution. Important concepts include heredity, genotype-phenotype, dominance-recessiveness, homozygous-heterozygous, the principle of segregation, the principle of independent assortment, and mutation.

EARLY VIEWS ON HEREDITY

Charles Darwin managed to deduce the operation of natural selection even though he was missing two major pieces of the evolutionary puzzle: knowledge of the source(s) of variation between individuals and knowledge of the mechanisms of heredity. Darwin knew only that in all species variations routinely occur in every generation and that offspring often inherit parental traits.

For decades after the principles of evolution had been formulated, these knotty problems remained: Why do living things vary, how do variations occur, and how are parental traits (including variations) inherited? It was clear that evolution functions through the selective preservation or elimination of the inherited differences between individuals, yet no one could say how such differences come about in the first place. To complicate the problem, people knew that traits were preserved by inheritance but did not know how a given trait was handed down from parent to offspring. Black-haired parents could produce a child with red hair, which the child inherited from a grandparent or an even more remote ancestor. Baffled, people fell back on the idea that heredity is somehow transmitted with the blood, and that a child bears a blend of the parents' bloods. So deeply rooted was this idea that it became a part of the language: people spoke of a prince "of royal blood" or a "blooded" mare and said, "Blood will tell."

Blending inheritance: an outmoded theory stating that offspring receive a combination of all characteristics of each parent through the mixture of their bloods; superseded by Mendelian genetics.

In Darwin's day, this idea of *blending inheritance* held sway, and yet it introduced a seemingly insurmountable problem. If each child is a blend of the parents' characteristics, the succession of generations must result in a loss of variation. The long-term effect of sexual reproduction within a population would have to be decreasing variability, until all individuals were almost exactly the same. And yet the opposite is true: variability is maintained over time and often increases.

Darwin was plagued for years by this problem. In an attempt to discover how traits are inherited, he experimented with the garden pea and other plants. For all the care he took, he could never figure out the pattern or order of inheritance that he felt certain must exist. Nor, apparently, could anyone else. Darwin read many scientific journals, but none enlightened him. And yet, by an ironic coincidence, the theory of evolution and the fundamentals of heredity were discovered independently, as we shall see, at about the same time.

WORK OF GREGOR MENDEL

Just as Darwin was turning at last to the final formulation of the theory of evolution, the Augustinian monk Gregor Johann Mendel (1822–1884) (Figure 2–1) launched the first of a series of experiments that were to demonstrate that inheritance, like evolution, is not chaos, chance, or miracle, but a matter of natural law. But Mendel's discoveries were not immediately seized upon and incorporated

FIGURE 2–1   Gregor Mendel's country childhood gave him deep knowledge and sympathetic understanding of the plant world. As a monk with some leisure, he took up plant breeding in the monastery garden, with remarkable and brilliant results.

into the theory of evolution. Darwin never heard of Mendel's work, and the monk's reports lay ignored by the scientific world for more than 30 years.

Mendel was born on July 22, 1822, in a little village in what is now the Czech Republic. His father, Anton, was known for his fine fruit trees, and he taught young Johann how to improve them with grafts from the orchards of the local manor house. In addition to learning much from his father, Johann did well in his classes and was recommended for higher schooling, but there was little money to pay for it. By the time he had gone on to a two-year philosophy course at the Olmütz Institute, he knew that he would have to look for a profession in which he would be "spared perpetual anxiety about a means of livelihood." A teacher suggested that he enter the Augustinian monastery at Brünn. When he was accepted in 1843, he began religious studies there, assuming the name Gregor.

From his youth, as he said, Mendel had been "addicted to the study of Nature." In the monastery, as long as he continued his religious studies, he was free to work on botanical experiments. In a small strip of garden Mendel began experimenting with crossbreeding flowers. He soon discovered that when he crossed certain flower varieties the same characteristics kept appearing with surprising regularity. The books he consulted helped very little. Many people had studied hybridization, the crossing of two varieties or species, but no one had detected any pattern in the offspring. The varieties that resulted seemed to follow no rule, occurring in all sizes, colors, and forms.

First Experiments

It struck Mendel, who was remarkably free of preconceptions, that the studies themselves had been chaotic. No one had bred hybrids systematically for generation after generation and recorded exactly what individual characteristics appeared in each plant; no one had even worked out the kinds of experiments that would make this systematic study possible. Mendel decided to develop a workable procedure, realizing as he started that the experiments would have to be done on a large enough scale to rule out small accidents of chance.

To begin with, he needed *true-breeding* plants, plants that show little variation from generation to generation. He also needed a plant easily protected from all foreign pollen, for if an insect or a breeze should fertilize a plant with pollen from outside his garden, an experiment on the inheritance of some selected characteristic would be ruined. Legumes most nearly fulfilled his needs, and after some testing Mendel chose the common garden pea as the ideal experimental plant. The pea ordinarily fertilizes itself and is easily protected from outside pollen.

One of Mendel's greatest assets was that he worked step by step in patient, well-disciplined ways. Instead of trying to compare plant with plant in all possible respects, a procedure that would soon have led him into difficulties, he decided to study a few easily compared pairs of characteristics of the pea. He selected seven, illustrated in Figure 2–2:

1. The form of the ripe seed—round or wrinkled
2. The color of the peas—yellow or intense green
3. The color of the seed coats—gray or white
4. The form of the ripe pods—inflated or constricted between the seeds
5. The color of the unripe pods—green or vivid yellow

True breeding (breeding true): situation in which the members of a genetic strain resemble each other in all important characters and show little variability.

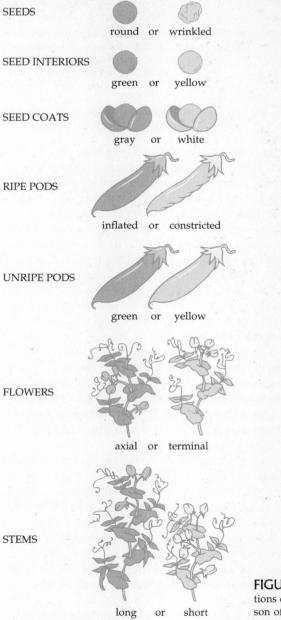

SEEDS

round   or   wrinkled

SEED INTERIORS

green   or   yellow

SEED COATS

gray   or   white

RIPE PODS

inflated   or   constricted

UNRIPE PODS

green   or   yellow

FLOWERS

axial   or   terminal

STEMS

long   or   short

FIGURE 2–2 Mendel's pioneering observations of the pea plant were based on a comparison of these 7 easily identifiable characteristics.

6. The position of the flowers—axial (distributed along the stem) or terminal (bunched at the top of the stem)

7. The length of the stem—long (6 or 7 feet; about 2 m) or short (9 to 18 inches; about 35 cm)

Mendel was now ready to produce hybrids, and he decided to start by crossing wrinkled-seed plants with round-seed ones. As soon as buds formed on the vines, Mendel opened those of each wrinkled plant and pinched off the stamens to prevent the pea from producing pollen for its own fertilization. To prevent any

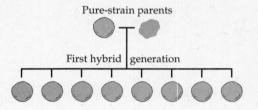

Pure-strain parents

First hybrid generation

FIGURE 2–3 This diagram shows the results obtained when Mendel crossed a plant produced by round seeds with one produced by wrinkled seeds. The hybrid seeds show the character of only one parent (round); this character Mendel termed *dominant*. Mendel got similar results with the other 6 pairs of characteristics.

Dominant: describes a trait that is expressed in the phenotype even when the organism is carrying only one copy of the underlying hereditary material (one copy of the responsible gene).

Recessive: describes a trait that is expressed only when the organism is carrying two copies of the underlying hereditary material (two copies of the responsible gene).

outside pollen from being carried in, he tied a little paper or calico bag around each bud. Then he collected pollen from the round-seed plants. This pollen he dusted on the stigmas of the wrinkled flowers, removing the protective bags to do so. He then performed the same interchange with each of the other pairs of characteristics he was testing. Altogether he fertilized 287 flowers on 70 plants.

Then he could only wait until time, sun, and rain performed their work. Finally, he was able to open the pods of his round-wrinkled hybrids. In them nestled only round peas. The wrinkling, a trait of half of the parents, had disappeared as completely as though it had never existed. So it was with the other six characteristics he tested: when he crossed tall plants with short ones, all the offspring were tall; when he mated yellow peas with green, all the offspring were yellow. In each test plot, one characteristic and only one appeared in this first hybrid generation (Figure 2–3).

During the winter, as Mendel worked with his jars of labeled pea seeds, he decided to call the characteristic that prevailed (like roundness or yellowness) *dominant*, and the one that seemingly disappeared (like wrinkledness or greenness) *recessive*. Thanks to his methodical approach, he knew what had gone into his hybrids. The next step was to see whether the recessive characteristics had survived the crossing. To find that out, he planned to let the hybrids fertilize themselves in the normal manner of peas. In the spring he planted his hybrid seeds and waited.

Once again the critical time came when the pods could be opened. Mendel broke open the first. Inside lay both round and wrinkled peas, side by side in the same pod! The wrinkling of the wrinkled grandparent, lost in the first generation, had reappeared. Mendel harvested 7,324 peas: 5,474 were round and 1,850 wrinkled. The ratio was nearly three round to one wrinkled.

It was the same for the other characteristics in the second generation. In the experiment on color there were three yellow peas to each green. Overall—ruling out a few small deviations introduced by chance—the ratio was always 3:1. Here was no haphazard recurrence of the traits of the grandparents, but an exact recurrence (Figure 2–4).

What would happen in the third generation? The next year Mendel planted his 3-to-1 group and again permitted each plant to fertilize itself. Now the wrinkled seeds (those showing the recessive characteristic) produced only wrinkled peas, and as long as Mendel continued to plant their descendants (he planted seven generations), they produced only wrinkled peas.

The story was remarkably different with the round seeds, however. In appearance they were all indistinguishable, but internally some were different from others. When Mendel planted them, these differences appeared (see Figure 2–5). Two out of three of the plants produced both round and wrinkled peas, in the ratio of 3:1. One out of three plants bore only round peas. Why did seemingly identical peas produce such varied descendants? With this question, Mendel began to solve the riddle of heredity. The true hereditary nature of the round peas was hidden

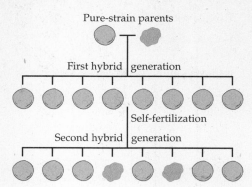

Pure-strain parents

First hybrid | generation

Self-fertilization

Second hybrid | generation

FIGURE 2–4 The production of a second hybrid generation by the self-fertilization of the plants produced by the seeds in Figure 2–3 showed that the first-generation hybrids had carried the characteristics of both their parents, but with the wrinkled characteristic hidden. The new generation of seeds was made up of both kinds (like the pure-strain parents), but came in the proportion of 3 round ones to 1 wrinkled.

deep within their cells. Some were truly round and produced only round descendants. Others merely looked round and produced both wrinkled and round descendants. Which was which could be revealed only by planting them and seeing what kinds of seeds they would produce. This test disclosed that two out of three plants that looked round were actually hybrids containing both the round and the wrinkled trait; only one in three was a true round. (Today, we call the hereditary qualities of a plant or animal its *genotype* and their physical expression its *phenotype*. A pea whose phenotype is round might have either a round or a round-and-wrinkled genotype.)

Mendel labeled the dominant characteristics *A* and the recessive ones *a*. When *A* and *A* came together, it meant two dominants; if these plants self-fertilized, they would produce nothing but round peas. These peas are described as *homozygous*. When *a* and *a* came together, it meant two recessives—and as

Genotype: the genetic makeup of a plant or animal; the total information contained in all genes of the organism.

Phenotype: the observable characteristics of a plant or an animal; the expression of the genotype.

Homozygous: having identical versions of a gene (alleles) for a particular trait.

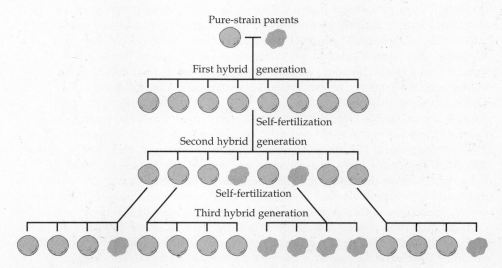

Pure-strain parents

First hybrid | generation

Self-fertilization

Second hybrid | generation

Self-fertilization

Third hybrid generation

FIGURE 2–5 Mendel found the explanation of the 3:1 proportion shown in Figure 2–4 when he allowed the second generation plants to self-pollinate. In the third hybrid generation he found new combinations of characteristics. The wrinkled seeds had bred true (and would always do so); some of the round peas also bred true, while others repeated the 3:1 ratio.

Hybrid parents

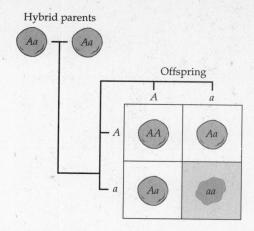

FIGURE 2–6   The experiment described in Figure 2–4 was explained by Mendel in this way. Using the letters *A* and *a* for the characters smooth and wrinkled, he accounted for the 3:1 proportion by proposing that *A* is always dominant to *a* in every hybrid.

Heterozygous: having different versions of a gene (alleles) for a particular trait.

long as the plants self-fertilized, there would be nothing but wrinkled peas, also a homozygous condition. It was only when *A* was combined with *a* to form the *heterozygous* type *Aa* that hybrids occurred. Though the phenotype was characterized by *A*, these hybrids could produce different kinds of offspring in future generations (see Figure 2–6).

Experiments Using Many Characteristics

Mendel had concentrated so far on single contrasting characteristics. What would happen, he next asked, if two or more diverse characteristics were studied together? To see, he crossed round yellow peas (peas showing two dominant characteristics) with wrinkled green peas (with two recessive characteristics). As he anticipated, all first-generation offspring were round and yellow. But in the next plantings, the round yellows revealed their inner nature: their genotype. As Mendel broke open the pods, he found that some had four kinds of peas: round yellow, wrinkled yellow, round green, and wrinkled green. The ratio was almost exactly 9:3:3:1 (Figure 2–7).

It is a remarkable fact that Charles Darwin, in similar experiments, also had obtained the 3:1 division in the hybrids. Being no mathematician, however, he had failed to understand the significance of what he was seeing. But Mendel grasped it easily. If each trait marked a separate hereditary factor, then he was obtaining every combination that could possibly be formed. Combine *A* and *a*, and only one unit could be formed: *Aa*. But if *Aa* and *Aa* came together, three different combinations could be made: *AA*, *Aa*, and *aa*. Thus from a cross of a pair of hybrids (*Aa* × *Aa*) 3 kinds of offspring would be produced; from a cross of a pair of double hybrids, in which two kinds of characteristics are studied (*AaBb* × *AaBb*), 9 kinds would be produced (as shown in Figure 2–7); from a triple-hybrid cross, 27. The combinations would pile up three times three times three, in cubic power. In short order the possible variations could reach an astronomical number.

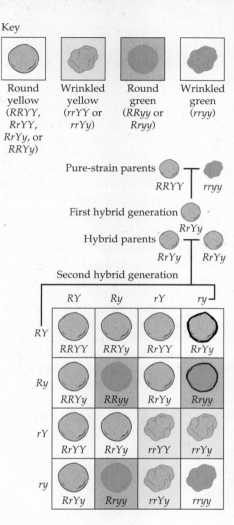

Key

Round yellow (*RRYY*, *RrYY*, *RrYy*, or *RRYy*)

Wrinkled yellow (*rrYY* or *rrYy*)

Round green (*RRyy* or *Rryy*)

Wrinkled green (*rryy*)

Pure-strain parents   *RRYY* | *rryy*

First hybrid generation   *RrYy*

Hybrid parents   *RrYy*   *RrYy*

Second hybrid generation

	RY	Ry	rY	ry
RY	RRYY	RRYy	RrYY	RrYy
Ry	RRYy	RRyy	RrYy	Rryy
rY	RrYY	RrYy	rrYY	rrYy
ry	RrYy	Rryy	rrYy	rryy

FIGURE 2–7 The Punnett square shows Mendel's law of independent assortment. A pea with two dominant characteristics (roundness and yellowness, *RR* and *YY*) is crossed with a pea having two recessive characteristics (wrinkledness and greenness, *rr* and *yy*). The hybrid combines all four genes of its parents (*RrYy*). If these hybrids are crossed, their genes produce the combinations shown: four kinds of peas appearing in a ratio of 9:3:3:1.

Principles of Segregation and Independent Assortment

Mendel lacked the microscopic techniques to peer into the inner structure of his peas and search out the physical units of heredity that his experiments told him must exist. His results, however, were explicable in no other way. Mendel proceeded to formulate the biological laws that he saw must underlie his findings:

1. Heredity is transmitted by a large number of independent, heritable units (now called *genes*). These occur in pairs in individuals. The pairs are separated during the production of gametes (eggs and sperm or ovules and pollen) so that a gamete has only one of each kind. This is the principle of segregation.

2. When each parent contributes the same kind of factor (producing a homozygous offspring), a similar characteristic is produced in the progeny. If each furnishes a different kind (producing a heterozygous offspring), a hybrid results, and when the hybrid forms its own reproductive cells the two different units

"liberate" themselves again. The hereditary units are unaffected by their long association in an individual.

3. Hereditary units for different traits are generally inherited independently of one another. This is the principle of independent assortment.

Finally, in late 1864, after eight years of work and innumerable crosses, Mendel wrote the paper that would demonstrate for the first time how individual traits are transmitted from parent to offspring. On a frosty night in February 1865, Mendel read his paper before the Brünn Society for the Study of Natural Science. The members listened in unbroken silence to his discussion of the unvarying ratios in pea hybrids. At the next meeting Mendel went on to explain what the ratios meant. The combination of mathematics and botany was unheard of, and the idea that lay behind it, a vast shuffling of unseeable, unknown units, ran completely contrary to the belief that heredity was a matter of blending. The minutes of the meetings recorded no questions and no discussion, but Mendel was invited to prepare his paper for publication in the society's proceedings. The monk's monograph, "Experiments in Plant Hybridization," appeared in 1866. Copies of the publication were sent, as usual, to more than 120 other scientific organizations and universities in Europe and America. Once more there was silence. No one praised or disputed Mendel's work or gave it any attention at all. Probably no one saw that it had any significance. Soon after, Mendel attempted to establish that his results were applicable to other plants, but during experiments with beans upsetting results began to appear. Only in certain characteristics did bean flowers follow the same laws as peas. When Mendel crossed a white-flowered, white-seeded bean with a bean having reddish purple flowers and red seeds flecked with black, all of the first generation bore pale red flowers unlike either parent. In the next

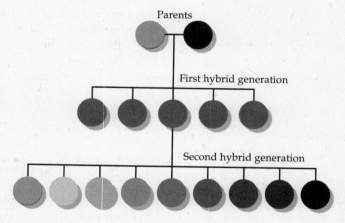

FIGURE 2–8 The question of flower color in beans proved complex. When red- and white-flowered strains were crossed, the first generation bore flowers of a single intermediate color, whereas the second bore flowers of many intermediate shades. By a brilliant insight, Mendel explained this result by postulating that two hereditary characters are responsible for flower color in this species. This meant that 1 in 9 of the second generation plants would bear flowers similar to each parent stock and the remainder would be intermediate.

hybrid generation Mendel was greeted with a range of color, from pure white through a wide spectrum ending in reddish purple. He saw colors that had not previously appeared in any of his test plants.

Could he have been wrong? Could an error have been made in his first results, which had shown that the first hybrid generation resembled the dominant parent? As Mendel puzzled over the in-betweenness of the pale red flowers of the first generation and the many colors of the second, it occurred to him that the nonconforming results could be explained if color is determined in some species not by a single hereditary unit, but by two units acting together. The two units could produce nine variations of color, as shown in Figure 2–8.

Mendel's explanation for the in-between appearance of many offspring was that more than one hereditary unit enters into the production of certain traits. Though Mendel knew nothing of how the hereditary units might be arranged in the cell, he had come upon yet another of the basic laws of heredity.

In 1868 Mendel was elected abbot of the monastery. At first he thought that the new post would afford wider opportunities for his work, but this proved a futile hope. Other duties pressed on him, and soon his experiments with hybridization had to be dropped entirely. Death eventually came to the abbot on January 6, 1884. The townspeople and civil and religious authorities gathered for the funeral of a man they held in the highest esteem. But in all that gathering—and indeed in all the world at large—no one realized that a great scientist, the man who had laid out the basic patterns of inheritance, had gone, or that his fame would be everlasting. Most of Mendel's experimental notes and records were burned by the monks.

MENDEL'S WORK REDISCOVERED

Darwin had died two years before Mendel, never having found the answer to the ever-present problem of the evolutionary base—the causes of the variations—on which natural selection acts. With the passing of the years, the problem became increasingly critical; the answer had to be found if the theory of evolution was to be accepted. In the 1880s one of those asking how the variations and modifications of life come about was Hugo De Vries (1848–1935), a botanist at the University of Amsterdam. De Vries (Figure 2–9) accepted Darwin's thesis that descent with modification is the main law of nature in the organic world. But if natural selection has only small, individual variations to act on, how can wide differences between species be produced?

De Vries knew that breeders could produce only limited changes when they had only small individual differences to work with. By selecting the redder tulips in their gardens they could breed a more intensely red flower. But for a completely different shade of red, they had to wait for nature to produce what De Vries called a *mutation*, a radical change from previously existing qualities. Darwin had used the word *sport* for such suddenly appearing new characteristics and had emphasized their importance but could offer no conclusive evidence in support of that emphasis. Some of his followers, in their all-out insistence on natural selection, tended to dismiss the effect of these sudden changes.

Mutation: generally, a spontaneous change in the chemistry of a gene that can alter its phenotypic effect. The accumulation of such changes may contribute to the evolution of a new species of animal or plant.

FIGURE 2–9 Hugo De Vries was a Dutch botanist of great distinction. From his observations of the evening primrose *Oenothera lamarckiana*, De Vries developed a theory of mutation that was to prove very important in our understanding of genetics. He was also the first to recognize the importance of Mendel's observations—35 years after Mendel announced them.

De Vries's Work on the Evening Primrose

De Vries decided to watch for the occurrence of mutations. He thought that they would most likely be found in some place where a plant was adapting to new living conditions. One afternoon in 1886, as he walked through the countryside near Hilversum, Holland, a yellow mass of the evening primrose *Oenothera lamarckiana* caught his admiring eye. The tall plants with the golden flowers had recently escaped from a nearby park and were multiplying rapidly in a former potato field. De Vries noticed that they varied widely. They differed in the shape of their leaves, in their mode of branching, and in their height. In one corner of the field De Vries found plants with such distinct traits that he concluded they were a new primrose species. De Vries had found the perfect radically varying plant for his studies.

During the next decade, De Vries raised or observed thousands of primrose plants. They showed remarkable independent variations in numerous traits, and De Vries noted that once a new plant type had appeared it tended to breed true rather than revert to the ancestral form. Based on his primrose studies, in 1900 De Vries reached the same conclusion that Mendel had formulated 35 years earlier: the characteristics of organisms are produced by "distinct, separate, and independent" hereditary units.

As he prepared his results—which he believed to be completely original—for publication, De Vries made a thorough literature search for related material. In the course of that search, he came across a reference to Mendel's paper and soon realized that to a great extent he had simply replicated the main findings of the Moravian monk. In his scientific report, De Vries gave full credit to his predecessor, and at long last Mendel's discoveries were properly recognized.

By a remarkable coincidence, Mendel was also rediscovered in 1900 by Karl Correns of Germany and Erich Tschermak of Vienna. The triple rediscovery undid the neglect of decades. Mendel received the scientific acclaim that had never come in his lifetime. The world, for its part, gained its first true understanding of the most immediate and ancient of mysteries: how the distinctiveness and the very form of all living things are passed down from parents to offspring. The theory of evolution at last had its base.

MUTATION AND NATURAL SELECTION

It began to seem to Hugo De Vries, once he had studied *Oenothera* and rediscovered Mendel's work, that evolution could never get anywhere by the slow process of natural selection alone. To him the sudden structural novelties that he called *mutations* (whose products he was overeager to label as new species) were the chief force in evolution. Natural selection, he argued, is not a force of nature but only a sieve that separates which organisms live and which die. It has nothing to do with the single steps of evolution; only after a step has been taken does the sieve act. It was clear to De Vries that novel characteristics—mutants—have to be put in the sieve before it can make a selection.

The Darwinians battled back. Natural, gradual selection is everything, they said, and large, sudden mutations in species are meaningless in evolution's long run. De Vries retorted that "the general belief in slow changes has held back science during half a century." The battle became fierce.

The Case of Mimicry

The mutationists for a time thought they had found incontrovertible proof in the phenomenon of mimicry (see Figure 2–10). In the Orient lives a handsomely marked butterfly, *Danaida tytia*. Its grayish upper wings are patterned in a strong tracery of black, and its lower wings are etched in brown. In some of *Danaida*'s territory, the butterfly *Papilio agestor* also lives. Its wings bear the same coloring and markings as *Danaida*'s and are even very nearly the same shape, though they are slightly wider; in every important way *Papilio* is an excellent mimic of *Danaida*. The latter has another mimic in southwest China, *Neptis imitans,* just as close a replica, with the same striking colors and designs. Even a careful observer—or a careless bird—may mistake the mimics for *Danaida*. And this is the point of the mimicry. For all its delicate appearance, *Danaida* is a tough, rubbery insect. Naturalists have seen it flutter away unharmed after being seized by a bird and dropped because of its bad taste. And so birds avoid *Danaida*. On the other hand, *Papilio* and *Neptis* are tender morsels. They have found safety in mimicking the unpalatable *Danaida*; the more they resemble it, the better is their chance of not being eaten.

The mutationists decided that such wonderful resemblances could have arisen only by mutation. How else could an elaborate design on the wings of a butterfly come into being? Mimicry, they said, is the outstanding proof of mutation, or the

FIGURE 2–10   Mimicry occurs quite widely among animals (and even some plants). In this example, the monarch butterfly *Danais plexippus* (top) is mimicked by the Nymphalid butterfly *Limenitis archippus* (bottom). Both butterflies have an orange ground and black and white markings. Experiments have demonstrated the function and effectiveness of this mimicry: The monarch butterfly is protected from predators by its unpalatability; *Limenitis* is protected by mimicking it.

"discontinuous" origin of species (the Darwinians argued for the "continuous," or steady, evolution of species caused by natural selection).

Mathematical Evidence

The dispute was a standoff until such men as Sir Ronald Aylmer Fisher, J. B. S. Haldane, and Sewall Wright entered the fray with a new weapon, mathematics. Because they can be counted, such things as hereditary units, degrees of difference, and alterations in natural populations are subject to mathematical analysis and testing. Fisher, a statistician, mathematician, and, later, a professor of genetics at Cambridge, brought mathematical analysis to bear on the mutationists' pet phenomenon, mimicry. His calculations showed that only natural selection acting on relatively small variations could bring about such intricate adaptations as the matching of mimic to model. The double occurrence of patterns and shapes by the randomness of mutation is so unlikely as to be mathematically impossible.

   Nor could mutation explain the proximity of model and mimic, which are always found in the same regions and in the same season. Often *Danaida* and its imitators are captured flying together. If their similarities had arisen by mutation, why should the same patterns not have occurred in other butterflies in other places? Fisher also pointed out that the mimic resembles the copied species no more than is necessary. Beneath the obvious, eye-deceiving colorings, shapes, and movements, model and mimic are as unlike as any two species.

Role of Mutations

After additional proofs confirmed Fisher's findings, natural selection was unequivocally assigned the role of evolution's prime agent. Mutation was given a supplementary role. Mutation alone was no longer credited for the amazing adaptations of the natural world, but research showed that it at least supplies raw material for these changes. Mutation is indeed the major source of new genetic material in all organisms. Without the new opportunities produced by mutation, evolution would surely stagnate, its products unable to adapt to such changes in the physical environment as ice ages, long droughts, and the slow elevations and subsidences of the earth's crust, or to such changes in the living environment as the appearance of a swifter predator, a deadlier germ, or a new competitor for food.

"The function of a mutation," wrote Fisher, "is to maintain the stock of genetic variance at a high level." If this analysis was right, some seeming contradictions had to be resolved. Work in many laboratories was showing that most mutations are detrimental, and most drastic ones lethal. They are steps in the wrong direction, in the sense that any random change in a smooth-running, well-adjusted organism is likely to be for the worse. Most bearers of radical mutations never survive long enough to pass the changes along to offspring. How, then, can mutations build up a "stock" for variation?

In fact, whereas a big change in an organism is often fatal, a tiny change or adjustment may be an improvement. A few mutations, generally small ones, may prove beneficial to the individuals that carry them. The next question for geneticists was: How can a rare, tiny, beneficial change—say, a minute change in the color or pattern of a butterfly's wings—spread through a species with a large population? Will it not be swamped by the fact that the mutant will be vastly outnumbered by the normal individuals? Not at all, said the mathematicians. Assume that a mutation offers an advantage of only one percentage point to the organism in which it arose, meaning the survival of 100 mutants as against 99 unmutated individuals. In a short time (as evolution goes)—say, 200 generations—the mutant would replace the original as the population's normal type. And so, by natural selection even a small change in adaptability spreads relatively quickly throughout the species. Although harmful or useless mutations may crop up, vanish, and reappear, the ones that ultimately pervade a species and become part of its normal makeup are either neutral or beneficial.

To Fisher, the great contrast between populous species and unpopulous ones lay in the fact that an abundance of individuals means an abundance of possible mutations and hence more possibilities of adapting to new conditions. With fewer possible mutants to help it cope with changes in the environment, a small species might eventually dwindle into extinction. But a numerous species, such as humankind, is likely to have a varied enough genetic pool to meet almost any change that might confront it. If a species had only 100 characteristics that would exist in two forms, Fisher computed, more than 1,000,000,000,000,000,000,000,000,000,000 genetic combinations would be possible when two of its members produced offspring. Mendel's conclusion that the number of combinations would increase in mathematical ratio was amply borne out. Evolution, Fisher realized, could head off in many directions and along tangents no one could conceive of. Haldane, from his own calculations, reached conclusions that agreed with Fisher's. Recently it has become clear that, although structure imposes limits, natural populations possess an enormous reservoir of genetic variation, much of it not expressed in the phenotype.

"It has not so often been realized," Fisher commented, "how far most species must be from a state of stagnation, or how easily, with no more than one hundred factors, a species may be modified to a condition considerably outside the range of its previous variation." In *The Genetical Theory of Natural Selection* (1930), Fisher proved that this richness of genetic variability is directly related to fitness for survival. What counts is not the single plant surviving the drought or the one rabbit eluding the fox, but the nature and the preservation of the genetic material that makes it possible for the plant species or the rabbit species as a whole to survive. Fisher saw organic evolution as the evolution of the mysterious, almost infinitely variable hereditary units whose existence Mendel had inferred.

SUMMARY

The problem of heredity was a stumbling block to Darwin. He was not aware of the work of Mendel, who published the results of his experiments with peas (1866) and formulated his two laws of heredity: that of segregation and that of independent assortment. His work was recognized only in 1900, when De Vries (who gave us the concept of mutation) and others read Mendel's publications.

The problem of mutation and its role in evolution continued to be a matter for research and discussion until it was to a great extent resolved by the mathematical approach of Fisher, Haldane, and Sewall Wright.

Darwin, Mendel, De Vries, Fisher, and Sewall Wright are just five of a group of distinguished biologists who have revolutionized our view of the natural world. As time has passed, we have come to understand that everything they learned about nature—about finches, peas, evening primroses, or butterflies—was equally true of humankind. We now realize that the science of biology holds the key to many secrets of our nature and our origin.

REVIEW QUESTIONS

1. How did Gregor Mendel's work contribute to the theory of evolution proposed by Charles Darwin (and still in use today)?

2. In retrospect, De Vries, Correns, and Tschermak would have been saved considerable time and effort if they had discovered Mendel's work *before* conducting their own studies of heredity. Discuss the importance of thorough preparation (including a literature review) before beginning a research project.

3. How does mutation contribute to the process of evolution by natural selection?

4. Why are large-scale mutations usually *selected against*, while small-scale mutations are often preserved?

POSTSCRIPT

Gregor Mendel's pioneering studies went a long way toward disproving the old notion that inheritance worked through a blending, or fusing, of parental traits in each offspring. To be sure, because of the effects of the principles of segregation and independent assortment, each offspring represents a mixture of parental characteristics, but within the genotype, the integrity of individual hereditary particles (genes) is maintained across the generations. Later work by Mendel's scientific successors showed how genes (and their phenotypic effects) can be altered by mutation—but once altered, mutant genes seem to follow the principles of particulate inheritance like their unaltered counterparts.

Very recent research, however, has revealed a new kind of genetic blending in nature. This blending, which still falls short of gene fusion or melding, involves the remarkable combination of genetic material between species through the action of bacteria and viruses. Bacteria are single-celled creatures whose genetic material is not contained within a nucleus (thus, they are classified as *prokaryotes*, "before a nucleus"; cells with a nucleus are *eukaryotes*). Bacteria contain a single chromosome (see Chapter 3), and in addition, they may carry accessory pieces of self-replicating, semiautonomous genetic material called *plasmids*. Plasmids have the interesting property of being able to travel from one bacterium to another, including being able to move between bacterial species. Within its new bacterial "home," an immigrant plasmid's genes supplement the genetic material of the host cell, sometimes with interesting results. For example, unfortunately for humans' ability to fight disease, many bacteria are now resistant to penicillin. This resistance is due not to an inherent capacity of the bacterial cell, however, but to a plasmid-carried gene that produces a substance (the enzyme beta-lactamase) that breaks down penicillin. Bacteria can thus "evolve" the ability to resist penicillin by acquiring a plasmid with the appropriate gene and by combining that plasmid's genetic material with its own. Ironically, the subsequent use of penicillin will bring about the selection of newly penicillin-resistant bacteria. Biologically neat— but from our standpoint, not particularly nice.

A second sort of interspecific genetic "blending" is very much in the news these days, and that is the combination of viral genes with those of a host organism—the sort of blending that leads to AIDS (acquired immune deficiency syndrome) in humans. Viruses are not living cells. They are essentially protein-encapsulated packets of genetic material (DNA or RNA; see Chapter 3) that depend on host cells for support and reproduction. The viruses that produce AIDS have been given the name HIV (human immunodeficiency virus). They are examples of retroviruses, so-called because they carry an enzyme that enables the virus to integrate its genetic material into that of the host cell. Infected cells thereafter faithfully copy the foreign genes until at some point they are reconverted into new human immunodeficiency viruses, which, when released, spread the infection by entering new host cells. HIV thus tricks the host into contributing to her or his own destruction.

The lesson to be learned from these studies is that nature always has a few tricks up its sleeve for each new generation of investigators. As Mendel showed, it is still true that genes are particulate hereditary units that are mixed during sexual reproduction, not blended in a way that destroys their integrity. Alterations in the character of genes typically occur by mutation, but occasionally—as shown by the bacterial and viral studies—*additions* to established genotypes can occur by a sort of blending or combination that may even cross species' boundaries. It is discoveries like these that make genetics and evolutionary biology such exciting and dynamic fields a century after Mendel and Darwin.

CHAPTER

3

Evolutionary Mechanisms
II. Genes and Populations

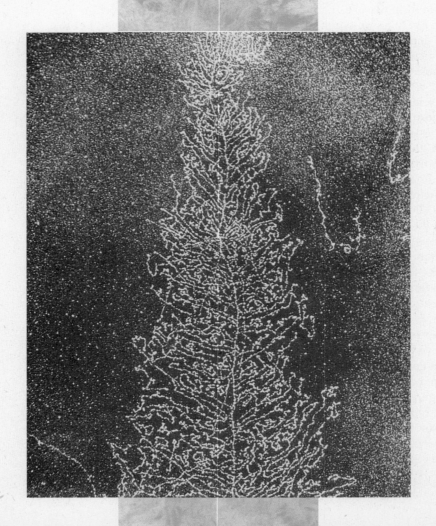

*T*he object is to combine certain ideas derivable from a consideration
  of . . . a population of organisms, with the concepts of the factorial
scheme of inheritance, so as to state the principle of Natural Selection
in the form of a rigorous mathematical theorem.
              R. A. FISHER, 1890–1962. *The Genetical Theory of Natural Selection.*

OVERVIEW

Chapter 3 summarizes the tremendous advances in both genetics and evolutionary theory that occurred during the twentieth century. Using improved analytical
techniques, scientists discovered the detailed anatomy of the cell. Mendel's hereditary units also yielded to researchers' efforts, and the structure and chemistry of
genes became known, as well as the mechanisms of gene mutations. An understanding of mutations plus observations of chromosomes during cell division produced critical information about the source of phenotypic diversity within a
species—a major piece of the evolutionary puzzle that Darwin was missing. Perhaps most important of all, after geneticists and evolutionary biologists combined
efforts in the 1940s, evolutionary processes—particularly natural selection and
speciation—could be understood in genetic terms. This was the beginning of
"population genetics," which has since grown to be a major field of investigation.
Finally, additional insights were gained into the death of species through extinction. Important concepts from this chapter include cell division, gene chemistry
(DNA, RNA), protein synthesis, mutation, chromosomal recombination during
gamete production, population genetics, speciation, fitness, sexual selection, and
extinction.

UNITS OF HEREDITY

Chromosomes

In spite of his extraordinary achievements, Gregor Mendel had no way to discover
what form the hereditary units that he believed to exist might take, or where they
might be located in plants and animals. But data from a variety of sources were
converging on a crucial biological insight. Cells, those fundamental structural
units of life, had been discovered in the seventeenth century, and by the 1830s
some biologists were convinced that all organisms were constructed of cells (Figure 3–1). And while Mendel's monographs sat unread on library shelves,
researchers using improved microscopes found tiny, threadlike structures in cell
nuclei. Initially, of course, no one made the connection between these structures—
named *chromosomes* ("colored bodies") because they had to be stained to be seen
microscopically—and the mechanisms of inheritance. However, it was noted that
within each species all somatic cells (cells other than the sex cells, or *gametes*) had
the same number of chromosomes in the nucleus (now called the species' *diploid*

Chromosomes: coiled, threadlike structures of DNA, bearing the genes and found in the
nucleus of all plant and animal cells.

Gametes: reproductive haploid cells generated by meiosis, which fuse with gametes
of the opposite sex in reproduction. In animals, the
female gamete is the ovum;
the male gamete, the sperm.

FIGURE 3–1 This simplified diagram of an animal cell shows the nucleus (containing the gene-bearing chromosomes) separated from the remainder of the cell's contents (the cytoplasm) by the nuclear membrane. Important structures to note within the cytoplasm include the ribosomes, which contribute to protein synthesis and the mitochondria, which contain nonnuclear DNA.

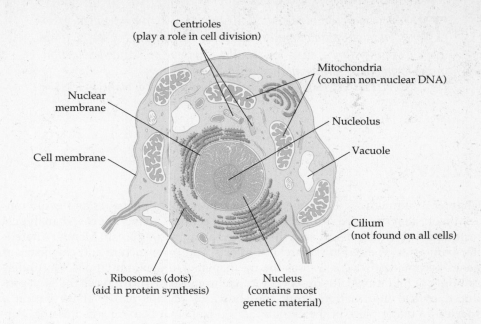

Centrioles
(play a role in cell division)

Mitochondria
(contain non-nuclear DNA)

Nuclear
membrane

Nucleolus

Cell membrane

Vacuole

Cilium
(not found on all cells)

Ribosomes (dots)
(aid in protein synthesis)

Nucleus
(contains most
genetic material)

Diploid number: the full chromosome count in somatic cells (all cells other than gametes).

Mitosis: cell division in somatic cells; two identical diploid cells result.

Chromatid: one of the two elements in a duplicated chromosome.

Centrioles: minute granules present in many cells outside the nuclear membrane. The centriole divides in cell division (*mitosis*), and the parts separate to form the poles of the spindle.

Cytoplasm: the contents of a cell excluding the nucleus.

Meiosis: cell division resulting in the formation of sex cells, each of which will have half the number of chromosomes present in the original cell (the haploid number).

Haploid number: the number of chromosomes carried by gametes; equal to one-half the full chromosome count of somatic cells.

number and symbolized $2n$). There were 20 in the cells of corn, 24 in the tomato, 14 in Mendel's pea plants, 8 in the fruit fly, 40 in the house mouse, 48 in the chimpanzee, and 46 in humans. Furthermore, close observation revealed that during somatic cell division, called *mitosis,* the chromosomes go through remarkable maneuvers (Figures 3–2 and 3–3). First, each chromosome undergoes replication, producing two *chromatids* and temporarily doubling the genetic material (Prophase). Next (during Metaphase), all chromatid pairs align themselves near the equator of a framework of microtubules called the *spindle* that stretches between the *centrioles.* Then the members of each pair separate, and one chromatid moves toward one pole of the spindle as its twin moves in the opposite direction (Anaphase). Cell division then proceeds to completion with a division of the *cytoplasm,* and the end result is two identical diploid ($2n$) cells where previously there had been only one (Telophase). (As we will see shortly, the cell division process called *meiosis,* which leads to sperm and egg cells, is very similar to mitosis with two important differences: the chromosome count is reduced by half to the *haploid number* [n], and significant scrambling of the genetic material occurs, producing genetically unique gametes.)

It was not until 1902, two years after the discovery of Mendel's work, that the suggestion was made independently by Walter Sutton in the United States and Theodor Boveri in Germany that chromosomes might be the containers of Mendel's hereditary units. In their coming together and pulling apart, they supply the kind of mechanism needed to produce Mendel's results.

A few years later William Bateson and R. C. Punnett, experimenting with sweet peas, crossed a purple-flowered plant having a long pollen grain with a red-flowered, round-grained plant. Instead of obtaining the independent segregation of characteristics that Mendel found in garden peas, these English researchers found that the red flower and the round pollen grain tended to stay in constant association. Other investigators came upon the same phenomenon. Certain traits seemed to be coupled; perhaps they were controlled by the same chromosome.

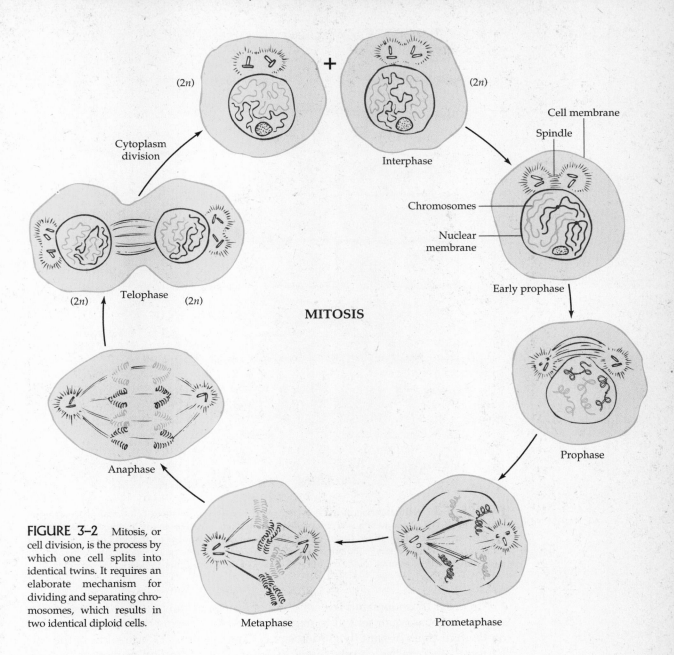

(2n)

Interphase

(2n)

Cytoplasm
division

Cell membrane

Spindle

Chromosomes

Nuclear
membrane

Early prophase

(2n) Telophase (2n)

MITOSIS

Prophase

Anaphase

FIGURE 3–2 Mitosis, or
cell division, is the process by
which one cell splits into
identical twins. It requires an
elaborate mechanism for
dividing and separating chromosomes, which results in
two identical diploid cells.

Metaphase

Prometaphase

Morgan's Work on Fruit Flies

Thomas Hunt Morgan was one of those finding associated characteristics. They
kept cropping up in the fruit flies with which he was working. For example, in
1910, about a year after he began studying *Drosophila melanogaster,* the little flies
that orbit ripe fruit, a male fly with white eyes appeared in one of the milk bottles
Morgan used for incubators. Since the wild flies have red eyes, Morgan felt certain
that this was a mutation. A series of crossings revealed that the mutant eye color
occurred only in males. It was therefore a *sex-linked trait.*

Sex-linked trait: an inherited
trait coded on the sex chromosomes and thus having a special distribution related to sex.

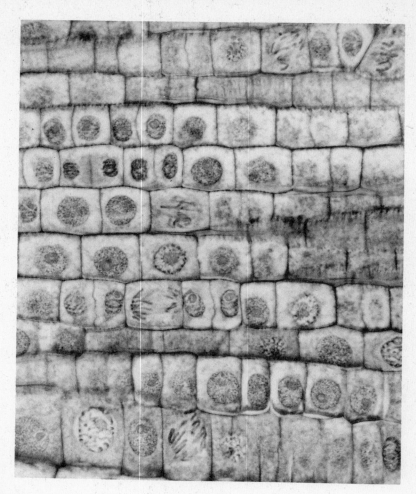

FIGURE 3–3   A thin section of the growing root tip of an onion shows cell division occurring in many places. The phenomenon is accompanied by remarkable changes in the nucleus (the dark circular zone in each rectangular cell), in which the chromosomes appear as threadlike structures that divide and are pulled apart as though by magnets. This is the process called *mitosis*, common to plants and animals, which ensures the distribution of copies of the entire genetic material to every cell.

In order to understand the coupling of traits and the role of chromosomes in such linkage, Morgan set out to map the hereditary factors that he suspected lay on the four pairs of fruit fly chromosomes. The task took 17 years, but in the end he found the precise chromosomal locations that controlled numerous specific characteristics in the fly, including body color, eye color, bristle type, and wing shape and size. One pair of chromosomes was even found to contain the factors that determine sex. The location of the mutant white-eye factor on the male-determining chromosome explained its sex-linked pattern. (The *sex chromosomes* are now known to differ strikingly between females and males in many species; Figure 3–4). The trait-determining hereditary units on chromosomes were named *genes* in 1909 by W. Johannsen.

It was soon discovered that the notion of "one gene–one trait" was overly simplistic, and that many traits (*polygenic traits*) were controlled by groups of genes.

Sex chromosomes: those chromosomes that carry genes that control gender (maleness or femaleness).

Polygenic traits: traits determined by more than one gene.

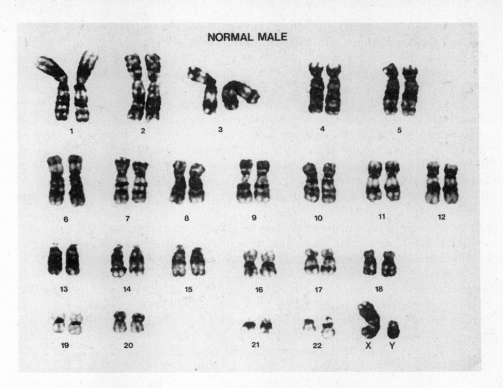

FIGURE 3–4   Humans have 46 chromosomes as 23 matching pairs. The sex chromosomes (labeled X and Y) are indicated in this photograph of male human chromosomes. Only males have the small Y chromosome, and so in this sex, the twenty-third pair cannot be matched. Females have two similar X chromosomes.

Nonetheless, inheritance was found to be particulate (as Mendel had already claimed), operating through the transmission of discrete bits of self-replicating matter, and also cooperative, with genes often combining or interacting to produce their effects. Furthermore, it was clear that Mendel's second principle, of independent assortment, was true only if the genes were on separate chromosomes. By some strange chance, or possibly as a result of trial and error, Mendel had chosen such independent characters of his pea plants, each on a separate chromosome. In reality many genes are linked on particular chromosomes and remain together through meiosis. With these realizations, not only did genetics find a firm scientific base, but the relations between genetics and evolution were put on a new and satisfactory footing.

Genes

But what *are* genes, how do they determine phenotypic traits, and what happens when they mutate? The answers to these and many other questions have come through the dedicated efforts of numerous researchers throughout this century. Thanks to the work of Morgan, H. J. Muller, F. H. C. Crick, J. D. Watson, F. Lipmann, and many others, we can now give a detailed (though by no means complete) description of the structure and functioning of genes.

Gene: primarily, a functional unit of the chromosomes in cell nuclei, which controls the coding and inheritance of phenotypic traits; some genes also occur in a closed loop in the mitochondria.

Mitochondria: granular or rod-shaped bodies in the cytoplasm of cells that function in the metabolism of fat and proteins. Probably of bacterial origin.

Locus: the position of a nuclear gene on a chromosome; each locus can carry only one allele of a gene.

Alleles: genes occupying equivalent positions in paired chromosomes, yet producing different effects in the phenotype when they are homozygous. They are alternative states of a gene, originally produced by mutation.

DNA (deoxyribonucleic acid): chemical substance found in chromosomes and mitochondria which reproduces itself and carries the genetic code.

Genes can be defined and understood in several ways. The vast majority of genes, including all those in the cell nuclei, are chromosomal segments, each with the potential to affect an organism's phenotype in some way. (Additionally, a few genes occur on closed loops in the *mitochondria*. These mitochondrial genes are discussed further in Chapter 16 and will concern us no further here.) This is the functional and commonsense definition of genes in which each gene is identified with the trait it affects. There are structural genes, such as those for skin color, eye color, and body shape and size, and also regulatory genes, which control the metabolic, energetic, and biosynthetic activities of the organism. Each nuclear gene tends to occupy a particular location (*locus*) on a particular chromosome (for example, the gene responsible for maleness in humans—the "testis-determining-factor"—occupies a locus on the short arm of the Y chromosome). A gene may also have several variant forms called *alleles* (such as the *R* and *r* alleles that control pea shape, as discussed earlier). Since chromosomes occur in pairs (one from each of an organism's parents), individuals either have similar alleles at a particular locus (the homozygous condition) or different alleles (the heterozygous condition).

A second definition for a gene is based on its molecular makeup. Chromosomes consist of long strands of *DNA (deoxyribonucleic acid)* a substance that was first discovered in 1869 by Friedrich Miescher and whose composition and structure were worked out by James Watson and Francis Crick in 1953. Since most genes are subunits of chromosomes, it follows that they are also subunits of chromosomal DNA. For a more exact molecular description, we must take a closer look at the makeup of DNA.

The DNA of a chromosome consists of two long, interlocking polynucleotide chains arranged in a double helix (Figure 3–5). The backbone of each chain is a

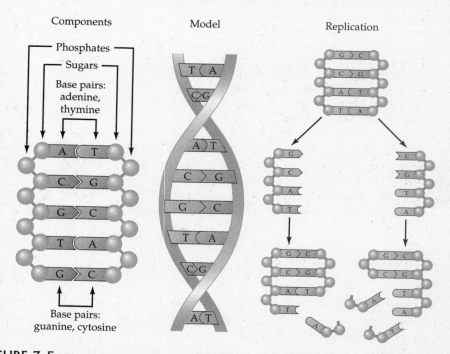

Components   Model   Replication

Phosphates
Sugars
Base pairs: adenine, thymine

Base pairs: guanine, cytosine

FIGURE 3–5   The DNA molecule is a double spiral (or helix) linked by four interlocking chemical subunits: the base pairs. Replication and protein synthesis take place by the splitting of the double helix: each separate strand replicates by synthesizing its mirror image from the unit molecules floating in solution, as shown here.

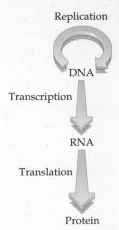

Replication

DNA

Transcription

RNA

Translation

Protein

FIGURE 3–6 The relationships between DNA and RNA that function during gene replication and protein synthesis.

series of linked sugar and phosphate molecules (deoxyribose phosphates), and each sugar-phosphate unit is bonded to a single *nucleotide* base. These bases come in four varieties—(A) adenine, (T) thymine, (G) guanine, and (C) cytosine—and the two chains are held together in a helical structure by the bonds between complementary nucleotide pairs (A with T, G with C). If the two chains are separated for individual analysis, each can be described by its sequence of *nucleotides*, for example, ACGTTGCAA. The nucleotides work in groups of three adjacent bases (e.g., ACG; such a triplet is called a *codon)* to code for the production of particular *amino acids* as part of protein synthesis within the cell (this is the first step in the production of phenotypic traits). Each gene consists of a long sequence of codons (humans' genes range in size from a few hundred to tens of thousands of base pairs) that work together to produce a particular protein. So, in summary, a gene can be identified in several ways: by the phenotypic trait it influences, by its chromosomal locus, and by its characteristic sequence of codons.

The DNA double helix actually becomes partially unraveled into two individual chains in two circumstances. First, during chromosomal replication in mitosis and meiosis, each chain serves as a template for the formation of its partner from newly synthesized polynucleotide units (Figure 3–5). Another name for this process, of course, is *gene replication.* And second, unwinding occurs during the transcription of DNA information into *RNA (ribonucleic acid)* as a step toward protein synthesis (Figure 3–6). A brief look at the process of protein synthesis reveals more details of the structure of genes and phenotype production.

Proteins are complex molecules composed of long chains of amino acids. They take a variety of forms, and collectively they coordinate and control our basic life processes, being involved in growth, development, reproduction, and bodily maintenance (one researcher has remarked that proteins "breathe life" into the information contained in genes). Examples of proteins include hemoglobin (responsible for oxygen and carbon dioxide transport throughout the body), collagen and keratin (building blocks of connective tissues and hair), the antibodies active within our immune system, and the enzymes that catalyze our biochemical reactions. The cellular process that results in protein synthesis begins with partial unwinding of the DNA helix (Figure 3–7). Transcription of the DNA information then starts as a strand of "messenger RNA" (mRNA) and is synthesized by complementary base pairing onto the DNA template. Interestingly, only certain portions of each gene's DNA, called *exon* segments, actually code for protein production. Long stretches of noncoding DNA, called *intron* segments, must therefore be

Nucleotides: organic compounds, consisting of bases, sugars, and phosphates; found in cells either free or as part of polynucleotide chains.

Codon: a nucleotide triplet that codes for the production of a particular amino acid during protein production.

Amino acids: a group of organic compounds that act as building blocks for proteins.

RNA (ribonucleic acid): a compound found with DNA in cell nuclei and chemically close to DNA; transmits the genetic code from DNA to direct the production of proteins. May take two forms: messenger RNA (mRNA) or transfer RNA (tRNA).

Proteins: molecules composed of chains of amino acids.

Exons: segments of a gene's DNA that code for protein production.

Introns: segments of a gene's DNA that do not code for protein production (so-called noncoding DNA).

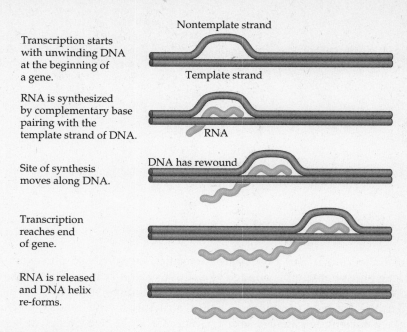

Transcription starts with unwinding DNA at the beginning of a gene.

RNA is synthesized by complementary base pairing with the template strand of DNA.

Site of synthesis moves along DNA.

Transcription reaches end of gene.

RNA is released and DNA helix re-forms.

Nontemplate strand

Template strand

RNA

DNA has rewound

FIGURE 3–7   The basic sequence of events during DNA-to-RNA transcription.

removed from the mRNA template after transcription is completed. This is done through a process called *splicing* that leaves the mRNA with only exon information (Figure 3–8).

Once a gene is completely transcribed, the mRNA strand is released, and the DNA helix re-forms. Messenger RNA is then engaged by particles called *ribosomes* that move along the mRNA chain and catalyze the translation of proteins, triplet codon by triplet codon (Figure 3–9). A key element in this process is the action of another form of RNA—"transfer RNA" (tRNA)—in engaging amino acids and

Ribosomes: cellular organelles that contribute to protein synthesis.

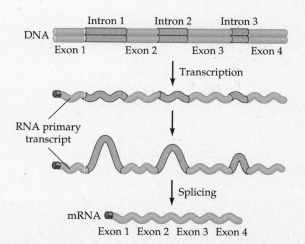

DNA

Intron 1   Intron 2   Intron 3

Exon 1   Exon 2   Exon 3   Exon 4

Transcription

RNA primary transcript

Splicing

mRNA

Exon 1   Exon 2   Exon 3   Exon 4

FIGURE 3–8   RNA splicing after transcription removes the noncoding introns and leaves only exon information.

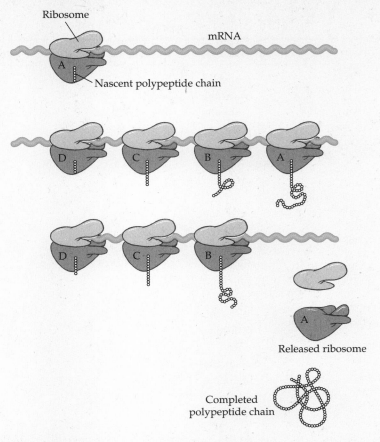

Ribosome

mRNA

Nascent polypeptide chain

Released ribosome

Completed
polypeptide chain

FIGURE 3–9 Multiple ribosomes sequentially engage mRNA after transcription and, aided by tRNA (not shown), catalyze the translation of the polypeptide chains that will form proteins. When a ribosome has completed its portion of polypeptide synthesis, it is released from the mRNA chain.

then positioning them on the mRNA template. Bit by bit, amino acids are assembled into long protein chains, all of which will contribute to the formation or operation of the organism's phenotype.

One of the strongest pieces of evidence supporting the theory that all life has evolved from a single source is the universal occurrence of the DNA genetic code (Table 3–1). In virtually all life forms, 61 DNA triplets encode the same 20 amino acids. One triplet (ATG) also functions as a "start" codon marking the beginning point for a protein coding sequence, while three triplets (TAA, TAG, TGA) function as "stop" markers. It is important to repeat, however, that not all of a cell's DNA actually contributes to protein production. Introns are noncoding sequences, and, surprisingly, they may account for ten times more DNA than do exons. Furthermore, at certain points on chromosomes, tandem repetitions of DNA sequences (called *satellite DNA*) tend to accumulate, and these are also likely to be noncoding. Satellite sequences probably account for around 5 percent of humans' DNA, while in some monkeys the figure may soar to 20 percent. How and why do these "silent" sequences of DNA accumulate, and what functions (if any) do they serve? At present, we have only partial answers for these and many other questions. Future studies promise to produce some surprises.

Satellite DNA: tandem repetitions of DNA sequences that accumulate at certain locations on chromosomes and are usually noncoding.

Table 3–1 THE GENETIC CODE

DNA Codon	Amino Acid	DNA Codon	Amino Acid
GCA	alanine	AGA	arginine
GCG	alanine	AGG	arginine
GCT	alanine	CGA	arginine
GCC	alanine	CGG	arginine
		CGT	arginine
GAT	aspartic acid	CGC	arginine
GAC	aspartic acid		
		AAT	asparagine
TGT	cysteine	AAC	asparagine
TGC	cysteine		
		GAA	glutamic acid
CAA	glutamine	GAG	glutamic acid
CAG	glutamine		
		GGA	glycine
CAT	histidine	GGG	glycine
CAC	histidine	GGT	glycine
		GGC	glycine
ATA	isoleucine		
ATT	isoleucine	TTA	leucine
ATC	isoleucine	TTG	leucine
		CTA	leucine
AAA	lysine	CTG	leucine
AAG	lysine	CTT	leucine
		CTC	leucine
ATG	methionine/**start**		
		TTT	phenylalanine
CCA	proline	TTC	phenylalanine
CCG	proline		
CCT	proline	AGT	serine
CCC	proline	AGC	serine
		TCA	serine
ACA	threonine	TCG	serine
ACG	threonine	TCT	serine
ACT	threonine	TCC	serine
ACC	threonine		
		TGG	tryptophan
TAT	tyrosine		
TAC	tyrosine	GTA	valine
		GTG	valine
TAA	**stop**	GTT	valine
TAG	**stop**	GTC	valine
TGA	**stop**		

Genes, then, are self-replicating units that ultimately code for various aspects of the phenotype (traits) or for phenotypic support and regulation. Of course, precisely how a trait is expressed in a given organism is the result of the interaction between genes (often working collectively if the trait is polygenic) and the environment; for example, persons who are undernourished in childhood may be stunted as adults even if they inherited genes for large body size. But many phenotypic differences between conspecifics cannot be attributed to environmental influences and must be due primarily to genetic differences. Since interindividual differences in phenotypic traits are essential for the operation of natural selection, information on the sources of genotypic variation is needed for a full understanding of the evolutionary process.

Mutations

Spontaneous changes in DNA sequences occur constantly and randomly in all living creatures. Such changes, called *point mutations,* can change the allelic identity of genes and influence an offspring's phenotype if they are carried on gametes and thus inherited. (Mutations in somatic cells also occur, but they cannot be inherited. Somatic mutations may contribute to the development of diseases such as cancer, however.) Mutations occur constantly, but at a very low rate per gene. The mutation rate may be increased, however, through exposure to environmental stimuli, such as radiation and certain chemicals (it also increases with age). H. J. Muller won the Nobel Prize in 1946 for his work on X-ray-induced mutations in fruit flies.

Point mutation: usually the substitution of one nucleotide in a single codon of a gene that affects protein synthesis and genotype; gene mutation.

Point mutations may be as small as the change (substitution, addition, or loss) of a single nucleotide base. Many point mutations are never expressed phenotypically because of DNA's extraordinary ability for self-repair back to the original condition. Even when expressed, mutations do not necessarily produce completely new (previously unknown) alleles and traits; they may simply alter a gene from one known allele to another (*A* to *a,* or *a* to *A*). Frequently, however, entirely new alleles are produced, and thus mutations are the primary source of new alleles in a species' *gene pool.*

But are constantly occurring point mutations responsible generation after generation for the vast amount of individual phenotypic variation seen in all species? Probably not. First of all, the mutation rate is too low. And second, most new mutant alleles are quickly lost from the gene pool. In some cases they are eliminated by natural selection, being selected against because they code for deleterious traits. Given the random nature of mutation, it is unusual for the process to produce beneficial genetic changes (just as a random adjustment inside a computer is unlikely to improve its performance, a random addition to a species' gene pool is unlikely to be useful to anyone who inherits it). In many other cases mutant alleles become extinct through chance loss alone. It has been calculated that even mutant alleles with small selective advantages stand a 90 percent chance of disappearing within 30 generations. Mutations do not serve, therefore, as the basis of most phenotypic variation. A much better candidate exists for that important role: meiosis, the cell division process that produces sperm and eggs.

Gene pool: all the genes of a population at a given time (summing genes within a species yields the species' gene pool).

Meiosis and Crossing-over

If the chromosomes go through remarkable maneuvers during mitosis, their behavior during meiosis is truly phenomenal (Figure 3-10). Meiotic cell division not only reduces the chromosome count of gametes to the haploid number (for

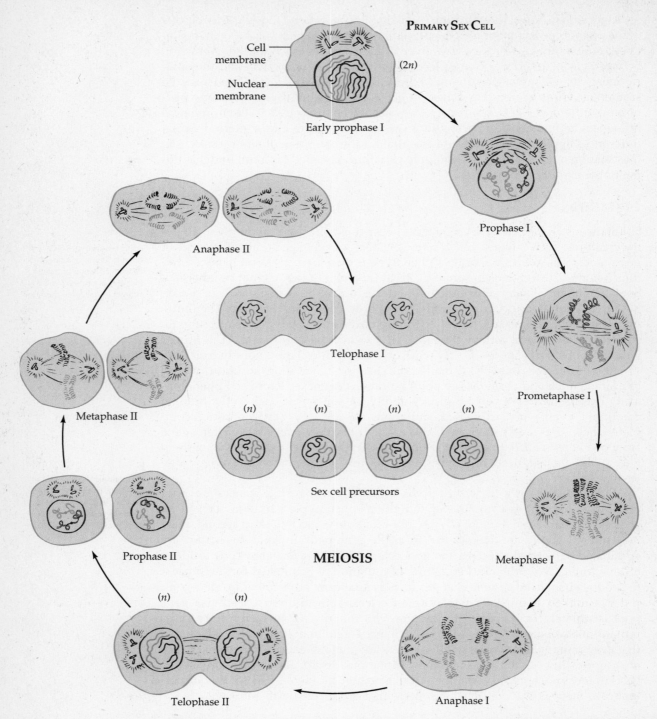

FIGURE 3–10 Meiosis. The single replication of genetic material occurs in Prophase I. Crossing-over within the tetrad takes place in Metaphase I, producing numerous reconstituted chromosomes. Two cell divisions then follow that (potentially) result in four haploid gamete precursors.

most organisms, the diploid number is restored at fertilization) but also provides the basis for extensive phenotypic variation within each species by producing genetically unique sex cells.

Meiosis involves one chromosomal replication and two cell divisions. Before the first cell division (during interphase), each chromosome replicates itself to produce two chromatids. The duplicated chromosome with its two elements then pairs with its homologous partner, and this pairing yields clusters of four chromatids called *tetrads*. As the tetrads line up at the equator of the spindle (Metaphase I), the chromatids in each may overlap at points called *chiasmata*. *Crossing-over*, or the exchange of sections between homologous chromosomes, may then take place at these sites (Figure 3–11). During the next stage (Anaphase I), the homologous chromosomes (each still consisting of two chromatids) separate and move toward opposite poles of the spindle (technically, the two halves of the dividing cell are now haploid, since we count chromosomes, not chromatids). At this point any or all of the four chromatids formerly making up a tetrad may contain a different mixture of genetic material from their original condition.

Chiasmata: points where the chromatids of a tetrad overlap and segment exchange may occur; crossover points (singular, chiasma).

Crossing-over: the exchange of sections between homologous chromosomes.

The first meiotic division is then completed, and the second begins (in females in some species—such as our own—the first division in potential egg cells begins prenatally, is suspended between birth and puberty, and is then completed—along with the second division—by a few cells every month between puberty and menopause). The second meiotic division occurs without further replication of the genetic material and involves the separation of chromatids (Anaphase II). The potential result of meiosis is the production of four haploid "daughter" cells (this term is used for both sperm and egg cells), each genetically unique. This potential is realized in men (four sperm cells from each original parent cell), while in women only one energy-rich egg is produced from every parent cell.

Evolutionary change via natural selection can proceed only if conspecifics vary phenotypically and trait differences are based, at least partially, on genetic differences (within a population, the proportion of phenotypic variance attributable to genetic variance is referred to as a trait's level of *heritability*). Meiosis, with its genetic and chromosomal mixing, provides the basis for gene-based phenotypic variations. The stage is now set for evolution at the levels of the population and the species.

Heritability: a property of phenotypic traits; the proportion of a trait's interindividual variance that is due to genetic variance.

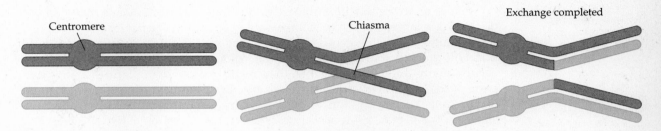

FIGURE 3–11 A simple example of crossing-over and segment exchange among the chromatids of a tetrad.

POPULATIONS AND SPECIES

Genotype and Gene Pool

In this short history of the science of genetics, we have dealt mainly with the structures that bring about replication of, and occasional variation in, the genotype, the genetic material of individual organisms. In looking at the process of evolution, we must look beyond the individual to the *population* and the species. Individuals are born, reproduce, and die, yet the population continues, changing and adapting to its environment.

Population: usually, a local or breeding group; a group in which any two individuals have the potential of mating with each other.

R. A. Fisher envisaged a gene pool of all the individuals in a species, a pooling of the total genetic material available to a species in adapting to its environment. The concept of the gene pool is an important one: the continuity we see in an evolving species is in truth the continuity and survival of the gene pool. Individuals—in particular, their bodies, or phenotypes—are little more than temporary homes of the genes they carry. The phenotypes can be seen as the genotype's means of survival in a range of environments over eons of geologic time.

When the individuals in a population reproduce sexually, genetic material is sorted, shuffled, and recombined during meiosis, and so variation among the offspring is increased. This increase in the potential for variation is the primary advantage of sexual reproduction. When species reproduce asexually, the variation available to natural selection is due to mutation alone, so that it is much more limited in its evolutionary possibilities.

Gene Flow, Speciation, the Founder Effect, and Genetic Drift

Sexual reproduction has another advantage. If two populations of the same species that have been isolated for some time come into contact, they can hybridize. Genes can pass between them, and their differing characteristics can be combined in future generations. In time, advantageous qualities that had previously been selected in only one population can pass to the other and so become available to both populations. This phenomenon is called *gene flow;* it allows the maintenance of genetic continuity between neighboring populations of conspecifics. Therefore gene flow increases variation within populations and decreases variation between them.

Gene flow: transmission of genes between populations through exogamy, which increases the variety of genes available to each and creates or maintains similarities in the genetic makeup of the populations.

This is an extremely important phenomenon because it means that a species occupying a large area without impassable geographic barriers may evolve as a whole, and any advantageous mutations that appear at one place in the population will quickly spread throughout the whole group. Thus, although humans occupy many different continents, they retain profound similarities and remain parts of the single species *Homo sapiens,* because gene flow occurs between them.

Allopatric speciation: the production of new species through the branching or splitting of existing ones. The process begins with the geographic isolation of one or more populations from the bulk of the parent species.

In contrast, interruption of gene flow by geographical barriers, called *geographic isolation,* may result in *allopatric speciation,* the creation of two species where one existed before (see Figures 3–12 and 3–18). In this case the variations accumulated over time in the different populations under the differing pressures of their two environments cause a genetic and phenotypic divergence between the populations. In the absence of gene flow, isolation will eventually allow large enough

1. The original frogs in this area interbreed with each other and constitute a single species.

2. Changes in the topography and drainage conditions of the region eventually create two distinct regions—swamp and forest—with a barrier between the two that the frogs cannot cross.

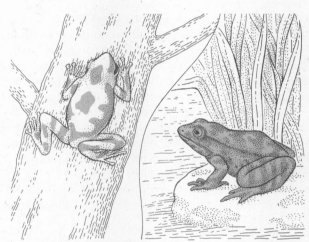

3. Over a long period of time, the frogs in the swamp and those in the forest adapt to their different environments. As they adapt and remain isolated from each other, the frogs in the two areas become different.

4. So many differences have now been selected in the two populations that the frogs do not interbreed even if they meet; they do not recognize foreigners as potential mates.

FIGURE 3–12   A simplified visual description of allopatric speciation in an imaginary frog population. In the last stage, two separate and independent gene pools now exist, eventually constituting two species where one existed before.

differences to develop between the two populations so that they come to form distinct species. The distinction comes about because variations will be naturally selected differently in the different environments (and no two environments are *exactly* the same). Should their geographical ranges overlap in the future, no interbreeding would occur. This leads us to the definition of a species: *a group of interbreeding natural populations that are reproductively isolated from other such groups.*

It is important to emphasize the word *natural*. Many closely related populations of animals that fulfill this definition in the wild will interbreed in the zoo or laboratory under special conditions. Such interbreeding occurs as a result of the breakdown of isolating mechanisms. Geographic isolation is the most common mechanism (it brings about speciation in the first place), but scientists have identified other mechanisms, the most important of which are behavioral. Typical behavioral mechanisms include differences in breeding seasons and courtship pattern. Courtship often involves complicated ritualistic behavior that is important in species recognition: it helps ensure that individuals will not mate with members of different but related species. Species that are closely related and whose ranges overlap are normally separated by behavioral mechanisms. They may also be prevented from interbreeding effectively because they have incompatible sex cells, which fail to fertilize, or because a hybrid that is produced will be sterile, as are mules (the offspring of horses and asses).

What is the actual effect of natural selection on a population? It is to alter the frequency with which different genes occur in the population, to increase beneficial genes (those that promote successful adaptation to the environment), and to decrease disadvantageous genes. One definition of evolution (and likely the best) is therefore the alteration of gene frequencies, that is, the alteration of the proportions in which different genes occur in a species, as a result of natural selection.

But what if information on gene frequencies is unobtainable and one has knowledge only of phenotypes in the population? (This is generally the case when one is dealing with fossils.) Is it still possible to show that evolutionary change has occurred? Yes, by documenting shifts in the average expression of traits (that is, by showing changes in the population's *collective phenotype;* Figure 3–13).

Collective phenotype: the set of phenotypic averages and norms that characterize a population or species.

It is important to recognize that to bring about evolutionary change, natural selection does not have to destroy less well-adapted individuals before they

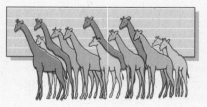

FIGURE 3–13   A common measure of evolution is change in the average expression of any characteristic in a species. A simple case is the lengthening of the necks of the ancestors of giraffes. Because long-necked giraffes have more reliable and extensive food sources in trees than short-necked ones, they are more successful and have more offspring over time. As a result, the average neck length slowly increases. Eventually all individuals are relatively long-necked. In contrast, Lamarck would have seen this change as a response of the individual to need and the continual stretching of the neck.

achieve reproductive age. Natural selection need only bring about a differential reproductive rate in the population, so that better-adapted individuals contribute more to the next generation than do the less well-adapted. A small difference in the genetic contribution across generations will eventually bring about the adjustments in gene frequencies and phenotypes that constitute adaptive evolution.

Natural selection does not always *change* things, however. The example given in Figure 3–13 shows *directional natural selection:* as long-necked giraffes are selected for (and short-necked ones are selected against), average neck length in the population is altered in the direction of the tallest phenotypes. But at times (probably often) natural selection acts to *preserve* current gene frequencies and phenotypic distributions. Such *stabilizing natural selection* occurs when the environment is relatively constant (unchanging), and it operates by selecting against all individuals that deviate from the prevailing phenotypic norms. Periods of *stasis* in the history of a species, when little or no evolutionary change occurs, are generally periods of stabilizing selection.

Directional natural selection: natural selection that operates in response to environmental change and produces shifts in the composition of a population's gene pool and collective phenotype.

Stabilizing natural selection: natural selection that operates during periods when the environment is stable and maintains the genetic and phenotypic status quo within a population.

Stasis: a period of evolutionary equilibrium or inactivity.

Natural selection is not the only evolutionary mechanism, but it ranks at the top of the list. In order to ensure your understanding of this important process, three clear examples of directional selection—including one from humans—are given in Box 3–1. In addition, a later section of this chapter explains the action of natural selection on humans' hemoglobin alleles, and Chapter 18 describes how the process has contributed to biological diversity among living people.

If a very small population becomes isolated from its parent species, various special factors may operate. First, this small *founder population,* as it is called, may not be a typical sample of its parent species. In that case, its successors will, from the very start, carry different gene frequencies and phenotypic norms from the parent species. These differences, which may be perpetuated if the isolated population flourishes and expands, can be ascribed to the *founder effect.*

Founder effect: genetic difference between a newly founded, separated population and its parent group. The founding population is usually different because its gene pool is only a segment of the parent group.

Small populations that have gone through a size-reducing bottleneck (e.g., as founder populations or because of decimation by disease) become good candidates for yet another evolutionary mechanism: *genetic drift.* This mechanism involves chance variations in allele frequencies between the generations of small populations (Figure 3–14). In such populations rare alleles may be quickly lost or "fixed" (widespread) in the gene pool because of several chance factors. For example, rare alleles may be lost when their few carriers die accidentally (no natural selection is involved here, just pure chance). Or perhaps the carriers survive but because of chance alone, fail to reproduce. Or finally, perhaps heterozygous individuals with rare alleles are lucky enough to survive and reproduce, but then just by chance the alleles are absent from the particular sperm or egg cells involved in reproduction. In a similar way, these examples could be reworded to explain how rare alleles may become fixed by chance alone. Studies suggest that weak environmental selection pressures are critical in the operation of genetic drift. Thus alleles with neutral or weak selective values should be good candidates for the effects of drift.

Genetic drift: genetic changes in populations caused by random phenomena rather than by natural selection.

In small populations that are isolated (and therefore experiencing little or no gene flow), the combined actions of genetic drift and natural selection can quickly lead to the evolution of genetic and phenotypic differences from other conspecific

BOX 3-1
THREE EXAMPLES OF NATURAL SELECTION AT WORK

1. Fur Color in Mice

In 1962, a mutant strain of house mice (*Mus musculus*) was discovered in a farm population in Missouri. Because of the effects of a single recessive allele, mutant animals had pink eyes and pale yellow fur in contrast to the dark eyes and dark (agouti) fur of normal mice. Mutants interbred freely with normal mice, and the two strains lived together in a granary used to store corn. The solid construction of the granary prevented the farm's numerous cats from entering.

In order to determine the relative proportions of mutants and normals, researchers periodically live-trapped the granary mice and released them (see table below). At the first trapping, the mutants accounted for about 28 percent of the population, and their representation increased steadily throughout 1962. In January 1963, because of an increase in the mouse population, the farmer made an opening in the granary wall to provide access for his cats. The cats immediately began to prey on the mice, and the pale yellow animals soon proved to be much more vulnerable to predation than their agouti conspecifics (probably because of greater visibility in

the dimly lit corn crib). Percentages of mutants in the population fell to zero soon after the cats began their deadly work.

The allele responsible for the mutant coloration had not been completely removed from the population, however. In September 1963, at the urging of the researchers, the farmer sealed off the cats' entrance, and within three months the pale-colored mice had rebounded to about 5 percent of the population. In this example from nature, heritable differences in fur color were strongly affected by predator pressure. (Data from L. N. Brown, 1965, *Journal of Mammalogy* 46:461–465.)

2. Body Size and Bill Dimensions in Darwin's Finches

A species of Darwin's finch (*Geospiza fortis*) was studied on the Galapagos island of Daphne Major between 1975 and 1978. Birds were trapped and measured regularly, and data were collected on their feeding patterns (they ate mostly seeds of various sorts and sizes).

In 1977 Daphne Major experienced a severe drought that resulted in a sharp food shortage for the finches. Seeds of all sorts declined in abundance, but

Date	Total Mice Trapped	Mutants as Percentage of Trapped Mice
Apr. 1962	32	28.1
Aug. 1962	44	40.1
Dec. 1962	58	46.6
(Jan. 1963—cats allowed into granary)		
Apr. 1963	22	0.0
Aug. 1963	29	0.0
(Sept. 1963—cats excluded from granary)		
Dec. 1963	37	5.4

small seeds declined faster than large ones, and the result was a strong overall increase in the average size and hardness of the available seeds (averages for the "size-hardness index" for the seeds increased from a predrought figure of just over 4 to about 6 during the drought). In response to these environmental changes, the finches suffered an 85 percent drop in population size. Small birds suffered greater decimation than large ones, apparently because the smaller birds (with their smaller bills) had difficulty cracking and eating large, hard seeds. That is to say, smaller birds were strongly "selected against" because of the drought-related changes in food. Measurements taken after the drought (1978, see table below) showed the effects of natural selection: average body size in the population had increased, as had average bill size.

3. Adaptations to Withstand Famine and Extreme Cold in Humans

During the winter of 1846, the Donner Party—87 pioneers headed to California—became snowbound in the Sierra Nevada. Food supplies were soon depleted, the weather was brutal, and before rescuers could reach the group in April of the next year, 40 people had died. Death did not occur randomly, however; it came most often to those who were least adapted biologically to survive famine and cold. Thus the pattern of death and survival in the Donner Party serves as a small-scale example of natural selection in humans.

The first factor to be considered in this retrospective analysis is sex. Overall, women are better adapted to survive famine and cold than are men. This better adaptation is due primarily to the fact that women carry somewhat more body fat than men and, importantly, they have a higher proportion of fat stored subcutaneously (thus providing insulation for the body's core). Despite having a higher body surface-to-mass ratio than men (which should increase heat loss), in response to extreme cold women experience smaller reductions in core temperature and smaller increases in metabolic rate, and they lose body heat at a lower rate than do men. Other things being equal, therefore, one would predict that in the face of cold and famine, women should outsurvive men by a significant margin.

A second important factor is age. Generally speaking, the very young and the very old are at much greater risk under conditions of cold and famine than are prime-aged individuals. The reason is that youngsters have few nutrients stored in the form of fat, while older people have a diminished capacity to respond metabolically to cold conditions. Thus a second prediction can be made: Under conditions of cold and famine, prime-aged individuals should outsurvive both the very young and the very old.

The following figures show that natural selection decimated the Donner Party pretty much according to retrospective predictions made from knowledge of differential biological adaptations. Females (age classes combined)

Finch Traits	Predrought Mean	Postdrought Mean
Weight (g)	15.59	16.85
Bill length (mm)	10.68	11.07
Bill depth (mm)	9.42	9.96

(Data from P. T. Boag and P. R. Grant, 1981, *Science* 214:82–85.)

(continued)

BOX 3–1 (continued)
THREE EXAMPLES OF NATURAL SELECTION AT WORK

proved to be much more "fit" than males under the harsh conditions and lost only 29.4 percent of their number. In contrast, 56.6 percent of males died (age classes combined). With regard to age, prime individuals outsurvived both the youngest and the oldest members of the group. Over 60 percent of the children between 1 and 4 years old died, as did over 80 percent of the individuals over 50. Although other variables, such as family size, also affected survival within the Donner Party, the biological correlates of sex and age seem to have been of major importance in differentiating fit and unfit individuals. Natural selection favored females over males and prime individuals over the young and old during that grisly winter of 1846.

Before Winter 1846 (Percentage)	*After Winter 1846 (Percentage)*
Proportion of females = 39.1	Proportion of females = 51.1
Proportion of males = 60.9	Proportion of males = 48.9
Proportion 1–4 years old = 18.4	Proportion 1–4 years old = 12.8
Proportion 5–49 years old = 74.7	Proportion 5–49 years old = 85.1
Proportion 50 or older = 6.9	Proportion 50 or older = 2.1

(Data from D. K. Grayson, 1993, *Evolutionary Anthropology* 2:151–159.)

populations. Indeed, some researchers argue that drift and selection often work together to produce rapid speciation (taking only 5,000 to 50,000 years).

Evidence for genetic drift has been obtained from experiments with small populations of the fruit fly *Drosophila*, but more interesting examples from natural populations can be found in the literature on human blood groups. (The nature and frequency of A, B, O, and other genetically determined blood groups are discussed in Chapter 18, but we shall refer to them here briefly in this connection.) An interesting instance of drift has been shown to have occurred among the polar Eskimos who lived near Thule in northern Greenland. This small band, which numbered no more than 271 people at any time, was isolated for generations. Another related band of Eskimos from Baffin Island spent several years trying to reach them, and when they made contact, the isolated band had come to believe that they were the only people in the world. In 1956 the American physical anthropologist William Laughlin took blood samples from both the isolated band and the parent population, and he showed that they differed quite significantly from their nearest relatives in two of their blood group frequencies. Other small and isolated communities have shown the same response, including some of the aboriginal tribes in Australia, the Dunker religious sect in eastern North America, and the Jewish community in Rome. These data are of interest because we believe that during much of human evolution the species consisted of small bands of between 200 and 500 individuals.

In summary, it seems probable that the founder effect has been of some importance in human evolution, especially where small populations have colonized

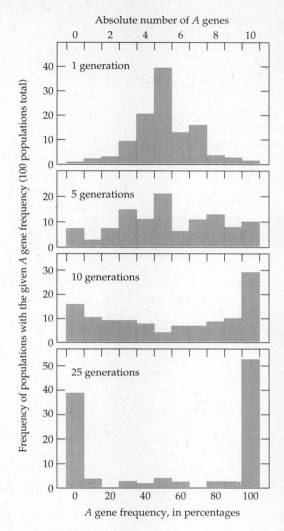

FIGURE 3–14 Computer simulations of genetic drift show how random changes across several generations may lead to either the elimination or the fixation of alleles in small populations. One hundred simulations for two alleles (*A, a*) at a single locus were conducted, and the figure shows the randomly generated frequency distribution of one allele (*A*) at Generations 1, 5, 10, and 25. Population size was set at five diploid individuals (10 genes) with *A* and *a* equally represented initially. (Data from L. L. Cavalli-Sforza and W. F. Bodmer, 1971, *The Genetics of Human Populations*, Freeman, San Francisco.)

islands or multiplied in isolation. The random effects of genetic drift may have played a smaller part in determining the human genotype because small isolated populations would have expanded rapidly and become subject to natural selection.

We can classify the biological processes we have described into those that *increase* genetic variability in a population and those that *decrease* it. Mutation, sexual recombination, genetic drift, gene flow, and increase in population size all increase population variability. Natural selection and the founder effect decrease variability. The interplay of all these factors determines the evolutionary potential of an evolving lineage.

Polymorphism and Genetic Load

All populations of plants and animals (and hundreds of millions of people) carry harmful unexpressed recessive genes. These are termed the *genetic load*. The genes constituting the genetic load are expressed only in the relatively rare recessive

Genetic load: recessive genes in a population that are harmful when expressed in the rare homozygous condition.

homozygote, when they may bring about a physical malformation or a fatal genetic disease. An example of such a phenomenon is sickle-cell anemia. Persons who are homozygous for the recessive sickle-cell allele (Hb^S) are characterized by anemia due to red blood cells that become crescent-shaped when oxygen levels are low (Figure 3–15). Homozygotes for the normal allele (Hb^A) have round red blood cells. Sickle-cell disease is a life-threatening condition that is common in certain regions of West and Central Africa (Figure 3–16). In many Central African populations, from 20 to 40 percent of individuals are Hb^A Hb^S heterozygotes; 1 to 2 percent are Hb^S Hb^S homozygotes, who usually die soon after birth.

Because natural selection would ordinarily select out such an undesirable trait, we have to ask why such a high frequency of the Hb^S gene is maintained. In 1954 A. C. Allison, a British doctor, showed that the sickle-cell trait in its heterozygote condition affords protection against malarial infection, and that the distribution of the Hb^S gene coincides with the distribution of the *Anopheles* mosquito, which carries malaria. The Hb^S gene was maintained by natural selection according to the balanced advantages and disadvantages that it offered: protection from disease for the Hb^A Hb^S carrier and death for the Hb^S Hb^S. This is an example of *balanced polymorphism. Polymorphism* usually refers to the expression of two or more alleles of a single gene in a population in more-or-less constant proportions. The human blood groups constitute further well-known examples.

Balanced polymorphism: maintenance in a population of different alleles of a particular gene in proportion to the advantages offered by each (e.g., sickle-cell and normal hemoglobin).

Today in the United States we live in an environment free of malaria, yet approximately 10 percent of Americans of African origin still carry the Hb^S gene. Thus it has become a complete liability and, in the rare homozygous state, is still a serious and often lethal condition. Clearly, a lifesaving adaptation in one environment is part of humankind's genetic load in another.

We can see, then, that the survival value of genes is determined by the environment in which they are expressed. We can see, too, how natural selection acting on genetic variability will often compromise between advantages and disadvantages, so that ordinarily lethal phenotypes are maintained in a population in balance with advantageous phenotypes. Of course, many rare recessive lethal genes are simply carried along in the gene pool because they are almost never expressed in a homozygote. Between balanced polymorphisms and rare recessives, it appears that most species will always bear the burden of a genetic load. But look on the bright side. Perhaps our genetic load represents a potential for variability that may in the future be necessary for survival, as it may have been in the past. Natural selection operates on phenotypes, that is, only on the expression of a proportion of the genotype. Hidden genetic variability is, to some extent, our insurance against environmental change.

The term genetic load also refers to the normal mutation rate that most commonly reduces fitness. In human populations genetic birth defects may affect up to 4 percent of births. Research has shown that in Britain 12 to 15 percent of all pregnancies that continue longer than four to five weeks end in spontaneous abortion before the end of the twenty-seventh week, and that more than 2 percent result in stillbirths. Some of these deaths may be due to external factors, but most are due either to inherited genetic factors or recent mutations in the germ cells. The latter may often be chromosomal abnormalities like Down's syndrome, in which the individual has an extra chromosome (46 + 1); Turner's syndrome, in which the Y chromosome (the sex chromosome that determines maleness) is missing (46 − 1); or Klinefelter's syndrome, in which individuals are XXY (phenotypic

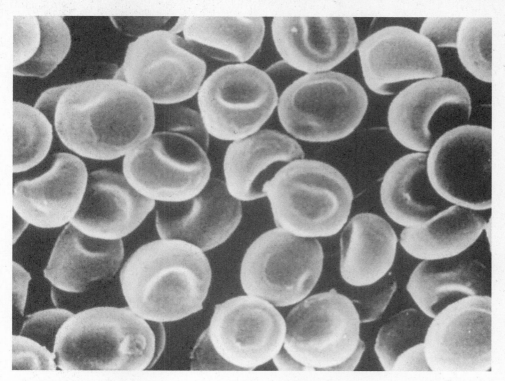

FIGURE 3–15   The sickle-cell trait is due to abnormal hemoglobin, which differs from normal hemoglobin in only 1 amino acid out of nearly 300 that constitute the protein. The red blood corpuscles in the top photograph appear normal; the bottom photograph shows the distortion that gives sickle-cell anemia its name.

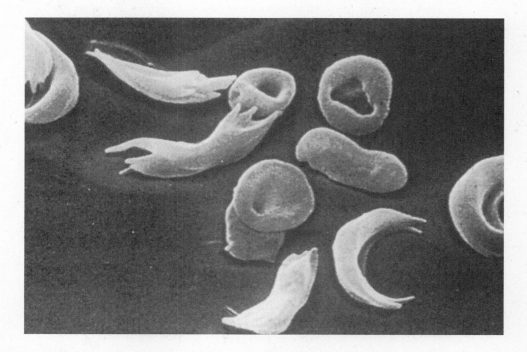

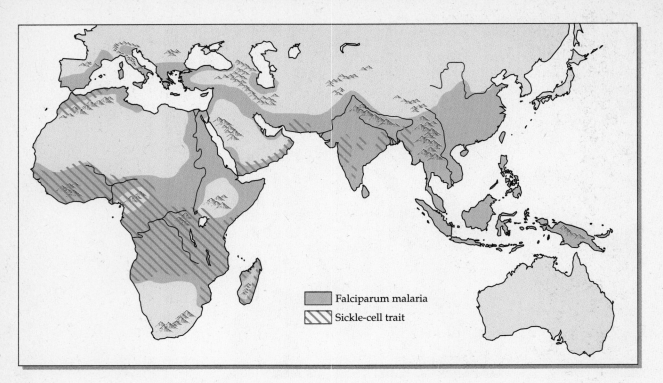

FIGURE 3–16 Coincidence of the sickle-cell trait and malaria in parts of the Old World led us to understand why the abnormal hemoglobin *Hb*ˢ appears in these areas. Though disadvantageous elsewhere, in malarial areas the sickling gene gives considerable protection against the dangerous malarial parasite. The two hemoglobin forms are in balance according to the advantages and disadvantages they offer. Therefore this instance of the phenomenon of polymorphism is termed *balanced polymorphism*. Other genes give similar protection in other parts of the world where malaria occurs.

males with two female X chromosomes; surviving individuals are sterile). Other chromosomal abnormalities include individuals who are XXX (super females with three X chromosomes) or XYY (super males with two male Y chromosomes). Such abnormal chromosome numbers are often associated with mental disorders.

Hardy-Weinberg Theorem

The preceding sections have established that evolution is a population-level phenomenon. Within their environments living creatures strive to survive and reproduce, and their success or failure in getting their genes into succeeding generations determines the evolutionary trajectories of their populations. The examples in Box 3–1 illustrate rapid evolutionary change in small populations, but as noted earlier, most of the time populations (particularly large ones) are probably in stasis, with little or no change occurring as long as the environment remains constant. It would obviously be very useful to be able to determine whether a population is in equilibrium (stable) for specific phenotypic traits, and geneticists have developed a procedure for this purpose: the Hardy-Weinberg test.

In 1908 the English mathematician G. H. Hardy and the German physician W. Weinberg independently developed a formula for describing the proportions of a pair of alleles within a stable population. This formula allows researchers to calculate the expected frequencies of genotypes and phenotypes once they have obtained information about allele frequencies. Here's how it works. Imagine the simplest possible condition: a trait that is controlled by a single pair of alleles (A, a). If we symbolize the frequency of the dominant allele (A) as p and that of the recessive allele (a) as q, then we can develop the equation:

$$(1)\ p + q = 1$$

This is true since the total proportion of the alleles at any given locus is equal to 100 percent. Furthermore, this equation can be expanded to produce the frequencies of the three possible genotypes (AA, Aa, and aa) that would be expected in a population at equilibrium:

$$(2)\ (p + q)^2 = 1$$

$$(3)\ p^2 + 2pq + q^2 = 1$$

Substituting the genotypes for their mathematical symbols, we get:

$$(4)\ AA + 2Aa + aa = 1$$

In other words, the frequencies of both homozygotes (AA and aa), plus the total frequency of the heterozygotes ($2Aa$), equal 100 percent of the population for the trait in question. Of course, with regard to their phenotypes, in this example both the AA homozygotes and the heterozygotes (Aa) would show the dominant form of the trait. Only the aa homozygotes would show the recessive phenotypic condition.

The genius of Hardy and Weinberg was to realize that under a certain set of conditions the allele frequencies p and q will reach equilibrium in one generation and, assuming the conditions are maintained, remain in equilibrium indefinitely. The necessary conditions, sometimes summarized by the term *random mating*, include infinitely large population size, no mutations, no selection, and no gene flow. Although these conditions may seem impossibly stringent at first glance, in fact, the Hardy-Weinberg theorem is rather robust and fits a number of natural populations rather well despite their failure to meet one or more of the criteria.

For simple single recessive allele traits, the frequency of q can be easily determined from the occurrence of individuals showing the rare phenotype. And once q is known, p (and thus all genotypic frequencies) can be readily calculated. For example, a rare disorder caused by a single recessive allele in modern human populations is Tay-Sachs disease. Most common in Jews of eastern European descent, Tay-Sachs sufferers experience nervous system degeneration, convulsions, and death at a young age. Although the frequency of Tay-Sachs disease varies strongly between populations, its global incidence is about 1 per 100,000 births, or 0.00001 ($= q^2$). The value of q is therefore 0.0032, making the frequency of the recessive Tay-Sachs allele 0.32 percent. From these figures p can be calculated as 0.9968 and p^2 (homozygous dominants) as 99.36 percent of living humans. Finally, of critical importance in the development of programs for the prevention and cure of Tay-Sachs disease, the frequency of unafflicted carriers of the disease (the heterozygotes, $2pq$) can be calculated as 0.0064, or about 1 person in 157 worldwide.

The Hardy-Weinberg theorem can also be used to test whether a population is at or near equilibrium with regard to particular phenotypic frequencies. One does this test by first determining p and q values, and then using those figures to calculate "expected" or predicted frequencies of the various phenotypes (p^2, $2pq$, and q^2). The set of predicted phenotypic frequencies can then be statistically tested against "observed" or actual frequencies found in the population. If the two sets of frequencies are statistically indistinguishable, the population is regarded as being at equilibrium for the trait. An example of this sort of equilibrium testing is shown in Figure 3–17, which uses data on the M and N blood group genes among the Quinault Indians of Washington State. In this case, M and N are alternate alleles at a single locus but they are *co-dominant* (neither is dominant to the other) and thus there are three distinct phenotypes: blood types M, N, and MN. Here p is simply assigned to M and q to N. Statistical testing of the predicted versus the actual phenotypic proportions proved the population to be in Hardy-Weinberg equilibrium.

Although all of the above examples were genetically simple, the Hardy-Weinberg formula can be expanded to cover cases with multiple alleles at a locus. This theorem has proved to be of exceptional value to population geneticists.

Sexual Selection

In discussing the action of selection and the transmission of characteristics in a population, and also in our discussion of the Hardy-Weinberg theorem, we have assumed that mating occurs randomly between members of the opposite sex of a population or species. Rarely is this so in practice, and a number of mating patterns can often be recognized. When struggle or choice enters into mating, we have what Darwin described as *sexual selection.* In 1871 he defined two kinds of sexual selection.

The first kind was the result of competition between members of one sex (usually males) for the opposite sex. Good examples are found among the higher primates, such as some multimale baboon groups (Chapter 5) where the alpha male may have primary sexual access to most females in a troop as they come into estrus. This reproductive pattern of behavior will select the genes for powerful and impressive males.

Darwin's second kind of sexual selection involves differential choice by members of one sex for members of the opposite sex: this usually takes the form of the female's choice of some males in preference to others and is well known among both birds and primates (see Chapter 5). Both these phenomena are most commonly observed among polygamous species and play a much smaller part in a purely monogamous species in which every individual has a mate.

The importance of sexual selection in human evolution is not yet understood, but it is clearly not a significant factor in a monogamous society with a 50:50 sex ratio. Insofar as human societies permit polygamy (and very many do), and insofar as the historical pattern was probably not monogamous (Chapter 9), it is possible that sexual selection has indeed brought about the evolution of traits that are not the product of natural selection (and that in theory could become nonadaptive if developed to excess). The kind of characteristics in humans that may be a prod-

Co-dominant: the term for alleles that, in heterozygous combination, produce a phenotype distinct from either type of homozygote.

Sexual selection: a category including intrasexual competition for mates (usually aggressive and among males) and intersexual mate selection (usually of males by females).

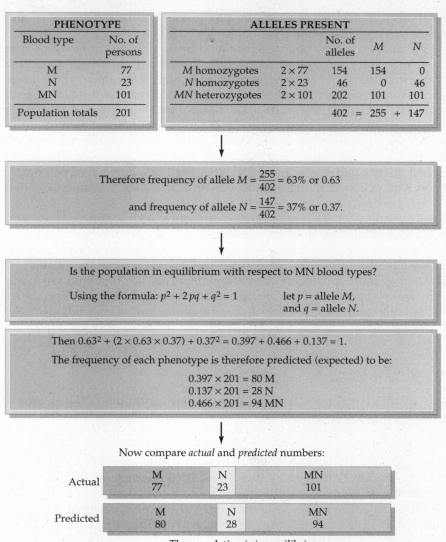

PHENOTYPE			ALLELES PRESENT			
Blood type	No. of persons			No. of alleles	M	N
M	77		M homozygotes	2 × 77	154	154	0
N	23		N homozygotes	2 × 23	46	0	46
MN	101		MN heterozygotes	2 × 101	202	101	101
Population totals	201				402 = 255 + 147		

Therefore frequency of allele $M = \dfrac{255}{402} = 63\%$ or 0.63

and frequency of allele $N = \dfrac{147}{402} = 37\%$ or 0.37.

Is the population in equilibrium with respect to MN blood types?

Using the formula: $p^2 + 2pq + q^2 = 1$ let p = allele M, and q = allele N.

Then $0.63^2 + (2 \times 0.63 \times 0.37) + 0.37^2 = 0.397 + 0.466 + 0.137 = 1$.

The frequency of each phenotype is therefore predicted (expected) to be:

$0.397 \times 201 = 80$ M
$0.137 \times 201 = 28$ N
$0.466 \times 201 = 94$ MN

Now compare *actual* and *predicted* numbers:

Actual

| M 77 | N 23 | MN 101 |

Predicted

| M 80 | N 28 | MN 94 |

The population is in equilibrium.

FIGURE 3–17 The Hardy-Weinberg theorem is a probability statement that predicts the phenotype frequencies in a population given the allele frequencies. Thus the Hardy-Weinberg theorem may be used to determine whether a population is undergoing change. Here we see the computation of such frequencies based on an actual example published by Frederick Hulse. The *M* and *N* blood-group genes constitute a simple two-allele trait, neither of which is dominant to the other. Genetic stability in these traits is indicated by the fact that the observed frequencies are not significantly different from those predicted.

uct of sexual selection are those which appear to advertise sexuality, such as hair patterns and types, body shape and breast development in women, and penis size in men. The second type of selection (differential choice of mate) has probably been more important in human evolution than the first. The elucidation of this problem depends on knowledge of the mating pattern of early peoples—information that is probably unobtainable. Were matings a result of free choice, or were they arranged by parents or elders for political and economic reasons? The present arrangements may not tell us much about the past.

Inbreeding: mating among related individuals.

Outbreeding: mating among unrelated individuals.

Other nonrandom mating systems found in animals and humans are *inbreeding* and *outbreeding*. Inbreeding occurs when sexual partners share a recent common ancestor (that is, when they are genetically related to some degree). In small, isolated animal and human populations, inbreeding may be the typical pattern, but it has its costs. It often results in the homozygous pairing of recessive genes, so that the recessive trait becomes expressed in the phenotype. As we have seen, recessive genes are often harmful, and in due course they will tend toward elimination by natural selection. Until then, their expression may be accompanied by increased disease and higher mortality rates, both of which have been predicted and observed in inbred animal populations (in humans the frequency of stillbirths is much higher for related parents).

Outbreeding is characteristic of human groups with extensive incest taboos, such as those groups that insist on marriage with members of other clans for political and economic reasons. Outbreeding has the opposite genetic effect of inbreeding: Variation increases, and lethal recessives remain unexpressed, and possibly accumulate, although the population may show improved health and lower mortality.

The mating system is therefore an important characteristic of a species and is linked not only to the species' social life as a whole, but, as we shall see, to many of its most striking anatomical adaptations.

Measures of Fitness

As this chapter has shown, individual organisms contribute to the evolutionary process simply by trying to survive and reproduce within their particular environment. Because of the action of the Darwinian mechanisms of natural selection and sexual selection, and because of "non-Darwinian" forces such as genetic drift, individuals differ in their degrees of success in surviving, reproducing, and getting their genes into succeeding generations. Such differences between individuals are often described in terms of *fitness*.

Fitness: individuals' relative degrees of success in surviving and reproducing, and thus in gaining genetic representation in succeeding generations.

Traditionally, fitness has been measured in terms of personal reproductive success, that is, how many offspring an organism produces and successfully rears. Since each offspring carries 50 percent of each parent's genes (in most organisms) and many parental traits, personal reproduction is a primary path to evolutionary fitness. (Obviously, survival to adulthood is necessary for personal reproductive success, but surviving without reproducing does not equal fitness as measured here. Equally obviously, simply possessing traits that are likely to lead to survival, such as strength, stamina, and general good health—the popular meaning of "being fit"—doesn't qualify as evolutionary fitness.)

Inclusive fitness: the sum total of an individual's personal reproductive success (number of offspring) plus portions of the reproductive success of genetic kin.

Recently, the definition of evolutionary fitness has been extended in important ways. Thanks to the work of W. D. Hamilton and many others, we now realize that personal reproductive success is only one component of an individual's *inclusive fitness*. A second important component is the reproductive success of one's genetic kin. After all, in diploid organisms, parents and offspring and full siblings have 50 percent of their genes in common, half-sibs 25 percent, first cousins 12.5 percent and so on. Assisting a relative to survive and reproduce is therefore a perfectly good way to get copies of one's own genes into future generations. This realization also appears to explain several previously puzzling aspects of animals' (and perhaps humans') behavior. Animals often appear to behave altruistically, doing things that benefit others while inflicting a cost on the actor (there are many examples, such as alarm calling, intervening in fights, and sharing food). But if the recipients of such *bioaltruism* are the actor's kin, then acts that appear to be altruistic may in fact reap a genetic reward for the actor by helping relatives survive and reproduce. This insight is the basis for yet another evolutionary mechanism known as *kin selection*. Kin selection may well be the process by which behaviors that are apparently altruistic, but that in reality are likely to serve genetic self-interest, may have evolved.

In summary, the old notion of the survival of the fittest has little meaning to modern evolutionary biologists. Fitness involves getting copies of one's genes and traits into the next generation, and we now know that there are several avenues to that goal. An organism's inclusive fitness combines personal reproduction with the reproductive success of genetic kin. In social animals kin selection has probably acted to produce numerous bioaltruistic behaviors that aid kin and thus increase the actor's inclusive fitness. This newly discovered evolutionary mechanism may have been particularly important among the long-lived and highly social primates (including humans).

Extinction

One final aspect of evolution remains to be discussed: the loss of species (or larger units such as genera and families) through *extinction*. To begin with a clarification, when a species becomes truly extinct, all of its members die—and their genes die with them. Species can disappear in other ways, however. The term *phyletic transformation* describes the process by which an entire species is gradually transformed by natural selection into a different species (Figure 3–18). This is not generally considered a form of speciation since there is no increase in the number of coexisting species (A is lost as B evolves), and neither is it a form of extinction since there is no loss of a species "life line." Rather, phyletic transformation produces a type of pseudoextinction that should not be confused with the real thing.

Disappearance, either by extinction or transformation is the inevitable fate of all species (humans included). While species typically last about 4 million years (within the human family, the average is closer to 1 million years), it remains true

Bioaltruism: behavior that appears to be altruistic, but that in fact is believed to benefit the animal indirectly, by increasing its *inclusive fitness*.

Kin selection: the selection of characteristics (and their genes) that increase the probability of the survival and reproduction of close relatives.

Extinction: the loss of a species due to the death of all its members.

Phyletic transformation: the conversion (through gradual natural selection and gene flow) of an entire species into a new species.

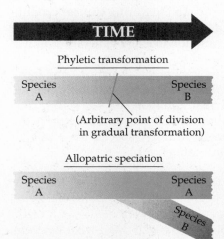

FIGURE 3–18 Phyletic transformation involves the gradual conversion (mainly through natural selection) of an entire species into a new species. While it probably occurs in nature, it is not a true form of speciation because it does not lead to an increase in species diversity. In contrast, allopatric speciation involves branching of an existing species (usually due to the isolation of one or more populations) with the result that the total number of species is increased.

that the vast majority of all species that have ever lived are now extinct. But why do species become extinct? Is it, as D. M. Raup asked in a recent book, a matter of "bad genes or bad luck"? Raup tends to side with bad luck, and there is a good deal of evidence supporting this point of view. It appears that, regardless of how well a species is adapted to its normal environment, sooner or later it will be exposed to such extraordinary biological or physical stresses that it will die. Examples of possible extinction-causing stressors include new and intense inter-specific competition; extreme environmental changes due to fluctuations in sea level, global climate, and large-scale volcanism; and environmental and ecological disasters resulting from collisions of the earth with extraterrestrial objects (comets and asteroids). Raup favors the collision hypothesis as an explanation for many mass extinction events, particularly the event that killed off the dinosaurs 65 million years ago (see Figure 6–1 for the dates of the five largest mass extinctions).

The data on extinction—and especially the mass events—suggest that contrary to the teachings of Lyell and despite a day-to-day appearance of regularity and predictability, when one views the earth over geological time it is clearly a dangerous and rather unpredictable place, periodically liable to large-scale, devastating environmental fluctuations. The extinctions that result from such fluctuations have played an important part in shaping the history of life on earth, and the existence of each living species is the result of a unique history of adaptation, speciation, and extinction. While natural selection has tended to improve species' adaptations to their normal environments and has combined with processes like genetic drift to produce new species, extinction has operated to reduce species' diversity and to open up ecological niches. Happily for humans, vacating ecological niches tends to open the way for new evolutionary experimentation. Had the dinosaurs not become extinct, mammals might never have diversified, and primates (including humans) might never have evolved.

SUMMARY

During the present century the science of genetics has yielded numerous secrets that allow us to understand the workings of evolution. Phenotypic traits are encoded in genes—hereditary units, consisting of DNA, that occur on chromosomes within the nucleus of the cell. Offspring tend to look like their parents because of inherited genes, but because of genetic mixing during gamete production, offspring never look exactly like their parents or each other (with the single exception of identical siblings). This heritable variation in every generation allows natural selection to improve the degree of adaptation of a species.

Working along with other factors, such as geographic isolation, mutation, founder effect, and genetic drift, natural selection can lead to speciation. Species exist for varying amounts of time—some for many millions of years—but ultimately all species disappear. Some (several?) mass extinction events have probably been caused by comets or asteroids hitting the earth. Every species has a unique history of speciation, adaptation, and, in the end, extinction.

REVIEW QUESTIONS

1. What are genes, how do they determine phenotypic traits, and what happens when they mutate?

2. Both point mutations and meiosis contribute to phenotypic variation in each generation. Discuss how and to what degree these processes produce interindividual variation.

3. Women produce one egg (ovum) for every primary sex cell (oocyte), while men produce four sperm for every primary spermatocyte. Discuss what effect (if any) this imbalance may have on the "reproductive strategies" of the two sexes.

4. What is meant by the phrase "survival of the fittest"? How can an individual's evolutionary "fitness" be measured?

5. How does natural selection operate to enhance the level of adaptation of a species? Does natural selection operate for the good of every individual?

6. Discuss the possibility of the extinction of our species. What circumstances could result in the extinction of *Homo sapiens?*

POSTSCRIPT

Every passing year brings an increase in humans' control over their own evolutionary future. Technological advances now enable many of the world's people to effectively short-circuit natural selection as we use new means of controlling our environment, health, survival, and reproductive success. Is a geographic region too hot or cold or dry or humid for comfortable human living? No problem. We simply build artificial environments featuring cooling, heating, humidifying, or dehumidifying systems that allow easy living in any climate regardless of one's phenotype. Poor vision is corrected with eyeglasses, poor hearing with hearing aids, and lost teeth with dentures. Light-skinned people live and work safely in areas of high solar radiation thanks to clothing and sun-screen creams.

Advances in medical technology now routinely enable the survival of premature infants who would have died only a few decades ago. Immunizations allow us to avoid many life-threatening diseases, and the eradication of vectors has brought other diseases under control. Artificial hormones are now synthesized for use by postsurgical patients or by individuals with impaired natural hormonal production. Organ transplantation allows life-saving replacements for people with kidney or heart disease.

In the field of genetics, increased knowledge of the mechanisms of the inheritance of various diseases and pathological conditions allows genetic counseling of high-risk would-be parents. In addition, procedures such as amniocentesis allow early detection of chromosomally abnormal fetuses and give the parents the option of terminating the pregnancy. At present, a major effort is under way to map the entire human *genome*—an accomplishment that will open the way for increased genetic engineering involving the addition, subtraction, and modification of genes affecting the health and reproduction of carriers.

Genome: the totality of the DNA unique to a particular organism or species.

Although the traditional set of evolutionary mechanisms (natural selection, mutation, genetic drift, and gene flow) continues to have some effect on humans (more on some populations than on others), it is clear that we are becoming something of a special case with regard to further evolution. And with increased control over our evolutionary trajectory comes a plethora of difficult questions and decisions. Consider the following issues:

- What are the implications of assisting increasing numbers of genetically and/or physically impaired people to be born and to reproduce? Will the genetic load of the species increase? Would the denial of medical assistance to *any* impaired individual (fetal or postnatal) be consistent with humane behavior?

- Should we attempt to eliminate undesirable human traits and develop desirable ones? If the answer is yes, who should decide which traits are which and how should the decisions be made? And how should such "species engineering" be accomplished? (Humans have a very checkered history of such eugenics projects.) Are there long-term disadvantages in reducing genetic and phenotypic variability within our species?

- How should we ensure that new genetic and medical advances are not put to improper use? For example, will amniocentesis be used to select against one sex or the other (female feticide following sex identification by amniocentesis may already being occurring in some countries) or against fetuses with a different mix of phenotypic traits from those desired by the parents?

Bioethicist: a person who specializes in exploring the ethical dimensions of biological decisions.

With increased biomedical knowledge comes increased responsibility for wise, informed, and humane action. The issues related to the evolutionary future of humans promise to be complex and challenging for *bioethicists* and laypersons alike.

II

THE ORIGIN OF HUMANKIND

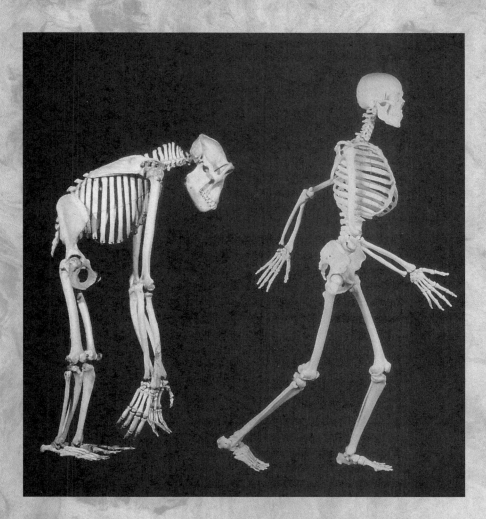

CHAPTER

4

Humans Among the Primates

What a piece of work is a man! How noble in reason! How infinite in faculties! In form and in moving, how express and admirable! In action how like an angel! In apprehension how like a god! The beauty of the world! The paragon of animals!
WILLIAM SHAKESPEARE, 1564–1616. *Hamlet*, II, ii.

OVERVIEW

The order Primates—that subgroup of mammals that includes prosimians, monkeys, apes, and humans—is quite ancient and this chapter is devoted to its description. First appearing at least 60 million years ago, the order is represented today by over 200 widely diverse species. Originally shaped by life in the trees and an insectivorous diet, primates have evolved an array of distinctive adaptations, including freely moving limbs with grasping hands and feet, keen vision, and (at least among the anthropoids) complex brains. Humans are in many ways typical primates, and our distinctive features can be best appreciated when considered against the primate background. Human specialities include habitual bipedal locomotion, extreme brain complexity, language and speech, and a cultural way of life. Thanks to cultural adaptations, humans have gained considerable control over their evolutionary future. Important topics in the chapter include classification systems, general primate characteristics, prosimian traits, anthropoid traits, the arboreal theory, the visual predation theory, and the numerous distinctive traits of humans. Particular attention is given to the ways humans differ from their close evolutionary relatives, the apes.

NAMES AND CLASSIFICATIONS

The first three chapters have shown how evolution works, but before we can start examining our past, we must first learn something about what we are like today. We cannot completely—or even partially—answer this question until we have answered simpler questions about our similarities to and differences from other animals. Humankind is biologically classified under the Latin name *Homo sapiens; Homo* means "man," and *sapiens* "wise." The human has been called the thinking animal. The human has also been labeled a political animal, a tool-using animal, a social animal, a speaking animal, and the animal that is aware of itself. We are all these things, and more.

   The Latin name *Homo sapiens* was coined by the great Swedish biologist Carl von Linné (1707–1778) as part of his classification of all plants and animals. Though a practicing doctor for part of his life, Linnaeus (the Latinized form of his name, by which he is more commonly known) collected plants and animals in Europe and received specimens from collectors throughout the world. He began to develop a system for naming and classifying most of the then-known living organisms. He used a binomial (two-name) system to label each one, choosing Latin for the names because it was a convenient international language. He published his system of names in his famous book *Systema Naturae*, which ran to 12 editions between 1735 and 1766.

   It was already clear to biologists that some creatures were more similar to each other than to others; they seemed to be created on the same general plan. Linnaeus

Homo sapiens: among living primates, the scientific name for modern humans; archaic members of the species first appeared about 400,000 years ago.

grouped the similar ones in classes and orders to form a hierarchic arrangement. In 1735, Linnaeus had put *Homo* in his first class of Quadrupeds in the order Anthropomorpha, with the apes (Simia) and the sloth. In the tenth edition (1758) he called humans *Homo sapiens* and placed them with monkeys and apes in the order called *Primates*. Although not based on a theory of evolution, this classification indicated anatomical similarities—similarities that disturbed Linnaeus, among others. In 1766 he wrote: "It is remarkable that the stupidest ape differs so little from the wisest man."

Linnaeus's classification scheme is still used because his method has proved to be of immense value. An international system of nomenclature (the rules of naming) has become essential in the development of the biological sciences, and the Linnaean system has survived the development of evolutionary biology since Darwin. The use of a language, such as Latin, that is no longer spoken, means that the terms do not undergo the changes through time that are characteristic of spoken languages. The theory of evolution changed the basis of the system, however, making it clear that the similarities seen by Linnaeus and others were in many

Clade: members of an evolutionary cluster (e.g., sister species) plus their common ancestor.

BOX 4–1
VARYING APPROACHES TO HUMAN AND GREAT APE TAXONOMY

Phenetic, cladistic, and traditional evolutionary classifications provide three different ways of arranging the taxonomy of modern humans and the great apes. The basis for each classification scheme is described below.

Phenetic Classification

Phenetic classification schemes are based simply on overall morphological similarities and differences among organisms. In a phenetic scheme, humans are separated from the four ape species, which are clustered together. This arrangement reflects the fact that the apes share such traits as long arms and short legs, grasping feet, projecting canine teeth, and relatively small brains, while humans have short arms and long legs, nonprehensile feet, short canines, and enormous brains.

Cladistic Classification

Cladistic systematists attempt to arrange organisms in groups that reflect their history of evolutionary branching. Members of a related cluster (or *clade*) are recognized by the possession of shared, derived traits. Furthermore, in cladistic classifications all traits are treated equally (i.e., viewed as being equally useful in establishing evolutionary relationships), and sister groups are always given equal taxonomic rank. A look at the division of great apes and humans shows how this system works.

Among the numerous traits shared by humans and the African apes are the fol-

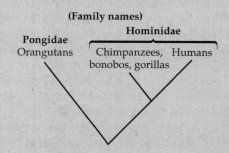

(Fig. 4–1b) Cladistic classification

(Family names)

Pongidae — Hominidae
Orangutans — Chimpanzees, Humans
bonobos, gorillas

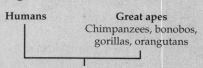

(Fig. 4–1a) Phenetic classification

Humans   Great apes
                Chimpanzees, bonobos,
                gorillas, orangutans

cases a result of evolutionary or phylogenetic relationships. Groups based on anatomical likeness often proved to share a common ancestor. The form of the system of classification remained but its meaning altered. The hierarchy came to reflect relationship, the species became variable and adaptable. The species was no longer the expression of an ideal type created by God, which Linnaeus believed it to be, but the changing product of natural selection.

Today we attempt in our classifications to reflect the evolutionary process so that the *taxonomy* we use is a *phylogenetic classification*. Where we lack knowledge of relationships, classifications can be based only on similarities and differences between species. Such a grouping scheme is called a *phenetic classification*. Linnaeus's system was phenetic, and it proved to require relatively little change with the coming of evolutionary biology because similarities do in fact often reflect relationship—but not always.

The contrast between a phenetic arrangement of species and one that is phylogenetic can be seen in the different ways one can group humans and the so-called great apes: chimpanzees, bonobos, gorillas, and orangutans (Box 4–1). A traditional

Taxonomy: classification of plants or animals according to their relationships, and the ordering of these groups into hierarchies; *taxonomic levels* are ranks within these classifications, e.g., *species* or *genus*.

Phylogenetic classification: taxonomy that reflects evolutionary descent and is based on the pattern of primitive and derived traits; in traditional evolutionary classifications, traits may be given different weights.

Phenetic classification: taxonomy based on physical similarities or differences between species or other taxa.

---

lowing features: a broad nasal opening, square orbits that are often broader than they are high, and widely spaced eyes. In contrast, the orangutan is characterized by a nasal opening that is higher than it is broad, small oval orbits that are higher than they are broad, and closely spaced eyes. These and many other features support the conclusion that humans and the African apes share a recent common ancestor to the exclusion of orangutans. The two sister groups (orangutan versus African apes plus humans) must have the same rank, and here they are placed at the family level.

Traditional Evolutionary Classification

Traditional evolutionary systematists differ from cladists in several important ways. First, they routinely place different weights on morphological traits since they maintain that some features are more useful than others in revealing evolutionary relationships. Second, traditional evolutionary systematists do not feel constrained to place sister groups at the same taxonomic level. In this scheme, sister groups are often ranked differently, in a ranking that reflects different

amounts of change from the common ancestral condition. Species that show extreme degrees of change from the ancestral condition are often described as having attained a new evolutionary *grade* compared to their near relatives. In the classification in Figure 4–1c, humans are placed in a different evolutionary grade from the apes because of their enlarged skull and brain, skeletal adaptations for bipedalism, incisiform canines, a fully *opposable thumb*, and so on. In contrast, ape–grade creatures share smaller brain size, skeletons adapted for some combination of quadrupedalism and suspension, elongated canines, and imperfectly opposable thumbs.

Grades: arbitrarily defined levels of evolutionary development (e.g., prosimians vs. anthropoids).

Opposable thumb: ability to hold thumb and index finger together in opposition, giving a *precision grip*.

(Fig. 4–1c) Traditional evolutionary classification

Ape grade   Human grade

(Family names)

Pongidae   Panidae   Hominidae

Orangutans   Chimpanzees,   Humans
        bonobos, gorillas

phenetic arrangement based on overall morphological similarity separates these creatures into two groups: humans on the one hand and the four apes on the other. In contrast, when traits are treated in evolutionary terms and primitive features (ancestral and ancient traits, broadly shared) are distinguished from *derived* features (recent innovations, shared by a small number of close species), orangutans are separated from the more closely related quartet of chimpanzees, bonobos, gorillas, and humans. But not all evolution-based classifications are alike. *Cladistic classification* views traits as having equal classificatory value and insists that *sister groups* be given the same taxonomic rank, that is, sister groups cannot be placed at different levels (say, genus versus family) within a classification. In contrast, traditional evolutionary systematists routinely give different weights to traits (that is, view some as more important than others in elucidating relationships) and argue that sister groups most definitely can occupy different taxonomic levels. Throughout this book, we rely primarily on traditional evolutionary taxonomies.

The close relationship of humans and the great apes with each other and with the lesser apes (the gibbons) has never been in question. The point was clearly made by T. H. Huxley in 1863 (Figure 1–10). Today they are all placed in the superfamily Hominoidea. As noted, Linnaeus classified this group (or taxon) with the monkeys and some other animals under the name *Primates*. Linnaeus then grouped the primates with other furry, warm-blooded creatures that suckled their young in the class Mammalia. We mammals have backbones and share an even more general structure with such animals as fish and birds, with whom we constitute the subphylum Vertebrata. Humans' position in the grand hierarchy of the animal kingdom is summarized in Table 4–1.

THE PRIMATES

The list of animals included in the order Primates has been modified substantially since Linnaeus's time. He had included the bats and colugos ("flying lemurs") as primates, but in 1873 these animals were removed by the English scientist St. George Mivart, who also provided a more detailed definition of the order. Mivart defined primates as placental mammals that possess the following traits: claws or nails; collarbones; eye sockets encircled by bone; *heterodont* dentition (specifically, having incisors, canines and molars); posterior lobe of the brain that includes a distinctive groove (the calcarine fissure); thumbs or big toes (or both) that are opposable; flat nail on big toe; caecum (pouchlike portion of the large intestine); pendulous penis; scrotal testes; and two nipples.

Mivart also arranged the primates in the two suborders of the Prosimii (or "premonkeys") and the Anthropoidea (monkeys, apes, and humans).

During the twentieth century, this anatomical definition of the primates was to a great extent superseded by a definition based on the order's evolutionary trends. According to the English anatomist W. E. Le Gros Clark (as presented in his influential book *The Antecedents of Man* in 1959), primates are characterized by the retention of generalized limbs tipped with five grasping digits; the replacement of claws by nails; retention of a tail; expansion and elaboration of the brain; emphasis on vision; deemphasis on olfaction; loss of some teeth from the ancestral condition; retention of a simple molar cusp pattern; delayed maturation; and reduction of litter size to single infants (Table 4–2).

Cladistic classification: evolution-based taxonomy that gives equal weight to traits and requires sister groups to be similarly ranked.

Sister groups: in *cladistics*, the groups resulting from a dichotomous evolutionary branching event; initially ranked as sister-species, these groups may change rank due to subsequent branching, but must always maintain the same *taxonomic level*.

Heterodont: having several different types of teeth (incisors, canines, etc.), each with a different function.

Table 4–1 CLASSIFICATION OF HUMANKIND

Taxonomic Category	Group Including Humans	Primary Characteristics	Members
Kingdom	Animalia	Organisms that move, and that feed by the mouth	Vertebrates and all other animals (e.g., insects)
Phylum	Chordata	Possession of a notochord at some stage of life	All animals with backbones, plus sea squirts, amphioxus, etc.
Subphylum	Vertebrata	Bilaterally symmetrical animals with flexible, internal segmented backbones and other bony skeletal structures	Mammals and all other animals with backbones (e.g., fish, birds, reptiles)
Class	Mammalia	Class of Vertebrates characterized by fur, warm blood, the feeding of live-born young by means of milk glands, and maternal care of young	Primates and all other warm-blooded furry animals that suckle their young (e.g., dogs, elephants)
Order	Primates	Order of Mammalia distinguished by grasping hands and feet, nails on digits, flexible limbs, and highly developed visual sense	Anthropoidea and Prosimii (lower primates: tarsiers, lorises, lemurs)
Suborder	Anthropoidea	Suborder of the Primates with evolved social organization, daytime activity, and notable development of intelligence and ability to learn	Hominoidea, Old World monkeys (e.g., rhesus), and New World monkeys (e.g., spider monkey)
Superfamily	Hominoidea	Superfamily of the Anthropoidea characterized by relatively erect posture, loss of tail, development of arms and shoulders for climbing, and (generally) five-cusped lower molars	Hominidae, Pongidae (orangutans), Panidae (chimpanzees, bonobos, gorillas), and Hylobatidae (gibbons, siamangs)
Family	Hominidae	Family of the Hominoidea characterized by bipedalism and a trend toward brain enlargement	Genera *Homo*, *Australopithecus*, and *Paranthropus*
Genus	*Homo*	Genus of the Hominidae characterized by a relatively large brain, skillful hands, and evolving traditions of tool use, toolmaking, and culture	*Homo habilis*, *H. rudolfensis*, *H. erectus*, and *H. sapiens*
Species	*Homo sapiens*	Species of the genus *Homo* characterized by a large brain, an advanced culture, technology, and language	Modern humans, plus early subspecies (such as *H. sapiens neanderthalensis*)

Table 4–2 MAJOR CHARACTERISTICS OF PRIMATES

A. CHARACTERISTICS RELATING TO MOTOR ADAPTATIONS

1. Retention of ancestral mammalian limb structure, with five digits on hands and feet, and free mobility of limbs with unfused radius and fibula.

2. Evolution of mobile, grasping digits, with sensitive friction pads and nails replacing claws. Palmar surfaces with friction skin.

3. Retention of tail as an organ of balance (except in apes and a few monkeys) and as a grasping "limb" in some New World monkeys.

4. Evolution of erect posture in many groups with extensive head rotation.

5. Evolution of nervous system to give precise and rapid control of musculature.

B. CHARACTERISTICS RELATING TO SENSORY ADAPTATIONS

1. Enlargement of the eyes, increasing amount of light and detail received.

2. Evolution of retina to increase sensitivity to low levels of illumination and to different frequencies (that is, to color).

3. Eyes that look forward with overlapping visual fields that give stereoscopic vision.

4. Enclosure of eyes in a bony orbit in all living groups.

5. Reduction in olfactory apparatus, especially the snout.

6. Internal ear structures enclosed within petrosal bone.

C. DENTAL CHARACTERISTICS

1. Simple cusp patterns in molar teeth.

2. In most groups 32 or 36 teeth.

D. GENERAL CHARACTERISTICS

1. Lengthened period of maturation, of infant dependency, and of gestation, compared with most mammals. Relatively long life span.

2. Low reproductive rate, especially among Hominoidea.

3. Relatively large and complex brain, especially those parts involved in vision, tactile inputs, muscle coordination and control, and memory and learning.

Today over 200 species of animals living in Africa, Asia, and the tropical Americas (Figures 4–2 and 4–3) are recognized as primates, and the diversity within the order is staggering. Primates range in size from the gorilla at an average weight of 258 lb (117 kg) to the tiny Demidoff's dwarf bush baby at 2.3 oz (65 g). Some primates are exceedingly intelligent creatures, others seem to have

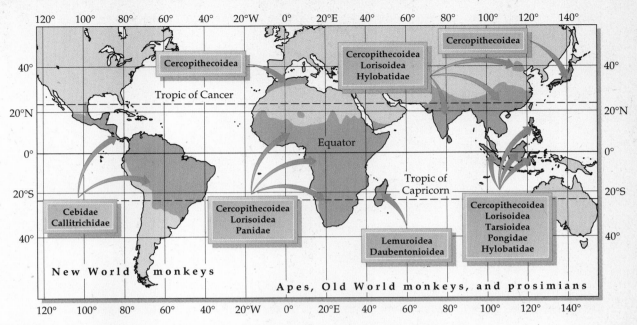

FIGURE 4–2 Worldwide distribution of nonhuman primates by superfamilies and families. Dark areas show the approximate ranges of nonhuman primates. (Adapted from J. Napier and P. Napier, 1967, *A Handbook of Living Primates*, London, Academic Press.)

run-of-the-mill mammalian intelligence. Most are very social creatures, but some live solitary lives; most are *diurnal*, but some are *nocturnal*. Dietary specialities range from insects to fruit to leaves (with humans adding a significant amount of animal flesh to the basic primate diet). In order to describe all of this diversity, a complex taxonomy based on the Linnaean classification system is required (Table 4–3).

Diurnal: active during the day, as apes, humans, and monkeys are.

Nocturnal: active during the hours of darkness.

Prosimians

Following Mivart, the primates are usually divided into two suborders: the prosimians and the anthropoids. Fossil discoveries indicate that the prosimians first evolved at least 60 million years ago (mya) and that this suborder gave rise to the anthropoids some 10 to 15 million years later. Living prosimians include the superfamilies Lemuroidea (the lemurs; Figure 4–4), Daubentonioidea (the aye-aye; Figure 4–5), Lorisoidea (lorises and bush babies; Figures 4–6 and 4–7) and, in most classifications, Tarsioidea (tarsiers; Figure 4–8). The tarsiers are actually quite difficult to classify since in many ways they are anatomically intermediate between undoubted prosimians and the anthropoids (monkeys, apes, and humans). In fact, some cladistic systematists prefer to group tarsiers with the anthropoids and refer them all to a suborder called Haplorhines, with lemurs, aye-ayes, and lorises remaining in a sister suborder called Strepsirhines. In this book we will follow the traditional placement of tarsiers among the prosimians while pointing out tarsiers' distinctive features where appropriate.

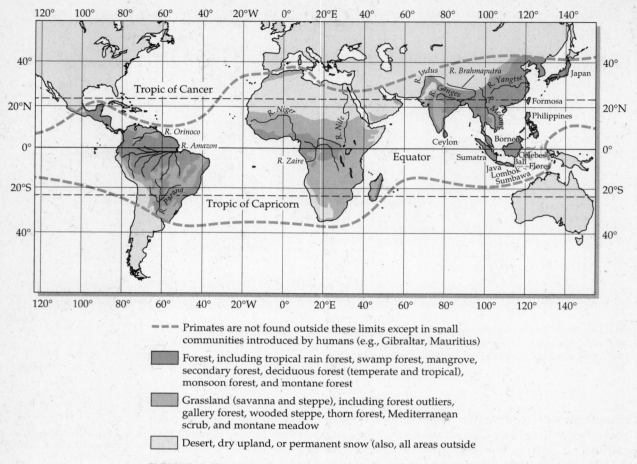

- - - - - Primates are not found outside these limits except in small communities introduced by humans (e.g., Gibraltar, Mauritius)

Forest, including tropical rain forest, swamp forest, mangrove, secondary forest, deciduous forest (temperate and tropical), monsoon forest, and montane forest

Grassland (savanna and steppe), including forest outliers, gallery forest, wooded steppe, thorn forest, Mediterranean scrub, and montane meadow

Desert, dry upland, or permanent snow (also, all areas outside

FIGURE 4–3   Approximate distribution of principal regions of vegetation within the range of non-human primates. (Adapted from J. Napier and P. Napier, 1967, *A Handbook of Living Primates*, London, Academic Press.)

Toothcomb: a dental specialization of prosimians in which the lower front teeth are closely spaced and forwardly inclined.

Today prosimians are found only in Africa, particularly on the island of Madagascar, and in Asia, and they are characterized by a suite of primitive traits (Table 4–4). In general, prosimians are small-to-medium-sized animals with a well-developed olfactory apparatus, visual features that suggest a current or ancestral adaptation to nocturnal activity, claws on some digits, prehensile hands and feet (but poor opposability of the thumb), and a dental specialization called a *toothcomb* that is used for both foraging and grooming (Figure 4–10). Prosimians are arboreal animals that move about the forests of the Old World quadrupedally or by clinging and leaping from one vertical support to another. On average they are somewhat less social than anthropoids, at least insofar as many prosimians forage solitarily or form small social groups (often monogamous breeding units). Prosimians are also more committed to insect eating than the average anthropoid (the only specialized primate insectivores are prosimians), although all eat fruit as well.

In several important ways, living prosimians bridge the anatomical gap between anthropoids and the primates' primitive mammalian ancestors. For one

Table 4-3 Living Genera of the Order Primates

Suborder	Superfamily	Family	Genus	Common Name	Location
Prosimii	Lemuroidea		9 genera	Lemurs	Madagascar
	Daubentonioidea		1 genus	Aye-ayes	Madagascar
	Lorisoidea		5 genera	Lorises and bush babies	Africa/Asia
	Tarsioidea		1 genus	Tarsiers	Southeast Asia
Anthropoidea	Ceboidea	Callitrichidae		*New World Monkeys*	
			Callithrix	Marmosets	Central/South America
			Cebuella	Pygmy marmosets	South America
			Saguinus	Tamarins	South America
			Leontideus	Golden-lion tamarins	Central/South America
			Callimico	Goeldi's marmosets	South America
		Cebidae	Pithecia	Sakis	South America
			Chiropotes	Bearded sakis	South American
			Cacajao	Uakaris	Central/South America
			Aotus	Douroucoulis	Central/South America
			Callicebus	Titis	Central/South America
			Saimiri	Squirrel monkeys	Central/South America
			Cebus	Capuchins	Central/South America
			Alouatta	Howler monkeys	Central/South America
			Ateles	Spider monkeys	Central/South America
			Lagothrix	Woolly monkeys	South America
			Brachyteles	Woolly spider monkeys	South America
	Cercopithecoidea	Cercopithecidae		*Old World Monkeys*	
			Cercopithecus	Guenons	Africa/Asia
			Erythrocebus	Patas monkeys	Africa
			Cercocebus	Mangabeys	Africa
			Mandrillus	Mandrills	Africa
			Papio	Baboons	Africa
			Theropithecus	Geladas	Africa
			Macaca	Macaques	Asia/Africa
			Cynopithecus	Celebes black ape	Asia
		Colobidae	Colobus	Guerezas	Africa
			Presbytis	Langurs	Asia
			Pygathrix	Douc langurs	Asia
			Rhinopithecus	Snub-nosed langurs	Asia
			Nasalis	Proboscis monkeys	Asia
			Simias	Pagai Island langurs	Asia
	Hominoidea	Hylobatidae		*Apes and humans*	Worldwide
			Hylobates	Gibbons	South/Southeast Asia
			Symphalangus	Siamangs	Southeast Asia
		Pongidae	Pongo	Orangutans	Southeast Asia
		Panidae	Pan	Chimpanzees and bonobos	Africa
			Gorilla	Gorillas	Africa
		Hominidae	Homo	Humans	Worldwide

Note: Authors differ in details of primate classification. This table presents a classification that is widely accepted.

FIGURE 4–4 The ring-tailed lemur (*Lemur catta*) is typical of the varied group of prosimian primates (Lemuroidea) from Madagascar. The most striking primate features of lemurs are large forward-looking eyes and long separated fingers on hands and feet. The ring-tail stands about 15 in (38 cm) high.

Postorbital bar: a bar of bone running around the outside margin of the orbits of prosimians.

thing, most prosimians lack the extensive eye protection found in anthropoids (Figure 4–9). While monkeys and apes show a complete bony eye socket, all prosimians except tarsiers display only a *postorbital bar* of bone extending from brow to cheekbone. Second, while both prosimians and anthropoids show a reduction in total tooth count from the ancestral dental formula (Figure 4–10), several prosimian species have retained the ancient 3-cusped pattern in their upper molar teeth. Third, prosimians still show the primitive clawed condition on some digits, while anthropoids show nails (usually flat, but sometimes compressed and recurved into "pseudoclaws") on all digits. Fourth, while prosimians show greater divergence of the thumb than nonprimate mammals and have grasping hands and feet, they lack the extensive thumb opposability (and precision gripping) that characterizes most anthropoids (compare Figure 4–11 with Figures 4–23 and 4–24).

Despite the retention of some primitive traits, however, prosimians show the distinctive primate combination of increased emphasis on vision plus grasping hands and feet. This pattern was inherited by the anthropoids, in whom further modifications of the sensory systems—such as a reduction of the olfactory sense—took place. But why did the combination of prehension and keen vision evolve

FIGURE 4–5 The aye-aye is a solitary and nocturnal prosimian with the most unusual dentition of the entire order. It has evolved enormous gnawing incisors, and the rest of its teeth have dwindled or disappeared.

among primates? There are two explanations, one traditional and one recent. The traditional explanation for the primate characteristics, especially grasping hands and feet and good vision, is called the *arboreal theory*. First developed by British scientists G. E. Smith and F. Wood Jones in the early twentieth century, this theory suggests that primate characteristics are essentially adaptations to life in the trees. Grasping extremities are viewed here as evolving for safe and lively movement through the irregular arboreal habitat. Similarly, keen vision is thought to have evolved to facilitate arboreal locomotion—particularly *stereoscopic vision*, with depth perception for judging distance before leaping—and for locating food and danger. The sense of smell was of limited use to arboreal animals, and its supporting structures (a long muzzle and large smell centers in the brain) dwindled.

The logic of the arboreal theory carried the day among anthropologists for over half a century. In the 1970s, however, American anthropologist Matt Cartmill began

Stereoscopic vision: vision produced by two eyes with overlapping fields, giving a sense of depth and distance; most highly evolved in hunting animals and primates.

FIGURE 4–6 The loris (*Loris tardigradus*) represents another group of prosimians (Lorisoidea) found in Africa and Asia. Lorises are smaller than lemurs but have very large eyes adapted for hunting insects and other small creatures at night. Lorises' bodies are about 8–14 in. (20–36 cm) long.

FIGURE 4–7 Hands are among the most characteristic features of primates. One striking primate adaptation is that of nails replacing claws. Both humans and the bush baby (*Galago*), which is just over 6 in. (16 cm) long, carry flat nails on their hands.

FIGURE 4–8   Three species of tarsier occur in Southeast Asia. With their enormous eyes, all are nocturnal, and most are forest living. Their diet consists mainly of insects. They weigh only just over 4 oz (120 g), but have long and powerful hind limbs adapted for leaping. They appear to have evolved little in 50 million years.

to probe that logic and the validity of the arboreal explanation. Cartmill observed that arboreal life does not necessarily select for primatelike characteristics. Many animals are perfectly at home in the trees without looking and acting like primates. Gray squirrels are a good example. Squirrels skitter about in the trees, moving through the branches and making leaps of many times their body length. Furthermore, they successfully locate food and detect danger in the trees. Squirrels manage all this even through their hands and feet are relatively nonprehensile and their eyes are much more wide-set and laterally oriented than those of a primate, producing poorer depth perception. Moving the eyes closer together and forward produces increased overlap of the left and right visual fields, and increased overlap leads to better stereoscopic depth perception at close range (Figure 4–12).

Cartmill began a series of careful comparisons of primates with other animals and found that relatively close-set, forwardly directed eyes (and thus good close-range depth perception) are characteristic of predators that rely on vision in hunting. Cats, owls, chameleons, and many other animals use their close-set eyes to locate prey and to judge the distance for a capturing leap or grab. For arboreal hunters, grasping feet stabilize the animal on its support, while grasping hands (one or both working together) make the capture.

Based on these discoveries, Cartmill fashioned the *visual predation theory* of primate evolution. This theory holds that, among the primates, grasping extremities

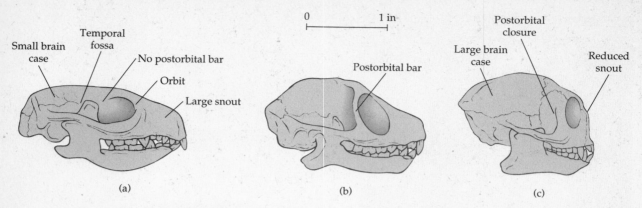

FIGURE 4–9 Comparative skull anatomy reveals several distinctive primate traits. Lateral views of (a) a nonprimate mammal (hedgehog), (b) a lemuroid prosimian, and (c) an anthropoid (New World monkey). Skulls not drawn to scale.

and keen vision originally evolved as adaptations for vision-directed predation on insects (such hunting is still common among some prosimians). Deemphasis on the sense of smell—and reduction of the olfactory apparatus—is viewed here as the result of a migration of the eyes in an anterior direction. Approximation of the eyes could have constricted the olfactory connections between the muzzle and the brain and thus could have led to a reduced sense of smell.

Cartmill's theory is currently carrying the day among anthropologists, but it has not gone unquestioned. American primatologist Robert Sussman has recently challenged the behavioral and anatomical evidence underlying the visual predation theory. While he agrees that many living prosimians show considerable insectivory, Sussman argues that they more often locate insect prey by smell or hearing than by sight, and that therefore "visual predation *per se* is not a sufficient explanation of [primates'] visual adaptations." Sussman counterproposes that primate traits first appeared during the Eocene as part of a diffuse coevolutionary interaction with the diversifying angiosperms (flowering plants). In his view, prehensile hands and feet evolved to allow movement in the food-laden terminal branches of angiosperms, while visual changes were adaptations for making fine discriminations among small plant foods. But is this scenario, although based on the latest information on plant and animal evolution, really very different from the older arboreal theory? Not by much, and thus it seems we still have only two major options concerning primate origins.

But are these two theories—arboreal versus visual predation—complementary or alternative explanations for primate traits? The most reasonable answer seems to be that they are complementary, the visual predation theory probably having more explanatory power. After all, Cartmill's visual predators were probably operating in a tree and bush habitat, and thus adaptations for successful hunting would also have satisfied the requirements of arboreal locomotion. Until someone produces evidence to the contrary, it seems that we should tentatively conclude that all living primates—humans included—are the descendants of ancient, prehensile, big-eyed insect hunters.

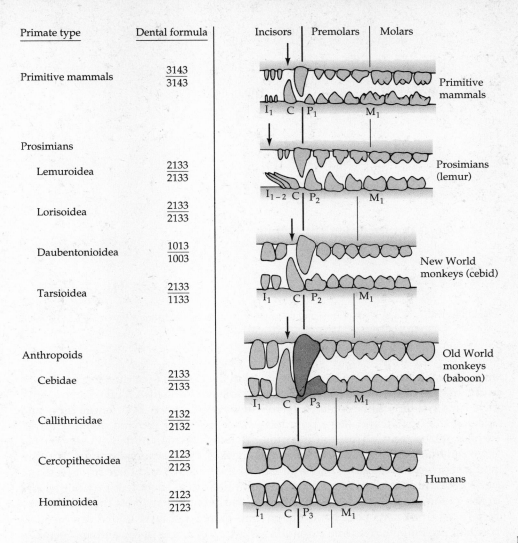

Primate type	Dental formula
Primitive mammals	$\frac{3143}{3143}$
Prosimians	
Lemuroidea	$\frac{2133}{2133}$
Lorisoidea	$\frac{2133}{2133}$
Daubentonioidea	$\frac{1013}{1003}$
Tarsioidea	$\frac{2133}{1133}$
Anthropoids	
Cebidae	$\frac{2133}{2133}$
Callithricidae	$\frac{2132}{2132}$
Cercopithecoidea	$\frac{2123}{2123}$
Hominoidea	$\frac{2123}{2123}$

FIGURE 4–10 Dental formulae and lateral views of several primate varieties. Dental formulae represent half of the upper dentition over half of the lower and count (from left to right) numbers of permanent incisors, canines, premolars, and molars. In lemurs, I_{1-2} and the lower canines make up the toothcomb. Arrows mark the presence of a *diastema*, or gap in the toothrow.

Diastema (pl. diastemata): space in the toothrow that accommodates one or more teeth in the opposite jaw when the mouth is closed.

Anthropoids

The earliest anthropoid fossils are 45 to 50 million years old. From that early beginning, modification and diversification have led to the living representatives of this suborder, including the monkeys of the New and Old Worlds (respectively, the Ceboidea and the Cercopithecoidea; Figure 4–13) and the hominoids (apes and humans; Figure 4–14).

As shown in Table 4–4, the anthropoids possess numerous anatomical differences from prosimians. Among anthropoids the sense of smell has been further reduced as the muzzle has been shortened and the *rhinarium* lost. The eyes of anthropoids are close together and forwardly directed, adapted for diurnal vision,

Rhinarium: the moist, hairless nose characteristic of all prosimians except tarsiers, and of most nonprimate mammals.

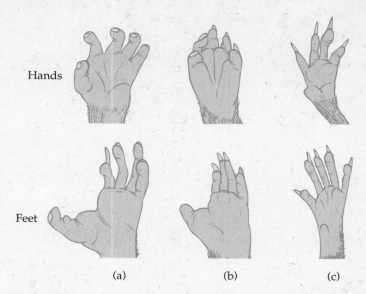

Hands

Feet

(a)   (b)   (c)

FIGURE 4–11 Comparisons of the hand and foot of (a) a prosimian primate (bush baby, Lorisoidea) with two nonprimate mammals: an opossum (b) and a gray squirrel (c).

and protected by complete bony sockets. With the exception of the tiny marmosets and tamarins of the New World, anthropoids have flat nails on all of their digits. (The small callitrichid monkeys have "reevolved" claws by compressing and curving their nails, and these pseudoclaws are used for moving about squirrel-fashion in the trees.) Most anthropoids are large, heavy animals, however, that have only nails; claws cannot bear the weight of a big arboreal animal. Anthropoids also have lower jaws that are fused at the midline, and their front teeth are vertically implanted (no toothcomb). And finally, as detailed in Chapter 13, anthropoids show increases in the relative size and complexity of the brain. Monkeys, apes, and humans all have a larger and more complexly folded cerebral cortex than prosimians. To some extent this is due to changes in the animals' sensory systems, but it is also related to increased intelligence.

For the purpose of further anatomical comparisons, anthropoids may be divided in several ways. Some authorities distinguish the *platyrrhines* from the *catarrhines*. The first category includes the New World monkeys (superfamily Ceboidea), all of which are marked by round nostrils that are widely spaced and face laterally, and by a total of 12 premolars in the adult dentition. Catarrhines include the Old World monkeys, apes, and humans (superfamilies Cercopithecoidea and Hominoidea), and they are characterized by compressed, closely spaced, and downwardly directed nostrils, and only eight permanent premolars (see Figure 4–13 for examples of both types). This division of New World versus Old World anthropoids will be useful when we begin to interpret the primate fossil record (Chapter 6), but for now a convenient classification separates all monkeys (Old and New World varieties combined) from all hominoids (apes and humans combined). Monkeys have long backs, narrow chests, laterally placed scapulae (shoulder blades) and a tail (Figure 4–15). Some ceboids have *prehensile* or grasping tails, but none of the cercopithecoids are so equipped. Monkeys also have a smaller range of motion at the shoulder than hominoids (Figure 4–16).

Platyrrhines: an infraorder of the anthropoids that includes the New World monkeys.

Catarrhines: an infraorder of the anthropoids that includes Old World monkeys, apes, and humans.

Prehensile: adapted for grasping.

Tree shrew
(primitive mammal)

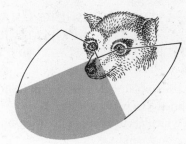

Lemur

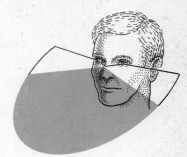

Human

FIGURE 4–12 Stereoscopic vision is of great importance to primates, probably for both arboreal movement and foraging activities. The primitive tree shrew's eyes look sideways, and the visual fields have small overlap; in the lemur the overlap is greater. In monkeys, apes, and humans the extent of visual field overlap is great. Upright posture permits easy head rotation, which compensates for the loss of backward vision. As the eyes moved to the front of the face in primate evolution and vision became the primary sense, the sense of smell became less important, the snout was reduced, and the face flattened. Heads not drawn to scale.

These anatomical traits are correlated with habitual *quadrupedal* locomotion both in the trees and on the ground (Figure 4–15). Generally speaking, monkeys walk, run, and leap about on all fours. This is not to say that monkeys don't or can't do other things—some species show a good deal of hanging and swinging by their arms (or tail)—but the majority of species usually move about quadrupedally along the tops of branches.

The anatomy of hominoids (apes and humans, members of the superfamily Hominoidea) differs significantly from that of monkeys. To start at the top, hominoids have larger brains than monkeys and this larger brain size is correlated with new functional capabilities such as self-recognition (in some species) and learning by insight. Hominoids also have certain distinctive dental traits. Their lower molars show a characteristic arrangement of five cusps and grooves called the *Y-5 pattern.* Old World monkeys, in contrast, show a pattern of lower molar cusp morphology called *bilophodonty:* four cusps that are arranged in two pairs (front and rear), with the members of a pair connected by a transverse ridge of enamel (Figure 4–17).

With regard to *postcranial* anatomy, all hominoids show broad chests with dorsal scapulae; short, stiff backs; long arms (relative to trunk length) with mobile wrists, elbows, and shoulders; and no tail. These traits are probably adaptations for suspensory locomotion and posture (arm swinging or hanging), behaviors that are shown to some extent by all living apes, though not by humans. A closer look at the variety of hominoid locomotor patterns, and their associated anatomical variations, is instructive.

The most obvious distinction between apes and monkeys is that apes are built for a different mode of travel, having short, wide, shallow trunks and long, free-swinging arms that rotate at the shoulders. These adaptations allowed early apes to reach out in all directions in the trees, climbing arm over arm.

From their probable beginning as efficient climbers, the different families of apes have adapted in different ways. The gibbons and siamangs (Hylobatidae),

Quadrupedal: moving on all four limbs.

Y-5 pattern: an arrangement of the cusps and grooves of lower molars that is characteristic of living hominoids.

Bilophodonty: the lower molar cusp pattern of Old World monkeys, featuring four cusps arranged in front and rear pairs.

Postcranial: referring to any anatomical feature that is behind the head (in quadrupeds) or below the head (in bipeds).

Table 4–4 DISTINGUISHING CHARACTERISTICS OF VARIOUS PRIMATE TAXA

PROSIMIANS

Long muzzle tipped with a rhinarium (rhinarium absent in tarsiers)

Tactile vibrissae (sensory whiskers)

Frenulum which anchors upper lip (frenulum absent in tarsiers)

Toilet claw on second toe

Postorbital bar only (tarsiers have a virtually complete eye socket)

Two-part frontal bones

Two-part mandible

Mandibular toothcomb in most species

ANTHROPOIDS

Reduced muzzle with a hairy nose (lack of rhinarium)

Lack of prominent whiskers

Reduced or absent frenulum

Nails (flat or modified) on all digits

Complete bony eye socket

Fused frontal bones

Fused mandibular symphysis

Lack of toothcomb

Retina that includes a *fovea* (also present in tarsiers)

Cerebral cortex that includes a central sulcus

Generally, extensive thumb and big toe opposability

HOMINOIDEA

Lack of tail

Broad chest

Shortened lower back

Dorsally placed scapulae (shoulder blades)

Great mobility at shoulders, elbows, and wrists

Higher ratio of brain size to body size than in other primates

Increased complexity of folding of cerebral cortex

Y-5 cusp pattern of lower molars

HOMINIDAE

Reduced canine length

Nonprehensile big toes

Pelvis and legs reflecting habitual bipedalism (short, wide iliac blades; enlarged iliac spines; close-knee stance)

Extreme brain enlargement and elaboration

Frenulum: the flap of skin that tethers the upper lip to the jaw in prosimians. It is reduced or absent in anthropoids and tarsiers.

Fovea: an area of the anthropoid retina that allows extremely detailed vision.

FIGURE 4-13 Old World monkeys (top): a long-tailed macaque (left) and a mandrill (right), both adapted to terrestrial quadrupedalism. New World monkeys, like the spider monkey (bottom), are highly adapted to an arboreal life. Notice the long prehensile tail in the New World monkey. Compare the form of the nostrils in the two groups.

FIGURE 4–14 Whereas the orangutan (upper left) and the gibbon (upper right) are still primarily arboreal, the gorilla (lower left) and chimpanzee (lower right) have developed knuckle walking as the form of locomotion most practical for their ground-based way of life.

Brachiation: an arboreal loco-motor pattern featuring man-ual swinging from branch to branch.

although they climb much of the time, especially when feeding, have evolved very long arms and hands and in this way are specialized for the horizontal arm-over-arm locomotion called *brachiation*. They can throw themselves from hand to hand, swinging under the branches through the treetops, often with their legs tucked up under their bodies. They can travel with considerable speed and extra-ordinary grace (Figure 4–18).

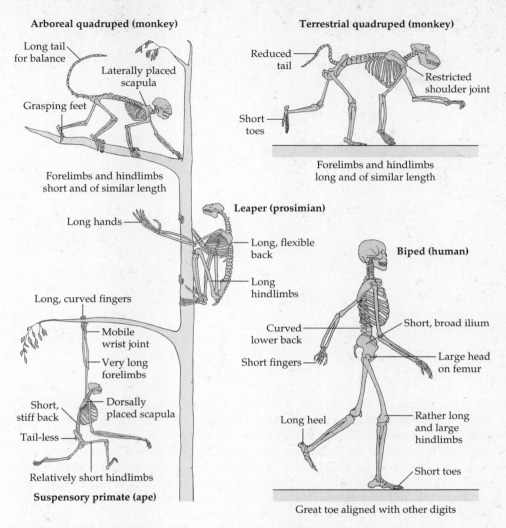

Arboreal quadruped (monkey)

Long tail for balance

Laterally placed scapula

Grasping feet

Forelimbs and hindlimbs short and of similar length

Terrestrial quadruped (monkey)

Reduced tail

Restricted shoulder joint

Short toes

Forelimbs and hindlimbs long and of similar length

Leaper (prosimian)

Long hands

Long, flexible back

Long hindlimbs

Biped (human)

Curved lower back

Short, broad ilium

Short fingers

Large head on femur

Long, curved fingers

Mobile wrist joint

Very long forelimbs

Dorsally placed scapula

Short, stiff back

Tail-less

Relatively short hindlimbs

Long heel

Rather long and large hindlimbs

Short toes

Suspensory primate (ape)

Great toe aligned with other digits

FIGURE 4–15 Monkeys are generally arboreal or terrestrial quadrupeds, while hominoids engage in arboreal suspensory behavior, knuckle walking, and bipedalism. This figure shows some of the anatomical features associated with each main type of primate locomotion.

The orangutan (*Pongo*) moves steadily, climbing through the trees with all four limbs. So flexible are its shoulder and hip joints that its legs are like arms in use: the animal almost appears to be four-armed and four-handed (Figure 4–14). On the ground the orang moves quadrupedally with clenched fists and feet, though it occasionally walks on the palms of its hands. Both the gibbons and the orang are fully adapted to arboreal life, however, and show no specific terrestrial adaptations.

The African apes (family Panidae), however, do show such adaptations, and the larger species, especially the mountain gorilla, have almost deserted the trees for the ground, though they still sleep in trees. Although the smaller chimpanzees are good

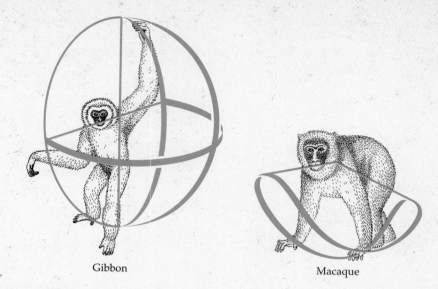

Gibbon   Macaque

FIGURE 4–16   One of the basic differences between apes and monkeys lies in the greater freedom of movement that the former have in their forelimbs. Apes are climbers; they can swing by their arms in trees and can move their arms freely in all directions (gibbon, left). Most monkeys, by contrast, are true quadrupeds. Since they travel on four limbs, they need move their front legs only backward and forward (macaque, right) and a little to the side. They leap and jump in trees.

climbers, all species of panids are adapted to terrestrial quadrupedalism, and they walk on the soles of their feet and the knuckles of their hands. The terrestrial skeletal adaptations are seen in the bones of their wrists and hands, which are modified to support the weight of the animals on their knuckles—on the second phalanx counting from the tip of the finger (Figure 4–14). Here, normal hairy skin is replaced by hairless friction skin such as we find on the palms of our hands and the soles of our feet.

   Thus the living apes, sharing a common ancestor which we believe was an arboreal climber that underwent a reduction in the tail, have each in their own way modified this original locomotor adaptation together with their skeleton and musculature. The tail was lost because a climber does not need an organ that balances and adjusts the aerodynamics of a leaping animal. Human ancestors have taken a fourth route—to terrestrial bipedalism. Although we are still quite able as climbers, our lower limbs have undergone profound changes in adaptation to *bipedal* walking on the ground.

Bipedal: moving erect on the hind limbs only.

Changes in Anatomy

Obviously, the adaptation that gave the apes the ability to climb with their arms and distribute their weight among several branches provided them with an opportunity for increased size. But having been granted this opportunity, what led them to exploit it? What advantage did the apes win by growing bigger?

   There was, of course, the competitive advantage that any big animal has over a smaller one when it comes to eating or being eaten. But there is also an extended life span. Big animals tend to live longer, and their rate of metabolism is slower

Top views

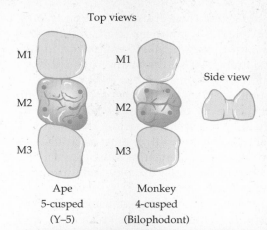

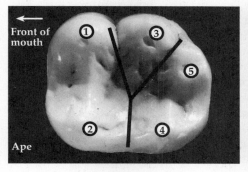

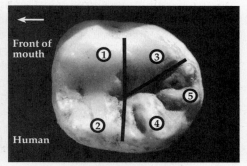

FIGURE 4–17 The cusp patterns of the lower molars enable us to distinguish apes and monkeys with ease. Old World monkeys show 4 paired cusps (the bilophodont pattern); front and rear cusps are clearly seen in a side view. In contrast, humans are relatively difficult to distinguish from apes on the basis of teeth: both have five cusps following a Y-5 pattern. In some human lower molars, however, the fifth cusp has been lost and it is commonly much reduced.

than that of small animals: their internal organs simply do not have to work so hard and therefore do not wear out as fast.

Any useful change often begets more change along the same line of development: it is a basic rule of evolutionary dynamics. Climbing prompted a series of further changes in the apes that altered the primate anatomy, providing on the one hand the potential for bipedal and tool-using humans and on the other the specialized adaptations of the modern anthropoid apes. As part of their adaptations for arboreal movement, the apes acquired a whole new complex of characteristics in their shoulders, their elbows, and their wrists that combined to make their arm

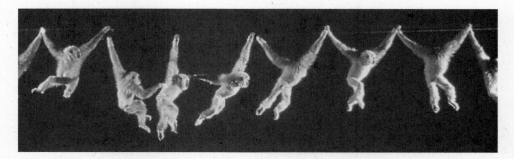

FIGURE 4–18 This photograph shows the hanging locomotion (called *brachiation*) of gibbons (here photographed brachiating along a rope in a cage).

movements much more flexible. Apes can swing their arms out in a wide circle from their shoulders. With their more flexible elbows they can straighten out their arms, and their wrists are much more mobile than a monkey's—more so, in fact, than a human's. An ape can hang from a branch by one hand and rotate its body completely around, thanks to the flexibility of its arm and wrist joints.

Nor did the changes that arose from climbing stop at the apes' arms and shoulders. Ultimately changes affected the whole of their upper bodies, giving them their characteristic short, relatively inflexible spine; the wide, shallow trunk with its resultant different arrangement of the internal organs; and a pelvis splayed out to provide additional room for the attachment of muscles. All these changes helped to produce animals that, from the waist up, physically began to remind us of the apes' evolutionary descendants—humans.

The results of the apes' evolutionary shift from quadrupedalism to climbing and brachiation are profoundly important. If an animal evolves greater erectness and arm flexibility, it can reach farther and grasp, pluck, hold, examine, and carry with greater ease. The more often a hand performs these acts, the better it gets at doing them. Despite their short thumbs, chimpanzees have the manual dexterity to strip the leaves from a twig (in other words, to make an implement) and to deftly insert that twig into a small hole in a termite mound so that they can lick off the termites that cling to the twig when it is pulled out (Figure 4–19). This remarkable act of food gathering requires not only careful manipulation but also intelligence. This is another way of saying that increased dependence on the hands has an evolutionary effect on the brain. It is therefore significant that apes are, as a group, more intelligent than monkeys, whose hands are dexterous enough, but whose quadrupedal way of life limits their use and thus limits the feedback that the use of the hands has on the evolution of the brain.

HUMAN CHARACTERISTICS

In the traditional evolutionary classification of Table 4–3, humans are the only living representatives of the primate family Hominidae, that is, the only living *hominids*. An abbreviated list of hominid traits is given in Table 4–4, but this list provides a most incomplete description of the attributes and abilities of modern people. What is it that makes humans different from the other primates? From among all the physical traits that separate humans from all other animals, four have overwhelming significance. The first three are a skeleton adapted for erect bipedalism (upright walking; Figures 4–15 and 4–20); eyes capable of sharp, three-dimensional vision in color; and hands that can both grip powerfully and manipulate things nimbly. These features are found in some degree in many primates; it is their elaboration and special combination with one another that distinguishes us. Controlling and making use of this equipment is humans' fourth significant trait: the brain—a physical organ itself, but one that introduces the capacity for rational thought and, with the body, makes possible that other most human of all our abilities, speech.

Bipedalism

These distinguishing attributes uniquely combined in humans interact with one another. It is impossible to say that one led to the next, or that one is necessarily more important than the others. Each reinforces the others and makes improve-

FIGURE 4–19 Jane Goodall observed chimpanzees fishing with short twigs for termites in mounds. The chimpanzees prepared the twigs by stripping off the leaves and breaking the twigs to a certain length: in fact, they made a tool.

ments in them possible. Nevertheless, one attribute stands out simply because it is so conspicuous: upright walking. It is a remarkably effective method of loco- motion, and no animal can use it as consistently as humans can.

For all its apparent simplicity, walking is an adaptation as specialized as fly- ing is to a bat or swimming is to a seal. True, humans are not the only animals able to stand on their hind legs; birds, bears, and a number of our primate cousins occasionally do so. But with the exception of a few flightless birds, such as the ostrich, humans are the only animals that depend exclusively on two legs for loco- motion. (The kangaroo, which may seem to be bipedal, actually uses its tail as a third limb and jumps rather than walks.) Using two legs, a human has the endurance to outrun a deer and can carry heavier loads, pound for pound of body weight, than a donkey. Only humans can swim a mile, walk several miles, and then climb a tree. Hominid bipedalism is specialized, yet it allows extraordinary versatility in locomotion.

Like horses, human beings have a variety of gaits; they amble, stride, jog, and sprint. The simple stride, though, is at once the most useful and the most peculiarly human way of getting from one place to another. Probably evolved on

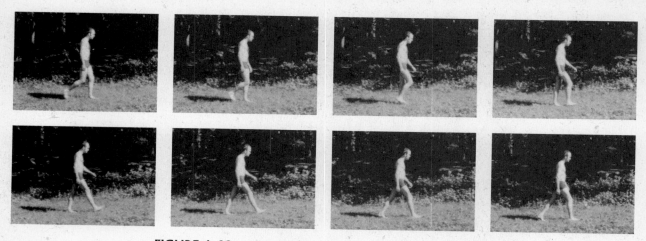

FIGURE 4–20   Bipedalism involves split-second balancing feats with precise muscular control. The right foot pushes off from the toe; the left foot bears the full body weight while the right leg moves ahead to land on the heel; then the left foot thrusts off. To run fast, human beings stay on their toes.

Savanna: tropical or subtropical grassland, often with scattered trees (woodland savanna).

the African grassland, or *savanna*, where our early ancestors often covered many miles in a day's food gathering or scavenging, the stride has taken us to every corner of the earth. Striding is no minor accomplishment. When compared with the way four-legged animals get about, human walking turns out to be a surprisingly complex feat (see Figure 4–20). "Without split-second timing," said John Napier, a British authority on primates, "man would fall flat on his face; in fact with each step he takes, he teeters on the edge of catastrophe." Human walking is actually a balancing act in which the muscles of the feet, legs, hips, and back are alternately contracted and relaxed according to synchronized orders from the brain and the spinal cord.

As Huxley showed in 1863, the human skeleton is closer in form to that of the African great apes than to that of any other animal. There are nevertheless striking differences between the human and the African ape skeletons—differences almost entirely due to the evolution in the human line of bipedal walking and in the ape line of quadrupedal knuckle walking (Figure 4–21). The human foot has lost the ability to grip with the big toe and the toe itself has become long and robust, forming the ball of the foot—an essential pivot for the act of walking. Human arms are short and legs long, in relation to the length of the trunk, while the apes have relatively long arms and short legs, indicating that the arms are more important in locomotion. The human knee has been modified for the transmission of weight and can be locked when extended. Fundamental changes have occurred in the pelvis to make the support of the trunk by the legs mechanically more efficient. The broader, shorter pelvis gives greater leverage to the muscles that hold the body erect, and the broad blade of the pelvis, called the *ilium*, anchors the buttock muscles, which do much of the work in walking. Almost every bone in the body reflects the remarkable evolution of these two distinct kinds of posture and locomotion.

Balanced bipedalism is uniquely human and strangely beautiful in its sheer efficiency and its superb adaptation of bone and muscle, brain and nerve, to the tricky problem of moving about on two legs rather than four. Our adaptations for bipedalism have not been perfected, however. Back trouble, foot ailments, and

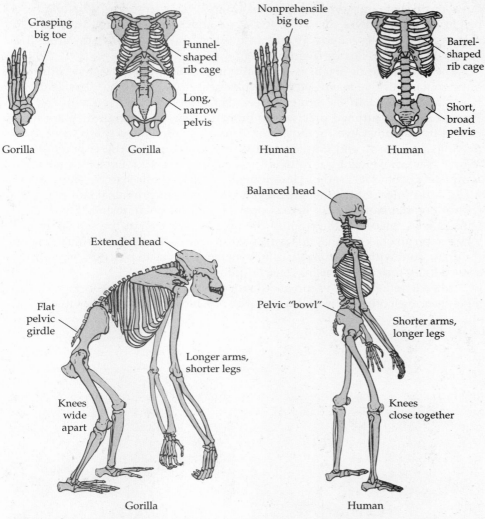

FIGURE 4–21 A comparison of key skeletal features of bipedal humans and quadrupedal apes.

difficulty in giving birth—common among humans—result partly from upright posture. Indeed, natural selection does not necessarily generate perfection in any trait. If a species survives, natural selection has brought about those traits required for survival—nothing more. To our eyes, the results often seem to constitute a kind of perfection, but most traits are compromises.

Vision

But why is it so important to human evolution that we stand erect and walk on two legs? Part of the answer has to do with the human head. The head is where the eyes are, and the taller an animal stands, the more it sees. A dog running through tall grass is forced to leap into the air time and again to get its bearings, but even on a smooth surface where no obstacles obstruct vision, the advantage of height is marked. Eyes that are 2 ft (0.6 m) above ground level can detect low objects about 6 miles (almost 10 km) away; eyes 5 ft (1.5 m) above the ground can see 9 miles (14 km) farther (Figure 4–22).

The advantage of height is especially important because vision is the most important of our five major senses. Scientists estimate that some 90 percent of the information stored in the brain arrives there through the agency of the eyes. Human eyes are attuned precisely to human needs. In general, they are unsurpassed by any other eyes in the world. A hawk can see more sharply but cannot move its eyes easily and must move its head to follow its prey. A dragonfly can follow faster movement but cannot focus a sharp image. A horse can see almost completely behind its head but has difficulty seeing objects straight ahead at close range. Most important, human beings and their nearest primate relatives have the special combination of full stereoscopic vision and color vision (Figure 4–12). Human eyes, placed at the front of the head rather than at the sides, can focus together on an object so that it is perceived as a single three-dimensional image in the brain. And within this image, color vision enables us to pick out details by hue as well as by form, relationship, and brightness.

Taken together, color vision and depth perception bring us enormous advantages over most other animals, the majority of which are either color-blind or have

FIGURE 4–22   More distant information about its environment is available to an animal with eyes 3 or 4 ft (about 1 m) above ground level (left) than to one of low height (right). These photographs, taken from different heights, are sharp at all distances, but animals other than primates can usually focus only at certain ranges of distance.

a relatively poor capacity to judge visual distances and to focus in fine detail on particular objects. Though it has stereoscopic vision, a dog sees, when it looks out over an open field, little more than what a black-and-white movie might show, though with some color sense, and the dog's distance focus is limited. The dog is unlikely to spot a rabbit in the field unless the rabbit moves—one reason rabbits and similar prey react to noises by freezing, which conceals them from their enemies. Human hunters, on the other hand, can scan a scene from their feet to the horizon in a few seconds by focusing sharply and selectively on a succession of images. And they see more images than any dog does because their eyes are raised at least 3 ft (almost 1 m) higher above the ground and their vision is in color.

Hands

Humans stand up partly in order to see and stay up partly because they see so well. But the freedom that this posture gives to their arms, and particularly their hands, has proved even more decisive in distinguishing humans from animals. Chimpanzees, though often upright and occasionally bipedal, are basically quadrupedal animals, and they lack free use of the arms. In an experimental situation they can get around with a bunch of bananas in their arms, but they must always be ready to maintain their balance with the help of a knuckle on the ground. Humans have far less need for caution. Babies may crawl on all fours; old people may rely on canes; but most humans go about with never a thought of support by anything but their two legs. Their hands are free to grab, carry, and manipulate.

Not needing our hands for support, we have been able to use them for more complicated and more creative tasks. With 25 joints and 58 distinctly different motions, the human hand is one of the most advanced mechanisms produced by nature. Imagine a single tool that can meet the demands of tasks as varied as gripping a tool, playing a violin, wringing out a towel, holding a pencil, gesturing, and—something we tend to forget—simple feeling.

Furthermore, while the hand itself may be a marvelous tool, it is used to full value only when it manipulates still other tools. This capacity is a second-stage benefit of upright walking. With our erect posture, our hands are free; with hands free, we can use tools; with tools, we can get food more easily and exploit the environment in other ways to ensure our survival. Humans are not the only animals that use tools, but they are the only ones that do so to any great extent and with any consistency.

There are two distinct ways of holding and using tools: the *power grip* and the *precision grip*, as John Napier termed them (Figure 4–23). Human infants and children begin with the power grip and progress to the precision grip. Think of how a child holds a spoon: first in the power grip, in its fist or between its fingers and palm, and later between the tips of the thumb and the first two fingers, in the precision grip. All primates have the power grip. It is the way they get firm hold of a tree branch. But only catarrhine primates have thumbs that are long enough or flexible enough to be completely opposable through rotation at the wrist, able to reach to the tips of all the other fingers and thus provide some degree of precision gripping. Apes and Old World monkeys differ in their grips, however, and, unexpectedly, the monkeys are somewhat more like humans. As an adaptation for arboreal arm-swinging and arm-hanging, apes have evolved

Power grip: a grip involving all fingers of the hand equally, as in grasping a baseball.

Precision grip: a grip that involves opposing the tip of the thumb to the tips of the other fingers, allowing fine control of small objects.

FIGURE 4–23   The power grip (left) and the precision grip (right) are illustrated in these photographs, together with the uniquely human independent control of the five fingers.

greatly elongated fingers, exclusive of the thumb. As a result, apes' thumbs are relatively quite short and, despite their full opposability, capable of only an impaired precision grip (Figure 4–24). Humans' long, fully opposable thumbs and the independent control of our fingers make possible nearly all the movements necessary to handle tools, to make clothing, to write with a pencil, to play a flute.

But the fine precision grip of humans would be a much less extraordinary adaptation without the complex brain that coordinates and directs its use. In the human family, manipulation, tool use, and the brain may have developed together. The hand carries out some of the most critical and complex orders of the brain, and as the hand grew more skillful so did the brain.

The Brain

The human brain is not much to look at. On the dissecting table, it is a "pinkish-gray mass, moist and rubbery to the touch . . . perched like a flower on top of a slender stalk" (the spinal cord). An ape's brain does not look very different. But there is a difference, and it is crucial. It lies in the extent of the gray layer called the *cortex*, which constitutes the outer layer of the largest part of the brain, the cerebrum. The cortex, scientists now know, plays the major role in reasoned behavior, memory, and abstract thought—and also supervises the delicate and accurate muscular movements that control the precision grip. The cortex is quite thin, but it represents 80 percent of the volume of the human brain and contains most of the brain's estimated 10 billion nerve cells, or *neurons*. If spread out flat, it would be about the size of a large newspaper page. It fits inside the head only by being compressed like a crumpled rag (the famous "convolutions" of the brain are mainly the folds and overlaps of the cerebral cortex). This compression demonstrates that the cortex has all but outgrown its alloted space. Indeed, the human

Neurons: nerve cells; the basic units of the nervous system.

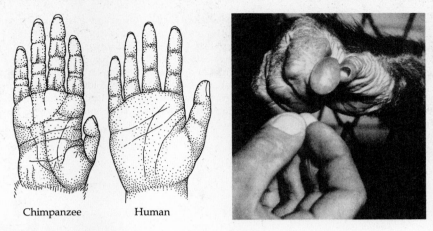

Chimpanzee   Human

FIGURE 4–24 Though superficially like a human hand, the hand of a chimpanzee has a relatively short thumb and less independent control of the fingers. As the photograph shows, when the chimpanzee picks up an object between finger and thumb, it does not (and cannot) oppose the tip of the thumb to the tips of the fingers as humans can. Thus, compared to humans (and Old World monkeys), the ape's precision grip is somewhat impaired.

brain is some three times larger than expected for an anthropoid of our body size. Somehow, the increase in the size of the cortex has helped make our brain the uniquely human thing it is (Figure 4–25 and see Chapter 13).

Although many mysteries about the brain remain to be solved, some of its secrets, particularly the importance of the huge cortex, are now well understood. The cortex is not only the seat of intelligence but also, and perhaps more significantly, the part of the brain where sense impressions and memories are stored to be called forth and acted on as circumstances suggest. The working of the human cortex follows no fixed pattern that dictates certain associations between experience and memory, as in some animal brains, and few predetermined responses are generated in the cortex. Among animals, many patterns of action are effectively automatic, performed by inborn programs or through previous conditioning. In humans, these patterns are, to some extent, performed consciously, or refrained from consciously, or replaced by completely new patterns, again consciously. This use of the brain results in what is known as *reasoned behavior,* a phenomenon typically human and rarely seen in other animals.

But of course the most impressive mental ability of humans is not the ease with which we solve problems or reason through behavioral decisions. Rather, it is our ability to look inward and observe our own mental processes: humans not only think but know they are thinking. We are conscious of what we know, believe, and feel, and we recognize knowledge, beliefs, and emotions in other people (we are also quick to manipulate others' beliefs, emotions, and knowledge to our own advantage). In a word, humans have a *mind*—but is this also true of other primates? Primatologists Dorothy Cheney and Robert Seyfarth have summarized much of what is known about the problem of mind among nonhuman primates in their book *How Monkeys See the World*. They find little evidence of mind among monkeys. Although monkeys know a lot about their physical and social environments, they differ from humans in their failure to use knowledge

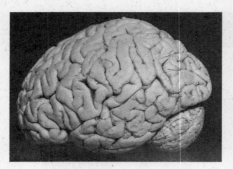

FIGURE 4–25 Conscious mental activity takes place at the surface, or cortex, of the cerebral hemispheres, the two halves of the cerebrum. This cortex has evolved so much in primate evolution that, in apes and humans, it is too large to be smooth, as it used to be, and is deeply folded. This series of diagrams illustrates the importance of the cerebrum and its cortex in humans. The photo shows a freshly dissected human brain.

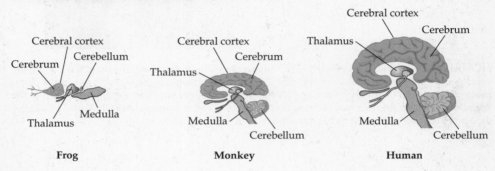

Frog   Monkey   Human

for personal gain—apparently because they "do not know what they know and cannot reflect upon their knowledge, their emotions, or their beliefs." Monkeys apparently are unable to attribute mental states or impute motives to other individuals, and therefore these concepts do not affect how they behave. Furthermore, monkeys appear to have little if any self-awareness. But, Cheney and Seyfarth continue, apes may be different. Research on apes (primarily chimpanzees) suggests that these animals may be far superior to monkeys in attributing mental states to each other: "There is strong suggestive evidence that chimpanzees, if not other apes, recognize that other individuals have beliefs and that their own behavior can affect those beliefs. Unlike monkeys, chimpanzees seem to understand each others' goals and motives. They deceive each other in more ways and in more contexts than monkeys, and they seem better than monkeys at recognizing both their own and other individuals' knowledge and limitations." In other words, apes may fall squarely between monkeys and humans with regard to the evolution of mind.

Language and Speech

Language: the cognitive aspect of human communication, involving symbolic thinking structured by grammar.

Speech: the oral expression of language (other expressions include signed or written language).

The uniquely large and complex human brain has combined with certain critical bodily modifications to produce our most important innovations: *language* and *speech.* Although virtually all animals communicate with their fellows, only humans think symbolically and transmit their thoughts by talking. Bees dance to direct hive mates to food; wolves warn off intruders by marking their territories with scent; one bird calls to announce danger, another to initiate courtship.

Besides using these ancient methods of communication, including bodily movements and simple sounds, humans also use speech, that most common physical expression of language, a repertory of short, contrasting sounds that can be combined in an almost infinite number of ways. While animals communicate emotional state and, on occasion, limited information about their physical or social circumstances, humans routinely engage in complex linguistic exchanges of information or ideas.

Language and speech are so clearly dependent on brainpower that their dependence on the body is often overlooked. The role of the body is most clearly demonstrated by studies of chimpanzees. Chimpanzees have brains that appear to be adequate for some degree of abstract thought and some learning by insight. They can stack several boxes on top of one another to reach a bunch of bananas, a simple act to us, but one requiring the imaginative combination of superficially unrelated elements. They can also produce a wide range of sounds. It seems that they ought, then, to be able to talk. Since the turn of the century scientists have been trying to teach chimpanzees to speak. The best anyone has been able to do, after years of patient tutelage, is to get a chimpanzee to say "mama," "papa," and one or two other infant words. Only recently has the reason for this failure been traced. It involves not simply brain size but another aspect of the anatomy. Chimpanzees and gorillas are indeed able to use very simple sentences—but they cannot speak them. These apes lack the kind of pharynx, mouth, and tongue that enable humans to articulate vowels. They can "speak" their sentences not with auditory symbols, but with visual ones, specifically, with the symbols of American Sign Language, originally designed for the deaf (see Chapter 13). The human remains the only creature that has developed both the physical structures and the powerful, specialized brain needed to produce speech.

Cultural Adaptation

Language was perhaps the last of our major biological characteristics to evolve. And with the gift of speech, we acquired an immensely powerful tool for the development and continuing evolution of our unique way of life—a way of life based on cultural adaptation. Unlike the other primates, humans are no longer wholly at the mercy of their surroundings. Faced with environmental challenges, we invent cultural solutions rather than evolve biological ones (apes also do this to a very limited extent, as described in Chapter 5). Clothes, shelters, and heating and cooling systems help us deal with harsh climatic conditions. Tools, irrigation systems, and pesticides help us aggressively exploit the environment for food. Medical technology helps us deal with diseases and physical handicaps. Furthermore, thanks to language, human knowledge is cumulative: it increases steadily as each new generation's innovations are added to the summed knowledge passed down to it. Thus *culture* evolves in a Lamarckian fashion, by the inheritance of acquired traits.

The importance of humans' evolution of a cultural way of life cannot be overemphasized. Our reliance on cultural adaptation has set us apart from the other primates. For better or worse, we are the only living primate species that exerts significant control over its own evolutionary future.

Culture: humans' systems of learned behavior, symbols, customs, beliefs, institutions, artifacts, and technology, characteristic of a group and transmitted by its members to their offspring.

SUMMARY

The first primates evolved at least 60 million years ago. Today the order is represented by over 200 species and is characterized by extreme physical and behavioral diversity. The most basic primate traits—grasping hands and feet, and stereoscopic vision with depth perception (plus the neural elaborations that go with these developments)—were most likely originally adaptations for predation on insects in an arboreal habitat. The primate order contains two suborders: Prosimii and Anthropoidea. The prosimians were the first suborder to evolve, and today they are characterized by the retention of several primitive anatomical traits, including a keen sense of smell and relatively unprotected eyes. At present these small (and often nocturnal) creatures are found only in Africa and Asia. The anthropoid suborder, today including monkeys, apes, and humans, first appeared about 45 to 50 million years ago. Compared to prosimians, living anthropoids show a reduced sense of smell, elaborated vision, complete loss of claws, and a more complex brain. Modern monkeys are found in Central and South America (superfamily Ceboidea) and in Africa and Asia (superfamily Cercopithecoidea). Most monkeys show some variety of quadrupedal locomotion in the trees.

The superfamily Hominoidea includes the apes and humans. While humans are found worldwide, apes are limited to Africa (chimpanzees, bonobos, and gorillas) and Asia (gibbons and orangutans). Apes tend to be large, tailless, arboreal arm swingers and arm hangers (or their terrestrial descendants), while humans have evolved into terrestrial bipeds. Hominoids display the largest, most complex brains of all primates. Humans have shown unparalleled brain expansion and elaboration, and they are characterized by the unique possession of mind. Other unique traits shown by humans include language and speech and cultural adaptation as a way of life. The latter has given humans considerable control over their evolutionary future.

REVIEW QUESTIONS

1. Review the relative merits of the arboreal and visual predation theories as explanations of the common characteristics of primates.

2. Compare the anatomy of prosimians to that of anthropoid primates. Can anthropoids be said to have *progressed beyond* the prosimian condition?

3. Why are humans classified as hominoids rather than monkeys? Describe how human anatomy resembles that of apes and differs from that of monkeys.

4. One can arrange the living primates so that it appears that evolution shaped primates to become increasingly humanlike. Discuss this notion of humans being the *goal* of primate evolution.

5. Do monkeys and apes have *minds?* Discuss the evidence, and consider the implications of how humans treat these animals.

6. What are the implications of humans' now being largely in control of their own evolutionary future?

POSTSCRIPT

Along with many other species, nonhuman primates are currently in a state of global emergency. Of the 200-plus primate species, over 50 percent are considered endangered or in some jeopardy, and 1 in 5 is likely to become extinct before the turn of the century if strict conservation measures are not begun immediately. Among the species at greatest risk are several of Madagascar's prosimians (aye-ayes, hairy-eared dwarf lemurs, golden and greater bamboo lemurs, and Perrier's sifaka), the muriqui monkeys and lion tamarins of South America, the Asian golden snub-nosed and Tonkin snub-nosed monkeys, the lion-tail macaques of India, and Africa's red colobus monkeys. Most of the living apes are endangered to some degree, although mountain gorillas—with only 400 or so individuals left—are clearly at the greatest risk of imminent extinction.

But who is responsible for bringing so many of our evolutionary relatives to the brink of disaster? Unfortunately, we have no one to blame but ourselves. Through our use of primates for food, pets, and research subjects and our destruction of their natural habitats, we have become monkeys', apes' and prosimians' worst enemy. Let's consider the problem.

The global population of humans is currently about 5.6 billion; this figure is predicted to rise to over 10 billion by the middle of the next century. Population growth is uneven from one country to the next, but the highest rates seem generally to be in underdeveloped tropical countries (around 3 percent annual growth). All of these people need—and demand—food and living space, and in their efforts to meet these needs, they are causing massive habitat destruction. Habitat destruction impinges most directly on primates when it affects the tropical and subtropical forests since, as explained in this chapter, this is where most species naturally occur—and the forests of the world are being ravaged. Every year some 67,000 sq mi (over 173,000 sq km) of tropical and subtropical forest are destroyed worldwide—an area almost as big as the state of Washington. About 180 sq mi (466 sq km) of forests are destroyed every day! The forests are cut down to make space for agriculture and ranching, for fuel to be used locally, and for exportable wood. And as the forests go, so do their primate inhabitants. The primate-rich Amazonian forests are expected to be reduced by half in the next 25 years, while the Congo basin forests will decrease 25 percent in the same period.

In addition to habitat destruction, humans contribute to primate extinction by hunting the animals for food and capturing them to sell. Primates are an important source of food in many parts of tropical South America and Africa. Additionally, even if they are not on the menu, when primates begin to raid farms and gardens they are hunted and killed as agricultural pests. Furthermore, tens of thousands of primates are captured each year for sale as pets or research subjects. Although capturing animals for sale has come under some control in the last few decades, it can still have a major impact on marginal species, and it is terribly inefficient: it has been estimated that traditional capture techniques result in five to ten animals killed for every one that is sold.

What, if anything, can (or should) we do about global habitat destruction and the plight of endangered primates? One response might be that we should do nothing; after all, extinction is a fact of life, and given enough time, the earth will surely adjust to humans' habitat and wildlife depredations. However, is this the wisest course? What do we stand to lose if the forests and their inhabitants are plundered completely? Perhaps we should move quickly to stop the destruction and save the endangered species, but how can we do it? After all, inhabitants of developed countries—comparatively well fed, well housed and secure—are hardly in a strong moral position to tell people in poor, underdeveloped countries to stop destroying the forests and the animals *for the global common good*. Hard questions. And also questions that demand immediate answers and carry high stakes. What's *your* position on these issues?

CHAPTER

5

The Behavior of Living Primates

*We love animals, we watch them with delight, we study their
habits with ever-increasing curiosity; and we destroy them.*
KENNETH CLARK, 1903–1983.
Animals and Men, CH. 5.

OVERVIEW

The fossilized remains of our extinct ancestors provide important direct information about their anatomy, but only limited (and indirect) information about their behavior. In order to make reasonable behavioral reconstructions, researchers often rely on analogues drawn from living human cultures (usually hunting-and-gathering peoples) and nonhuman primates. This chapter presents a broad summary of what scientists have learned about our nonhuman primate kin, including their diets, grouping patterns, social development, sexuality, dominance systems, and affiliative (friendly) relations. Particular emphasis is placed on the various living ape species, since the fossil record makes it clear that the human family is descended from ape stock. Important topics in the chapter include social group type, socialization, dominance, sexual behavior, sexual selection, friendly relations, territoriality, and feeding strategies. Also important are the behavioral profiles of baboons, gibbons, orangutans, gorillas, chimpanzees, and bonobos.

STUDYING PRIMATES

Fossils can provide a very good indication of the course of evolution, but they are less good at indicating precisely how evolution came about. This limitation has been a source of frustration to anthropologists for many years—so much so that many are now looking for answers elsewhere than in the fossil record. One alternative field that is fruitful is the study of humankind's primate relatives, the monkeys and apes; closely related to us, they are even more closely related to our ancestors.

As we have seen, recent developments in biochemistry have shown close similarities of DNA, cell proteins, and blood proteins including hemoglobin between humans and the other primates. Now, thanks to an upsurge in studies of monkeys and apes in their natural environments, it is becoming clear that in their social behavior, too, they stand much closer to us than we had suspected. Many live in highly organized groups in which following routines and sharing knowledge permit a relatively stable social organization. Others, like chimpanzees, live in more loosely organized groups. Whatever the size or structure of the group, some members are good friends, others dedicated enemies; some are collaborators, others rivals; some are popular, others despised. Infant apes and monkeys, as they grow up, must learn a code of behavior, much as a human child must, and all the members of a group are linked by an elaborate system of communication that uses both sounds and gestures and shows considerable sophistication.

The comparison of ape and monkey behavior with human behavior, of course, must not be pushed too far. Yet, in their daily routine and in many aspects of their relationships with their fellows, the nonhuman primates resemble humans in many surprising ways and throw much light on the roots of human behavior.

Early Work

Although new aspects of the connection between us and our primate kin are continually coming to light, the idea of studying primates is by no means a new one. In the parts of the world where humans live in close contact with monkeys or apes, accounts of their primate neighbors have dotted observers' writings for centuries; the Chinese general Wang Jeñ-yü, for instance, mentioned his pet gibbon Yeh-pin in his memoirs written in the tenth century. Western travelers to foreign lands were especially impressed by monkeys and apes, which in many ways were uncannily similar to themselves. In the mid-1800s, while writers like Edgar Allan Poe spun tales emphasizing the eerie aspects of the resemblance between ape and human, others who observed monkeys and apes in their natural habitat were awed by what they saw. In 1840 the English naturalist William Charles Martin, observing a female gibbon, wrote, "It is almost impossible to convey in words an idea of the quickness and graceful address of her movements: they may indeed be termed aerial as she seems merely to touch in her progress the branches along which she exhibits her evolutions."

Early in the twentieth century, casual observation of primates began to give rise to more serious study. In the 1920s psychobiologist Robert Yerkes observed captive chimpanzees in the United States and was so impressed by what he saw and so astonished by how little was known about the great apes that he sent two students, Henry Nissen and Harold Bingham, to Africa to study the chimpanzee and the gorilla, respectively. In 1930 Yerkes opened the Laboratories of Primate Biology at Orange Park, Florida, which later moved to Emory University in Atlanta and were renamed the Yerkes Regional Primate Research Center. Behavioral studies, including intelligence tests and other studies of social behavior, as well as studies of stress and other physiological matters, are carried out at the center, which today has the largest collection of apes in the country.

The first systematic investigations of the behavior of apes and monkeys living under natural conditions were made by C. R. Carpenter. In the early 1930s Carpenter journeyed to Barro Colorado Island in Panama to study howler monkeys and then traveled to Southeast Asia to observe gibbons. Later he set up a colony of rhesus monkeys on Cayo Santiago near Puerto Rico and observed them. Carpenter published some revolutionary findings on monkey behavior. The results he obtained by viewing primates in the wild pointed up the limitations of studying primates in captivity, which had been the practice up to that time.

Around the same period, the South African zoologist Solly Zuckerman was studying baboons—first, hamadryas baboons in the London Zoo and then chacma baboons in South Africa. Zuckerman was especially interested in what these creatures' behavior might suggest about that of humans. He concluded that sexual behavior was the original force behind social organization among primates, an idea that has since been alternately discredited and somewhat revived. But he was seriously misled by studying baboons in the zoo: their behavior in captivity was quite different from the way they were later found to behave in the wild.

Psychologists, too, took an interest in the behavior of nonhuman primates, particularly that of apes. In Germany, Wolfgang Kohler conducted experiments investigating chimpanzees' capacity to find solutions to problems, such as stacking boxes or using sticks to reach bundles of bananas. In Russia, Nadie Kohts studied chimps' ability to discriminate between objects by size, color, and shape. And in the United States, Harry and Margaret Harlow studied the mother-infant bond in rhesus monkeys. By using artificial surrogate mothers of varying design, the Harlows were able to show that tactile stimuli (i.e., the ability to cling to "mother") was much more important to young monkeys than access to milk. Furthermore, monkeys denied access to their mothers when young showed behavioral problems in adulthood—a finding with important implications regarding humans.

It is exceedingly difficult to do some kinds of experimental work in an animal's natural habitat, for example, surgery, chemical therapy, and experimental separations of mothers and infants. But however useful for gauging an individual animal's response to a specific stimulus or situation it is, observing apes or monkeys in artificial confinement provides little insight into normal primate behavior. The other handy spot for observation is the zoo, but there, too, the subjects' behavior is distorted by the abnormal environment (Figure 5–1). Small cages provide scant room for movement, there is no need for ordinary activities like seeking food, and the crowding found in many zoos transforms the animals' social relationships. For scientists interested in studying normal primate behavior, the only realistic option is to observe monkeys and apes in their natural setting.

A major development in field research occurred after World War II, when primatologists in Japan established the Primate Research Group to study native Japanese macaques under natural conditions. At Takasakiyama, by setting up feeding stations that a macaque colony with 200-odd members visited regularly, scientists were able to observe one group of monkeys over an extended period. On

FIGURE 5–1   Zoos are necessarily extremely unnatural environments for primates, which in nature are gregarious, inquisitive, and extremely active animals. In these photographs a gorilla attempts to use dry leaves to build a nest on a concrete floor. Neither hard floor nor dry leaves are present in a tropical forest, where nests are built from soft living vegetation folded to make a comfortable bed.

the island of Koshima, with an isolated macaque population, researchers not only recorded their subjects' customs but to some extent changed them, thereby gaining numerous insights into how the monkeys' behavior and social structure were determined.

Recent Studies

The trend toward studying primates in their native habitats really caught hold in the late 1950s. Led by various anthropologists, a large number of young field workers, including both women and men, began pouring out all over the world from universities and museums in a dozen countries. In the late 1950s they began by studying langurs and baboons. During the 1960s they studied rhesus and langur monkeys in India and gorillas, chimpanzees, and many forest monkeys in Africa. During the 1960s and 1970s they observed the gibbons and orangutans of Southeast Asia. At various times studies of New World monkeys have been conducted in Central and South America.

Primates turned out to be much harder to study than anyone had imagined. Many, like the mountain gorilla, live in inaccessible places. Many stay in the tops of trees in dense forest, where they are nearly invisible. Others, like the orangutan, are extremely rare. Most are shy. There is also the problem of what to look for and how to interpret it. Different species act differently in different areas, under different ecological influences, and even in different population densities. Primate behavior is not stereotyped, but complex and highly variable.

Yet, as we shall see, field studies have proved an invaluable source of information. Our knowledge of apes' behavior has greatly increased over the past three decades, thanks to the work of researchers like Vernon and Frances Reynolds, who studied chimpanzees in the Budongo Forest of Uganda; Adrian Kortland, who studied chimpanzees in West Africa; Jane Goodall, who spent decades at the Gombe Stream chimpanzee reserve in Tanzania; Toshisada Nishida, who studied chimpanzees in the Mahali Mountains of Tanzania; George Schaller, who observed gorillas on the mountain slopes of Central Africa; Biruté Galdikas, who studied orangutans in Kalimantan (Borneo); and the late Dian Fossey, who extended Schaller's work. As each new fact is unearthed, old prejudices are dispelled. The gorilla, whose size and appearance cast it for more than a hundred years as a fearsome forest monster, is now known to be shy and usually gentle. And the chimpanzee is not merely an amiable muncher of bananas but an enthusiastic hunter and a murderous adventurer on occasion.

BASIS OF SOCIAL ORGANIZATION

Although, as shown in Chapter 4, monkeys and apes differ from each other in important ways, they also share many characteristics. Of these, certainly the most interesting is that they are all social species (except the orangutan) and that their societies are highly organized. We first need to ask ourselves several questions: What are the advantages of social life? Why are so many mammal and bird species social and why have the Hominoidea developed this characteristic to such lengths? Four kinds of advantage are usually proposed by zoologists.

1. Several pairs of eyes are better than one in the detection of predators and in their avoidance. Defense by a group is also far more effective. Three or four

male baboons constitute an impressive display and can frighten any predator, even a lion. A lone baboon is a dead baboon.

2. Competing for large food patches is more successful when done by groups rather than by individuals. We shall see that in some monkeys social groups subdivide when food is sparse and widely scattered.

3. Reproductive advantages accrue from social groups because regular access to the opposite sex is ensured.

4. Social groups permit extensive socialization with peers and elders and the opportunity to learn from them. Among animals such as the higher primates, this is a factor of the greatest importance.

These factors are probably the most important in bringing about the selection of social life in animals such as primates. Although considerable variation may occur within a species, especially under different environmental conditions, only a few Old World primate species (including the gibbons and the siamang, a large gibbon) normally live in groups consisting of only an adult male, a female, and their young. The orang is unique in being more-or-less solitary. The remaining Old World monkeys and apes all live in social groups that number as high as 500 individuals but most commonly number between 10 and 50 (Table 5–1).

But how are these societies organized? Far from being a structureless collection of rushing, squalling animals, primate societies are remarkably complex and stable. Order is maintained in primate societies through a complex interrelationship of several factors. One is the animals' prolonged period of dependence: infant apes and monkeys, like human infants, are far from self-sufficient and maintain a close relationship with their mothers longer than most other animals. During this time they learn some of the roles they will play as adults. Other factors are dominance and hierarchy. In many species the adults of one or both sexes have quite a well-defined social rank within the group. Also important are the other relationships among adults, which to some extent are determined by kinship, friendship, sexual contacts and competition for food, sleeping sites, and any other limited resources.

Thinking about these factors, one quickly sees that they are among the most important regulators of human society as well. Thus, for a very long time (we may assume) and for many species—for humans, for chimpanzees, and for baboons—the problem of life has been, and still is, largely the problem of getting along in a group.

Learning in Childhood

What is meant by a prolonged period of dependence? A kitten has become a cat by the time it is a year old. A comparable-sized ring-tailed lemur takes about twice as long to reach adulthood. A male baboon takes 7 to 8 years to reach full social and biological maturity, a chimpanzee needs anywhere from 10 to 15 years, and a human even longer. As a result, family ties—and especially those based on *matrilineal kinship*—among higher primates tend to be strong and lasting. This slow development among a group of supportive relatives is necessary for a higher primate to learn all the things it must to fit itself into the complex society into which it is born. It needs time to learn. In a society in which an individual must deal with many daily choices and varied personal interchange, a long period of

Matrilineal kinship: kinship traced through the maternal line.

Table 5-1 Some Socioecological Characteristics of Old World Monkeys and Apes

	Japanese Macaques (Macaca fuscata)	Yellow Baboons (Papio cynocephalus)	Hanuman Langurs (Presbytis entellus)	White-Handed Gibbons (Hylobates lar)	Eastern Highland Gorillas (Gorilla gorilla beringei)	Orangutans (Pongo pygmaeus)	Chimpanzees (Pan troglodytes)	Bonobos (Pan paniscus)
Group size	35–55	10–185	10–65	Adult pair and 1 or 2 offspring	9–37	2 (mother and offspring)	20–105	50–120
Social structure	Multimale; multifemale	Multimale; multifemale	Multimale; unimale, and possibly age-graded; multifemale	Monogamous families	Unimale or multimale with one dominant silverback male; also lone males; multifemale	Mother and infant; lone males	Multimale; multifemale; dispersed community	Multimale; multifemale, dispersed community
Habitat	Seasonal, deciduous and evergreen montane and submontane areas	African middle belt, Acacia woodland, short grass savanna forest	Deciduous to moist evergreen forests; sea level to high Himalayas	Forest	Lowland and mountain rain forests and bamboo forests	Indonesian jungles; herbivorous (mostly frugivorous) diet	Deciduous woodland; omnivorous (mostly frugivorous) diet	Lowland rain forest and swamp forest; omnivorous (mostly frugivorous) diet
Home range	0.1–10.4 mi² (0.2–27 km²)	0.8–15.4 mi² (2.1–40 km²)	0.04–3 mi² (0.1–7.8 km²)	0.08–0.2 mi² (0.2–0.5 km²)	1.9–3.1 mi² (4.9–8.1 km²)	0.2–2.3 mi² (0.4–6 km²)	2–215 mi² (5–560 km²)	7.7–19.3 mi² (20–50 km²)

Sources: Cheney, D. L. "Interactions and Relationships Between Groups," in Primate Societies, ed. by B. Smuts, D. Cheney, R. Seyfarth, R. Wrangham, and T. Struhsaker. Chicago, University of Chicago, 1987; Nishida, T., and M. Hiraiwa-Hasegawa. "Chimpanzees and Bonobos: Cooperative Relationships Among Males," in Primate Societies, ed. by B. Smuts et al. Chicago, University of Chicago, 1987; Rodman, P. S., and J. C. Mitani. "Orangutans: Sexual Dimorphism in a Solitary Species," in Primate Societies, ed. by B. Smuts et al. Chicago, University of Chicago, 1987; Stewart, K. J., and A. H. Harcourt. "Gorillas: Variation in Female Relationships," in Primate Societies, ed. by B. Smuts et al. Chicago, University of Chicago, 1987; Melnick, D. J., and Mary C. Pearl. "Cercopithecines in Multimale Groups: Genetic Diversity and Population Structure," in Primate Societies, ed. by B. Smuts et al. Chicago, University of Chicago, 1987.

FIGURE 5–2   Each night, chimpanzees prepare new nests for themselves by bending tree branches over larger boughs to make a bed.

youthful learning is an absolute necessity. During this period the vulnerable young animal is protected by the group.

For a chimpanzee, childhood play is the equivalent of going to school. It watches its mother look for food, and looks for food itself. It watches her make nests and makes little nests of its own—not to sleep in, just for the fun of it (Figure 5–2). Later, during a long adolescence, it picks up from its peers the physical skills it will need as an adult, as well as the more intricate psychological skills required to get along with others: it learns not only how to interpret the moods of other chimpanzees but also how to respond to other individuals. Any chimpanzee that cannot learn to communicate fully with its fellows almost certainly will not live to grow up, for communication is the essential bonding of any society. All this time the learner is finding its own place among its peers, first in play, later in more competitive activity that will help determine its rank as an adult. In sum, two sources of learning and two sets of relationships make up primate society. One of these is the family relationship (usually, mother-infant and other matrilineal kin; occasionally, mother-father-infant-siblings). The other is the larger relationship of the individual to all other members of its troop.

Primate behavior, like that of some other highly evolved mammals, depends heavily on learning, in contrast to the less flexible behavior of simpler animals. For this reason the prolonged learning period is especially significant. The important role of learned behavior among primates also means that the group as a whole has more knowledge and experience than its individual members. Experience is pooled, and the generations are linked. This was demonstrated in the Nairobi game park, where a ranger had had to kill a baboon: for many years afterward, the troop that had lost its member avoided the site of the killing, even though all members of the troop had not witnessed the event.

FIGURE 5–3 A juvenile female langur (left) holds a complaining infant while adult females groom each other. As the infants get older, they become more adventurous (right).

Studies of Hanuman langurs in India (Figure 5–3) have yielded a wealth of information on how the infants of one monkey species learn. These large monkeys live in groups containing several adult females and one or more adult males (Table 5–1). The adult females are organized in a dominance hierarchy that is shown by their respective abilities to displace one another from food and other resources. Mothers lavish attention on the distinctively dark new infants, but they also allow other females to hold, carry, and groom the baby—and many females, particularly nulliparous youngsters and pregnant adults, are anxious to engage in such "aunting," or *allomothering,* behavior. Mothers must be careful, however, as they sometimes have difficulty reclaiming their infants. When confronted by a high-ranking allomother who refuses to return an infant, a low-status mother can only wait until the "aunt" tires of the baby and deserts it, or watch for an opportunity to snatch back her offspring.

Allomothering: typically, care or attention directed toward an infant by a female other than its mother (also called *aunting behavior*).

After the infant reaches the age of about 5 months, its dark coat lightens to the color of an adult langur. Now the females no longer vie to hold it. It follows its mother about, copying her actions, learning to forage. It also spends much of its time in energetic activity, running, climbing, chasing, and wrestling—skills that will be invaluable as it reaches adulthood. As it plays with its fellows, it learns to get along as a member of the group.

Once young langurs are weaned, around the age of 15 months, they become segregated by sex. The females stay near the center of the group, close to the adults, mixing more and more intimately with the adult females and their infants. Holding the infants and sometimes tending them while the mothers are away, they are gaining experience for their own future role as mothers. The male juveniles, meanwhile, spend most of their free time playing. As they grow older, their play becomes ever more vigorous and wide-ranging, and they drift toward the periphery of the group, away from both the adults and the infants. This is the young males' first step toward eventual emigration.

Other monkeys whose development has been studied include the baboons and the macaques. The patterns they follow illustrate interesting social differences among the various genera in the male attitude toward the infants of a group. In a langur group, adult males are inclined to behave like the traditional Victorian father who kept himself apart from his young children. Langur males in captivity do show an interest in newborns, particularly males, but on the whole young langurs grow up in an almost exclusively matriarchal atmosphere. On the other hand, Japanese macaque males have been observed to cradle 1- and 2-year-old infants during the birth season. Paternal attention of this nature, which may persist for some time, is somewhat similar to that of hamadryas baboons. The subadult or young adult hamadryas male in fact acquires females for his eventual one-male (and many-female) family unit by first "mothering" infant females. For months—often a year or more—a young female enjoys a protective relationship with a male that is similar to the protection she received from her mother. The male readily carries the young female on his back, helps her over difficult terrain when she walks, and lets her huddle next to him at night. She will in due course become an adult member of his one-male group—his harem of females. In savanna baboon groups, adult males also show an intense interest in infants and associate most closely with the babies of females with whom they share a special relationship. Usually an adult male will approach a mother, smacking his lips to show he means no harm, in order to enjoy the pleasure of playing with the mother's infant. The savanna baboons live in multimale groups in which one male does not control a particular harem of females.

Why these differences? They are adaptations acquired in the interests of survival and reproductive success in different environments. Comfortable as some langur species are on the ground, no langur ventures far from trees. Females do not require a male's protection, and they usually do not get it. If a langur group is alarmed, it is every monkey for itself (although langur males have been known to defend group-mates—particularly infants—against humans and hawks). Baboons, on the other hand, are organized differently, perhaps because they frequently range far from trees. Adult male baboons routinely defend infants against attacks from conspecifics. Furthermore, if a predator approaches the troop, the males *may* (depending on the degree of danger) position themselves between the threat and their group (including the infants). As noted above, however, the protective patterns of baboon males may reflect more than just a generalized concern for infants. These patterns may be one way the males maintain relationships with the infants' mothers—relationships that later may yield important benefits in the form of mating opportunities.

In summary we can note that monkey species are finely adapted to what may seem to us minor differences in their environment, such as food distribution (density and clumping), density and type of trees (if any), water resources, and terrain. We can reasonably suppose that hominid adaptations during human evolution have also been finely tuned to the environment. It is in these adaptations that we can detect natural selection at its most precise, as it brings about the endless modification of behavior.

The Dominance Hierarchy

Dominance hierarchy: rank structuring of a primate group, usually based on winning and losing fights. For some purposes, the ranks within a subset of animals, such as the adult males, may be analyzed separately.

Part of growing up in most monkey societies is establishing a place in the group's social hierarchy. The concept of a status or *dominance hierarchy* among social animals is well recognized from chickens to gorillas. Sometimes called a "pecking order," the idea is a simple one. But even though dominance of one kind or another is a central factor in the social life of many higher primates, it has proved a rather difficult concept to understand in practice.

We can define dominance simply as the relative social status or rank of an animal, as determined by its ability to compete successfully with other individuals for varying goals. Contested goals might include access to resources such as favorite foods or sleeping sites. Social resources, such as mates or grooming partners, are also contested. Dominant animals can also direct and control their own and others' aggression; in aggressive encounters dominant animals consistently defeat less dominant animals (Figure 5–4).

In some species dominance relationships are clear-cut and static, and a social hierarchy can be recognized. Sometimes such hierarchies are limited to one sex, but in other species both males and females are integrated into a general hierarchy within which some animals may share a similar rank.

However, dominance hierarchies are always subject to influence by animals' personalities and by social variables, and a particular animal may be dominant or submissive under different circumstances. Successful aggression is not the only behavior that generates high status. An ingratiating personality can gain allies and lead to high status, while an ill-tempered aggressive animal may get little social support. Alternatively, two or even three individuals may team up as a coalition to hold a top position that none alone could hold. High-ranking animals move confidently through their troop, others deferring to them as a matter of course. Supportive relatives are particularly important in maintaining status, and macaque and baboon mothers will pass down their status from generation to generation through the female line. Adult males, however, have to establish their rank from scratch whenever they move from one troop to another.

Dominance hierarchies are not usually stable for long. In one baboon troop studied over a long period, male ranks altered on average every 8 days, while female ranks altered on average every 57 days. Factors that brought about such changes included the movement of males in and out of the troop, births and deaths, and fighting within the troop.

FIGURE 5–4   Confrontations among savanna baboons usually result in one individual's either presenting its rump in defeat or scampering off. For these two well-matched baboons, however, confrontation has resulted in fighting.

Sex and Status

One of the most interesting questions for the evolutionary biologist is this: Do dominant individuals produce more young than subordinates? At first glance, this seems obviously to be the case for males, because in many species, such as baboons, dominance can increase a male's sexual access to fertile females. In fact, the situation is anything but straightforward. Several studies of baboons have reported positive correlations between male rank and reproduction. For example, American primatologist Glenn Hausfater found that higher-ranked males clearly out-copulated lower-ranked males within his study group. To a large extent, this was due to the alpha male's being able to achieve unequaled access to females at the peak of *estrus* (that is, on the day of ovulation). But results such as these seem to be matched by an equal number of studies that find no correlation between male rank and reproduction. Furthermore, since males of many species change ranks frequently, measuring sexual success rates for ranks may not tell us much about the success of individual animals (or at best we will obtain information on short-term reproductive success). That is, today's alpha male, with his high copulation rate, may well be tomorrow's subordinate male, stuck with a much lower reproductive performance. And males that live for many years may occupy several ranks and experience many fluctuations in their level of reproduction. Until longitudinal studies yield information on males' lifetime histories of rank and reproduction, firm correlations between these factors will remain elusive.

It is also important to record that female choice does play a part in any male's sexual achievements, and many males court females for long periods of time in order to win their favors. Dominance is not a ticket to unlimited sexual access, though it certainly helps.

The behavior of chimpanzees is most instructive in this matter and shows how flexible the relations between sex and status can be. Wild chimpanzee males show at least three mating strategies. If a male is sufficiently high-ranking (typically, the alpha male of the community), he may try to monopolize a sexually attractive female (a female with large "sex swellings"; see next section) by preventing the approach of other males. Such sexual possessiveness is often impossible for lower-ranking males, however, who usually opt for the strategy of frequent *opportunistic mating* (this can involve several males' nonaggressively sharing sexual access to a particular female that copulates promiscuously with them all). Finally a male of any rank may attempt—through skillful social manipulation and sometimes aggressive courting—to form a *consortship* with a female which he then leads away to the periphery of the community range for several days of exclusive mating. Thus wild chimpanzee males attempt to exert their dominance rank for reproductive gains whenever possible, but when this strategy is unworkable, they easily shift to other mating patterns, all of which include some likelihood of fathering infants. While the sexual behavior of captive chimpanzees (such as those at the Arnhem Zoo, to be described in a later section) may be rigidly controlled by male rank, this correlation does not hold in the wild, where animals range and associate freely, and where opportunities for concealment and seclusion are numerous.

Baboons have been studied in great detail over many years by Shirley Strum, at Gilgil in Kenya. It is now clear that adolescent males leave their home troops as a matter of course and move to neighboring troops. Here they attempt to become assimilated by making friends with high-ranking females. The approach to the female is made very slowly over a long period of time, and in due course, if the

Estrus: the period, usually around ovulation, of sexual attractiveness and activity by primate and other mammalian females.

Opportunistic mating: mating done whenever and wherever the opportunity presents itself, and with whatever partner is available.

Consortship: generally, a period of exclusive sexual association and mating between a female and a male

male is accepted, he begins to play with her infant for hours. Males generally make friends with infants as a means of winning female trust and of neutralizing the aggression of other males. If such a male becomes accepted by the female, he courts her and becomes her "friend," thereby becoming a full member of the troop. If he is sufficiently ingratiating and clever in developing his relationships, he may be able to copulate with this female or other females at estrus. Recent evidence suggests that, among the Gilgil baboons, sexual conquest can be achieved more effectively by building friendships than by achieving dominance in the male hierarchy.

Males' ranks and reproductive strategies are only half of the story, however, and primatologists have found that females' dominance and mating patterns are equally fascinating. Longitudinal observations of baboons and better knowledge of kin relationships within the baboon troop have revealed that the long-term stability of the group depends not so much on the males as on high-ranking females that constitute an ongoing aristocracy of their own, based on mother-daughter and sister-sister ties. Once established, this matrilineal aristocracy tends to perpetuate itself: the hierarchy of females is much more stable than that of males. The privileged—and usually related—females groom each other sociably, bringing up their infants in an atmosphere of comfort and security that is denied low-ranking females. The latter are forced to hang about at the edge of the group, alert to the possibility of a bite or a slap if they do not move aside for a higher-ranking animal. Unable to enter permanently into the established matriarchy at the center, they pass their timidity and generally low self-esteem on to their young. Not surprisingly, the young reared by the dominant mothers grow up with a far greater chance of achieving dominance themselves, having learned confidence and assurance from their mothers. Among rhesus and Japanese macaques, an individual's rank within its age group is based on its mother's rank. Among baboons, this is also true within each sex, but males of any age consistently dominate females of similar age.

With regard to the question of female rank and reproductive success, recent studies have shown that the situation is just as complex as among males. Observations of the baboons that inhabit Tanzania's Gombe National Park (best known for Jane Goodall's chimpanzee studies, to be described in a later section) have shown that high-ranking females enjoy significant *short-term* advantages in reproduction compared to low-ranking females. Probably because of greater access to food, dominant females have shorter interbirth intervals, greater infant survival, and accelerated maturation of their daughters. These results seem to provide clear evidence why competition for rank would be beneficial for female baboons.

But short-term benefits can be deceptive, and at Gombe no overall relationship exists between *lifetime* reproductive success and female dominance. This is because achieving and maintaining high rank takes a significant long-term reproductive toll on many females. Compared to low-ranking animals, dominant females experience a higher incidence of miscarriage and run a greater risk of being chronically infertile. Such stress-related reproductive failure represents the cost females pay for being at the top of the dominance hierarchy—a cost that is probably great enough to prevent female baboons from evolving into hyperaggressive status-seekers.

Overall then, high rank can produce short-term reproductive benefits for both males and females, but lifetime benefits have yet to be demonstrated for either sex. Nonetheless, status hierarchies, whether based on conflict and threat (Figure 5–5) or on kinship and personality, represent one means by which natural

FIGURE 5-5   Here a male savanna baboon is threatening the photographer. The main features of a baboon threat are the displays of the immense canine teeth and of the half-closed light-colored eyelids.

selection has brought order and organization to primate society. The tendency for an individual to attempt to increase its status is deep-seated and is expressed among most higher primates, and indeed most social animals. Human societies are no exception: status is just as pervasive and just as variable in its mode of expression as it is among other primates.

Sexual Physiology and Behavior

As we saw earlier, Solly Zuckerman's observations of baboons in the London Zoo during the 1930s led him to conclude that the members of primate groups are bound to each other by the continuous urge to satisfy their sexual needs. In many mammals—deer are among the most familiar examples—males and females are together only during the breeding season, forming separate societies during the rest of the year. Because Zuckerman thought that monkeys were sexually active the year around, he argued that sex was a logical explanation for the monkeys' staying together. This theory was bolstered by the effects of the crowded conditions under which primates were often studied in zoos or laboratories, for in such a situation animals use sexual behavior to establish dominance and submission. Studies of Japanese macaques at the Takasakiyama feeding station, for instance, revealed that a dominant male often mounts an inferior male—as he would when copulating with a female—to assert his right to a choice tidbit.

Actually, as recent field studies have shown, many monkeys—for example, the rhesus and the Japanese macaques—breed only in a specific season, and their closely knit societies continue even when there is no primary sexual activity. Thus, once again, the study of captive animals proved misleading. In the controlled environment of a laboratory, a monkey's endocrine system, which governs its sex hormones, is not subject to seasonal variations, and the monkey may copulate all year around. In the wild, however, its hormones are influenced much more heavily by such external factors as day length, humidity, and diet, and the result is that many species copulate during only a few months of the year. The existence of a mating season is one means of ensuring that the young will be born at an auspicious time, when they are most likely to survive.

All Old World monkeys, apes, and humans share a basically similar sexual anatomy and physiology. The ovarian-uterine cycle is about 28–35 days in length, with ovulation occurring near the middle and menstruation (shedding of the uterine lining) at the end. Counting the interval between periods of menstrual bleeding produces a measure of the *menstrual cycle.* Mapped on top of the menstrual cycle, however, is a pattern of behavioral fluctuation called the *estrus cycle.* In response to the changing levels of their sex hormones (mainly the estrogens and progesterone), primate females show monthly cycles in sexual *attractiveness* and *receptivity,* and in their tendency to initiate mating (this is called their degree of *proceptivity*). A sexually active female—one that is simultaneously attractive, proceptive, and receptive—is commonly labeled as being *in estrus.* (In some species—baboons and chimpanzees, for example—females in estrus also display large, colorful *sex swellings* around the vulva, but it is behavior and not swelling or color that marks a female as estrous.)

Old World monkey and ape females show great flexibility in the occurrence of sexual behavior throughout the menstrual cycle. Copulations may occur early in the cycle, at ovulation, or near menstruation (pregnant females also continue to mate). Indeed, females seem to have a moderate level of situation dependency in their sexual behavior that allows them to use sex to their advantage (perhaps to fool a potentially infanticidal male or to accommodate a sexually insistent one) regardless of their ovarian or hormonal condition. Nonetheless, among monkeys and apes *most* sex takes place near ovulation during a period of estrus that lasts a week or so.

One of the primary differences between nonhuman primates and humans is the fact that women do not show strong estrus-type peaks in sexual behavior. Extending the sexual flexibility characteristic of monkeys and apes, human sexual behavior is marked by extreme situation dependency and mating throughout the menstrual cycle and during pregnancy. Although humans may retain some mild mid-cycle remnants of estrus (experts disagree on this point), it is clear that our sexual behavior is much more flexible and less controlled by hormones than that of our nonhuman relatives. But it is important not to overstate the contrast. While humans no longer show clear-cut estrus, monkeys and apes seem to anticipate human behavior with their moderate degree of situation dependency. A pair of interesting questions (to be discussed in a later chapter) is how and why hominids evolved such an extremely flexible system of sexual behavior.

The overt activities of nonhuman primate sexual behavior contrast with the covert nature of most human sexual behavior. For example, among nonhuman primates, sexual advances and mountings may occur at any time to reduce tension and appease anger. Male-male, male-female, female-male, and female-female mountings are commonly seen. Touching of genitals may occur as a greeting and

Menstrual cycle: the interval (generally, monthly) between periods of menstrual bleeding; especially characteristic of catarrhine females.

Estrus cycle: the interval between periods of sexual attractiveness and activity of primate females; correlated with ovulation and the menstrual cycle, but with great flexibility among catarrhines.

Attractiveness: in primate studies, the aspect of female sexuality reflected by attention from males.

Receptivity: the aspect of female sexuality reflected by cooperating in copulation.

Proceptivity: the aspect of female sexuality reflected by inviting copulation.

Sex swellings: hormone-induced swellings on the hindquarters of certain primate females; generally correlated with ovulation.

is often seen in grooming sessions to solidify social relationships. Homosexual behavior, which is quite distinct from the social mountings mentioned above, has been described in several species. Sex is indeed a continuous and rich part of primate social life.

Sexual Selection Among Primates

In 1871 Charles Darwin noted that the sex that most competes for the other may be characterized by a larger body, and differences in body form, as well as in skin color and texture, muscularity, vocal and locomotor displays, decorative appendages, and so on, are common. In many primate species, males compete for females, since access to females sets an upper limit on males' reproductive success (this is true of all mammals). This may be the reason that males tend to be larger than females—a form of *sexual dimorphism* that is not uncommon. Great apes, various baboon species, and a number of other monkeys have very considerable differences between the sexes in body size, weight, and size of canine teeth. Shoulder breadth and strikingly handsome hair forms are often well developed in the males (Figure 5–6). Sex differences in size may vary from 50 percent among baboons (when females are 50 percent the size of males); to 75 percent among chimpanzees; to 85 percent among humans; and to 100 percent among gibbons—among whom females are the same size as males.

It is often claimed that the large, aggressive baboon males are selected as protectors of the troop against predators. If we look at higher primates as a whole, however, we can find a correlation between reproductive strategy and sexual dimorphism. *Monogynous* species, in which neither sex competes for additional mates (for example, siamangs and gibbons), show little sexual dimorphism. *Polyg-*

Sexual dimorphism: characteristic anatomical (and behavioral) differences between males and females of a species.

Monogyny: in zoology, generally having only one mate.

FIGURE 5–6 Hamadryas female with young, and a male. The male is larger and heavier, and he carries a magnificent mane, which makes him look even larger.

ynous species (such as savanna baboons), which live in multimale troops and offer greater sexual opportunities to powerful, successful males, are quite dimorphic. It seems that in such a dimorphic species both natural selection and sexual selection are generating large males. A comparison of dimorphism and the breeding system in a whole range of primates and other mammals, carried out by biologist Richard Alexander and his colleagues, tends to support this conclusion.

Another possible explanation for sexual dimorphism such as we find among baboons has been proposed: small females may be selected to reduce their nutritional requirements in a poor environment, subject to the requirements of their reproductive physiology. Anthropologist James McKenna summarized his conclusions on this topic as follows: "Body size might best be considered the result of genetic compromise between competing variables, such as male intrasexual competition, female reproductive physiology, infant care-giving patterns, feeding, foraging, and defence strategies." Indeed, the entire animal is just such a compromise. But by including among the variables male-male breeding competition, we are including a factor that is not a product of natural but of sexual selection and as such is of profound interest.

But as Darwin pointed out, sexual selection has two faces, and same-sex competition (such as the male-male competition discussed above) is only one. The second kind of sexual selection involves members of one sex exercising a deliberate choice of certain traits in the opposite sex. If two males fight over a female and the victor then forces his attentions on her, the female cannot be said to have exercised much choice—or she had a "Hobson's choice" at best (mate with any male you choose so long as you choose the winner of the fight). But female primates do much more than make Hobson's choices. Like males, females have sexual strategies shaped by evolution to maximize reproductive success, and an important part of those strategies is playing an active role in mate selection. Primatologist Meredith Small has recently reviewed the patterns of mate selection by primate females, and several of her conclusions are startling. She believes that females are more sexually assertive and less picky about their mates than has traditionally been held. Rather than waiting coyly for a male suitor, females are often sexually aggressive and actively solicit males. Further, females sometimes chose *not to be selective* and, as a result, mate rather promiscuously with the males of their group. Or they may make choices that seem to make little theoretical sense, as when they prefer outsiders (stranger males characterized by unknown fitness) over well-known male group-mates (characterized by "proven" fitness). Small concluded that primate females' main objective is to conserve time within their reproductive careers. "Get pregnant as soon as possible" seems to be the overriding guideline; the identity of the baby's father seems considerably less important. Small's views are sure to create a good deal of controversy among primate researchers, but they are of extraordinary value in reminding us that it's not only males who do the sexual choosing.

Grooming and Social Interaction

Perhaps the most commonly observed form of social contact between higher primates is grooming. One monkey or ape grooms another by picking through its fur to clean out dirt, as well as parasites and salt crystals, which it then eats. Physically, grooming is simply a cleaning mechanism, and it is highly effective, as one can see by comparing lions and baboons that inhabit the same area of the East

Polygyny: in zoology, the tendency for a male to have regular sexual access to two or more females.

African savanna. Although lions are clean animals, the backs of their necks, where they cannot reach to clean, are thick with ticks, whereas the baboons' hair is totally free of them.

But to primates, grooming is far more than a form of hygiene. It is the most important means of social interaction among members of a group, and it serves a variety of purposes. For example, grooming seems to be an effective instrument for reducing tension of all kinds, as shown by baboons, macaques, and chimpanzees. At other times, it serves simply as an enjoyable pastime when the group is not in search of food. Much as humans gather in conversation groups, monkeys gather in grooming groups. The same function is served: the maintenance of friendly social relations. Being groomed is obviously enjoyable: The groomed animal sits or lies in an attitude of beatific contentment (Figure 5–7). Most grooming is done by females. Mothers regularly groom their young from birth. Equals groom each other in approximately equal amounts, while subordinates groom their social superiors much more frequently than they are groomed in turn. As one might expect, dominant males get much grooming and give little. There is, however, a semblance of reciprocity in a female's grooming of a male: after she has worked over him for perhaps 10 minutes, she will turn and sit, inviting him to groom her. The male obliges by grooming her for about 30 seconds, then turns indolently and is groomed by the female for another 10 minutes. The significant function of grooming in monkey society is that it cuts across hierarchical lines,

FIGURE 5–7   Grooming has two main functions: to remove parasites and keep the fur clean and to establish and maintain social relationships. Here a relaxed female encourages a dominant male to groom her, while a lower-ranking male watches from a proper distance.

establishing friendly relationships between individuals on various levels of the hierarchy who might not otherwise interact.

It seems clear that the degree of awareness exhibited by chimpanzees and baboons is such that they are not merely conscious of the activities and status of other troop members but see deeper into personality. They show preferences; that is, they prefer to spend time with particular members of the troop, that are often their kin. In both species we see what looks very like friendship; certain pairs and trios (sometimes of different sex, but more often of the same sex) spend much time together and share experiences and food sources. When meat, a rare delicacy, is obtained, chimpanzees will share after the provider has had first pick; baboons will move aside to make room for a friend to get at the kill. It looks as if these primates are in some small way responding to each other's needs, even when they are adult and outside the mother-infant relationship. What we see is the innate bioaltruism that rearing an infant implies being extended to *reciprocal altruism* between adults. Insofar as the members of a troop help one another, this behavior has an obvious adaptive value for the social group as a whole.

> **Reciprocal altruism:** trading of apparently altruistic acts by different individuals at different times; a variety of bioaltruism.

The degree of cohesiveness of a group, in fact, directly reflects the potential danger that threatens its members. Gorillas live in comparatively little day-to-day danger, and so individual male gorillas feel free to go off on their own, and many do—even for weeks at a time. The situation among Gombe chimpanzees, which are also in little danger, is somewhat similar. They split into small units whose membership is constantly changing, and individuals often search for food alone, out of sight of the group's members. And chimpanzees seem little concerned about the safety of the group as a whole, because when alarmed, an individual chimpanzee will often run off without even giving a warning call.

One of the most noticeable characteristics of many primate species (from howler monkeys to chimpanzees) is their vocalizations. Most higher primates have a highly evolved means of communication, based on calls, facial expressions, and body language. Because language is a central characteristic of humans, we discuss primate communication in some detail in Chapter 13. In the present discussion it is sufficient to point out that complex social groups depend on sophisticated communication systems, and higher primate societies are no exception.

Variations in the social behavior of the higher primates are endless. Between species, and even within species, there are wide differences in behavior. It seems that the details of social interactions are learned and thus generate what in humans would be called *cultural differences* between populations within the species. This kind of variability is particularly striking among chimpanzees, which are not only highly intelligent and extroverted animals but occupy a broader environmental and geographical range than the gorilla and the orangutan.

We shall now see in more detail just how environment interacts with social behavior.

TERRITORY AND ECOLOGY

The relationship between the social group and its environment is ultimately determined by the distribution and density of the natural resources essential to the animals' survival, by the density of competing animals (including humans) and by the pressure of predators. The social group becomes associated with a recognizable area of land or forest—called the *home range*—which contains sufficient

> **Home range:** the area a primate group uses for foraging, sleeping, and so on in a year.

space, food, water, and safe sleeping sites for all its members. Behavioral mechanisms bring about this spacing, which reduces the possibility of overexploiting the food resources and of having conflict over those resources. The home range of savanna baboons may be partly shared with other groups of the same species; it is always shared with other species, often with other primate species. Within this range, it is usually possible to define smaller areas—called *core areas*—containing resources absolutely essential for survival, in this case sleeping trees (Figure 5–8). A core area becomes defended *territory* when it is actively defended against intruders from neighboring groups.

Different primate species use space in very different ways. In many species, such as savanna baboons (Figure 5–9), some vervet monkeys, orangutans, and gorillas, neighboring groups simply avoid each other by staying at a distance. At the other extreme, gibbons of both sexes display vigorously at the boundaries of their precisely defined territories to demonstrate their occupation of the area and their ferocity. Gray langur monkeys have also been observed to display at territorial boundaries. Other species, such as chimpanzees, rhesus monkeys, macaques, some langurs, and some baboons, may sometimes interact aggressively if they meet by chance, demonstrating a clear territorial sense.

Why do some species defend a territory while others do not? The answer is uncertain, and a number of factors may be in operation. The resource base seems to be the key, and it appears that, if food is patchy in space and unpredictable in time, an optimum feeding strategy is to form large groups and range over con-

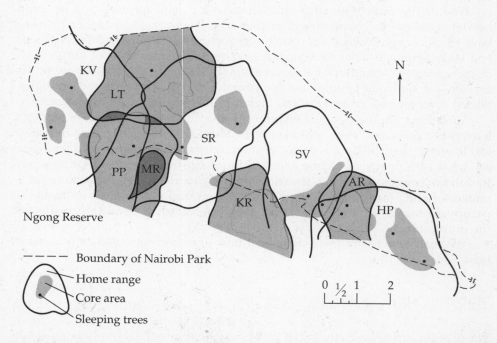

FIGURE 5–8   This plan shows the home ranges and core areas of the baboon troops in the Nairobi Park in 1960. The home ranges overlap considerably, but the core areas, which contain the baboons' sleeping trees, essential to each troop, are quite distinct. (The letters refer to the different troops studied by Washburn and DeVore.)

FIGURE 5–9   The sleeping trees, to which a savanna baboon troop returns each night, are an essential feature in the home range of every troop in open savanna country. In this photograph, the troop has left its grove of acacia trees at dawn and is preparing to move out into the open grasslands to feed.

siderable areas of land (e.g., savanna baboons). Where food is concentrated in space and reliable in supply, the smaller groups may occupy a fixed and limited area (e.g., gibbons), and it is both possible and worthwhile to defend such an area. In the case of gibbons, the ultimate small group has evolved: a monogynous pair.

For these animals, monogyny and a defended territory prevent competition for food, and each sex is assured a mating partner. Other monogynous species— siamangs in Southeast Asia and marmosets and titi monkeys in South America— also defend territories and show little sexual dimorphism. These species are also characterized by sexual equality of status and a sharing of social roles not found in other species.

In contrast, savanna baboons and some other monkeys that cover large home ranges are sexually promiscuous, having multimale groups. They do not defend their extensive home ranges and are not capable of doing so. The contrast in the use of space, the quality of the environment, and reproductive strategy is clear and significant.

It must be added, however, that food distribution is not the whole story. Other essential resources, such as sleeping trees or cliffs (in open savanna situations) and water supply and forest density may also contribute to how a primate species uses

Socioecology: the connection between species' ecological relations and their social behaviors; also the study of this connection.

its environment and what form its reproductive strategy will take. The exact mechanisms operating and the factors involved are still poorly understood. *Socioecology* is, however, a major branch of primate research, and much progress is now being made in this subject.

Socioecology of East African Baboons

During the course of human evolution our ancestors have passed through and adapted to a whole range of different environments. The first major adaptation of the hominids was to the relatively dry savannas of Africa, and for this reason it is worth looking in more detail at the adaptations of some well-known monkey species to this habitat.

Baboons are extremely adaptable animals; they have not become as physically specialized as many other species, and they are thus able to suit themselves to a wide variety of living conditions. With no material culture to rely on, however, baboons must change their behavior and social organization in order to adapt to different environmental conditions.

Of three species, the East African savanna baboon lives in the easiest surroundings: close to trees to which it can flee and in which it can sleep, and in a climate where there is a year-round abundance of food. In this setting the troop is the all-important social unit; family relationships, except for mother-infant ties, are secondary. The nearest thing to a social father is a dominant male or males, which as we have seen may exercise authority over troop members.

Gelada: species of terrestrial monkey related to baboons, found in the mountains of Ethiopia.

By contrast, *geladas* (a related genus but not a true baboon) are confined to mountain slopes in Ethiopia. There the climate is harsher, seasonal change is greater, trees are very rare, and food availability is more chancy. Male-female relationships, too, are very different from those which prevail on the savanna. The animals are found in large herds that, in areas or seasons of poor food supply, break down during the day into a number of separate wide-foraging polygynous units, each containing a single adult male with one or more females and assorted young. With this *harem polygyny* social structure, the relationship between a particular male and females is far more durable than it is among savanna baboons. In that respect it resembles the human nuclear family unit more closely than does the organization of the savanna baboon troop. Significantly, when the wet season comes to the dry Ethiopian hills and food starts to be more abundant, the one-male groups coalesce into the larger multimale troops.

Harem polygyny: in zoology, a group including one breeding male and multiple females; among humans, one husband and multiple wives and concubines.

Hamadryas society is different again. This baboon lives in country even drier than the gelada's terrain, in rocky sections of Ethiopia and the near-desert of Somalia. In this environment one-male groups are the rule the year round, though for safety many groups come together at night on the sleeping cliffs. The male-female relationship is more close-knit than among geladas. Each hamadryas male is continuously jealous of his harem, requiring his females to stay very close at all times. When he moves, they move—or get bitten.

Although these baboon adaptations appear at first sight to contradict the considerations of territoriality discussed in the preceding section, the principles enumerated do still apply. The food supply is patchy, widespread, seasonal, and unpredictable, and there is no defended territory. But we have seen that, under the exceptional circumstances of a very harsh and dry environment, where food is extremely widespread, small one-male (polygynous) groups are an appropriate response.

Finally, it is of great interest that there is some reason to believe that the one-male harem may be an ancient and widespread catarrhine pattern. If so, then the savanna baboon's and the chimpanzee's social adaptation of large multimale units may be considered the product of the abundant food supply available to these species.

Primate Feeding Strategies

Just as reproductive strategy refers to all those adaptations that maximize reproductive success, so a feeding strategy comprises the anatomical, physiological, and behavioral characteristics that permit animals to obtain energy efficiently by food acquisition. As before, the use of the word *strategy* implies no conscious intent on the part of the individual primate.

The strategy that should be favored by natural selection is the one that is most effective in metabolically converting food resources into energy and that is least expensive in terms of energy expenditure. Thus, to estimate the efficiency of a particular feeding strategy, we would need to know the nutritive, and especially the calorific, value of every food item eaten and the energy required to get it and digest it. A feeding strategy is optimal when, in addition to providing essential nutrients, its net energy yield per unit of time is at its highest.

Several kinds of feeding strategy can be identified among primates, but they all appear to fall, broadly, along a continuum between two extremes. On the one hand we have the generalist-opportunist approach, and on the other hand the specialist approach.

The generalist-opportunist shows selectivity with regard to the energy value of food. It eats according to availability and eats the most nutritive food available at any particular time. Then it moves on to other, sometimes very diverse, food sources. The South American howler monkey is a good example of such a generalist. In some species opportunism includes the consumption of significant quantities of high-energy insects and meat in addition to plant foods. Baboons, macaques, mangabeys, and chimpanzees have all been observed to eat meat in substantial quantities when the opportunity (sometimes rare) presents itself.

In contrast, specialists concentrate on only a few plant species. These either yield high energy or are abundant enough so that quantity will supplement what may be lacking in caloric density. Specialist strategies necessarily evolve in relatively stable environments where key foods are always available. Specialists have the considerable advantage of spending less time searching for food than do generalists.

Specialists have also evolved specialized digestive organs, such as the large stomach of the leaf-eating Colobine monkeys, which consists of a forestomach (in which cellulose is digested) followed by a series of saclike chambers. The ability to digest both young and mature leaves of common trees places specialist leaf-eating Colobines in a very advantageous position among primates.

Dietary specializations also tend to be correlated with dental differences among primate species. For example, animals such as tarsiers that eat insects usually have enlarged and pointed incisors and canines for killing prey, and tall, sharp cusps on their molars and premolars for shearing insects into tiny, digestible fragments. Specialized leaf-eaters likewise have high-crowned molars and premolars for slicing up foliage (this aids in the digestion of cellulose), but their incisors tend to be rather narrow. And finally, species that eat mainly fruits show yet another combination of traits: large, broad incisors with straight cutting edges (an adaptation for biting off chunks of tough-skinned fruits) and relatively small, low-crowned molars (which are adequate, because the inner flesh of fruit is generally soft and needs little chewing). Information on the dental adaptations of living primates can serve as a basis for inferring the food preferences of fossil species.

The concept of a feeding strategy helps us gain knowledge of how a species actually makes a living in a highly competitive environment. It also helps us to gain insights into early hominid feeding strategies. As shown in later chapters, early hominids were probably both generalist and highly opportunistic feeders.

THE APES

The environmental adaptations of the monkeys and their social organization make their study of particular interest to us, but it is, of course, not the monkeys but the apes that are our closest relatives among nonhuman primates.

Asiatic Apes: Gibbons and the Orangutan

Gibbons (six species including siamangs) and the orangutan are Asiatic apes. By a great number of external and internal measurements, including genetic ones, they are remarkably different from chimpanzees, bonobos, and gorillas. In fact, they are in some ways less like a chimpanzee than are humans. This difference indicates a separation far back in time, between 12 and 21 million years ago, long before the separation of human, gorilla, bonobo, and chimpanzee (see Table 1–2).

As we have seen, both gibbons and the orangutan are tree-dwelling animals today. Millions of years of climbing and total reliance on the fruits that grow in jungle trees have brought them to an extreme point of arboreal specialization. In the trees, they move superbly, each in its own way. The gibbon (Figure 5–10) is an airy flier that hangs from branches, swinging from one to another in a breathtaking arc, grabbing the next branch just long enough to launch itself in the direction of a third. For this brachiator, arms and hands are everything. Its fingers are extremely long, specialized to serve as powerful hooks to catch branches. As a result of this finger specialization, the gibbon has the poorest manual dexterity of any ape. And being the smallest ape, it has the smallest brain.

The orangutan is quite different, (Figure 5–11). It is much larger: adult males weigh over 150 lb (68 kg), compared to the gibbons' 10 to 25 lb (4.5–11 kg). Obviously an animal of this size cannot go careening through the branches. Orangutans have developed four prehensile hands well adapted to seizing or holding, and their limbs are so articulated that they can reach in any direction. There is almost nowhere in a tree that an orangutan cannot safely go, despite its great bulk, by careful gripping and climbing.

The grouping patterns and mating systems of gibbons and orangutans are very different. Gibbons form monogynous families that are stable and long-lasting. Adult males and females are *monomorphic* in body size and canine tooth length and, as a result, are often codominant (equally dominant). Both sexes

Monomorphic: both sexes showing the same trait (e.g., similar body size).

FIGURE 5–10 A gibbon hangs by an arm and steadies itself with a foot while feeding. See also Figure 4–18.

actively defend the family's arboreal territory (0.08–0.2 mi², 0.2–0.5 km²) against encroachment by neighboring families. Subadults of both sexes disperse from their natal units (often after aggression by their same-sex parent) and start their own families. In contrast, adult orangutans of both sexes live solitary lives, and the only real social unit is that of a female and her dependent offspring. Adult males are twice the size of adult females, and males (even as subadults) generally dominate females. Each adult inhabits a large home range (0.6–2.3 mi², or 1.5–6 km², for females), with an extensive overlap of males' and females' ranges. Adult males have several mating strategies. Some defend their ranges as territories from other adult males, while pursuing sexual interactions with overlapping females. Other males, both full adults and subadults, do not defend a mating territory; rather, they move over large distances and seek matings opportunistically. Since both males and females have access to multiple sexual partners, the orangutan mating system is best described as *promiscuous*.

Both gibbons and orangutans are basically frugivorous in their diets. Compared to other ape species, gibbons perform very little object manipulation and may be safely classed as non-tool-users (although there was one observation of a leaf being used as a sponge for water dipping), while wild orangutans show a few simple tool-use patterns, such as dropping twigs and snags as part of aggressive displays and rubbing their faces with leaves. In captivity, orangutans have shown quite extensive and complex tool use.

Promiscuous: both females and males having multiple sexual partners.

FIGURE 5–11 The orangutan of Indonesian Sumatra and Kalimantan (Borneo) is the most seriously threatened of the great apes. It has immensely long arms and relatively short legs with short thumbs and big toes. It is mainly arboreal but does cover considerable distances on the ground in emergencies. This is a juvenile.

But among the living apes, gibbons and orangutans are humans' most distant evolutionary kin. Biochemical and fossil data suggest that the orangutan lineage diverged from that of the other hominoids some 13 to 16 million years ago, with gibbons splitting off several million years earlier. In contrast, it appears certain that humans share a common ancestor with some of the African apes as recently as 5 to 7 million years ago (Table 1–2). Therefore we must examine our hominoid relatives from Africa in somewhat greater detail.

Gorillas: Research of Fossey

Much of what we know of the gorilla comes from the work of Dian Fossey, who began her extensive observations of mountain gorillas in 1967 and founded a research center in Rwanda. Fossey quickly discovered that, far from being the ferocious beasts of legend, gorillas are generally mild-mannered vegetarians who like to mind their own business (Figure 5–12).

While the orangutan and gibbon have evolved into specialized tree-dwellers, the gorilla's development has taken the direction of a great increase in size, along with a dietary switch from the fruit and leaves found in trees to a more general

FIGURE 5–12 In Central Africa, Dian Fossey walks through the forest near her isolated field station with two young mountain gorillas. She studied this endangered species in its native habitat from 1967 until her death in 1985. (Bob Campbell, © National Geographic Society)

menu of fresh bark, larger leaves, roots, bamboo shoots, and other plants—herbal as much as arboreal vegetation. These two specializations of size and diet go together: we may suppose size and strength have been selected because other animals will not attack the gorilla while it is on the ground eating. And because the gorilla is so large, it needs a great deal of just the kind of coarse vegetation that it finds in large quantities in the places it inhabits. This great ape retains the equipment for climbing and reaching: the long arms, the deft hands, and keen vision. Young gorillas are frisky and venturesome in the trees, but their elders are essentially ground animals. Having carved out a successful niche for themselves there, they have apparently been relatively stable members of the African rain forest community for millions of years.

With no predators to fear except humans, and with plenty of food available, the gorillas Fossey encountered lived most of the time in a state of mild and amiable serenity (Figure 5–13). Most of them live in groups of 9 to 37, each group led by a powerful silverback male, so called for the saddle of grizzled silver hair that the males grow when they reach the age of 10. His dominance over the group is absolute, but normally genial. Occasionally a young gorilla will get too frolicsome and will be silenced by a glare or a threatening slap on the ground by an adult. Sometimes a couple of females will begin to scream at each other until the leader glares at them, when they promptly quiet down. Except for particularly irascible

FIGURE 5–13   Here mountain gorillas (the silverback is on the left) relax on a fallen tree after a morning's feeding. The Central African mountain environment in which these animals live has very high rainfall and the vegetation is lush.

silverbacks, the leaders are usually quite approachable. Females nestle against them and infants crawl over their huge bodies. When a band of gorillas is at rest, the young play, the mothers tend their infants, and the other adults lie at peace and soak up the sun.

Gorilla groups are not territorial; rather, they move about within nondefended home ranges in search of food and other resources. They do not use tools to obtain food or for any other purpose. The gorilla mating system is one of harem polygyny, and a silverback male typically has several sexual partners, while females have only one. Both males and females routinely emigrate from their natal group as adults, and within a harem the strongest social bonds are between females and their silverback leader. Bonds between females are quite weak.

Like humans, gorillas yawn and stretch when they awake in the morning, and they sit, dangling their legs over the sides of their nests. They pick their noses, scratch themselves when puzzled, and, if nervous or excited, often begin to eat vigorously. Though there is great individual variation of temperament among gorillas, there is about them a curious reserve; they are normally rather quiet creatures and rarely use their immense strength.

Nonetheless, gorillas can exhibit strong feelings, especially when they feel threatened. They scream in alarm and as a warning to other members of the group. They toss leaves in the air. They also beat their chests. All gorillas, even very young ones, do this, rising up on two legs on the ground, or popping up amid the foliage of a tree to give a few brief slaps before fading out of sight. The full performance, however, which is given in response to more serious threat or high anxiety, is put on only by the silverback males, and it is as formal as the entrance of a fighter into the prize ring. It begins inconspicuously with a series of soft, clear hoots that gradually quicken. Already, the silverback expects to command attention because, if interrupted, he is liable to look around in annoyance. As he continues to hoot, he may stop, pluck a leaf from a plant nearby, and place it between his lips. This curiously incongruous and delicate gesture is a prelude to coming violence, and when they see it, the other gorillas get out of the way. The violence is not immediate. First, the gorilla rises to his full height and slaps his hands on his chest or his belly, on his thigh, or on another gorilla, producing a booming sound that can be heard a mile away. The chest beating over, the violence erupts. He runs sideways for a few steps; then he drops down on all fours and breaks into a full-speed dash, wrenching branches from trees and slapping at everything in his way, including any group members that do not have the wit to keep clear. Finally, there comes the last gesture: the silverback thumps the palm of his hand violently on the ground and then sits back, looking as if he is now ready to hear the applause.

Though gorillas present a mild demeanor to the outside world, protected as they are by their immense strength, they can be aggressive in rivalry between males over females and in other aspects of reproductive behavior. Males reaching full maturity as young silverbacks can form their own family groups only by kidnapping females from other groups, by usurping the position of the dominant silverback male (probably their father) in their own group, or by awaiting his death. Sometimes the females support an up-and-coming male against an older one. The group leaders, in turn, must defend their own females against kidnapping and must maintain their authority over their groups. The kidnapping is usually carried out by stealth as much as by overt aggression, but the takeover of a group from an aging male may be a very unpleasant affair. Sometimes two ambitious young silverbacks fight each other. One or more of the older females may be killed, and quite often the youngest infant or infants are killed by the victorious male. The new male then copulates with the females, which will now rear his progeny rather than the young of his predecessor. In this way the newly promoted dominant male begins mating and starts his own family without further delay.

Here we see one form of sexual selection. The intermale rivalry described by Darwin is selecting sexual dimorphism: gorilla males are about twice as big as females and have powerful jaws and large canine teeth. Thus some features of gorilla dentition are associated not only with diet but also with patterns of behavior that have evolved as a result of the social structure of the species.

The observation of *infanticide* is important. Until 1965 it was believed that the human primate alone had the dubious distinction of sometimes murdering its own infants. In that year, however, the Japanese primatologist Yukimaru Sugiyama observed the takeover of a langur monkey troop by an outside adult male. First, the incoming male chased away the old adult male; then he asserted his dominant position by threatening the females and other troop members. Finally, he set about killing the dependent infants. After a short time, the bereaved

Infanticide: the killing of infants.

FIGURE 5–14   Two older female langurs are chasing away a male that has recently taken over their troop and threatened a black infant. The black infants, under 6 months of age, are easily identified as the offspring of the deposed male. Sarah Blaffer Hrdy of the University of California at Davis has studied the Hanuman langurs of Mount Abu near New Delhi. She reports seeing nursing mothers repeatedly try to save their infants from a new dominant male bent on infanticide.

females stopped lactating and came into estrus. He copulated with them in turn, and in due course they raised his offspring in place of those they had been nursing before his arrival (Figure 5–14).

Similar observations have since been made among several other primate species. It has been proposed that such behavior is adaptive for the incoming male, which in this way can ensure the production of a large number of offspring at the expense of other males. His young would presumably be old enough by the time of the next takeover to avoid being killed. In other words, infanticide has been proposed as another component of sexual selection in action.

Whether the sexual selection explanation of infanticide is correct is controversial, however. Some workers believe that primate infanticide may be a product of environmental stress, such as overcrowding, or even merely a product of an especially aggressive takeover in which infants are killed more in error than by intent. Furthermore, say skeptics, neither the regularity nor the fitness effects of infanticide have been well documented. Nonetheless, for many primatologists the hypothesis of infanticide as a reproductive strategy is a compelling one. But the evidence so far is limited. Only further observations will help us to resolve this fascinating question.

What Dian Fossey observed among gorillas is valuable evidence that leads toward an understanding of the process by which young males can gain access to females. But Fossey's primary concern in more recent years was to protect the remaining mountain gorillas from the deadly work of poachers. Although the gorillas are a protected and endangered species, poachers, in order to obtain marketable tourist items, continue to kill them in the Parc National des Volcans in Rwanda. Fossey waged an unceasing war against poachers, doing her best to protect the dwindling numbers of animals in this remote part of Central Africa. In September 1985 she was brutally murdered, presumably by one of the poachers she had caught and punished. Today her successors continue observing these magnificent animals. Her pioneering contribution to our understanding of the gorilla is of priceless value, and her work will be read and discussed for generations to come.

Goodall and the Gombe Chimpanzees

As with the gorilla, long and devoted field observations have helped us understand something of chimpanzee behavior. Paleoanthropologist Louis Leakey knew of a troop of chimpanzees that lived in a hilly wooded tract near the Gombe Stream, a river running into Lake Tanganyika in western Tanzania. He was interested in anything that had to do with primates; furthermore, he thought that the present-day stream, with its woodland and grassland environment, closely resembled the environment inhabited by early hominids. He persuaded Jane Goodall to undertake a study of the Gombe troop.

In 1960, when Goodall arrived in what is now the Gombe National Park, she set up camp near the lakeshore and began to spend her days roaming the hills and valleys, looking for chimpanzees in an area of about 15 sq mi (39 km^2). Her plan was to watch the animals discreetly, not getting too close, just accustoming them to her presence, as a preliminary to closer acquaintance. Many months later she was still watching from a distance, still treated with suspicion by the shy chimpanzees. Ultimately, after a period of rejection that would have discouraged a less dedicated person, she was accepted, not by all the chimpanzees, but by many of them (Figure 5–15). She became very friendly with a few of them. Eventually she spent thousands of hours with them, sometimes in actual physical contact—handing out bananas, playing with a baby, and more often just sitting quietly and watching a society of unimagined subtlety and complexity gradually unfold. Goodall's studies (summarized in a book called *The Chimpanzees of Gombe*) reveal the chimpanzee to be an animal whose nature and social organization provoke all kinds of speculations about the emergence of humankind.

Chimpanzees occur in a broad band across West and Central Africa from Senegal and the Ivory Coast in the west to Tanzania, Uganda, and Zaire in the east (Figure 5–16). Of all the great apes, the chimpanzee is the least specialized. In size it is a neat compromise: small enough to get about in trees, and big enough to take care of itself on the ground against predators, particularly since it usually travels in bands, which are sections of a larger community. As a result, it is at home in both worlds. Although still a fruit eater whose favorite staple is ripe figs, it is a generalist-opportunist and will eat a wide variety of other fruit and vegetation, together with some meat: birds' eggs or fledglings, insects, lizards, or small snakes, and occasionally a young baboon, colobus monkey, or bush pig.

Chimpanzee society is not typical of the higher primates. The Gombe animals live in dispersed communities of from 40 to 60 individuals, and the bonding between them is loose. The term *fusion-fission* has been applied to chimpanzee society. Individuals of either sex have almost complete freedom to come and go as they wish. The membership of temporary subgroups is constantly changing. Adults and adolescents can and do forage, travel, and sleep alone, sometimes for days at a time. An individual rarely sees all the members of the community on the same day and probably never sees them two days in succession. An animal may travel one day with a large, noisy, and excitable gathering and the next day completely alone. Females may spend many days alone or with their young; males tend to be more gregarious. This flexibility of chimpanzee society is one of its most remarkable characteristics.

Fusion-fission community: a society that includes several individuals of both sexes and all ages and is characterized by the formation and dissolution of temporary subgroups.

FIGURE 5-15 Jane Goodall has been a pioneer in the study of wild animals. By undertaking a long behavioral study of wild chimpanzees since 1960, she has contributed greatly to our understanding both of chimpanzees and, by implication, of ourselves.

In addition to their fusion-fission characteristic, chimpanzee communities can be classed as multimale-multifemale since they contain several adult individuals of each sex. Young females habitually emigrate from their natal community to live and breed elsewhere as adults, while males routinely remain in the community of their birth. Although there is considerable variation among chimpanzee populations, this emigration pattern typically results in relatively weak social bonds between females but strong bonds (often based on kinship) between males. Heterosexual social bonds also appear to be rather weak, and grooming between the sexes is less common than grooming between males.

As noted earlier, male chimpanzees strive to achieve high dominance rank, and within each community one male can be recognized as the alpha animal. Males form strong alliances with one another, and support from allies (often kin) may be crucial to achieving and maintaining high rank. Dominance relations exist among females, but they are not as clear-cut as the male hierarchy, although older females generally dominate younger ones.

Nishida and the Mahale Mountain Chimpanzees

In 1966, not long after Goodall set up camp, Toshisada Nishida and Junichiro Itani, with a small team from Kyoto University in Japan, set out to study another

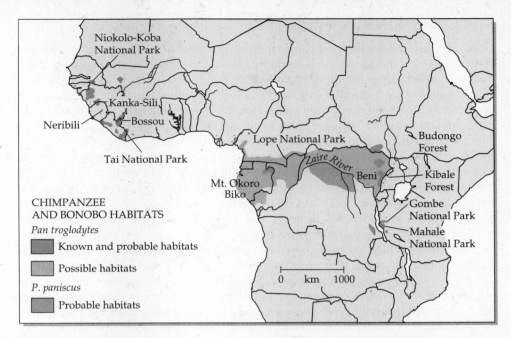

FIGURE 5–16 Chimpanzee and bonobo distribution follows the band of tropical rain forest across Central Africa. A number of study areas are identified. The chimpanzee is today an endangered species because of both poaching and continued logging in forest areas. There is apparently still a world demand for baby chimpanzees, and as long as it continues, the outlook for the species is not good. (Based on Jane Goodall, *The Chimpanzees of Gombe*, Cambridge, Harvard University Press, 1986, Figure 3.1, p. 45.)

group of chimpanzees not far south of Gombe, in the Mahale Mountains of Tanzania. Since that time they have maintained almost continuous observation of a large community of more than 100 apes. This work constitutes an admirable comparative study that can throw extra light on Jane Goodall's well-known observations. The first most striking impression is that this large community has a far greater density of males, with the result that there is far more intermale rivalry and a much more marked dominance hierarchy. In place of the more easygoing ways of the Gombe males, we see a situation in which the alpha male dominates the matings of all females in season and plays a more central role in all the troop's activities. Interactions generally seem to be more intense and more highly structured. We see social behavior responding to a difference in population size and density.

The important result of comparisons of this sort—and we now have studies from parts of West Africa to compare with those of East Africa—is the realization that chimpanzees have a very flexible and adaptable behavior repertoire. There are subtle (and not so subtle) differences between the behaviors of every community, and it is only by studying a considerable number of different populations, living under slightly different conditions, that we can begin to learn the full repertoire of chimpanzee behavior and come to gain some insight into the total potential of this remarkable and very intelligent animal.

The Chimpanzee as Hunter

Goodall reports that a hunting chimpanzee is unmistakable. Compared with other chimpanzee behaviors, there is something out of the ordinary about hunting behavior, observed much more often among males than among females. There is in it something purposeful, tense, and inward that other chimpanzees recognize and respond to. Sometimes they just watch the hunter intently. Sometimes other chimpanzees move to adjacent trees to cut off the escape of the quarry, a young baboon or a small arboreal monkey. On several occasions observed by Goodall, the quarry was a young baboon whose screams brought adult baboons rushing to its defense. In the ensuing hullabaloo the youngster more often than not escaped. But Goodall saw chimpanzees eating infant baboons often enough to realize that a small but fairly steady toll was taken of them.

Chimpanzees are excited by meat and are clearly very fond of it. They chew it long and reflectively, usually with a mouthful of leaves added. Wads of this mixture are occasionally given to other begging chimps. Sometimes the carcass is shared by the successful hunter, which tears off pieces and hands them out (Figure 5–17). Such sharing in response to begging gestures by group-mates is striking, but not all transfers of meat are so orderly. In fact, immediately after a successful hunt all hell may break loose around a carcass. Individuals with meat may be attacked or threatened by those without, and sometimes fights break out among the throng of have-nots. When sharing does occur, it often involves transfers between male allies (often kin) or between males and estrous females. Females with meat almost never share it with other females.

Observations by Nishida and others in both East and West Africa confirm that chimpanzees are hunters and carnivorous when they have the opportunity.

FIGURE 5–17   The upper chimpanzee is holding the rib cage of a small monkey; the two lower chimpanzees are begging. Frequently the hunter will share the remains of the kill.

In the Tai National Park, Ivory Coast, chimpanzees have been studied for more than ten years by Christophe Boesch and Hedwige Boesch-Achermann of the Swiss Center for Scientific Research. Here the chimpanzee is found in tropical rain forest—quite distinct from the savanna woodland environment of many of the East African chimpanzee communities. The surprising fact is that in this dense rain forest the chimpanzees hunt in a much more organized way—with a larger group of males and more complex strategies, often involving one or two drivers, pursuers, and encirclers. There is much more cooperation between males and more generous sharing of meat. Regular sharing of the kill presumably encourages future cooperation. Rather than killing whatever they come across as they do in East Africa, West African chimpanzees concentrate exclusively on the two common species of colobus monkey. When Jane Goodall made her first observations of hunting, it was supposed that this was an unusual adaptation to the more open savanna woodland of Gombe. Now we find not only that hunting is probably universal among chimpanzees, but that it is most developed in the rain forest communities. One of the delights of scientific research is the continuous accumulation of knowledge, which results in the sometimes surprising modification of hypotheses.

The revelation that chimpanzees hunt and eat meat—and share it as well, although often reluctantly—has enormous implications in explaining the development of hunting and sharing among hominids. It now becomes possible to speculate that these traits were brought to the savanna from the forest. We no longer have to puzzle over how a propensity for meat eating got started in a creature with a fruit-eating ancestry; it was already there, as we now know it is in most primates. All this propensity needed was encouragement in a new environment.

The First Herbalists?

To this brief section on chimpanzee diet and food strategies, we can now add a most remarkable and unexpected postscript. Jane Goodall's observations and other more recent studies in East Africa by Richard Wrangham of Harvard University and Toshisada Nishida have revealed that on certain occasions chimpanzees will chew the pith or eat a few leaves of particular plants that have been shown to have medicinal properties. The chimps seem to know when they need these plants, and they evidently have the knowledge to select particular species. How do we know they are medicinal? In the first place, they are certainly not part of the chimp's regular diet and are eaten only quite uncommonly and when other more popular food plants are available. The leaves are not particularly palatable, for the chimps do not chew them but swallow them like a pill. Second, the local Tongwa people use some of these same plants, in particular, species of *Aspilia*, in the same way. Finally, the plants turn out on analysis to contain an antibiotic (thiarubrine-A) that is potent against bacteria, viruses, fungi, and even parasitic worms!

Although it has not been proved, it does appear that chimpanzees—and occasionally, gorillas and bonobos as well—are deliberately dosing themselves, when they feel unwell, with one or more of a number of species of plants that have very definite medicinal qualities. Research is now proceeding apace, not only to study the chimpanzees' diet more intensively, but to look into any value these plants may have in Western medicine.

Tools and Weapons

Although chimpanzees are tool users and toolmakers in a limited way, they do not *need* tools. Nevertheless, we know that the chimpanzee can develop a tradition of elementary tool use. We cannot know when the chimpanzees at Gombe first learned to fish for termites with twigs (as shown in Figure 4–19) or how long this took to become an established activity. Goodall has shown that each new generation learns it from the previous one. The youngsters have an opportunity to learn from their elders: they watch them intently, often copying what they do.

Another talent Goodall observed among the Gombe chimpanzees was for throwing things. Her accounts reveal that this activity was well established in the Gombe troop; a number of males tried it, and in a variety of circumstances. Even often woefully inaccurate throwing seems useful to a chimpanzee. In chimpanzee life there is a great deal of bluffing and aggressive display. During such activity an animal will jump up and down, wave its arms, hoot, shriek, and charge forward. This behavior looks especially disconcerting if it is accompanied by a shower of sticks, waste, or stones (Figure 5–18). The fact that throwing is useful as an aggressive display explains why it is now established as part of the species' behavior.

At its present stage of throwing development, the chimpanzee is scarcely a star athlete, by human standards. Through lack of practice it cannot throw far or accurately; it cannot count on hitting anything more than 4 or 5 ft (1.5 m) away. But the performance does not have to impress humans, only other chimpanzees, baboons, leopards, and the like. For that audience the display is extremely effective. Throwing clearly has selective value, and we can speculate that, if chimpanzees are left to themselves long enough, they may become better throwers than they now are.

Even now, potential for improvement exists among individual chimpanzees. There was one such at Gombe called Mr. Worzle (Goodall named all the chim-

FIGURE 5–18   Throwing stones and other objects is typical of chimpanzees trying to scare a threatening intruder or merely letting off steam.

panzees as fast as she could recognize them, for ease of identification). Mr. Worzle accomplished the remarkable feat of becoming a superior stone thrower as a result of being exposed to an unusual challenge. In order to attract the troop to the camp area, where it could be more easily observed, Goodall made a practice of putting out bananas. This unnatural concentration of food also attracted baboons that lived in the vicinity, leading to abrasive confrontations. The baboons quickly learned which chimpanzees, mostly females and juveniles, they could intimidate by rushing at them. But they never could dislodge Mr. Worzle, who stood his ground, picking up whatever was handy and throwing it at them. Sometimes it was leaves. Once, to the delight of the baboons, it was a bunch of bananas. But slowly Mr. Worzle learned that rocks were best, and as time went on he depended more and more on rocks and started using bigger and bigger ones. Mr. Worzle's response indicates the ability to improvise that exists in an intelligent and physically adept animal when confronted by a new situation or given an opportunity to deal with an old one in a new way.

More recently, primatologists Yukimaru Sugiyama and Jeremy Koman, who have studied undisturbed chimpanzees near Bossou, in Guinea, West Africa, experienced "aimed throwing" of branches of considerable intensity and accuracy, which repelled everyone present except Sugiyama! These chimpanzees had clearly hit on a most effective way of dealing with predators and other intruders—a technique that surely would have been equally valuable to early hominids.

This is only one of the many new sites, particularly in West Africa, to which chimpanzee studies have been extended. It is now clear that, in different regions of their range, chimpanzees show "cultural" differences in behavior generally, and in tool use. Different kinds of probes are used in "fishing" for termites, and at some sites in Rio Muni, termite hills are very hard and are broken into with much stronger sticks; then the termites are dug out and eaten by hand. The hominid use of digging sticks is foreshadowed by these primates.

At other sites, chimpanzees have been observed using sticks and stones to break open nuts. At Bossou, chimpanzees used two stones to smash open palm nuts. They placed the nut in the cavity of one flat stone (platform stone) and smashed it with a hammer stone (Figure 5–19). As Sugiyama and Koman, who observed this behavior, pointed out, it is almost identical to that attributed to early hominids, and if these stones had been found in an excavation, they might have been identified as a product of hominid tool use.

Thus among chimpanzees we have evidence of the use of tools as weapons, digging sticks, and nutcrackers, and as implements for the collection of social insects such as termites and ants. Even the use of stone tools—so important in hominid evolution—is seen in chimpanzees' hammer-stone-and-anvil nut-processing. But two additional interesting and suggestive observations must be made: female chimpanzees appear to use tools more often and more efficiently than do males. As noted by primatologist W. C. McGrew in *Chimpanzee Material Culture*, most chimpanzee tool use occurs during sessions of insect gathering (termite fishing and ant dipping), and females show much higher levels of insectivory than males. With regard to nutcracking behavior, Boesch-Achermann and Boesch reported that at Taï, chimp females were considerably more efficient than males at opening nuts. Tool use rarely occurs in the context of hunting and eating mammalian prey—which, as noted earlier, are primarily male activities—although sticks are occasionally used to pick marrow from broken bones, or leaf wads are used to clean out an opened braincase. Can these findings on sex differences in chimpanzee tool use be applied to early hominids? In McGrew's words, "If the

FIGURE 5–19 Chimpanzee using a hammer stone and an anvil to crack open oil palm nuts.

parallels between observed ape and hypothesized proto-hominid data are genuine, then the evolutionary origins of tool-use are more likely to have come from solitary, female gathering and not from social, male hunting." Further data bearing on this point are eagerly awaited.

Murder and War

Observations have revealed that encounters between chimpanzee communities may in fact be sought and may become very aggressive. The best data come from Goodall's observations at Gombe. Here it was observed that parties of up to ten adult males, sometimes accompanied by females and young, might patrol peripheral areas near the boundary of the community territory and actively search for signs of neighboring groups. Contact might result in displays until one or both groups gave up or fled and returned to the core area of their range. When single chimpanzees or very small parties were encountered, they might be chased and even attacked, often brutally. Males have been observed setting out as a small group with the clear intention of stalking a neighbor. They silently moved through the forest, avoiding the crackle of branches or leaves underfoot. Such behavior is known to have resulted in what can only be called brutal murder, clearly cold-blooded and calculated. Jane Goodall has described one four-year period at Gombe as essentially a war, during which an entire community was annihilated, so that the victorious males and their females were able to move into the unoccupied territory. This behavior looks all too familiar, and the whole question of intercommunity relations and aggression among chimpanzees is now a subject of active research. Understanding it is important to those studying the evolution and nature of human violence.

Chimpanzee Politics

Studying chimpanzees and gorillas in the wild may seem the ultimate step in behavioral research, yet it has one serious disadvantage. It is extremely difficult to follow the behavior of groups of individuals for long periods in great detail; trees and undergrowth, the natural shyness of wild animals, and their tendency to move about can interrupt observations at critical moments. On the other hand, observations of captive apes are unreliable insofar as their behavior is distorted in captivity by the unnatural conditions under which they live.

In 1971 an attempt was made to overcome this problem. A large 2-acre (0.8 ha) moated enclosure was built at the Burghers' Zoo in Arnhem, Holland. Here a group of chimpanzees was settled—males, females, and young—and they have developed into a most successful breeding colony that now numbers 25 individuals. Observation platforms were built, and observers were able to watch the behavior of the inmates in extraordinary detail. In his *Chimpanzee Politics*, Frans de Waal describes the social life of these chimpanzees in a way that was never before possible. What he has found is truly remarkable: the chimpanzees exhibit political behavior (defined as social manipulation designed to secure and maintain power status) of a kind previously believed to be found only among humans.

Throughout the past three decades, since Jane Goodall began her research at Gombe, we have been surprised (and delighted) again and again by the extent to which chimpanzees have been found to foreshadow humans in their social behavior: first, the greeting and nursing behavior, then the intermale competition, then the interest in using and making tools, then the enthusiasm for hunting, then the aggression, ambition, and apparent cold-blooded cruelty. Now, de Waal reveals to us that the whole social structure is based on political infighting; that whole passages from Niccolo Machiavelli (1469–1527) describing humans' political manipulations seem to be directly applicable to chimpanzees; and that the struggle for power and the resultant opportunism are so marked among chimpanzees that their social organization seems almost too human to be true. But it is true. The observations are sound, and their interpretation is unavoidable. Not all the political mechanisms seen at Arnhem are necessarily present in all wild communities, but they probably are present, and there is no doubt that the potential for this kind of political maneuvering is indeed part of chimpanzee nature.

The main difference between the wild and the captive chimpanzees is one of leisure time: the wild animals spend most of their waking hours in the quest for food. In contrast, the captive chimpanzees were fed daily, each evening, and therefore had far more time at their disposal to devote to politics and intrigue.

The work at Arnhem has given us important insights into many areas of chimpanzee behavior, which we can only briefly summarize here. In that group there was a clear-cut rank order, at least among the dominant individuals. The urge to power was a primary determinant of all male behavior. Second, female relationships were less hierarchic and much more stable than those of males. Senior females were influential and even mediated between competing males. They occasionally confiscated rocks from the hands of an angry male!

Hidden beneath the power struggle and its resultant hierarchy was a network of positions of influence. Thus the most influential troop members at Arnhem were the oldest male and the oldest female, no longer dominant in the obvious sense, but highly influential and able to pull strings behind the scenes. Newly dominant individuals were usually much less influential and dependent on coalition and alliance. Thus there is an overt and a covert aspect to chimpanzee politics. Altogether, power politics reigns supreme and is able to give chimpanzee society a logical coherence and even a democratic base. Every individual searches for social significance and continues to do so until a temporary balance is achieved, determining new hierarchic positions. Thus the hierarchy is a cohesive structure and brings stability that makes possible effective child care, play, cooperation, and undisturbed sexual activity. But the balance of power is tested daily and, if found to be weak, is challenged; then the social structure is rebuilt.

At Arnhem, it appears that the rewards of power were more limited than in nature, for food was rationed and fairly distributed among the chimpanzees. Thus the rewards to males of high status were mainly sexual: access to estrous females. This limitation, however, did not prevent the apes from exhibiting almost every political subterfuge known to humans, including dominance networks and coalitions, power struggles, alliances, divide-and-rule strategies, arbitration, confiscation, collective leadership, privileges, bargaining, and frequent reconciliations (which usually took the form of kissing, open-mouthed).

Reconciliation: the act of restoring friendly relations.

The importance of *reconciliation* and peacemaking has been stressed by de Waal in a more recent book, where he has extended his studies to three other species, including bonobos. It is clear that peacemaking and other stabilizing social mechanisms of reconciliation are vital for a stable, adaptive, and successful society. Almost all these behaviors have been at least briefly observed or suspected in wild populations, but they were never recorded with the frequency or in the detail made possible at Arnhem. The significance of the Arnhem observations is that they show us yet more of the behavioral potential of an ape such as the chimpanzee.

Bonobos: The Best Evolutionary Model for Early Hominids?

One ape species remains to be described: *Pan paniscus*, the bonobo (pygmy chimpanzee). Although recognized for over half a century, this species remained essentially unstudied until the last two decades. As data on bonobos have been forthcoming, however, they have been particularly tantalizing for anthropologists, since in some ways these are the apes that most closely resemble humans in their behavior. Some scientists feel, therefore, that bonobos are an especially good model for studies of early hominid evolution.

Bonobos are found in Central Africa, in the lowland rain forests and swamp forests south of the Zaire River (Figure 5–16). They are about the size of the smallest subspecies of chimpanzees (*Pan troglodytes*), although bonobos are somewhat more slender, with narrower shoulders and longer legs. In addition, bonobos have smaller brow ridges and ears, and lighter-colored lips, than chimpanzees, and the hair on their heads is parted down the center (Figure 5–20). As in the other African apes, sexual dimorphism in body size is significant among bonobos, and females' body weight is about three-quarters that of males.

FIGURE 5-20 Bonobo (*Pan paniscus*) female and infant. Bonobos are somewhat more slender than chimpanzees, and their hair is parted in the center.

Bonobos live in multimale-multifemale communities that are characterized by the fusion-fission subgrouping already described for chimpanzees: females appear to emigrate from their natal communities, but males do not. Interestingly, the tendency of bonobo males to remain in their natal communities is not correlated with strong male-male relationships or clear-cut male dominance, as it is among chimpanzees. The strongest social bonds among adult bonobos are (depending on the study population) either between females or between males and females. Adult males tend not to develop close relations with one another, but rather they remain strongly bonded to their mothers, associating with them frequently. Newly immigrated females use affiliative and sexual interactions (genito-genital rubbing, see below) to establish friendly relationships with resident females, and coalitions of bonded females dominate males and limit males' access to preferred feeding sites. Bonobo females develop distinct dominance relationships, and the support of a high-ranking mother can enhance an adult son's rank among the males. In general, bonobo females have much more influence within their communities—and bonobo males have less—than is true for their chimpanzee counterparts.

A community of bonobos includes between 50 and 120 animals and inhabits a range of about 8–19 mi^2 (20–50 km^2). Within their range the apes spend most of their time in the trees foraging for fruits, a diet that is supplemented with other plant parts, insects, and some meat. Unlike chimpanzees, bonobos apparently do not use tools to obtain or process either plant or animal foods (in fact, the only established tool-use pattern for wild bonobos is using leafy twigs as shelter from rain). Encounters between animals from different communities are marked by avoidance or aggression, and although more data are needed, it appears that males cooperatively defend a community's territory.

Among the similarities claimed for bonobos and humans, most are sexual, but one is postural. Studies of captive animals have suggested that bonobos stand and walk bipedally more often (and with greater ease) than chimpanzees or gorillas (Figure 5–21). While this may be true, no one is claiming that bonobos are habitual bipeds. In fact, a recent field study showed that bipedalism represented less than 2 percent of the total locomotion of its wild bonobo subjects.

The similarities in sexual behavior, however, are more striking and possibly more important. Bonobo females show rather long sexual cycles of 35–49 days, and between menstrual flows they may be maximally sexually swollen for up to 49 percent of the time. This is a considerably longer period of sexual attractiveness and mating activity than is recorded for chimpanzees, whose females are maximally swollen for 27–40 percent of their menstrual cycle. Humans, of course, engage in sexual behavior throughout all or most of the menstrual cycle, rather more like bonobos. But the sexual similarities take two more interesting twists.

FIGURE 5–21 Bonobos stand and move bipedally much more often than chimpanzees.

First, while virtually all chimpanzee copulations are ventrodorsal (the male mounts the female from the rear), some 25–30 percent of bonobo matings are ventroventral. Of the two sexes, female bonobos seem to be particularly fond of face-to-face sex; several instances have been recorded of females interrupting ventrodorsal copulations in order to change their position and embrace the male ventrally. And second, bonobos are without doubt the most inventive of all the apes in their sexual variations. Bonobos show all of the possible combinations of sexual partners: opposite-sex, same-sex, and old and young. Pairs of females frequently embrace ventrally and rub their genitals together, while males mount one another and occasionally "fence" (mutually rub) with their erect penises. Sex is used by bonobos to reduce tension and resolve conflicts, and some researchers feel that frequent female-female and male-female sexual contacts explain why these relationships are stronger among bonobos than among chimpanzees.

Studies of bonobos are in their infancy. Assuming that humans allow (and assist) bonobos to avoid extinction, this species promises to yield critical information for interpreting human evolution.

Speculations About Ape-Human Common Ancestors

Studies of chromosomes and DNA are beginning to allow fine-grained distinctions about humans' evolutionary relationships with the African apes. Most molecular research suggests that humans, bonobos, and chimpanzees are a clade with a common ancestor that lived about 5 to 7 million years ago—the gorilla lineage having diverged a couple of million years before. These studies further suggest that the chimp and bonobo lines may have separated only within the last 2.5 to 3 million years, so that they are extremely close sister species. Not everyone agrees with this phylogeny, however, and anatomists argue that it implies that knuckle walking evolved independently twice—once in the gorilla lineage and once in the ancestors of chimps and bonobos after the divergence of hominids—a seemingly unlikely occurrence. Nonetheless, on balance the molecular evidence seems the more convincing, and thus, based on data from living humans, chimpanzees, and bonobos, we can speculate cautiously about the probable characteristics of their last common ancestor (an ape-grade creature whose exact identity has yet to be established).

As summarized in Table 5–2, it seems likely that humans' last ape ancestor formed multimale-multifemale communities that were characterized by fusion-fission subgrouping. Female emigration from the natal community was probably the prevalent pattern, as was range defense by males. Sexual behavior was probably variable and situation-dependent (that is, hormonal control of sex was moderate to low, and mating may have occurred throughout much of the menstrual cycle). Males almost certainly had access to multiple mates, and the same may have been true of females. The common ancestor probably engaged in some tool use (the extent is uncertain), included meat in its diet, and, at least occasionally, shared food. And finally, bipedal standing and walking almost certainly occurred on occasion, although not habitually.

Beyond this admittedly sketchy characterization, speculations become very tenuous, but even this incomplete picture of our last ape ancestors is useful in generating evolutionary hypotheses for further testing. Humans appear to be the

Table 5-2 CHARACTERISTICS OF CHIMPANZEES, BONOBOS, HUMANS, AND THEIR COMMON ANCESTOR

Trait	Chimpanzees	Bonobos	Humans	Common Ancestor
Social group[a]	MM-MF community; fusion-fission	MM-MF community; fusion-fission	MM-MF community; fusion-fission	MM-MF community; fusion-fission
Females or males change groups?	Females	Females	Females more often	Females
Male-male bonds	Strong	Weak	Strong	?
Female-female bonds	Weak	Strong	Weak	?
Male-female bonds	Weak	Strong	Strong	?
Territorial defense?	Yes, by males	Probably, by males	Yes, by males	Probably, by males
Mating system	Promiscuity	Promiscuity	Mild polygyny	Multiple mates for males (for females too?)
Sexual swelling?	Yes	Yes	No	?
Sexual activity[b]	27–40%	35–49%	Near 100%	?
Hormonal control of female sexuality	Moderate	Moderate to low	Low	Moderate to low
Copulation pattern	Ventrodorsal	Ventrodorsal > ventroventral	Variable	?
Paternal investment by males	Slight	Slight	Great	?
Tool use?	Frequent and variable	Rare (one pattern)	Very frequent and variable	Probably present (variable?)
Meat eating?	Yes	Yes	Yes	Yes
Food sharing?	Routinely	Rarely	Frequently	Yes
Bipedal stance?	Rare	More common than in chimps	Habitual	At least occasionally

[a]MM, multimale; MF, multifemale.
[b]Percentage of menstrual cycle with mating.

descendants of social, territorial, polygynous-to-promiscuous, tool-using apes that relished a bit of meat in the diet and at least occasionally stood and moved upright. But what was involved in the evolutionary transformation of such a creature into a hominid? To begin to answer that question, we need to focus not on shared traits, but on behavioral and anatomical differences between apes and humans. We will examine such differences in the next chapter as we take a look at some fossil candidates for the office of Common Ancestor.

SUMMARY

Knowledge of the behavior of living primates is an important component in the study of human origins and human nature. Since they began in the early part of this century, primate studies have produced much useful information about our evolutionary relatives, the monkeys and apes. As shown in this chapter, primates are extremely social creatures whose complex behavioral repertoires are based mainly on learning. Their societies are structured by several types of relationships, especially dominance relations, kinship, and affiliative relations (the last based commonly on grooming). Patterns of sexual behavior vary from species to species, but the levels of reproductive success and the identities of sexual partners are commonly influenced by dominance and female choice. Among the apes, chimpanzees and bonobos are clearly the closest evolutionary relatives of humans; gorillas rank third. Comparisons among chimpanzees, bonobos, and humans have revealed much about the likely traits of our common ancestor and enable us to formulate numerous evolutionary hypotheses for testing.

REVIEW QUESTIONS

1. Studies of primate behavior are commonly conducted both in the field and in captivity. Discuss the strengths and weaknesses of research in these two settings.

2. Why do most primates live in groups? What are the advantages and disadvantages of social living? What mechanisms have the animals evolved to cope with the disadvantages of group life?

3. How does the sexual behavior of primate males and females differ? How is sexual behavior affected by rank, age, kinship, and hormonal condition? What is "situation-dependent" sex?

4. How do primates relate to their habitat? Define and compare the following three concepts: home range, core area, territory.

5. Describe tool use among chimpanzees, and explore the implications of the chimp data for the evolution of tool use among hominids.

6. Why do some anthropologists think that bonobos make a better model for hominid evolution than chimpanzees? Develop some questions about hominid evolution to which one could apply a bonobo model.

7. Describe the (speculative) characteristics of the chimpanzee-bonobo-human common ancestor.

POSTSCRIPT

Do chimpanzees have culture? A deceptively simple question perhaps. A knee-jerk answer might be "No, of course not—they're animals!" But how does one classify an animal that makes and uses tools, and that shows regional variation in both tool use and social behavior? The British social anthropologist E. B. Tylor defined culture in 1871 as the "capabilities and habits acquired by man as a member of society." The only kind of culture then known was human culture and it was therefore defined as a specifically human characteristic, dependent on language. Early cultural anthropologists (who produced nearly as many definitions as they themselves numbered) were certain about culture's unique state as a human attribute and did not consider the question of its development from prehistoric times.

The nascent science of archaeology forced the issue of cultural origins in the nineteenth century. Early collectors of stone tools and other artifacts were properly cautious, however, and talked of the beginning of human "material culture." This qualified term reflected the view (since confirmed by animal studies) that simple tools are not always accurate indicators of a total cultural system. This view follows from the fact that toolmaking skills can be learned by observation alone, without language-based instruction. The implication was, and still is, that material culture might well have preceded the full range of cultural manifestations in the course of human evolution.

Modern anthropology has made progress in understanding culture and its definitive features, but there is still room for debate. A modern revision of Tylor describes culture as *the totality of behavior of a social group that is passed down the generations by learning and symbolic means.* This broad definition covers all modern cultural manifestations—rituals, beliefs, material objects, social institutions, and so on—and grounds them in the three key elements of learning, symbolic transmission, and behavior as the property of society.

But to return to the original question: How well do chimpanzees and other nonhuman primates match our current understanding of culture? Following the revised definition, we can recognize some apparently cultural behavior among monkeys as well as among toolmaking chimpanzees. But for many workers, the critical addition of symbolic transmission to the definition seems clearly to distinguish human *culture* from the nonsymbolic *protoculture* of nonhuman primates. As most anthropologists—and nearly all cultural anthropologists—understand things, the transition from protoculture to culture came with the evolution of symbolic language.

Not everyone agrees with the prevailing wisdom, however, including W. C. McGrew, primatologist and author of the book *Chimpanzee Material Culture.* His book takes on the problem of culture among apes, and the title says it all about McGrew's opinion. McGrew sets out eight criteria for identifying cultural acts among nonlinguistic creatures such as chimps: innovation, dissemination, standardization, durability, diffusion, tradition, nonsubsistence, and naturalness. He concludes that no single chimpanzee population satisfies all eight conditions, but that all conditions (except perhaps diffusion) are met by the behavior of some chimps in some cases. He also describes differences in grooming patterns between chimp populations that would automatically be described as cultural differences if shown by humans, but that are denied that label when they are shown by apes. McGrew's argument strongly implies that while definitions of culture are important *heuristic devices* for social scientists, they usually also have the unspoken function of separating humans from all nonhumans.

Heuristic devices: devices that facilitate or stimulate further investigation and thought.

Of course, the problem with definitions and labels that establish a clean break between humans and nonhumans is that they are hard to reconcile with the fact of evolution. After all, modern people are the descendants of nonhuman ancestors: at least one type of ape and also an entire series of premodern hominid forebears. What sort of terminology should we apply in that gray zone of evolutionary intermediacy? As an example, the earliest known hominid tools (Oldowan tools, about 2.4 million years of age) are only slightly more complex than chimpanzee implements. Should the makers of these tools (presumed by most to be nonlinguistic early *Homo,* probably *H. habilis*) be welcomed as "cultural" creatures *simply because they are hominids* while chimpanzees are excluded from the fold? Do we gain or lose anything by labeling early *Homo* as protocultural? And how will we ever identify the point where protoculture graded into true culture?

It should be clear that the question of chimpanzee culture is only the tip of a philosophical and terminological iceberg. Rudimentary technology has been documented among living apes and early hominids, but the significance of such discoveries to the origins of what we moderns understand as culture are hard to determine. Furthermore, one can make the case that we are biased toward limiting culture to members of the human family, despite arguments by some researchers that chimpanzees are equally qualified. Are we being anthropocentric and/or practicing poor science in our construction and application of cultural definitions? What do you think?

Apes and Other Ancestors
Prehominid Evolution

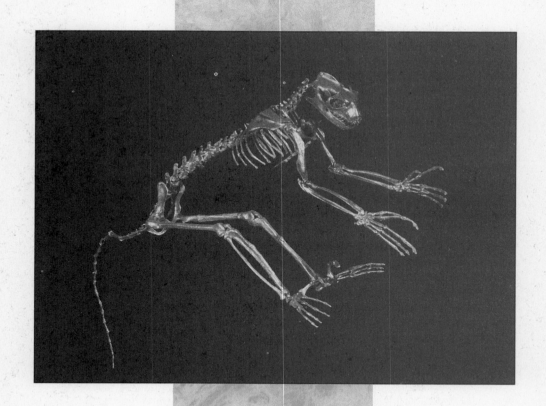

*It is an axiom of mine that when you have excluded the impossible,
whatever remains, however improbable, must be the truth.*
ARTHUR CONAN DOYLE, 1859–1930. *The Adventures of Sherlock Holmes:*
THE BERYL CORONET.

OVERVIEW

This chapter describes the evolutionary beginnings of the primates, a mammalian order that has been around for at least 60 million years and probably much longer. Judging from the fossil record as currently known, the primate order first evolved in Africa during the Paleocene epoch, and its original representatives were prosimian-grade creatures. Anthropoid primates—with their improved vision, reduced sense of smell, and more complex brains—did not appear for perhaps another 10 million years. Around 17 to 20 million years ago (mya)—again in Africa—the superfamily Hominoidea made its evolutionary appearance. The early hominoids are best described as *dental apes,* since their teeth, but not their limbs, marked them as the ancestors of today's apes and humans (postcranially, they were more like monkeys). After a period of considerable success, when evolutionary radiations increased their diversity, and geographic expansion carried them into Europe and Asia, the apes began to decline in numbers and variety during a period of late Miocene climatic cooling. It was at this time—some 5–7 mya—that modern humans' last ape ancestors are thought to have lived, although their precise identity is still unknown. We do know, however, what it took to convert those apes into hominids: primarily the remodeling of quadrupedal creatures into bipeds. And because understanding this conversion is an essential prerequisite to studying the hominid fossil record, the last sections of the chapter are devoted to a description of the anatomy of bipedalism. Important topics in Chapter 6 include primate evolution, continental drift, hominoid evolution, ape anatomy, and the anatomy of bipedalism. Important fossils include the plesiadapiforms, *Altiatlasius, Algeripithecus, Eosimias, Amphipithecus, Pondaungia,* the oligopithecines, *Aegyptopithecus, Proconsul, Oreopithecus,* and *Sivapithecus.*

THE EARLIEST PRIMATES

The study of prehistoric humans is, of necessity, the study of their fossil remains. To begin to understand who our ancestors were and what they were like, we must be able to interpret the fragments of them that are coming to the surface in increasing numbers. Given fairly reliable methods to determine their age, we can now turn with more confidence to primate fossils for an answer to the all-important question: How do we tell monkeys, apes, and humans apart? For present-day species we have no problem; all have evolved sufficiently so that they no longer resemble one another. But since they all have a common ancestor, the further back we go in time, the more similar their fossils begin to look. There finally comes a point when they are indistinguishable. The construction of a primate fossil family tree is, however, essential if we are ever going to discover the line of descent from early primate to modern human.

We must therefore sort through the teeth and bones that have survived through the ages to see what physical changes took place in our ancestors and how these changes led to modern humans. Each step along the way is equally important. The new developments that characterize each new link of the chain of life that leads to humankind were made possible only by earlier developments. To understand precisely what we are, we must consider the entire chain and look behind apes and monkeys to the earlier animals from which they sprang. Traits that would later emerge as distinctly human had their origins in the anatomy and behavior of these distant creatures, the earliest primates.

As noted in Chapter 4, the oldest known primate fossils are about 60 million years old and are from the late *Paleocene* epoch of geologic time (Figure 6–1). Although this date sounds solid enough, it should be taken only as a rough approximation of the first appearance of primates. The reason is the enormous gaps in our knowledge of the fossil record. The 200-plus fossil varieties currently known represent only 2 to 4 percent of an estimated 5,000–7,000 extinct primate

Paleocene: the geologic epoch extending from 65 to 58 million years B.P. (before present).

Years B.P.	Eras	Period	Epoch	Years B.P.	Main Events
	Cenozoic	Quaternary	Pleistocene	10,000 to 1.6 million	Humans first learn to use and control fire in temperate zones
			Pliocene	1.6 to 5 million	Genus *Homo* appears Age of *Australopithecus, Paranthropus*
			Miocene	5 to 25 million	First hominids First apes
		Tertiary	Oligocene	25 to 35 million	Catarrhines and platyrrhines separate
			Eocene	35 to 58 million	First anthropoids
65 million			Paleocene	58 to 65 million	First primates: prosimians
	Mesozoic	ME Cretaceous		65 to 135 million	First flowering plants Disappearance of large dinosaurs
		Jurassic ME		135 to 180 million	First birds
225 million		Triassic		180 to 225 million	First mammals Age of Reptiles begins
	Paleozoic	ME Permian		225 to 280 million	
		Carboniferous ME		280 to 345 million	First coniferous trees First reptiles
		Devonian		345 to 395 million	First forests First amphibians, insects, and bony fish
		Silurian ME		395 to 430 million	First land plants First fish with jaws
		Ordovician		430 to 500 million	First vertebrates: armored fish without jaws
570 million		Cambrian		500 to 570 million	First shell-bearing animals
	Precambrian			600 million	First multicellular animals
				3.5 billion	First living things: algae, bacteria
				4 billion	Formation of primordial seas
				4.5 billion	Formation of earth

FIGURE 6–1 Geologic time scales are of such immense duration that it is hard to comprehend fully the great period of time during which nature and humankind have evolved. If the almost 500 million years of vertebrate evolution are symbolized by 1 hour of time, then primate evolution took 7 minutes, and human evolution occurred in the last 12 seconds of that hour. ME = mass extinction event.

species. As additional discoveries are made, it seems inevitable that the origin of our order will be pushed millions of years further back in time—perhaps even into the late Cretaceous period.

But for now the late Paleocene marks the origin of primates, and those first members of our order emerged into a very different world from today. For one thing, the positioning of the continents was different. Studies of *continental drift* have indicated that the Paleozoic supercontinent Pangaea II (Figure 6–2) split during the Mesozoic to form a large northern landmass—including the modern continents of North America, Europe, and most of Asia—and an even larger southern landmass combining Africa, South America, Antarctica, India, Madagascar, and Australia. By the Paleocene, South America and India had drifted away from Africa, and Africa had been separated from Eurasia by high sea levels. In the north, Eurasia and North America were still contiguous and remained so for several million years (Figure 6–3).

Continental drift: a theory that describes the movements of continental landmasses throughout the earth's history.

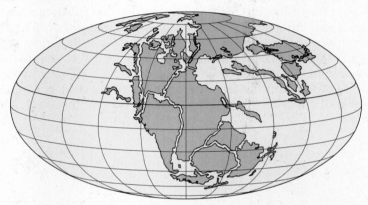

Pangaea II: 200 million years ago

FIGURE 6–2

This reconstruction of the supercontinent Pangaea II at 200 million years B.P. shows the precursors of most of the modern continents. At about this time, Pangaea II split into a northern landmass, Laurasia, and a southern continent, Gondwanaland.

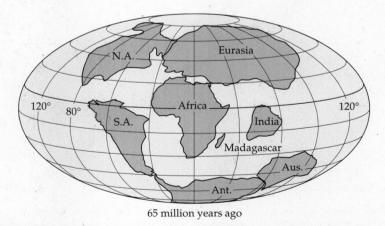

65 million years ago

FIGURE 6–3

By the beginning of the Paleocene epoch, South America and India had separated from Africa, while North America and Eurasia were still linked.

Not only was the configuration of the continents different during the Paleocene, but in consequence global climate patterns and habitat zones were as well. Tropical forests spread much farther north and south from the equator; France and Germany were moist, humid jungles, as was much of Africa and nearly everywhere in between. Parts of North America were similarly forested, and the forest avenue between North America and Eurasia allowed extensive mammalian dispersal.

Within this moist, forested world, the first primates arose from some primitive, semiarboreal mammalian ancestor. Although that ancestor's exact identity remains to be discovered, it may well have resembled modern insectivorous tree shrews (Figure 6–4). In response to the challenges of arboreal living and of visual-manual predation on insects (see Chapter 4), the early primates began the order's evolutionary trajectory toward grasping hands and feet (Figure 6–5), keen vision, and a reduced sense of smell.

One diverse group of animals once thought to be basal primates can now be eliminated from the order. The *Plesiadapiformes* from the Paleocene and *Eocene* of North America and Europe have been classified by some authorities as a primate suborder on dental grounds, even though they lacked such defining features as postorbital bars (Figure 6–9). Recent findings, however, have brought this classification into question. For example, some plesiadapiforms are now known to have differed from undoubted primates in the anatomy of the *auditory bulla*. In all true primates, the bulla develops from one particular bone of the skull, while in the

Plesiadapiformes: fossil mammals of the Paleocene and Eocene that were once thought to be primitive primates but are now classified as relatives of *colugos*.

Eocene: the geologic epoch extending from 58 to 35 million years B.P.

Auditory bulla: the bulbous bony development that houses the middle ear region.

FIGURE 6–4   Tree shrews are found in Southeast Asia. They are primitive animals and are probably similar to the first primates. Their appearance is somewhat similar to that of the squirrel, but they are quite distinct from any rodent. Their bodies are about 5 in. (13 cm) long.

The Living Apes

After their evolutionary heyday during the Miocene epoch, apes experienced a strong reduction in diversity, until today they are represented by only four genera: *Hylobates* (gibbons and siamangs), *Pongo* (orangutans), *Gorilla* (gorillas), and *Pan* (chimpanzees and bonobos). These remarkable creatures are humans' closest living relatives, and studies of their anatomy, ecology, and behavior promise to yield important insights into our evolutionary development—unless they are pushed over the brink of extinction by hunting and habitat destruction. The following photographs attempt to communicate the intelligent gaze and distinctive personalities of various living apes.

◆　　◆　　◆

In this painting, entitled *Darwin and Friends*, artist Stephen Nash has depicted a wide variety of living primates. From left to right, one encounters prosimians, monkeys, apes, and humankind represented by Darwin himself.

The white-handed gibbon (*Hylobates lar*) is a monogynous inhabitant of the forests of Southeast Asia. A master brachiator, the gibbon hooks supporting branches with its long fingers as it swings through the trees.

Also an inhabitant of Southeast Asia, a mother orangutan (*Pongo pygmaeus*) is shown with her infant. Once widely spread from India to China and as far south as Indonesia, orangutans are now found only on the islands of Sumatra and Borneo.

An adult male gorilla (*Gorilla gorilla*) munches his way through a leafy meal. So large and powerful that they have few natural predators, gorillas—particularly the eastern "mountain gorillas"—are nonetheless losing the battle for existence because of human activities.

With their lengthy period of sexual activity and frequent bipedal posturing, bonobos (*Pan paniscus*) are thought by some scientists to be the best living models for early hominids. Field studies of these Zairian apes are in their infancy.

An adult male chimpanzee (*Pan troglodytes*) strikes a thoughtful pose. Intelligent and highly social, chimpanzees are without doubt the best hunters and toolmakers among the nonhuman primates, and some anthropologists believe they demonstrate a primitive sort of culture.

This painting by artist R. E. Hynes gives a good idea of the relative sizes of the various hominoid species. Furthermore, a comparison of females (shown on the left for all species except humans) and males demonstrates the amount of sexual dimorphism in body size within each species. From upper left to right the species are gibbons, orangutans, bonobos, common chimpanzees, gorillas, and humans.

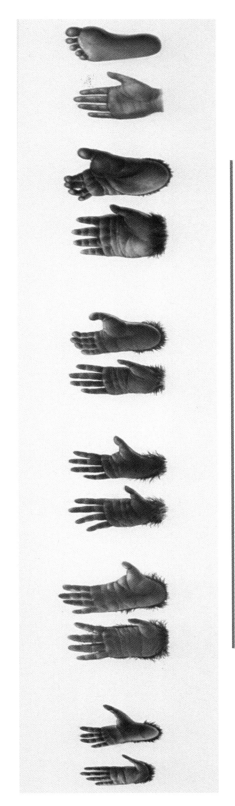

In this illustration R. E. Hynes shows a representative hand and foot for each of the hominoid species. The species are in the same order as on the facing page.

Tree shrew   Slow loris   Macaque

FIGURE 6–5 The hands of a tree shrew, a prosimian, and a macaque monkey are illustrated. The tree shrew, like all insectivores, carries claws. The loris has nails on all digits except its second toe, where a claw has survived for grooming. Macaque monkeys have nails on all digits and relatively long thumbs, giving them a good precision grip.

plesiadapiform genus *Ignacius* it grew from a different bone entirely. Further evidence comes from the anatomy of the hand. Some plesiadapiforms possessed elongated digital bones that may have served to support webbing between the fingers. From this last discovery, it has been suggested that the plesiadapiforms may be evolutionary relatives of the colugos: living nonprimate mammals from Asia known for their arboreal gliding habits and misnamed flying lemurs. In all, despite certain dental similarities, the plesiadapiforms just don't work as basal primates—which leaves the beginnings of our order shrouded in mystery.

UNDOUBTED PRIMATE FOSSILS

It is perhaps to be expected that the earliest primate fossils should be difficult to distinguish from related groups, with the result that their status is often controversial. At present, the earliest fossil primates have been found in Morocco at a site named Adrar Mgorn, at the foot of the Atlas Mountains. Here, in late Paleocene sediments, together with remains of 23 other mammalian species, have been found ten isolated molar teeth of a very small (2–4 oz; 50–100 g) creature named *Altiatlasius*. Not much to go on, perhaps, but enough to make a strong case for an African origin for the primate order, for the teeth are undoubtedly the teeth of early prosimians. This claim is supported by later finds from the early Eocene of Algeria, Tunisia, and Egypt.

Altiatlasius: oldest known primate fossil; prosimian from the late Paleocene of North Africa.

We also have fossils of about this age, or a little later, from Europe, Asia, and North America. It was previously thought that North America contained the earliest fossil primates, and some believe that Asia is a more likely place of origin for the order, but the evidence for an African origin is rapidly accumulating.

Judging from the remains of *Altiatlasius* and many other, more complete fossils, the earliest primates can be classified confidently as prosimians. In clear contrast to the plesiadapiforms and other nonprimate mammals, they possessed forwardly directed eyes, postorbital bars, grasping big toes, and nails on most digits instead of claws. They have been arranged into two extinct families—the *Adapidae*

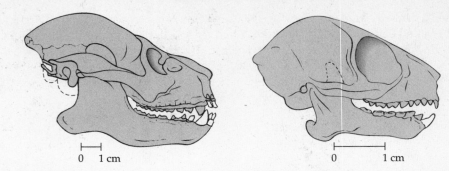

FIGURE 6–6　Representative skulls of early prosimians. Adapid (*Leptadapis magnus*) shown at left and omomyid (*Necrolemur antiquus*) to the right. Both are from European mid-Eocene deposits.

Adapidae and Omomyidae: families of Eocene prosimians, now extinct.

and the *Omomyidae* (Figure 6–6)—and their diversity during the Eocene epoch (we recognize some 40 genera) shows that they underwent a strong evolutionary radiation shortly after their origin. Although there is disagreement among paleontologists and more fossil evidence is needed, the adapids appear to be evolutionary predecessors of modern lemurs and lorises, while the omomyids may be more closely linked to modern tarsiers. *Altiatlasius* has been interpreted as a very early form of omomyid.

The anatomy of these Eocene prosimians indicates that they were agile arborealists that ate a mixed diet of fruit, leaves, and insects. Furthermore, they anticipated one of the main characteristics of modern primates by showing larger brains for their body size than most other Eocene mammals.

But for all we know about the first primates, we still cannot determine which form gave rise to the anthropoids. None of the known adapid or omomyid skulls shows the beginnings of such defining anthropoid traits as complete bony eye sockets or fused frontal bones (Table 4–4), and all of the Eocene prosimians very likely had a rhinarium. Still, by the middle of the Eocene some prosimian variety had given rise to creatures we can recognize as basal anthropoids, creating a major fork in the primate family tree. At first, the emerging anthropoids could not be called anything more than super prosimians, because the differences between them and the older prosimian species were too small to be significant. But as these differences began to build up, by giving a survival advantage to the individuals that had them, the trees became filled with smarter, swifter, defter, altogether abler animals. The surviving prosimians remained nocturnal or died away in many places because they could not compete. Nevertheless, those first Paleocene and Eocene primates do point to the first pieces of the puzzle of humankind's evolution.

THE FIRST HIGHER PRIMATES

Oligocene: the geologic epoch extending from 35 to 25 million years B.P.

Dating the emergence of the anthropoids (higher primates) from prosimian stock is a tricky business. Anthropoids were clearly well established and diversified by the *Oligocene* epoch (35–25 mya), but their actual origin was probably much earlier. The oldest fossils likely to be anthropoids come from the site of Glib Zegdou in the North African country of Algeria. These remains (consisting of three molar teeth) have been named *Algeripithecus minutus* and date from the middle or even early Eocene. But while the teeth show a number of anthropoid-like features, the fragmentary nature of the fossil argues for a conservative interpretation. At present, the classification of *Algeripithecus* as an anthropoid should be viewed as strictly tentative. If further discoveries—particularly of fossils showing diagnostic anthropoid cranial features—validate the claim, then the appearance of higher primates probably occurred in Africa over 50 mya.

Algeripithecus: tentatively, the oldest known anthropoid primate from North Africa's early-middle Eocene.

The African case is not airtight, however, and there are a number of Asian fossils just slightly younger than *Algeripithecus* that also appear to be anthropoids. Among the most exciting are some very recent discoveries from mid-Eocene deposits in China. In 1994 a joint American-Chinese research team announced the discovery of a rich deposit of fossil primates near the village of Shanghuang. Dating about 45 million years old, the Shanghuang primates include adapids, omomyids, the earliest known tarsiers, and also fossils assigned to a new genus, *Eosimias* (the "dawn ape"). But don't be misled by the name. In fact, *Eosimias* was not an ape at all, but a generalized creature that showed a strong combination of derived (anthropoid) and primitive (prosimian) traits. A very small primate (body weight of 2.4–4.8 oz, or 67–137 g), *Eosimias* shared a number of dental traits with modern anthropoids but still resembled prosimians in its unfused mandibular symphysis (see Table 4–4). Neither a monkey nor an ape, *Eosimias* seems to fill the bill nicely as a basal anthropoid.

Eosimias: probable basal anthropoid from the mid-Eocene of China.

Other possible anthropoids from Asia include *Amphipithecus* and *Pondaungia* from Burma. Known from fragmentary dental remains recovered early in this century, *Amphipithecus* and *Pondaungia* date to the late Eocene. The new fossils from Shanghuang, coupled with evidence from *Amphipithecus* and *Pondaungia*, suggest to some researchers that the anthropoid suborder originated in Asia, not Africa. *Eosimias* in particular appears to be only slightly younger than *Algeripithecus*, and the dates for both fossils involve considerable estimation. Although Africa may still hold a slight edge in the contest, theories of an Asian origin of anthropoids must be given careful consideration.

Amphipithecus and *Pondaungia:* possible anthropoids from the late Eocene of Burma.

But if the early and mid-Eocene glimmers of the anthropoids are faint and confusing, their presence had solidified by the end of the epoch, and for that story we must return to northern Africa and Egypt's Fayum Depression, a region renowned for its fossil remains. In the Fayum, deposits straddling the Eocene-Oligocene boundary have yielded several undoubted anthropoids belonging to an extinct subfamily called the *oligopithecines*. Located in the desert about 60 miles southwest of Cairo, the Fayum Depression is currently one of the driest places on earth—hardly good anthropoid terrain. In Eocene and Oligocene times, however, the Fayum was a tropical and swampy region lying along the southern shore of the Mediterranean. Heavily wooded in parts and laced with rivers, it was a fine place for early anthropoids to live and evolve—and evolve they did, as the diversity of the oligopithecines attests.

Oligopithecines: late Eocene anthropoids; many have been collected from Egypt's Fayum Depression.

The oligopithecines date to the latest Eocene of northern Africa (about 36 mya) and include three genera: *Oligopithecus, Proteopithecus,* and *Catopithecus.* All were small-bodied (≤2.2 lb, or 1 kg) forest-dwellers that ate, most probably, a mixed diet of fruit and insects. Among the fossils of *Catopithecus* is a well-preserved skull (Figure 6–7) that demonstrates such diagnostic anthropoid traits as bony eye sockets and fused frontal bones. But the oligopithecines were not typically anthropoid in all of their features. Demonstrating that anthropoid traits

Catopithecus: a particularly well-known oligopithecine from the Fayum in Africa.

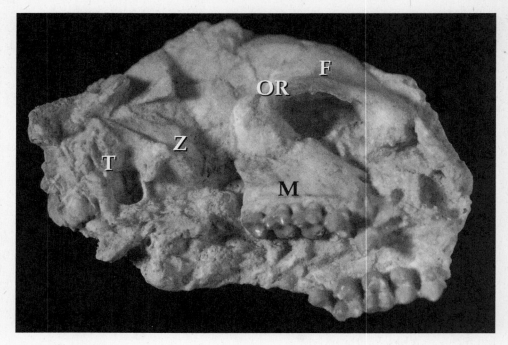

FIGURE 6–7   Distorted fossil skull of *Catopithecus browni*, an oligopithecine anthropoid from the late Eocene of Egypt. Crushing has moved the right orbit over the grinding teeth. The upper teeth P3 through M3 are preserved on both sides. As in this case, fossils are sometimes difficult to interpret because of damage and distortion during fossilization. The key to the skull bones is as follows: F, frontal; M, maxilla; OR, orbital rim; T, temporal; Z, zygomatic.

evolved in mosaic fashion rather than all at once, the oligopithecines still showed a low ratio of brain size to body size as well as some prosimian-like features in their teeth. Interestingly, the oligopithecines varied somewhat in their dental formulae: while *Catopithecus* had a total of 8 premolars, *Proteopithecus* had 12. Although too generalized to be classified as either monkeys or apes, the oligopithecines give us a good view of the anatomy, diet, and habitat of early, undoubted anthropoids.

Oligocene Anthropoids

Aegyptopithecus: a basal catarrhine from the Fayum in Africa; dated to the Oligocene epoch.

By the early Oligocene epoch, anthropoids were enjoying much success in Africa. Several genera had evolved, including *Parapithecus, Propliopithecus* (Figure 6–8), *Apidium* (Figure 6–9), and *Aegyptopithecus* (Figures 6–9, 6–10, and 6–11). Although these creatures showed some advances over their Eocene ancestors, analyses of their total morphological patterns show that they were still very primitive. *Parapithecus* and *Apidium* are best classified as basal anthropoids that preceded the evolutionary separation of platyrrhines and catarrhines. *Propliopithecus* and *Aegyptopithecus,* on the other hand, can be identified as catarrhines, although both were too primitive to be classified further as either monkeys or apes. A detailed

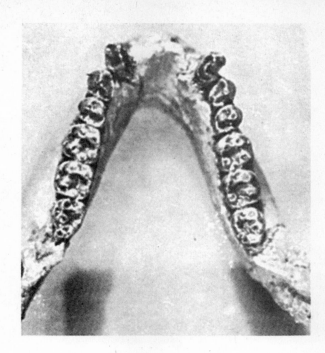

FIGURE 6–8 *Propliopithecus* had a five-cusped pattern on its lower molars. This early primate could possibly have given rise to Old World monkeys, apes, and humans.

analysis of the total morphology of *Aegyptopithecus* shows how such a conclusion is reached. Although certain dental features suggest that *Aegyptopithecus* had evolved into an ape-grade creature—2123/2123 dental formula, five-cusped molars, rectangular dental arcade (Figure 6–10)—other features are distinctly monkeylike. *Aegyptopithecus* was an arboreal quadruped rather than an arm hanger or arm swinger, sported a tail, and had a monkey-shaped skull (Figure 6–11; see also Figure 6–12 for anatomical comparisons of modern monkeys and apes). Thus, given their mosaic anatomy, *Propliopithecus* and *Aegyptopithecus* are best regarded as generalized catarrhines that were, however, on or near the ances-

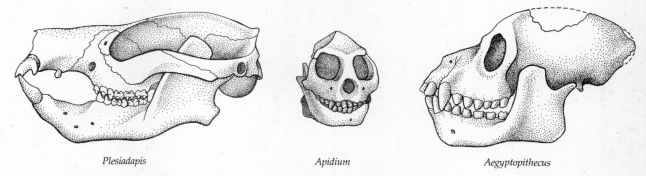

Plesiadapis   *Apidium*   *Aegyptopithecus*

FIGURE 6–9 The orbits of living primates are surrounded by a ring of bone that constitutes a lateral extension of the frontal bone joining the cheekbone. This structure protects the large, forward-pointing eyes. Fossil anthropoids such as *Apidium* had these laterally bounded orbits and also a full bony socket, as did the more advanced *Aegyptopithecus*. In more primitive mammals, such as *Plesiadapis*, the orbit was open at the back and side. The scale is 60 percent of actual size.

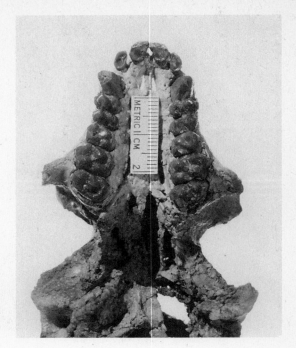

FIGURE 6–10   The palate of *Aegypto-pithecus* shows a somewhat apelike dentition and almost rectangular dental arcade. The creature, however, was very small, as indicated by the scale. This specimen was discovered by Elwyn Simons in the Fayum region of Egypt. It is dated about 32 million years B.P.

FIGURE 6–11   Finds of *Aegyptopithecus* bones are now so numerous that a full reconstruction is possible. This drawing of the 12-lb (5.4 kg) creature was made under the direction of Elwyn Simons. Notice that this catarrhine carried a long tail.

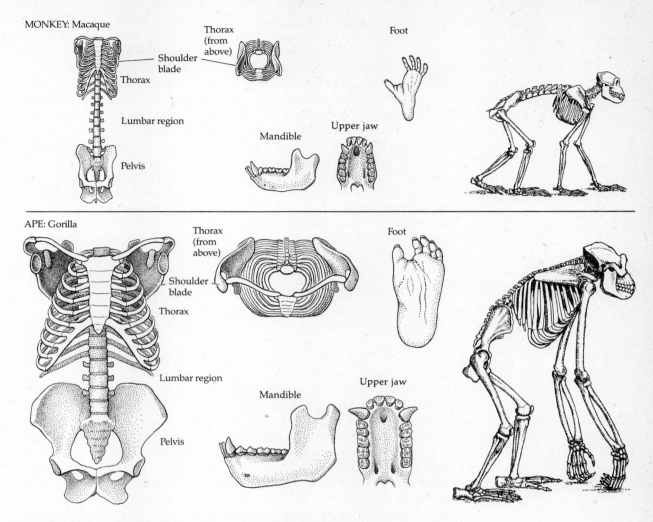

FIGURE 6–12 Ape and monkey skeletons have much in common. Apes are more like humans than like monkeys in skeletal structure. Note the different proportions of limbs; the form of the rib cage and shoulder blade; and the use of hands in locomotion. Scale is approximately one-twentieth actual size. Note that the macaque shown has a relatively short tail. See Figure 4–15 for more typical monkey tails.

tral line for all later anthropoids of the Old World. The stage was set for the evolution of the modern superfamilies of monkeys and apes.

Evolution of the New World Monkeys

Humans are catarrhine primates whose evolutionary origins reside in the Old World. That being the case, the history of the New World monkeys is of rather secondary importance to the story being told here. Nonetheless, the evolutionary appearance of these "second cousins" of ours deserves at least a brief description before we move on to fossil apes.

Branisella and *Szalatavus:* Oligocene platyrrhine monkeys from Bolivia.

The oldest fossils of platyrrhine monkeys come from late Oligocene deposits in Bolivia. Two genera are recognized—*Branisella* and *Szalatavus*—and both are about 27 million years old. Thus, on the basis of fossil evidence, anthropoid primates showed up in the New World at least 9 million years later (and possibly as much as 20 million years later) than in Africa. Couple these dates with the present lack of evidence of separate prosimian ancestries for platyrrhines and catarrhines, and one is forced to conclude, although tentatively, that the New World monkeys are descended from African anthropoid stock. But how could they have migrated across the South Atlantic—a sizable span of water even in Oligocene times—to a new neotropical home? It's hard to accept, but the best answer seems to be that they crossed by a combination of island hopping (a series of mid-Atlantic islands may have existed off the coast of Sierra Leone and elsewhere) and rafting aboard floating mats of vegetation. Once in South and Central America, the platyrrhines diversified strongly to produce the great variety of New World monkeys alive today. They made no contribution, however, to the evolution of humankind.

The Miocene: Apes at Last

Miocene: the geologic epoch extending from 25 to 5 million years B.P.

Early members of the superfamily Hominoidea—that is, early apes—first appear in the fossil record about 17–20 mya. With one possible exception (*Dionysopithecus;* see Table 6–1), these early *Miocene* fossils come from East Africa or nearby Saudi Arabia (Figure 6–13), and thus an African origin for hominoids seems a safe conclusion. Cercopithecoid monkeys appear in the fossil record not long after the apes—at about 15–17 mya—but details of the evolutionary differentiation of the two living catarrhine superfamilies are unclear at present. The earliest catarrhine monkeys are classed within the extinct subfamily *Victoriapithecinae*, and many species used more open habitats than those favored by the evolving hominoids. Although interesting in their own right, the Cercopithecoidea made no contribution to hominid evolution, and therefore they will concern us no further.

Victoriapithecinae: extinct subfamily of the earliest catarrhine monkeys.

The apes do concern us, however, and during the early Miocene they were busy adapting to a warm East African environment covered mostly by forests and woodlands. As shown by the lists in Figure 6–13 and Table 6–1, these early apes were a diverse lot, and their evolutionary relationships are not at all clear. Primarily forest animals that ate a mixture of fruit and leaves, they varied from monkey-sized beasts to creatures as large as modern chimpanzees. A close look at one fairly well known genus, *Proconsul* (Figure 6–14), allows us to understand them better.

Proconsul: an ape from East Africa that lived during the Miocene epoch.

Proconsul is probably best described as a *dental ape*, since its postcranial skeleton actually had few similarities to those of living apes. As a member in good standing of the catarrhines, *Proconsul*'s protruding muzzle showed a dental formula of 2123/2123. In addition, it had projecting and pointed canine teeth, upper canines that sheared against the lower anterior premolar, and postcanine toothrows that were generally parallel. Other features worth mentioning are *Proconsul*'s strongly receding forehead and low-vaulted braincase. Despite its apelike teeth and skull, however, *Proconsul* showed few similarities to modern apes from the neck down. As summarized in Table 4–4 and illustrated in Figure 6–12, modern apes have a broad chest, a short lower back, no tail, and shoulders and arms modified for forelimb-dominated locomotion (arm hanging and arm swinging). Although *Proconsul* did lack a tail, the similarities stop there. In contrast to mod-

Table 6–1 CLASSIFICATION OF FOSSIL APES[a]

SUPERFAMILY HOMINOIDEA

Family **Proconsulidae**

Dendropithecus	Early Miocene (Africa)
Dionysopithecus	? Early Miocene (Asia)
Limnopithecus	Early Miocene (Africa)
Micropithecus	Early Miocene (Africa)
Proconsul	Early Miocene (Africa)
Rangwapithecus	Early Miocene (Africa)

Family **Oreopithecidae**

Nyanzapithecus	Early-mid Miocene (Africa)
Oreopithecus	Late Miocene (Europe)

Family **Pongidae**

Dryopithecus[b]	Mid-late Miocene (Europe)
Gigantopithecus	Late Miocene-Pleistocene (Asia)
Lufengpithecus	Late Miocene (Asia)
Sivapithecus[b,c]	Mid-late Miocene (Africa, Europe, Asia)

Family **Pliopithecidae**

Laccopithecus	Late Miocene (Asia)
Pliopithecus	Mid-late Miocene (Europe)

Family *incertae sedis*

Afropithecus	Early-?mid Miocene (Africa, Saudi Arabia)
Turkanapithecus	Early Miocene (Africa)
Otavipithecus	Mid Miocene (Africa)

[a]With the exception of *Otavipithecus*, information from G. Conroy, 1990, *Primate Evolution*, New York, W. W. Norton.
[b]*Rudapithecus* (Figure 6–16) is lumped with *Dryopithecus* by some authors and with *Sivapithecus* by others.
[c]Includes *Ouranopithecus, Kenyapithecus*, and the Pasalar fossils from Figure 6–16, and also *Ramapithecus*.

ern apes, *Proconsul* had a long, flexible spine; a narrow torso; and monkeylike limb proportions (Figure 6–15). Judging from its postcranial remains, *Proconsul* was a rather generalized quadruped, certainly not an animal adapted for forelimb-dominated arboreal movement.

By the mid-Miocene, apes had migrated into Eurasia. Fossil remains have been found from Spain in the west to Turkey in the east, and in South Africa the recently discovered species called *Otavipithecus namibiensis* shows that apes were living in the southern part of that continent as well as in their old East African haunts. Adaptive radiations occurred in both Africa and Eurasia, greatly increasing ape variety.

Late Miocene times witnessed the greatest diversity of apes and found them spread throughout Europe and Africa, and also across southern Asia as far east as China (Figure 6–16 lists some important late Miocene genera and gives approximate time ranges). These apes tended to be moderate to large in body size (some, like *Gigantopithecus,* were enormous), and they primarily inhabited dense woods and forests. Their diets were probably as diverse as their body sizes. Some genera,

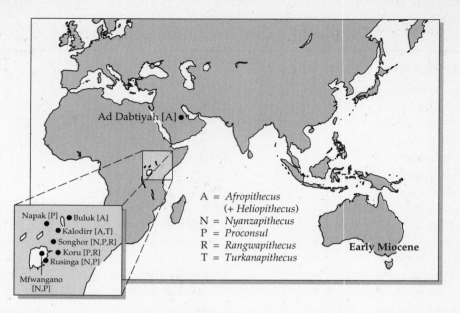

FIGURE 6–13 Map of the Old World showing the sites that have produced ape remains dating to the early Miocene. Note that these earliest apes were concentrated in Africa.

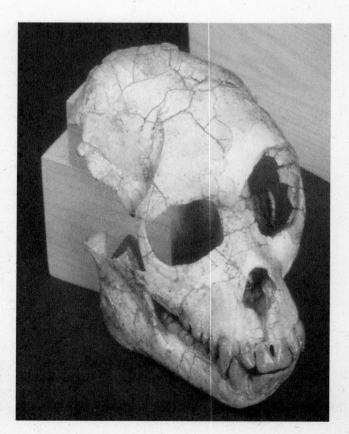

FIGURE 6–14 The skull of *Proconsul* is a typical ape skull. It combines a low cranial vault, projecting muzzle, and large anterior teeth.

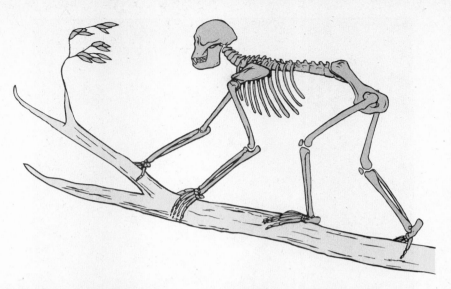

FIGURE 6–15 Reconstructed skeleton of *Proconsul*. Note the slender torso, the monkeylike limb proportions, and the lack of a tail.

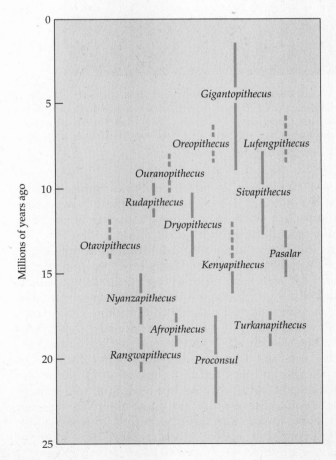

FIGURE 6–16 Various fossil ape genera are shown here along with their time ranges (solid lines denote well-known ranges; dashed lines indicate probable ranges).

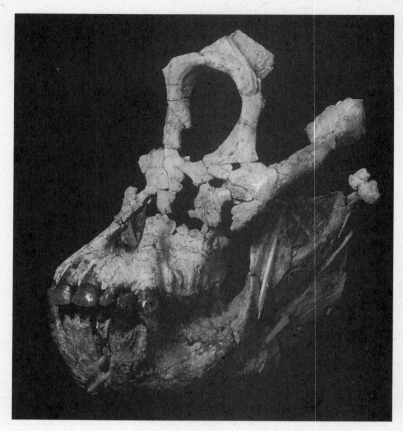

FIGURE 6–17 This *Sivapithecus indicus* skull was found in northeast Pakistan with no other fossils except a mouse tooth. The skull had a bite mark in it, indicating that a hyena must have carried it to the spot where the head and the jaw were found within 2 ft (0.6 m) of each other. The site excavations by David Pilbeam and his research team from Harvard (previously from Yale) have been ongoing since 1973.

Sivapithecus: a genus of Miocene apes that includes *Ramapithecus;* probably ancestral to the orangutan.

such as *Sivapithecus* (Figure 6–17) and *Gigantopithecus,* had thick-enameled grinding teeth and probably subsisted on tough, hard food items. Others showed dental evidence of more frugivorous diets, while the enigmatic European genus *Oreopithecus* (Figure 6–18) probably tended toward folivory.

Although there are some indications among the late Miocene hominoids of the beginnings of suspensory locomotion like that of modern apes, few species showed extensive adaptations for arm hanging or swinging. *Rudapithecus* and *Sivapithecus,* for example, had elbow joints adapted for arboreal suspension, but the rest of their postcranial skeletons suggest quadrupedal walking. The exceptional species, and the one showing the clearest adaptations for suspension, was *Oreopithecus bambolii* from Europe (Figure 6–18). This unique creature had a short trunk and a broad thorax, long arms and short legs, and elbow joints like those of living apes. Unfortunately the evolutionary relationships of *Oreopithecus* are extremely obscure. It seems likely, however, that the line leading to *Oreopithecus* diverged from the main hominoid lineage fairly early and therefore was not directly ancestral to modern apes. In summary, the specialized, forelimb-dominated locomotion common to living apes is apparently a rather recent evolutionary development that can be neither dated nor described accurately at present.

Oreopithecus: enigmatic late Miocene hominoid from Europe that showed adaptations for suspensory locomotion.

FIGURE 6–18   Skeleton and reconstructed habitual posture of *Oreopithecus*, an enigmatic ape from the late Miocene of Europe.

Ape diversity declined strongly in the very late Miocene in association with global climatic changes, principally continental cooling and drying. Forests shrank in size as open habitats expanded. We know that the ancestors of the modern large-bodied apes and hominids had to be sorting themselves out at this time, but we know very little about the process because of a paucity of relevant fossil material. The orangutan lineage probably diverged between 13 and 16 mya, and it can be said with some certainty that the fossil genus *Sivapithecus* (now understood to include *Ramapithecus*, a genus once thought to be an ancestor of hominids) is an evolutionary ancestor of the Asian great ape (Figure 6–19). Unfortunately the evolutionary histories of the African apes, chimpanzees, bonobos, and gorillas—humans' closest living primate kin—are very poorly known at present. The African habitat was strongly affected some 8 mya by geologic activity that produced the Rift Valley running down the eastern side of the continent (see Figure 7–1). Because of changes in air circulation and rainfall, the area west of the Rift remained humid and forested, while to the east a drier climate produced open savannas. Biomolecular studies suggest that the gorilla lineage may have branched off around the time the Rift Valley was formed, with hominids separating from the chimpanzee-bonobo lineage shortly thereafter. It appears that humans' last ape ancestors lived in Africa (as Darwin so wisely believed) during the late Miocene, some 5–7 mya (Table 1–2). But precisely what those apes were, what they looked like, and how they behaved all remain to be discovered. But big changes were afoot: by early in the succeeding *Pliocene* epoch, unequivocal hominids had evolved.

Pliocene: the geologic epoch extending from 5 to 1.6 million years B.P.

Apes to Hominids: The Anatomical Criteria

We are now poised to review the fossil record of the human family, the family Hominidae. Indeed, most of the remainder of this book is devoted to that purpose. Before surveying the hominid remains, however, it is important to set out very clearly the minimum criteria for including a fossil species in that category. As

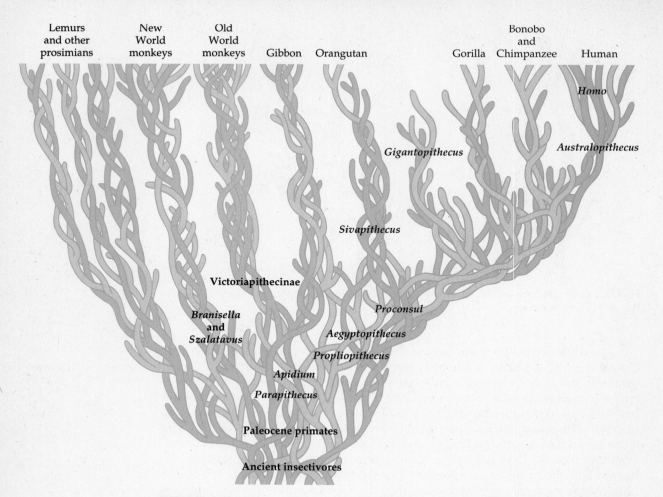

FIGURE 6–19 Evolutionary "trees," or dendrograms, are always greatly oversimplified and in certain ways inaccurate, but they nevertheless give a good indication of the relative ages and phylogenetic relationships of the species shown. The multiplicity of lines indicates that any evolving lineage contains an unknown number of divergent populations that may or may not be different species. Many such populations become extinct. The chart is highly speculative.

reviewed in Chapter 4, living hominids (modern humans) are distinguished by several traits, including short, incisorlike canine teeth (Figure 6–20); skulls with flat faces and huge brains (Figure 6–21); fully opposable thumbs that give us a fine precision grip; and numerous adaptations of the back, hips, legs, and feet that facilitate bipedal locomotion. Of these traits, only two—the first to evolve—are useful markers of the earliest hominids: reduced canine length and adaptations for bipedalism. But even these two are not equally useful. Some of the late Miocene apes (*Ouranopithecus*, for example) had relatively short canines, while those of some early hominids were relatively long in comparison to those of later members of the human family. Therefore, in the final analysis only evidence of habitual bipedalism unmistakably marks a fossil species as hominid.

Modern apes are long-armed and short-legged arborealists. They climb, swing, or hang about in the trees using forelimb-dominated movements, and

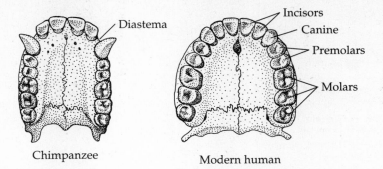

FIGURE 6–20 The dentition of the upper jaw of an ape (a chimpanzee) and a human is here compared. Notice the distinct shape of the dental arcade, as well as the large ape canines, and their diastemata.

when they come to the ground they walk quadrupedally. As adaptations for these locomotor patterns, apes have evolved (or retained) a distinct suite of postcranial traits. They have short, stiff, straight backs; tall, narrow pelvic bones similar to those of monkeys; widely spaced knees and feet (a *wide-knee stance;* Figure 6–22); and divergent big toes capable of grasping branches during climbing. Specifically with regard to the pelvis, the following distinctive anatomical traits can be identified in apes (Figure 6–23): (1) the *iliac blade* is long and narrow and shows no sign of forward curvature into a "pelvic bowl"; (2) the *anterior inferior iliac spine* is very small and undeveloped; (3) the shaft of the *ischium* lies essentially in a straight line with the main portion of the ilium; and (4) the *sacrum* (the wedge of fused vertebrae that articulates with the pelvic bones) is relatively narrow. Additionally, with regard to the *femur,* or thighbone, the ape's wide-knee stance results in the lack of an angled shaft at the knee (Figure 6–22).

Equipped with this set of anatomical features, apes are capable only of energetically expensive and (somewhat) unstable bipedalism. A bipedal ape stands in a bent-hip, bent-knee posture with its center of gravity high above and anterior to the hip joints (Figure 6–24). This semi-upright posture is needed to produce an

Wide-knee stance: standing with the feet and knees about as far apart as the hip joints.

Iliac blade: the broad portion of the *ilium,* one of the bones of the pelvis.

Anterior inferior iliac spine: a projection from the ilium that serves as an attachment point for certain thigh muscles and also the iliofemoral ligament.

Ischium: one of the bones of the pelvis.

Sacrum: the part of the vertebral column that articulates with the pelvis and forms the dorsal portion of the pelvic girdle.

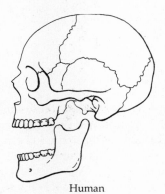
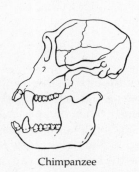

FIGURE 6–21 The ape and human skulls are quite distinct. The chimpanzee has a large jaw with large canines, especially in the male skull shown here. In humans the teeth are smaller, and the canines often project no farther than the other teeth. Humans also show a distinct chin, whereas apes do not. The enlarged braincase of humans brings about a more vertical alignment of the face and jaws. The scale is approximately one-fifth actual size.

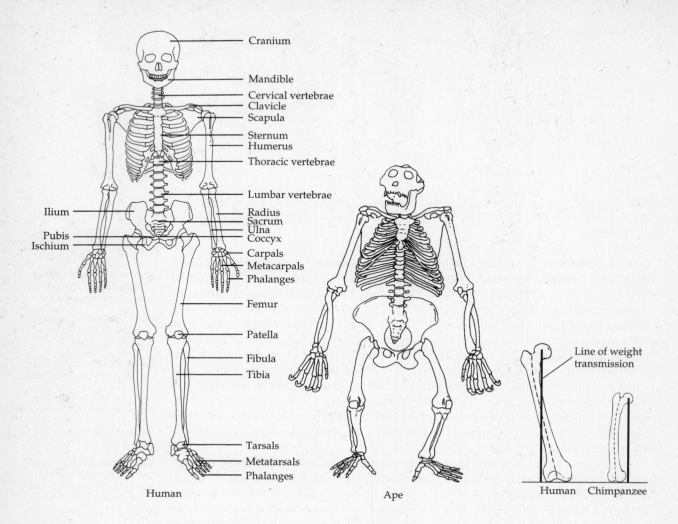

FIGURE 6–22 Humans (left) have evolved a close-knee stance, while bipedal apes (center) show a wide-knee posture. Postural and locomotor differences are reflected in the ape's lack of an angled femoral shaft in contrast to humans, who have one (right).

Hamstrings: muscles of the hips and the back of the thigh; thigh extensors.

angle between the ischium and the femur—an angle that allows the *hamstring muscles* to extend (retract) the thigh—but it is maintained only with considerable muscular effort. When an ape walks, it takes short steps (the knee never passes behind the hip joints) and it balances by swaying its trunk to one side as the opposite leg is swinging forward (Figure 6–25). This "waddle-and-teeter" bipedalism is the best an ape can do, given its anatomy, but it is a most imperfect means of locomotion.

Sciatic notch: a deep indentation of the dorsal edge of the hominid ilium.

In contrast to apes, the human pelvis (Figure 6–23) features (1) a short iliac blade that has been widened and bent posteriorly (as shown by the deep *sciatic notch*); (2) anterior curvature and lateral flaring of the iliac blades to produce a bowl-shaped pelvic girdle; (3) strong enlargement of the anterior inferior iliac

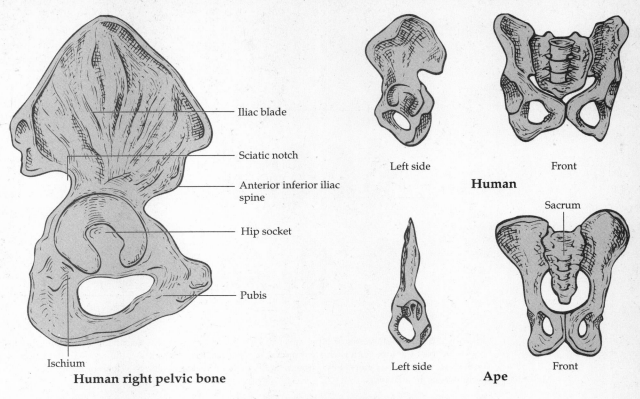

Iliac blade

Sciatic notch

Anterior inferior iliac spine

Hip socket

Pubis

Ischium

Human right pelvic bone

Left side

Front

Human

Sacrum

Left side

Front

Ape

FIGURE 6–23 The right pelvic bone of a human (left) has a broad iliac blade, a deep sciatic notch, and a large anterior inferior iliac spine. The two pelvic bones plus the sacrum form a distinct pelvic bowl in humans (top right), while the iliac blades of an ape show no bowllike curvature (bottom right). Drawings on right are not to scale.

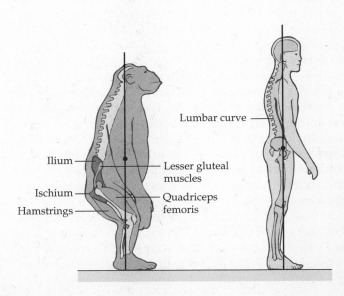

Lumbar curve

Ilium

Lesser gluteal muscles

Ischium

Quadriceps femoris

Hamstrings

FIGURE 6–24 A bipedal ape (left) stands with its feet wide apart and with a bent-hip, bent-knee posture. The ape's center of gravity (see dot) is located high above and anterior to the hip joints. In contrast, a bipedal human (right) has its feet close together, and the center of gravity is located within the pelvic girdle.

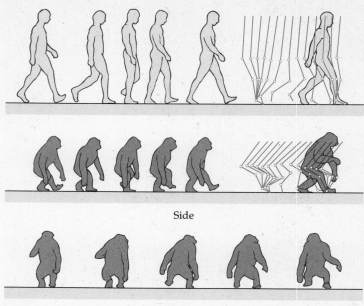

Side

Rear

FIGURE 6–25 Side views of bipedalism in humans and apes reveal that the human knee extends backward past the hips with each step, producing a long stride. In contrast, the ape waddles forward with short steps. A rear view shows how a bipedal ape teeters from side to side in order to balance its weight over the fixed leg.

Lumbar curve: forward curvature of the vertebral column in the lower back that helps bring the hominid trunk over the hip joints.

Gluteus medius and gluteus minimus: muscles of the hip; lateral stabilizers of the pelvis in modern humans.

Iliofemoral ligament: ligament that prevents backward movement of the trunk at the human hip.

Close-knee stance: standing with the feet and knees closer together than the hip joints.

spine; (4) realignment of the ischium relative to the ilium; and (5) a wide sacrum. These evolutionary modifications went a long way toward perfecting bipedal walking. In conjunction with the development of a *lumbar curve* in the back, posterior expansion and bending of the iliac blades brought the human trunk over the hip joints and allowed straightening of the legs, while lowering the center of gravity to a point within the pelvic bowl (Figure 6–24). This greatly increased the energy efficiency of bipedalism and reduced its instability. The evolution of a "pelvic bowl" with broad, flaring walls allowed the lesser gluteal muscles (*gluteus medius* and *gluteus minimus*) to function as powerful lateral stabilizers of the trunk during walking (no more teetering to balance the body and free the swing leg; Figure 6–26). Expansion of the anterior inferior iliac spine facilitated pulling the thigh forward (flexion) and also provided space for humans' large *iliofemoral ligament*, an anatomical feature that stabilizes the trunk against backward movement at the hips (Figure 6–26). And finally, realigning the ischium relative to the ilium resulted in an angle between the ischium and the femur that allows the thigh-extending hamstrings to work well with the body fully upright. This last change, in turn, allowed humans to take nice long strides on knees that swing back past the hips (no more waddling; Figure 6–25).

Two other changes in humans' postcranial anatomy deserve to be mentioned. We evolved a *close-knee stance* that pulled our feet nearer the body's midline, making lateral balancing of the trunk much easier than in wide-kneed apes and producing an angled femoral shaft (Figure 6–22). Additionally, we evolved nondiver-

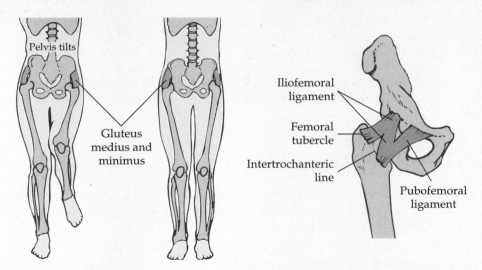

FIGURE 6–26 (Left) The lesser gluteal muscles of humans (gluteus medius and gluteus minimus) provide lateral stabilization of the pelvis over the fixed leg during bipedalism. (Right) A front view of the pelvis and the femur also shows the position of humans' iliofemoral ligament.

gent and nonprehensile big toes that function to propel our bodies forward during bipedal movement.

The pelvic anatomies of living apes and humans reveal two ends of an evolutionary continuum. We can expect the pelvic remains of early hominids to be intermediate between these extremes, with the very first members of our family resembling apes more than people. But the primary criterion for classifying a fossil species as hominid is clear: evidence of habitual bipedal movement. This criterion should be kept firmly in mind as we review the evidence of the beginnings of the hominid family in the next few chapters.

SUMMARY

As currently known, the fossil record indicates that the primate order originated about 60 mya (during the late Paleocene epoch) in Africa. This date is an approximation, however, based on very incomplete evidence, and future discoveries are likely to push the actual point of origin several million years back in time. Despite the uncertainty on dates, the earliest primates can be classified confidently as prosimians—not enormously different from today's lemurs, lorises, and tarsiers. By perhaps 45–50 mya, the ancient prosimians had given rise to the first anthropoids, although whether this occurred in Africa or Asia is hotly debated. By the Eocene-Oligocene boundary (35 million B.P.) the anthropoids were well established. Too primitive to be classified as either monkeys or apes, the early anthropoids nonetheless had such distinctive features of higher primates as bony eye sockets and fused frontal bones. The Oligocene epoch saw anthropoids differentiate into catarrhines and platyrrhines, and by 17–20 mya (the early Miocene), the first hominoids (apes) had evolved in Africa. These ancient apes differed significantly from their modern ape descendants, however. The Miocene apes tended to be generalized quadrupeds, while living apes show strong adaptations for fore-limb-dominated movements, suggesting that habitual suspensory locomotion is a rather recent evolutionary development. Finally, during the late Miocene epoch, the Hominidae—the human family—evolved from an as-yet-undiscovered African ape ancestor. Marked by distinctive adaptations for bipedal locomotion, the early hominids began the evolutionary journey that would culminate in modern humans.

REVIEW QUESTIONS

1. The Plesiadapiformes were once included among the primates. What aspects of plesiadapiform anatomy now convince many anthropologists that these creatures were *not* members of our order?

2. When and where did the suborder of the anthropoids arise? Describe the fossil evidence of the appearance of anthropoids.

3. Compare fossil apes with living apes with regard to postcranial anatomy and locomotor behavior.

4. What do we know about the age, location, identity, and behavior of humans' last ape ancestor?

5. Describe hominids' anatomical adaptations for habitual bipedalism.

POSTSCRIPT

What makes an ape an ape? Or in slightly more stylish form, what is the essence of apeness? Answering this question is easy if we think only of living apes: Apes are big primates with distinctive five-cusped molar teeth (Figure 4–17), relatively large brains, and no tail. Furthermore, their locomotor patterns are distinctly fore-limb-dominated; in the trees they often hang or swing about by their arms, and as adaptations for this sort of movement they have short, stiff backs; long arms; and shoulder and elbow joints that allow a wide range of movement. So far, so good. But as this chapter has shown, the suite of features that characterizes modern apes was not present in its entirety at the beginning of ape evolution—and this creates a terminology problem.

The very earliest catarrhines, such as the Oligocene primate *Aegyptopithecus*, showed a mixture of primitive traits that were sorted out differently in the evolutionary lineages leading to today's monkeys and apes. These early catarrhines are described as *generalized* because they combined certain apelike dental features (including five-cusped molars) with a monkeylike, tail-equipped body that was adapted for arboreal quadrupedalism rather than forelimb suspension. By the mid-Miocene, the Old World monkeys had emerged as a distinct evolutionary family that retained the old pattern of arboreal quadrupedalism and combined it with new dental specializations such as four-cusped, bilophodont molars (Figure 4–17). The emergence of the dentally distinct Old World monkeys left a group of anthropoid "remainders" (*Proconsul* is a good example) that continued to show the primitive combination of five-cusped molars and a body designed for quadrupedalism. For lack of a better term—and because they seem to be generally on or near the evolutionary track toward today's bonobos, chimps, gorillas, orangs, and gibbons—these creatures are commonly called *apes*.

Such "dental apes" with monkeylike bodies existed for a long time. Only hints of suspensory adaptations appear in the known hominoid fossils, even those from the latest Miocene. Nonetheless, since all living apes show forelimb-dominated locomotion, and human anatomy indicates descent from a hanging-swinging ancestor, we must conclude that at some point (or points) the apes showed a general shift from arboreal quadrupedalism to suspensory movement. Precisely when and where this occurred is unknown at present. Given the widely spaced divergence times for the modern ape lineages (perhaps 18 mya for the gibbon line, 13 mya for orangutans, and 5–7 mya for the hominid-panid split), it appears that suspensory locomotion may have evolved independently more than once. Only after the evolution of arboreal suspension, however, would the modern meaning of the term *ape* have been applicable. So what makes an ape an ape? As with so much else in science, it depends to a great extent on the definitions we choose to adopt. But it is also very important to remember that, because of the continuity in the evolution of lineages, the definition of grade boundaries (in this case the attainment of the ape grade), which are never clean in nature, will always present difficulties.

CHAPTER 6 TIMELINE

	YEARS B.P.	FOSSIL RECORD	PRIMATES
Cro-Magnon, Neandertal, and *Homo erectus*	Pleistocene →		*Homo*
CENOZOIC	2 million —	Early *Homo*	
Early prosimians	Pliocene →	*Paranthropus*	
65 MILLION	5 million —	*Australopithecus*	Australopithecines
Basic insectivores		Earliest *Australopithecus*?	
		Sivapithecus in Asia and Europe	
		Dryopithecus in Asia	
MESOZOIC	Miocene →	*Dryopithecus* in Europe	
		Proconsul in Africa	
First mammals			Apes
225 MILLION	25 million —		
	Oligocene →		Catarrhines and platyrrhines
	35 million —	*Propliopithecus* and *Aegyptopithecus* at Fayum	
		Oligopithecines in Africa	
		Amphipithecus and *Pondaugia* in Burma	
PALEOZOIC			Early prosimians
	Eocene →	*Eosimias* in China	
		Algeripithecus in Algeria	
First vertebrates	58 million —		
		Altiatlasius in Morocco	First primates
570 MILLION	Paleocene →		
PRECAMBRIAN	65 million —		

BACK BEYOND THE APES

The time scale of primate evolution is immense. The first half of the 60 million years of primate history was the age of the prosimians, which occupied much of the Old and New Worlds.

By 17–20 million years ago the apes were established in Africa, and for this reason we too find our origin on this continent. By about 15 million years ago the apes had spread into Eurasia.

CHAPTER
7

The Transvaal Hominids

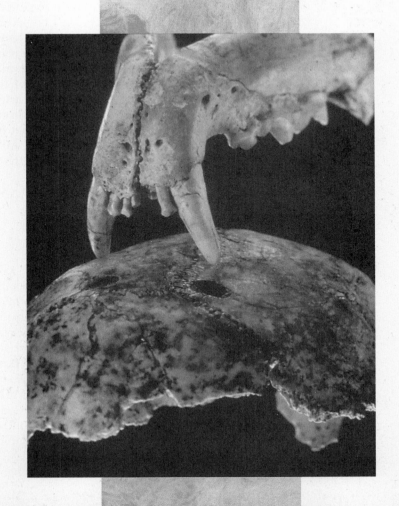

In each great region of the world the living mammals are closely related to the extinct species of the same region. It is, therefore, probable that Africa was formerly inhabited by extinct apes closely allied to the gorilla and chimpanzee; and as these two species are now man's nearest allies, it is somewhat more probable that our early progenitors lived on the African continent than elsewhere.

CHARLES DARWIN, 1809–1882. *The Descent of Man.*

OVERVIEW

The human family—the family Hominidae—branched off from ape stock some 5 to 7 million years ago (mya). All members of that family, living and fossil, are referred to as *hominids*, and all hominids can be placed in one of two subfamilies: Australopithecinae (containing the genera *Australopithecus* and *Paranthropus*) and Homininae (containing the genus *Homo*). The australopithecine subfamily was the earliest to evolve, and the first fossil evidence of these ancient bipeds was discovered in South Africa by Raymond Dart in 1925. Dart named his discovery *Australopithecus africanus* and claimed that it was intermediate between modern apes and humans. Dart's claims were largely dismissed by the scientific community until additional, and more complete, australopithecine materials were discovered by Robert Broom in the 1930s. Included in the new finds were the fossils of a more rugged species of australopithecine equipped with massive grinding teeth. Broom named this new creature *Paranthropus robustus*. Today the hominid status of the australopithecines is firmly established, and it is known that they roamed South Africa from 3 million years B.P. to just a million years ago. Although the issue is somewhat controversial, there appears to be no solid proof that the South African australopithecines manufactured stone tools.

DART'S DISCOVERY OF THE TAUNG SKULL (1924)

The importance of bipedalism cannot be overestimated. Bipedalism is much more than a mere rearing up and running about. As we have seen, apes and monkeys have all sorts of structural handicaps that hamper them in this respect; they stand with knees bent, unable to extend their legs fully, and they walk on the sides of their feet. They can move on two legs and sometimes do for short distances, but they are not made for it. Humans, however, cannot function properly in any other way. Somehow, somewhere, in the late Miocene or early Pliocene, the adaptations of bipedalism made their appearance in at least one kind of primate.

The first tangible evidence that a two-legged primate existed in the distant past came from an unexpected place, the Transvaal region of South Africa. Raymond Dart (1893–1988), professor of anatomy at the University of the Witwatersrand in Johannesburg, South Africa, encouraged his students to send him rock fragments that contained fossils. In 1924 a student brought him a fossil baboon skull that had

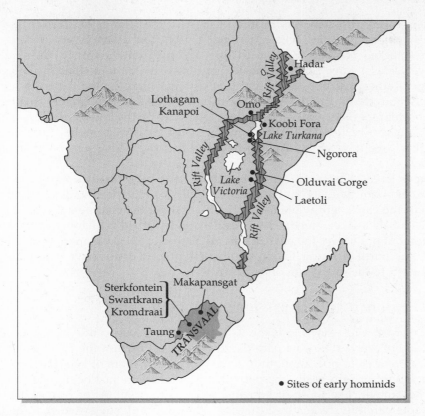

FIGURE 7–1   The earliest knowledge of australopithecines came from the Transvaal in South Africa. At a number of sites in this area, fossils were preserved in caves and hollows in the dolomite bedrock. Although their absolute age is not accurately known, they are broadly dated between 3 and 1 million years B.P.

come from a limestone quarry at a place named Taung, 200 miles (320 km) from Johannesburg (see Figure 7–1). Hoping to obtain more fossils, particularly another baboon skull, Dart persuaded the quarry owner to save bone-bearing rocks, and in due course he was sent two boxes of broken rock containing fossils.

Dart found nothing of great interest in the first box, but his eye hit on something very strange in the second. On the top of the heap lay not a skull, but the next best thing to it: an oddly shaped rounded piece of rock that appeared to be the mold of the inside of a skull. Scarcely allowing himself to think what this might mean, Dart went through the rest of the box and found another piece of rock with a curved depression into which this mold fitted: part of the skull itself. In this second rock Dart could dimly perceive the outline of a broken piece of skull and the back of a lower jaw. He was looking from the rear at the inside of something's, or somebody's, head.

An *endocast* (a fossilized cast of the interior of a skull) of any species of primate would have been a notable discovery, but one look at this antique fragment sent Dart's mind racing. Here was no fossil baboon. The animal's brain capacity appeared to be three times larger than an ancient baboon's, and perhaps even larger than a modern adult chimpanzee's. The exciting thought struck Dart that he might be holding in his hands the "missing link" between ape and human.

Endocast: a fossilized cast of the interior of a skull; may reveal much about brain size and shape.

Dart's first problem was to free the rest of the strange skull from the surrounding stone. Working with a hammer, chisels, and a sharpened knitting needle, he "pecked, scraped and levered" bits of stone from the front of the skull and the eye sockets. After days of painstaking dissection, an incredible face began to emerge. Rather than the long projecting jaw and large canine teeth that clearly identify both existing and fossil baboons, this face had the relatively smaller jaw and shorter face of an ape; yet it was not overhung by the low brow of an ape, but surmounted by a forehead. From then on, Dart lay awake nights "in a fever of thoughts" about what kind of ape might have lived long ago on that grassy plateau.

Apes lived in tropical forests, but there have been no such forests in South Africa for more than 100 million years. While ice advanced and retreated over much of the earth, and while mountains rose along the continental coasts, South Africa had always remained a dry, relatively undisturbed veld, much as it is today. Throughout prehistory the nearest natural habitat of apes was more than 2,000 mi (3,200 km) north of Taung. Could some different kind of ape have found a way to adapt itself to life in an arid, open land?

The Evidence and Dart's Interpretation

Dart continued his exacting labor with the baffling fossil until, on the seventy-third day of work, the stone parted and he saw before him the face and most of the skull of a child now thought to have died at 3–4 years of age (Figure 7–2). It had a full set of milk teeth; the permanent molars were just beginning to erupt; and the canines, like those of humans, were quite small. After Dart studied his find more carefully, he realized that the set of the skull suggested that the child had walked upright. One thing that made him feel sure he was dealing with a true bipedal creature was the position of the *foramen magnum,* the large hole through which the spinal cord passes into the skull on its way to the brain. In apes and monkeys the foramen magnum is near the back of the skull, reflecting the sloping position of the spinal column in quadrupedal posture. But in the Taung skull it faced almost directly downward (Figure 7–3): the Taung child had carried its head over its spine like a sphere balanced on the top of a pole. Whatever verdict the scientific establishment would eventually pass on the Taung child, Dart was certain that the creature had stood erect.

Foramen magnum: large opening in the cranial base, through which the spinal cord passes to the brain.

All previous discoveries of human predecessors were then thought to be authentic, if early, human beings, including Neandertal man and Java man. All are now classified as *Homo* despite certain primitive features. The child's face before Dart seemed the reverse: an ape with human features. It could not possibly be a human. It was too primitive, too small-brained. A prehuman, then, a link with the ape past? Taking a deep breath, Dart announced to the world in 1925 that he had found a human ancestor that was not yet human. He gave it the formidable name of *Australopithecus africanus* (from *australis,* "southern," and *pithekos,* "ape"): African southern ape.

Australopithecus africanus: gracile australopithecine species that inhabited South Africa 3.0–2.5 mya.

Because he was so confident of the significance of his find, Dart publicized his momentous news in record time. Less than four months after the skull had come into his hands, he wrote a full scientific report for the February 7, 1925, issue of the British scientific journal *Nature.* His report included the provocative statement, "The specimen is of importance because it exhibits an extinct race of apes intermediate between living anthropoids and man . . . a creature well advanced beyond modern anthropoids in just those characters, facial and cerebral, which

FIGURE 7-2   In 1924 Raymond Dart startled the anthropological world by his discovery of a small fossil skull from a quarry at Taung in South Africa. (The height of the skull and jaw is about 5 in. or 13 cm.) The following year he named the Taung specimen *Australopithecus africanus* and boldly declared it to be a human ancestor. His claim was derided, but finds made many years later proved that his fossil was indeed hominid.

are to be anticipated in an extinct link between man and his simian ancestor." That day, in South Africa and around the world, the headlines proclaimed that the missing link had been found. It was also the first link in a long chain of discoveries that would establish Africa as the place of origin of humankind.

Dart's Claims Dismissed

Dart's report was intensely interesting to a number of scientists in Europe, not so much for the human attributes he claimed for the Taung creature as for the inexplicable presence of an ape so far south. The general conclusion was that this was a young specimen of an ancient chimpanzeelike or gorillalike species, but how it had wandered where no ape had ever before been known to go was extremely puzzling. As a result, Dart's claims about the Taung child had to endure a long period of skepticism.

This suspicion may seem strange. After all, anthropologists spend their lives looking for increasingly primitive, ever more apelike fossils. Why are they so reluctant to recognize one when it turns up? There are numerous reasons. For one, there are many false alarms. If this book were to catalog all the mistaken claims

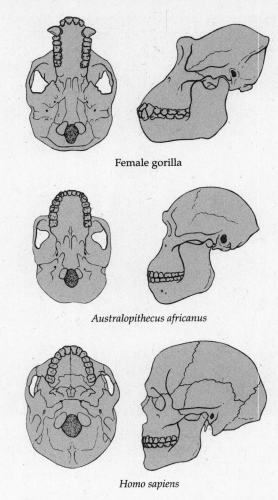

Female gorilla

Australopithecus africanus

Homo sapiens

FIGURE 7–3 Improvement in the balance of the head during human evolution has involved movement of the occipital condyles and the associated foramen magnum (shown stippled) forward. (The occipital condyles are the bearing surfaces of the skull on the uppermost vertebra—the atlas; the foramen magnum is the hole in the base of the skull through which the spinal cord passes.) In this important characteristic of the skull base, *Australopithecus* is intermediate between apes (here a gorilla [top] is illustrated) and modern humans (bottom). Scale is approximately one-fifth actual size.

about hominid fossils made by laity and experts alike, it would have to be far longer than it is. At the time that Dart discovered the Taung skull, the fraudulent Piltdown skull (Chapter 10) represented the generally held concept of our early ancestors. It suggested that early humans already had large brains but still had apelike faces—a concept that satisfies modern human vanity, with its emphasis on the special quality of the human intellect. Dart's fossil was not so agreeable. It suggested the opposite; that face and teeth began to become recognizably human while the brain was still very small. And so anthropologists and anatomists were cautious, even prejudiced, and attacks on Dart were not long in coming. Dart's child, several critics suggested, was only "the distorted skull of a chimpanzee." There may also have been jealousy that some remote colonial professor, rather

FIGURE 7–4 Robert Broom was a passionate fossil hunter and distinguished paleontologist. He kept working until his death at age 85.

than a distinguished European, had made what was surely to become the greatest discovery of the age. Taung became something of a byword; it was ridiculed in songs and on music-hall stages.

Despite the criticism, Dart was encouraged by a warm congratulatory letter from Robert Broom (1866–1951), a Scottish physician who had hunted fossils, particularly fossils of mammallike reptiles, in many parts of South Africa (see Figure 7–4). Two weeks after the letter arrived, Broom himself appeared at Dart's laboratory. He spent a weekend studying the Taung child intensively and became convinced that, as "a connecting link between the higher apes and one of the lowest human types," it was the most important fossil discovered up to that time. He said so firmly in an article in *Nature*. After the first flare-up of attention, however, Dart's child was either forgotten or dismissed by most scientists. Nonetheless, Dart and Broom continued to study the skull.

Dentition of Taung

For his part, Dart worked away at the skull almost daily for more than four years. In 1929 he succeeded in separating the upper and lower jaws, which had been cemented together in a rock-hard mass of breccia (a mixture of sand, soil, and pebbles cemented by lime) that enclosed them. For the first time he could examine the entire pattern of the teeth and get a good look at their grinding surfaces.

What he found strengthened his case that the fossil was clearly not an ape or a baboon. In apes, as we have seen (Chapter 6), the front teeth are large, because they are used for threat and for tearing up the tough vegetable matter that forms much of an ape's diet. Ape canines, in particular, are so large that there must be spaces (diastemata) between the teeth of the upper jaw to accommodate the lower canines when the jaw is closed (Figure 7–5). At the same time, apes' jaws are relatively longer than humans' jaws, and heavier, too, and the muscles needed to move them are more massive. The Taung child, although a young individual and therefore lacking typical adult characters, could be judged to be distinctly more humanlike than apelike in all these characteristics. Its nicely curved jaw was shorter than a young ape's and more lightly made. Its canines and incisors were relatively small and set closely together. In fact, though the molars were larger than is now normal, most of the teeth could have belonged to a child of today (Figure 7–6).

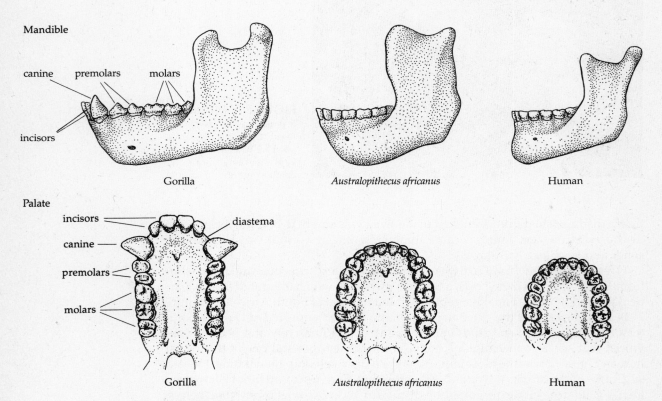

FIGURE 7–5   These drawings show a lateral view of the mandibles (lower jaws) and the palates (upper jaws) of a gorilla, an adult *Australopithecus africanus*, and a modern human. The striking difference in the size and form of the canine teeth is clear, and in the gorilla palate we can see the gaps or diastemata, into which the lower canines fit on each side. The difference in the shape of the dental arcade in ape and hominid is also striking. The lateral view also shows distinct tooth wear: the ape teeth are used to crush and tear; the hominid teeth are used to crush and grind, which causes the typical flat wear of the hominid dentition. The drawings are not to scale.

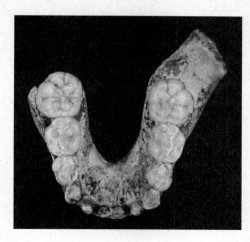

FIGURE 7–6 Lower dentition of the Taung child (*Australopithecus africanus*). The largest teeth are the first permanent molars.

In the minds of Dart and Broom, any lingering doubts about the hominid nature of the creature vanished; but skeptics, they suspected, would take more convincing. What was needed was an adult skull, and also some legs or pelvic bones, to support the claim of erect posture that the position of the foramen magnum suggested. Broom was determined to find this evidence, but it was not until the 1930s that he was free to begin a serious search.

DISCOVERIES OF ROBERT BROOM

The way was opened when Broom became curator of vertebrate paleontology at the Transvaal Museum in Pretoria. For the next year and a half, he was occupied with digging out, describing, and naming 44 new fossil species of reptiles. He also unearthed a baboon jaw that at first appeared to be *Australopithecus*. It was not, but the publicity it engendered led two of Dart's students to tell Broom about some small skulls they had found in a quarry at Sterkfontein, a village not far from Pretoria (Figure 7–1).

A Skull from Sterkfontein (1936)

Ever since the first mining camps were opened during the South African gold rush of 1886, the people of the Sterkfontein area had been picking up fossilized remains of baboons, monkeys, and perhaps, unknowingly, hominids. By some extraordinary quirk of fate, the limeworks at Sterkfontein had even issued a little guidebook: "Come to Sterkfontein and Find the Missing Link." When Broom first visited the quarry, the manager, who had worked at Taung and knew about the *Australopithecus* child's skull, promised Broom that he would keep a sharp lookout for anything resembling the skull of a hominid.

When Broom returned on August 7, 1936, the manager asked, "Is this what you're after?" and handed him two-thirds of a superb brain cast, which had been blasted out only that morning. Broom anxiously dug into the debris to find the skull that had served as the mold. Though he worked until dark, he found nothing. The next day, as he sorted the piles of breccia, he recovered not only both sides of the upper jaw, but also fragments of the braincase. When the fragments were pieced together, Broom had parts of the skull of an adult *Australopithecus*.

Paranthropus robustus at Kromdraai

For three years Broom, now in his 70s, continued to visit his fossil gold mine. One June day in 1938, the quarry manager met Broom and handed him an upper jaw with one molar in place. He had obtained it from a schoolboy who lived on a farm at Kromdraai, less than a mile away. Broom found the boy, who responded to Broom's first questions by pulling out of his pocket "four of the most wonderful teeth ever seen in the world's history." The boy also gave Broom a piece of a lower jaw. During the next two days, Broom and the boy sifted earth and found a number of scraps of bone and teeth. When the pieces were put together, Broom had most of another skull, though this one was different: the face was flatter than that of the Sterkfontein *Australopithecus*, the jaw was heavier, and, though the incisors and canines were still small, the molars were larger and less human.

When the newest findings were published, the situation seemed even more confused. The Kromdraai adult differed so markedly from both the Taung child and the Sterkfontein adult that it appeared increasingly likely to Broom that there were two species of early hominids in South Africa: the smaller, more slender "gracile" type with smaller molars that Dart had named *Australopithecus africanus*, and the heavy-jawed "robust" Kromdraai type with extremely large molars. Broom established a new genus and species for the Kromdraai type: *Paranthropus robustus*, or "robust near-man."

Broom's action in setting up a new genus for the Kromdraai fossils did not sit well with his paleontological colleagues, who thought he was going too far. Despite the apparent differences between the Kromdraai and Sterkfontein hominids in body size, muscularity, and dental proportions, many scientists thought the new genus was uncalled for. "Of course the critics did not know the whole of the facts," said Broom. "When one has jealous opponents one does not let them know everything." What he had not disclosed was that the fossils of animals found with the Kromdraai fossil were less archaic than the ones excavated with *Australopithecus africanus* and thus represented a different period. Fossil horses abounded at Kromdraai; none apparently occurred at Sterkfontein, only 1 mi (1.6 km) away. Many other fossil animal species were not shared by the two sites. Also, the breccia itself in which the Kromdraai creature lay seemed to be of a different age from that which had held *Australopithecus africanus*. If the sites were occupied at various times—from several million to a half million years ago—then each might well have sustained a different species of hominid. Broom came to the conclusion that some of his *P. robustus* finds were as much as a million years younger than the Sterkfontein fossils—and this is still considered a more-or-less correct interpretation. Today, the controversy over generic names—*Australopithecus* versus *Paranthropus*—continues unabated. For a variety of reasons (see the Postscript at the chapter's end), we agree with Broom's original naming system and recognize two genera of early hominids: *Paranthropus* (including *P. robustus* and other species described later) and *Australopithecus* (including *A. africanus* from South Africa and two East African forms, *A. afarensis* and *A. ramidus*, the last

Paranthropus robustus: robust australopithecine species that lived in South Africa 2.0–1.0 mya; formerly *Australopithecus robustus*.

Australopithecus: a genus of the family Hominidae, subfamily Australopithecinae; contains three species: *A. africanus, A. afarensis,* and (provisionally) *A. ramidus.*

Paranthropus: a genus of the family Hominidae, subfamily Australopithecinae; contains three species: *P. robustus, P. boisei,* and *P. aethiopicus.*

Table 7–1 HOMINID TAXONOMY

FAMILY HOMINIDAE (COMMON NAME: HOMINIDS)

Subfamily Australopithecinae (Common name: australopithecines)

   Genus *Australopithecus*
      Species   *Australopithecus ramidus* (provisional)
                                                    Australopithecus afarensis
                                                    Australopithecus africanus

   Genus *Paranthropus*
      Species   *Paranthropus aethiopicus*
                                                    Paranthropus boisei
                                                    Paranthropus robustus

Subfamily Homininae (Common name: hominines)

   Genus *Homo*
      Species   *Homo rudolfensis*
                                                    Homo habilis
                                                    Homo erectus
                                                    Homo sapiens

Homo: a genus of the family Hominidae, subfamily Homininae; contains at least four species: *H. habilis, H. rudolfensis, H. erectus,* and *H. sapiens.*

included provisionally). Members of both genera are commonly referred to as *australopithecines.* A modern classification of living and fossil hominids is shown in Table 7–1.

Broom continued to search, and in due course he had more robust fossils to work with, having struck a rich find in a cave at Swartkrans (Figures 7–7 and 7–8) just across the valley from Sterkfontein. But the more new robust material he found, the more puzzled he became. Of the two types of hominid, *Paranthropus robustus,* the larger and more recent, seemed somehow the more primitive. Although a million years closer to us, it was not more humanlike, nor was it more apelike (Figure 7–9). Its jaws and molars were massive, less like those of modern humans than were the jaws and molars of *A. africanus.* These grinding teeth were huge in proportion to the size of the front teeth, for the canines were very small. Also, on its skull *P. robustus* had a bony ridge or crest, called a *sagittal crest,* to anchor large jaw muscles. These characteristics suggested that the creature was a vegetarian, and chewed up large quantities of tough vegetable food, as a gorilla does today.

Could the younger, robust type be the human ancestor? That just did not make sense. How could a less human hominid occur so much later than a more human one? Assigning *P. robustus* a role in human ancestry raised awkward problems. For one thing, an animal does not get specialized jaw equipment—a heavy jaw, oversized grinding teeth, and a bony ridge on its skull—overnight. It could be assumed that *P. robustus* had been following an evolutionary course toward a vegetarian life for a long time. Therefore the most reasonable expectation would be that the creature would continue to do so. Evolution does not work capriciously or fast. It would be much more logical to assume that, since humans were known to have eaten all sorts of things (to be omnivores) for at least three-quarters of a million years, they probably had done so for a much longer time.

Sagittal crest: a ridge of bone running front to rear along the midline of the skull; serves to attach certain jaw muscles. A *sagittal keel* is a slight elevation of the bone in the same location.

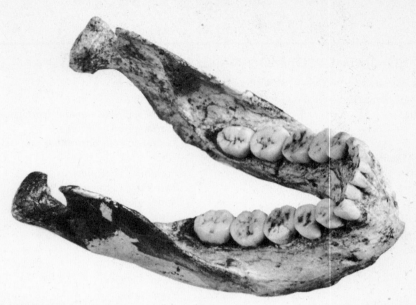

FIGURE 7–7   The almost perfect jaw of *Paranthropus robustus* found at Swartkrans. Note the huge molars and premolars and the diminutive front teeth that characterize the robust genus. This photograph is approximately three-quarters actual size.

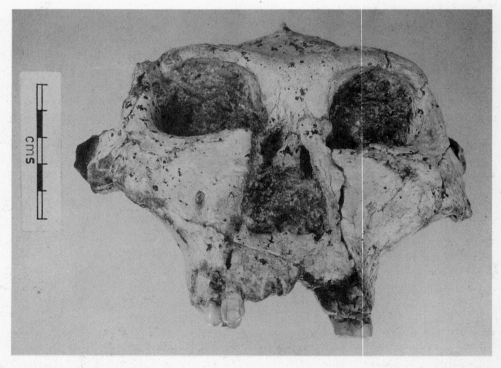

FIGURE 7–8   A skull of *Paranthropus robustus* from Swartkrans (museum catalog number SK48). Note the broad face, the large zygomatic arches, and the sagittal crest.

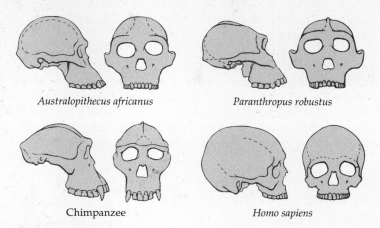

Australopithecus africanus   Paranthropus robustus

Chimpanzee   Homo sapiens

FIGURE 7–9   The skulls of two australopithecine species are here compared with those of a chimpanzee and a modern human. Notice the absence of the sagittal crest in *A. africanus* and its presence in *Paranthropus*. The large ape canine is not found in either australopithecine species. In the human specimen, notice the increase in the relative size of the braincase and the relatively smaller jaws. The pictures are not drawn to the same scale.

Age of *Australopithecus africanus*

Broom set out to calculate the age of *Australopithecus africanus*, a task that was not easy. Accurate dating is impossible in South Africa because of the way the fossils were obtained and, more important, because ofthe unique geologic structure of the area. Most South African finds were made in lime-cemented breccia that had filled in ancient caves. This material had to be removed from quarries by blasting, which, of course, destroyed the stratigraphic pattern. In addition, because of the distinctive geology of South Africa, with no volcanic activity to deposit datable layers of ash, whatever stratigraphic clues could be discovered could not be matched with better-known and better-dated layers in other parts of the world. About the best Broom could do was to carefully examine the animal fossils associated with the *Australopithecus* remains. To Broom's frustration, not only were all the large mammals extinct, but they also were not known in any other place; there was nothing he could compare them with. The very fact of their extinction suggested, however, that they must have been at least a million years old, possibly much older. Making a bold guess, Broom announced that *Australopithecus africanus* was probably 2 million years old, of the Pliocene epoch.

His choice of 2 million years turned out to be more extraordinarily shrewd than it was shaky. For the moment, however, his announcement was greeted by the scientific community with derision. What bothered other scientists who examined the fossils or read about them was not the jaws but the rest of the head. They could not believe that a human ancestor with a brain scarcely bigger than a chimpanzee's had been running around on two legs in South Africa 2 million years ago.

As this creature was estimated to be more than twice as old as any other known hominid, it did not seem remarkable to Dart or Broom that this peculiar mixture of ape and human characteristics should exist in a fossil. Two million years, they reasoned, might bring one pretty close to a common ancestor for humans and apes. That ancestor could well display a confusing and unexpected mingling of characteristics.

World War II came and went, and still *Australopithecus* was scarcely recognized in the scientific world. This was partly because Dart was an anatomist and all but unknown to the paleoanthropological establishment, all of whose brightest stars were in the United States, England, France, and Germany; it was also partly because the brains of these South African fossil creatures just were not big enough to satisfy other scientists prejudiced by the Piltdown skull (see Chapter 10). Perhaps *Australopithecus* was simply an aberrant chimpanzee.

Further Discoveries at Sterkfontein (1947)

Meanwhile fossil evidence continued to accumulate. In 1947, soon after the end of the war, Broom resumed working at Sterkfontein. One day a blast in some unpromising cave debris revealed the first of a series of important discoveries. When the smoke cleared away, the upper half of a perfect skull (Figure 7–10) sparkled brilliantly in the sunlight. Lime crystals encrusting its inner surface caught and reflected the light like diamonds. The lower half of the skull lay embedded in a block of stone that had broken away. The glittering skull was believed to be that of an adult female. Her jaw protruded and her forehead was low, but to the trained eye there was an unmistakable quality of humanness about her. Her cranial capacity was 485 cc (see Box 7–1). Her discovery was fol-

FIGURE 7–10   The magnificent skull of *Australopithecus africanus* found at Sterkfontein by Robert Broom in 1947. Although the teeth and jawbone are missing, the skull is otherwise complete and undistorted—a rare find. The photograph is approximately one-half actual size.

lowed by other important finds (Figures 7–11 and 7–12): first, a male jaw with an intact canine tooth worn level with the other teeth, as human canines are, and then, in August 1947, a nearly perfect female pelvis. This was, after the skull, the most important discovery. There was no doubt that it had belonged to a creature that had walked and run upright, much as we do, although given the

BOX 7–1
CHARACTERISTICS OF THE SOUTH AFRICAN AUSTRALOPITHECINAE[a]

Trait	Australopithecus africanus	Paranthropus robustus
Height	F: 3.8 ft (115 cm) M: 4.5 ft (138 cm) (F is 83% of M)	F: 3.6 ft (110 cm) M: 4.3 ft (132 cm) (F is 83% of M)
Weight	F: 55–66 lb (25–30 kg) M: 90–132 lb (41–60 kg) (F about 54% of M)	F: 71–88 lb (32–40 kg) M: 88–176 lb (40–80 kg) (F about 60% of M)
Brain size (sexes combined)	445 cc mean (405–500 cc range)	530 cc mean (range unknown)
Cranium	Prognathic face; lacks sagittal crest; low, flat forehead; low-vaulted braincase; lacks flexure (arching) of cranial base[b]	Face is wide, flattish, and "dished"; sagittal crest; low, flat forehead; low-vaulted braincase; some flexure (arching) of cranial base[b]
Dentition	Parabolic toothrow; short, incisorlike canines; no diastemata; lower P3s have two cusps; smaller grinding teeth than P. robustus	Parabolic toothrow; short, incisorlike canines; small anterior teeth; no diastemata; lower P3s have two or more cusps; very large grinding teeth
Diet	Mostly fruits and leaves?	Harder, tougher items than A. africanus (more nuts? gritty tubers?)
Limbs	Longer arms and shorter legs than modern humans	Longer arms and shorter legs than modern humans
Pelvis	Short, broad ilia; pelvic bowl nearly complete; short ischial shafts realigned in modern manner; pelvis wide between hip joints	Short, broad ilia; weak iliofemoral ligaments(?); shortening of ischial shaft(?); pelvis wide between hip joints
Locomotion	Bipedalism (swaying gait?)	Bipedalism (swaying gait?)
Known dates (million years B.P.)	3.0–2.5	2.0–1.0

[a]Mean values for height, weight, and brain size are sometimes based on small samples and may change with additional fossil discoveries.
[b]A fully flexed (arched) cranial base suggests the presence of the throat anatomy that allows modern speech (see Chapter 13).

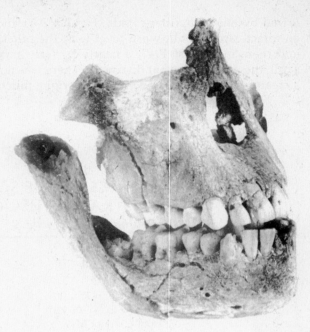

FIGURE 7–11 These beautifully preserved jaws were found in 1949 at Sterkfontein by John Robinson, Broom's successor as curator at the Transvaal museum. This specimen has unusually large canine teeth for *Australopithecus africanus*.

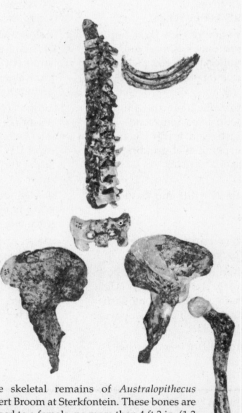

FIGURE 7–12 The skeletal remains of *Australopithecus africanus* found by Robert Broom at Sterkfontein. These bones are believed to have belonged to a female, no more than 4 ft 3 in. (1.3 m) tall. The pelvic bones were of exceptional importance in proving that *Australopithecus* was bipedal, as Dart had claimed in 1925. The photograph is approximately one-quarter actual size.

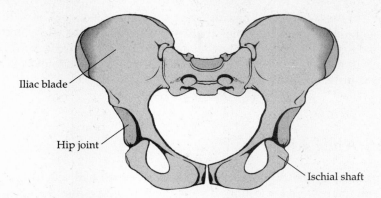

Iliac blade

Hip joint

Ischial shaft

FIGURE 7–13   The restored pelvic girdle of *Australopithecus africanus* from Sterkfontein. The wide pelvis has short, broad iliac blades; forwardly curved ilia producing a nearly complete bowl; and short ischial shafts that have been realigned in the modern manner. It is clearly the pelvis of a biped. Not drawn to scale.

width of its pelvis, it probably swayed laterally a little for balance as it moved. Other fragments of pelvis and femur confirmed bipedalism many times over (Figure 7–13).

Assessing *Australopithecus* and *Paranthropus*

By 1949 the remains of more than 30 gracile and robust individuals had been recovered from the South African caves, and Wilfrid Le Gros Clark, professor of anatomy at Oxford University, undertook an impartial, definitive study. He studied the South African fossils and compared them in every detail of shape and structure with a series of skulls and skeletons of modern apes. His verdict was unqualified:

> It is evident that in some respects they [the australopithecines] were definitely ape-like creatures, with small brains and large jaws. But in the details of the construction of the skull, in their dental morphology, and in their limb bones, the simian features are combined with a number of characters in which they differ from recent or fossil apes and at the same time approximate quite markedly to the *Hominidae*. All those who have had the opportunity of examining the original material are agreed on these hominid characters: the real issue to be decided is the question of their evolutionary and taxonomic significance.

By the mid-1950s a total of five sites had yielded several dozens of individuals of both *Australopithecus africanus* and *Paranthropus robustus*. The growing fossil record confirmed Broom and his assistant, J. T. Robinson, in their certainty that they were dealing with two quite different creatures (Table 7–1). Furthermore, another South African, C. K. Brain, had made detailed studies of the sediments at the various sites, and his findings had begun to produce more evidence of the relative age of the two types. The smaller, *A. africanus,* specimens were invariably more ancient, and at the site of Makapansgat, which Dart had excavated in 1947, they seemed to evolve toward somewhat larger forms. By contrast, the robust type was always of more recent date. It seemed that throughout its known existence it had evolved little, or not at all.

FOSSILS AND ARTIFACTS

Which, if either, of the two South African fossil types had led to humans still remained an unanswered question. If stone tools could be found associated with either type, some light might be shed on the matter.

Australopithecus at Makapansgat

At first, Dart and Broom were preoccupied with the fossils. The australopithecines were such ancient and controversial characters that for a number of years after their discovery the argument was less over whether they were or were not tool users than over whether they were or were not apes. In 1947, after 18 years of concentrating on his work in anatomy at the University of Witwatersrand, Dart returned to the search for "dawn man." He analyzed thousands of fossilized animal bones associated with further remains of gracile *Australopithecus* that had been found in cave deposits 200 mi (320 km) to the north of Sterkfontein, at Makapansgat (Figure 7–14). He called the collection an *osteodontokeratic culture* (meaning a culture of bone, tooth, and horn). His arguments, though ingenious, were not widely accepted. Today it seems clear that these extensive deposits were not of tools but of bones collected and gnawed by carnivores or, surprisingly, by porcupines (which are vegetarian rodents). The study of the origin and formation of assemblages of fossils such as these is termed *taphonomy.* It is, as we shall see, a branch of paleontology which has proved of immense value in understanding prehistoric environments and early hominid behavior (see Table 1–1).

The deposits at Makapansgat are of interest and importance, however, because they contain the oldest *A. africanus* fossils from South Africa, dating, according to Elizabeth Vrba, from about 3 mya. It would appear that they were the stem population from which the other groups of South African *Australopithecus* may have evolved.

Broom sought other clues, other cultural objects essential to hominid status. For years, he and his colleagues hunted for stone tools that might be associated with either the robust or the smaller, gracile hominids. For years they found none. Then, in 1953, two years after Broom's death, some simple pebble tools were discovered on a terrace in the Vaal valley, which had been formed during what was thought to be the same dry period in which the hominids had lived; the tools were fist-sized pieces of stone from which a few chips had been removed. At the time it seemed impossible to most archaeologists that they could have been made by *Australopithecus,* whose brain was no larger than that of a modern ape, and so the question of tools continued to haunt paleoanthropologists.

Osteodontokeratic culture: the culture of bone, tooth, and horn tools hypothesized by Raymond Dart for *A. africanus;* now largely dismissed.

Taphonomy: scientific study of the conditions under which objects are preserved as fossils.

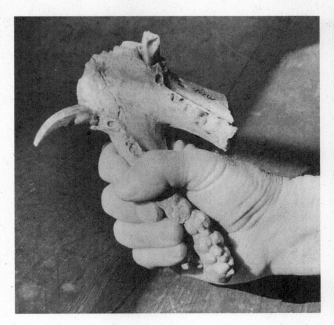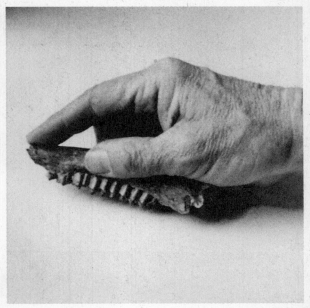

FIGURE 7–14 Raymond Dart firmly believed that *Australopithecus africanus* used animal bones as a wide variety of tools. He demonstrates a pick (left) and a scraper (right).

Pebble Tools at Sterkfontein

But in 1957, once again new evidence was discovered. Working close by the cave at Sterkfontein that was yielding up a gratifying supply of *A. africanus* remains, Broom's successor, J. T. Robinson, and an archaeologist, Revil Mason, dug into a layer of red-brown breccia and found several hominid teeth and nearly 300 pebble tools. To the untrained eye these objects would have looked like naturally fractured stone, but close examination showed that chips had been flaked off two sides; the head of the stone was left round (Figure 7–15). A hammer stone held in the hand and guided by understanding had shaped these pebbles to cut, scrape, and crush. Not only their shape and the fact that they had been worked indicated that these were tools, but their location also did. The Sterkfontein cave is near the top of a hill where stones of that kind do not occur naturally, but such stones are common in the valley about half a mile (0.8 km) away. Because stones do not climb hills unaided, they must have been carried to the site of the cave.

For 15 years the situation was not entirely clear. The breccia that had yielded the teeth and stone tools was believed to be somewhat more recent than that which had yielded the skulls and teeth of *Australopithecus africanus*, but there were not enough teeth from the breccia containing tools to permit exact identification of the teeth with *Australopithecus* or with later hominids. Since 1966 a very thorough and painstaking excavation has been carried out by Phillip Tobias, Dart's successor as professor of anatomy at the University of Witwatersrand, and his assistant, Alun Hughes. This work has made it clear that the teeth and the stone tools excavated by Robinson and Mason come from a more recent period

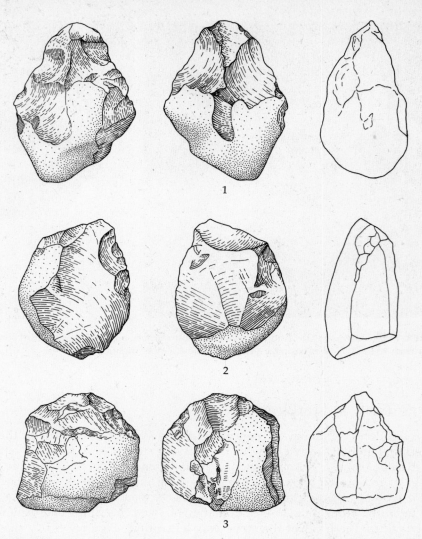

FIGURE 7–15   These primitive stone choppers from Sterkfontein were the first to be discovered in association with hominid remains in South Africa. Recent research has shown that they were associated not with *Australopithecus africanus*, but with *Homo habilis*, and are from a higher level of the cave deposits. This type of simple stone tool is discussed in Chapter 9. (These drawings are approximately 40 percent of natural size.)

than the *Australopithecus africanus* fossils. Indeed, Tobias and Hughes found, along with stone tools, a fragmentary skull that is much more advanced than that of either *Australopithecus* or *Paranthropus* and that clearly belongs to an early member of the genus *Homo*. It now seems quite certain that toolmaking humans lived in the Sterkfontein cave after *Australopithecus africanus*. Recent faunal and stratigraphic research suggests that the *Australopithecus*-bearing strata at Sterkfontein date from between 2.5 and 2.8 million years B.P., while the early *Homo* and tool-bearing strata date from 1.8–2.0 million years B.P. Thus the Sterkfontein site has failed to produce evidence that *A. africanus* made stone tools.

Since 1965, C. K. Brain, assisted by Elizabeth Vrba, has been working at Swartkrans. In a meticulous excavation they have resolved many of the problems associated with this site. In the first place, they estimate that the fossil-bearing strata there date from 1.6–1.8 mya (roughly contemporary with the more recent Sterkfontein bed). Second, they have established that the *Paranthropus robustus* fossils that characterize the deposits are accompanied by fossils of *Homo* and stone tools, similar to those from the more recent Sterkfontein bed. Thus we now have good evidence of the contemporaneity and age of early *Homo* and *P. robustus* in South Africa. (More recent deposits in the Swartkrans cave have yielded a jaw likely to be from *Homo erectus;* see Chapter 10).

Since 1977, Vrba has been reexamining Broom's famous breccia-filled cave at Kromdraai. She has already found further specimens of *P. robustus* and, on the basis of extensive faunal analysis, has suggested a date of about 2.0 million years B.P. for these deposits.

New Finds at Swartkrans

More recent discoveries at Swartkrans (1979–1986) and a detailed analysis of the hominid remains by Randall Susman of the State University of New York have revealed a great deal more about *Paranthropus robustus.* Previously these creatures had been known almost entirely from cranial remains, and postcranial relics were very scarce indeed. Now, with more postcranial finds, Susman has been able to draw some interesting conclusions about the behavioral potential of this species.

First, judging by the massive masticatory apparatus, there is still little doubt that we are dealing with a vegetarian species of australopithecine. The size of the teeth and the kind of wear that they exhibit make this abundantly clear.

Second, the footbones reveal that the great toe was incapable of apelike opposition to the other toes and was indeed humanlike. Though there are minor differences from a human foot, the evidence demonstrates that *P. robustus* was capable of a kind of bipedal locomotion not very different from our own, although probably involving swaying balancing because of great pelvic width.

Third, bones of the hand reveal that this creature had a fully opposable thumb and was capable of a precision grip. In fact there is no anatomical reason why *P. robustus* could not have used, or even made, tools.

Finally, these hominid remains are associated in the Swartkrans breccia with a fairly rich collection of both stone and bone tools. Following the guidelines set out in Chapter 9, scholars have tended to associate the tools with the contemporary species of *Homo* that is also found in these breccias. In view of the anatomical potential of *P. robustus,* we now have to recognize the very real possibility, or even likelihood, that this species was a tool user and possibly even a toolmaker. The wear on the bone tools suggests that they may have been used for digging, and indeed, there is no logical reason to assume that stone tools imply meat eating. Some would argue that this conclusion is reinforced by the fact that there are 20 times as many *P. robustus* individuals represented in the deposits as there are *Homo* individuals. Whether *P. robustus* was a tool user or toolmaker may never be known. Nevertheless, from our knowledge of chimpanzee behavior and of australopithecine anatomy, we can now say that these early hominids undoubtedly had that potential, whether or not it was used and developed.

SUMMARY

In 1924 Raymond Dart recognized the first *Australopithecus africanus* skull from Sterkfontein and claimed that it stood halfway between apes and humans. His claims were dismissed by most anthropologists, but Robert Broom started working in the dolomite caves of the Transvaal and soon found more material, including *P. robustus*. After pelvic bones and other skeletal remains were found in 1947, Wilfred Le Gros Clark of Oxford assessed the finds and pronounced them hominid—and bipedal. Pebble tools were found in 1957 but have yet to be linked unequivocally with the australopithecines.

Extensive excavations at all the main Transvaal sites since 1966 have established that *Australopithecus africanus* inhabited the region between about 3.0 and 2.5 mya (Box 7–1). A half a million years later, *Australopithecus africanus* was long gone, and *Paranthropus robustus* and early *Homo* roamed southern Africa. While *A. africanus* may have been ancestral to later, more modern hominids (this possibility is discussed further in Chapter 8), it now seems certain that *Paranthropus robustus* was destined to become extinct without descendants.

REVIEW QUESTIONS

1. In 1925 Raymond Dart claimed that *Australopithecus africanus* was an evolutionary link between apes and people. Why was his claim rejected by most of his anthropological and anatomical colleagues?

2. Describe the anatomical and behavioral differences between the two South African australopithecine genera.

3. Should the South African australopithecines be placed in a single genus or two genera? What are the arguments on each side of the question?

4. At present, most anthropologists conclude that the South African australopithecines did *not* make stone tools. Review the evidence, and evaluate the strength of that conclusion.

POSTSCRIPT

How many genera of australopithecines inhabited southern Africa in the late Pliocene and the early Pleistocene? Can all of the South African fossils be accommodated within *Australopithecus*, or is a second genus—*Paranthropus*—needed for the robust forms? The question is not an easy one, and both options have loyal and vocal supporters. The basic issues are as follows.

When Raymond Dart and Robert Broom described and named their newly discovered hominids during the first half of this century, they followed a grand paleontological tradition of emphasizing the differences between fossils rather than their commonalities, and they created a plethora of new species and genus labels. The Taung child was christened *Australopithecus africanus*. Gracile fossils from Sterkfontein were first named *Australopithecus transvaalensis* and later *Plesianthropus transvaalensis*, while similar bones from Makapansgat became *Australopithecus prometheus*. The larger, more muscular hominids from Kromdraai were called *Paranthropus robustus*, but equally robust specimens from Swartkrans were dubbed *Paranthropus crassidens*. By mid-century, at least three genera and five species of australopithecines had been suggested for southern Africa.

More recently, the original "splitting" of the South African fossils into numerous taxa has been countered by a trend toward "lumping" them into a minimal number of species and genera. Arguing that all of the South African australopithecines represent a single evolutionary grade of organization, and emphasizing the anatomical features they have in common, paleoanthropologists of the last few decades have tended to recognize only one genus (*Australopithecus*) and two species (*A. africanus* and *A. robustus*). Acknowledging diversity within unity, however, the two species were often described as representing a "gracile lineage" and a "robust lineage."

Within just the past few years, the argument for splitting the lineages into separate genera have been renewed with vigor. Much of this argument is based on the results of modern cladistic analyses that show, in the words of paleoanthropologist F. E. Grine, "that the 'robust' australopithecines [from both South and East Africa] form a monophyletic clade [indicating] the validity (and the necessity) of the generic name *Paranthropus*." (In this case, a monophyletic clade is a group of species marked by shared derived traits and containing only species more closely related to each other than to any species outside the clade.) Harvard's professor emeritus of anthropology William Howells agrees with the revival of *Paranthropus*, noting that the anatomical differences between gracile and robust australopithecines at least equal those between living chimpanzees and gorillas, which are classified in separate genera (*Pan* and *Gorilla*). Numerous other authors, including British scientists Bernard Wood, Christopher Dean, and Christopher Stringer, and American researchers Leslie Aiello, B. Holly Smith, and Randall Susman, are also using the two-genus scheme.

We find the arguments convincing that the South and East African robusts form a monophyletic clade and that anatomically they are significantly different from the gracile forms. Therefore in this book we have adopted the two-genus classification for the australopithecines. But do we consider the matter settled? Not by a long shot. Most paleoanthropologists—particularly in the United States—still use (prefer?) the more conservative one-genus classification. One can only hope that additional fossil finds and new analyses will settle the issue definitively in the future.

CHAPTER 7 TIMELINE

HOLOCENE

10,000

CENOZOIC

Proconsul

*Apidium, Parapithecus,
Aegyptopithecus,* and
Propliopithecus

Amphipithecus

Eosimias

Early prosimians

65 MILLION

MESOZOIC

First mammals

Age of reptiles

225 MILLION

PALEOZOIC

YEARS A.D.	DISCOVERIES
1990 —	
1988	Susman's assessment of *Paranthropus robustus*
1977 —	Vrba starts work at Kromdraai
1966 —	Tobias starts work at Sterkfontein
1965 —	Brain starts work at Swartkrans
1957 —	Robinson and Mason find tools at Sterkfontein
1950 —	Definitive assessments by Le Gros Clark published
1948 —	*Paranthropus* found at Swartkrans
1947 —	*Australopithecus africanus* skull and pelvis found at Sterkfontein; Dart discovers *Australopithecus* at Makapansgat
1938 —	*Paranthropus robustus* discovered by Broom at Kromdraai
1936 —	Broom's first adult *Australopithecus* found at Sterkfontein
1925 —	Dart's publication on *Australopithecus africanus*
1924 —	Dart discovers *Australopithecus africanus* from Taung

YEARS B.P.	FOSSIL RECORD	
	Homo sapiens	
Pleistocene ◆	*Homo erectus*	
2 million —	*Paranthropus robustus* at Kromdraai and Swartkrans with *Homo*	*Homo* and *Paranthropus robustus*
	Australopithecus africanus at Sterkfontein and Makapansgat	*Australopithecus africanus*
Pliocene ◆		
5 million —	? Origin of bipedalism	
Miocene ◆		Ancient apes
	Sivapithecus in Europe and in Asia	
10 million —		
15 million —		
	Proconsul in Africa	

THE TRANSVAAL HOMINIDS

The history of discoveries in South Africa is a fascinating story still unfolding (top right). The age of the fossils (bottom right) is still a matter of some uncertainty because potassium-argon dating is not applicable in the area, owing to the absence of volcanic activity there during the Cenozoic.

The Great Savanna

Ex Africa semper aliquid novi. ("Africa always has something new.")

PLINY THE ELDER, 23–79. *Natural History,* BOOK VIII.

OVERVIEW

Hominid fossils have been discovered not only in South Africa, but at numerous locations in East Africa as well. Sites centered on the Rift Valley have produced the remains of both lineages of australopithecines (gracile and robust) and several extinct species belonging to the genus *Homo.* Although specialists disagree somewhat on species and genus names and the assignment of particular fossils, the following list of extinct East African hominids from the *Plio-Pleistocene* seems reasonable: four australopithecines—*Australopithecus ramidus* (the earliest and least known), *A. afarensis* (the oldest widely accepted member of the hominid family), and robust species *Paranthropus boisei* and *P. aethiopicus;* and three hominines—*Homo habilis, H. rudolfensis* (collectively referred to as "early *Homo*"), and *H. erectus.* East Africa has produced the earliest evidence of bipedalism (clearly shown in the anatomy of *A. afarensis* fossils and the preserved footprints from the Laetoli site) and the manufacture of stone tools (a behavior currently understood to be limited to hominines). Combining the fossil evidence from East Africa with that from the southern part of the continent suggests that some variety of *Australopithecus* gave rise to the genus *Homo,* while the *Paranthropus* clade went extinct without descendants. Important topics in Chapter 8 include the various fossil species and their characteristics (and, in particular, the intermediate natures of *A. ramidus* and *A. afarensis* between apes and more modern hominids); the first evidence of habitual bipedalism; problems involved in the recognition and naming of extinct species; the varying lifestyles of the early hominids; and the evolutionary relationships binding the australopithecines to the genus *Homo.*

Plio-Pleistocene: a combination of the last two epochs of the Cenozoic era; the Pliocene lasted from 5 to 1.6 million years B.P. and the Pleistocene from 1.6 million to 10,000 years B.P.

DISCOVERIES AT OLDUVAI

Fifty million years ago the grasses evolved and began to spread throughout the world. They were adapted to particular climatic conditions: intermittent wet and dry seasons that provided insufficient rain to support forest. As rainfall patterns changed, particularly during the Miocene, the grasses spread over great areas of North America, East Asia, and Africa; in Africa they extended down the eastern side from Ethiopia to the continent's southern tip. The grasslands usually contained scattered trees, but essentially they constituted an open habitat distinct from forest and woodland, a habitat to which a whole new range of herbivorous animals were destined to become adapted. These vast African plains, known as savannas, were to play an important part in hominid evolution.

The questions that archaeologists were trying to answer in the Transvaal—whether the early hominids made tools and where the first stone tool industries occurred—brought the attention of anthropologists to another part of the African

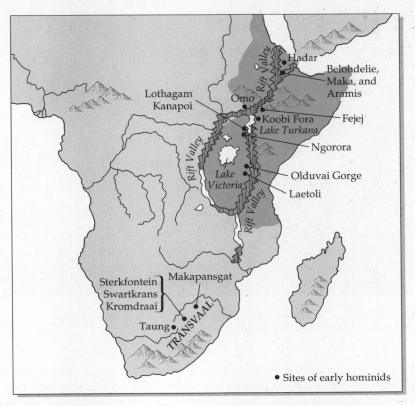

FIGURE 8–1   Southern and Eastern Africa, showing some of the many sites in which australo-pithecine fossils have been discovered. All lie on the eastern side of the continent, where parkland and savanna have proliferated during the past 10 million years.

savanna. During the 1950s, Louis and Mary Leakey, both distinguished archaeol-ogists, were finding the remains of an extensive pebble-tool industry 2,000 mi (3200 km) north of the Transvaal grasslands of South Africa in a dry river canyon in northern Tanzania (Figure 8–1).

Olduvai Gorge is an abrupt rent in the earth, some 25 mi (40 km) long and 300 ft (90 m) deep. Like a miniature Grand Canyon, its sides display different strata laid bare by the cutting of an ancient river (Figure 8–2). A German entomologist named Wilhelm Kattwinkel found the gorge in 1911 when he almost fell into its depths as he broke through some bush on the edge. A hasty exploration showed the place to be a rich source of animal fossils. Some of the fossils that Kattwinkel took back to Berlin were so unusual that an expedition, headed by Hans Reck, was sent out in 1913 to explore further. Its investigations were ended by World War I, and after the war Reck was unable to raise funds to resume operations. Eventu-ally he wrote to Louis Leakey (1903–1972), the young curator of the Coryndon Memorial Museum at Nairobi, Kenya, urging him to take over, but Leakey had to wait until 1931 before he could raise the money for an expedition to Olduvai.

One season spent exploring the gorge was enough to convince Leakey that Olduvai was a site "such as no other in the world." He found pebble tools in his first year there, long before they were discovered in South Africa, and no doubt he won-dered if they could have been made by a creature similar to *Australopithecus*. For

FIGURE 8–2   Olduvai Gorge is a remarkable landform as well as a fossil gold mine. In this photo-graph the layers of sedimentary rock are obvious.

years Leakey searched the clearly stacked strata of the gorge in vain, unable to find the maker of the tools. As money and transport permitted, Leakey returned to the gorge, along with his wife Mary (b. 1913) and their sons. From each of the four prin-cipal beds that overlie one another from the river bottom to the surface of the plain some 300 ft (90 m) above, the Leakeys eventually recovered an enormous number of animal fossils. They identified and classified more than a hundred species, most of them extinct and some unknown to science until the Leakeys discovered them.

Discovery of *Paranthropus boisei* (1959)

For 28 years the Leakeys (Figures 8–3 and 8–4) were engaged in one of the most persistent and unrewarding efforts in the history of anthropology. Olduvai was far from the museum at Nairobi where Louis Leakey worked, and they could seldom spend more than a few weeks a year at the gorge. The trip was expensive, and in the early years it took several days to get to Olduvai on the very rough road from Nairobi. The gorge was stiflingly hot, and water had to be hauled from a spring 35 mi (55 km) away. It was not until the 1950s that the Leakeys were able to begin extensive excavation at Olduvai, and until July 17, 1959, all they knew was that they were the possessors of a small collection of what they believed to be the old-est implements ever seen, collectively called the *Oldowan tool industry*.

On that morning Louis Leakey awakened with a fever and a headache. His wife insisted that he remain in camp. But the work season was drawing to an end, and the day could not be lost, so Mary Leakey drove to the point where the party was working. As she walked slowly along the hillside of Bed I, the lowest layer of the gorge, a piece of bone exposed by recent erosion caught her eye. She recog-nized it as a piece of skull. Searching higher along the slope, she suddenly saw two big teeth, brown-black and almost iridescent, just appearing from the eroding hill. She marked the spot with a small piece of stone and sped back to camp.

Oldowan tool industry: earli-est known stone-tool culture, dating 2.4 million years into the past and first made by early *Homo*. The products were very crude stone chop-pings and flakes.

FIGURE 8–3 A distinguished archaeologist, Mary Leakey worked at numerous African sites, including Olduvai and Laetoli, until her retirement in 1984.

Louis heard the car racing up the road and sprang up in alarm, thinking that his wife had been bitten by a snake. But as the car stopped, he heard Mary shout, "I've got him!" The "him," she felt sure, was a hominid fossil—the early human they had been seeking for so many years. Louis's fever and headache forgotten, he jumped in the car, and the couple drove back as fast as they could.

The Leakeys went to work with camel's hair brushes and dental picks. The palate to which the teeth were affixed came into view, and then fragments of a skull emerged. In order not to lose a single precious scrap, the couple removed and sieved tons of scree (fine rock debris) from the slope below the find. At the end of 19 days they had about 400 fragments.

While undertaking the delicate task of assembling the bits and pieces, the Leakeys continued to excavate the site. Not only had they discovered the oldest hominid skull found to that time in eastern and central Africa, but they had also unearthed what appeared to be a campsite of this ancient creature. Scattered on what had been the margins of an ancient lake were many tools made of flaked stone and pebbles, along with waste chips. Lying about, too, were the fossil bones of animals: complete remains of rats, mice, frogs, lizards, birds, snakes, tortoises, and some young pigs, and parts of small antelopes. But there were no remains of

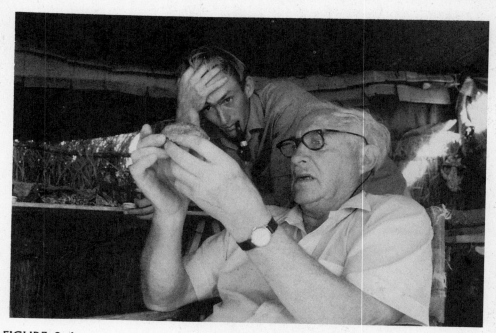

FIGURE 8–4 Louis Leakey was somewhat eccentric, and a passionate, brilliant man. Here he is examining some of his important and numerous discoveries with his son, Richard.

large animals. Nearly all these bones were broken, but the near-human skull and tibia and fibula (the two bones of the lower part of the leg) that appeared at the same site were not. It seemed to the Leakeys that the hominid had killed the other animals.

The skull that took shape from the fragments uncovered at the campsite was that of a nearly mature male (Figure 8–5). That the wisdom teeth were unworn and that the suture joining the two halves of the skull, the *sagittal suture*, had not yet closed indicated that it was a young adult. In brain size and in general appearance, the young male broadly resembled *Paranthropus robustus* of the south. The molars were extraordinarily large and heavy, but detailed study confirmed that they were, in their structure, undoubtedly hominid teeth. The skull had the characteristic massive face and teeth and rugged low cranium of *P. robustus* but was even larger and more specialized. These differences led Louis Leakey to set up a new genus for what he believed was the earliest tool user, and he named it *Zinjanthropus boisei*. (Zinj means "Eastern Africa" in Arabic; *boisei* honored Charles Boise, who had helped to finance the Leakeys' search for early humans.) Today the skull is classified as *Paranthropus boisei*. The skull is so much more heavily built than that of *P. robustus* that it is often described as *superrobust*.

Age of *P. boisei*

Fortunately the approximate age of the Leakeys' fossil could be determined because it had been found sandwiched between layers of volcanic ash. Geologists

Sagittal suture: the line of union joining the two main side bones of the braincase.

Zinjanthropus boisei: original name for the australopithecine species now called *Paranthropus boisei*.
Paranthropus boisei: robust australopithecine species that lived in East Africa 2.4–1.3 mya; formerly *Australopithecus boisei*.

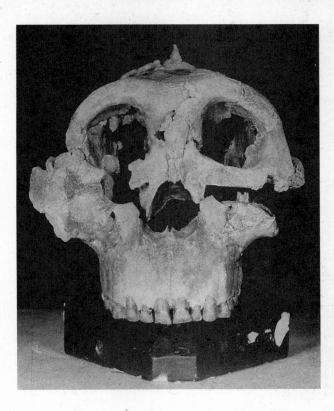

FIGURE 8–5 *Zinjanthropus,* the immense skull found by Mary Leakey at Olduvai in 1959. It is now classified as *Paranthropus boisei.* This photograph is approximately 45 percent actual size.

extracted minerals containing potassium from the volcanic ash covering *P. boisei* and also from an older volcanic bed that underlay the site. When they analyzed these layers by the then-new method of potassium-argon dating, they were able to fix the startling age of about 1.75 million years, an age repeatedly confirmed by later potassium-argon tests. This dating of the fossil was extraordinary in itself, and it also had a valuable side effect: suddenly Broom's original claim of an age of 2 million years for the early South African hominid *Australopithecus africanus* changed from being a wild guess to being an inspired deduction.

The question of which of the early hominids (Figure 8–6) was the first to use tools, and when, continued to haunt paleoanthropologists. The evidence from Olduvai seemed to suggest to the Leakeys that *Zinjanthropus* might be the tool-maker. But only a year after they had found the first skull, they found another.

Discovery of *Homo habilis* (1960–1964)

Early in 1960 the Leakeys' son Jonathan uncovered some teeth and bone fragments of the second hominid. Though found at broadly the same stratigraphic level as *P. boisei* and not far away, these bones, Louis Leakey realized, represented a creature far closer to humankind than the heavily built *P. boisei.* Two years passed before further specimens were found to confirm this interpretation, but by 1964 the Leakeys and their collaborators were ready to announce their new discovery.

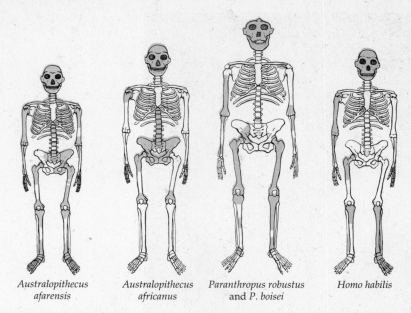

Australopithecus   Australopithecus   Paranthropus robustus   Homo habilis
afarensis   africanus   and P. boisei

FIGURE 8–6   The skeletons of *Australopithecus afarensis* from Ethiopia, *A. africanus* and *Paranthropus robustus* from South Africa, and *P. boisei* and *Homo habilis* from East Africa are reconstructed from fragments of many individuals. In the case of *P. boisei* and *P. robustus*, the drawing is highly imaginative and the skeletal material is combined, for we have very limited remains (shown in color). *Australopithecus africanus* was approximately 4 ft (1.2 m) tall, and the others are drawn to scale.

Homo habilis: one of the two species of "early *Homo*"; inhabited South and East Africa 2.0–1.6 mya.

Though as old as *P. boisei*, the new fossils represented a distinct species. It was clearly of the gracile type and even more humanlike than the gracile South African *A. africanus*. In fact, it seemed sufficiently human to be separated from the known *Australopithecus* species altogether. Louis Leakey and his co-workers described the fossil species as a true human that deserved to be classified in the genus *Homo*. He christened his find *Homo habilis*, "handy" man, believing that now he really had discovered the toolmaker.

That *Homo habilis*, and not the superrobust *P. boisei*, was indeed the toolmaker has now been widely accepted. The Leakeys subsequently collected from Olduvai a whole series of *Homo habilis* fragments, indicating that this type lived there for more than half a million years, using much the same primitive tool culture the entire time. In the mid-1980s, Donald Johanson and Tim White visited Olduvai for four seasons and recovered a very fragmentary skeleton of *Homo habilis*. There is doubtless much more material awaiting recovery from this famous canyon when circumstances permit. (*Homo erectus* fossils were also discovered at Olduvai, together with a more advanced stone culture; see Chapters 10 and 11.)

Homo erectus: hominid species that inhabited much of the Old World 1.8–0.3 mya; successor to "early *Homo*."

Classifying *Homo habilis*

Homo habilis earned neither name nor credentials easily. It was primitive and still relatively small-brained. A few anthropologists preferred to identify it as an advanced type of the gracile *A. africanus* not deserving *Homo* status at all. Some still identify it in this way. Its qualifications as a distinct species have been in question from the day it was named.

Should it be called *Homo habilis* or *Australopithecus habilis?* Compared to the certified human beings of the genus *Homo* that came after, it seems scarcely human; compared to the more primitive types that preceded, its human credentials suddenly improve. This disconcerting shift of perspective always occurs when the eye runs down a series of fossils that are related to one another through direct descent. The differences between them are often differences in degree—not in kind—and obviously become more pronounced as one takes one's examples from more widely separated time zones. The more obvious characteristics of *Homo* are comparative: an "increasingly large" brain, a "higher" forehead, a "more delicate" jaw, and "longer" legs. But in a continuous series, where does one draw the line?

The Question of Brain Size

The question of brain size continues to arise, but it is conceivably the wrong question. Since all creatures are bundles of characteristics, many of which may be evolving at different rates, drawing a line that is based on these characteristics always causes trouble. Early in this century, the British anatomist Arthur Keith chose to draw the line marking the appearance of humanity where the brain capacity touched 750 cc. Anything below that, according to Keith, was not human; anything above it was (*Homo sapiens* is usually within the 1,200–1,600 cc range; see Table 8–1). More recently, Wilfrid Le Gros Clark put the minimum at 700 cc. Clark's choice, unlike Keith's, was not arbitrary; it reflected the state of the fossil record at the time it was made: no accepted "human" skulls were known to exist with cranial capacities of less than 700 cc. Implicit in this situation, of course, was the possibility that an apparently human specimen with a slightly smaller brain might be discovered any day.

Homo habilis laid this problem right on the scientists' doorstep. The great difficulty in deciding whether it was human lay in the fact that the so-called type specimen, the first one to be found and named *Homo habilis* by the Leakeys, had a brain capacity estimated to be about 657 cc—just under Clark's limit. Since then five other *H. habilis* skulls have been measured by two experts: Phillip Tobias and Ralph Holloway. They came up with surprisingly uniform figures for these skulls. They range in capacity from 509 to 674 cc and average about 612 cc. Too small-brained for a human? Perhaps, but probably too large-brained for a typical gracile *Australopithecus*, whose mean cranial capacity was only about 440 cc.

What is the meaning of brain size? How significant is the steady increase in cranial capacity that we find in human evolution? Large brains are found in large animals generally, and the brains of elephants and whales are very much larger than those of humans. As a general rule, among mammals brain size can best be interpreted when it is related to body size, and a doubling of body size during the evolution of a lineage usually results in a considerable increase in brain size (see Chapter 13). When we look at the figures in Table 8–1, therefore, we should consider the size of the animal itself. For example, the stature of *A. afarensis* varied from 3.3 to 5 ft (1–1.5 m) tall, while that of modern humans varies from approximately 4.5 to over 6 ft (1.4–1.8 m). The difference in relative brain size is therefore not quite as great as the table might suggest. It should not be forgotten, however, that many human populations—of pygmies, for example—

fall into the range of stature for *A. afarensis* and yet have brains in the region of 1,200–1,350 cc; three times as large. A consideration of stature is therefore not going to alter very seriously the significance of the figures for the Hominidae listed in Table 8–1.

By the mid-1960s, the situation was becoming complex. Two varieties of australopithecine had been discovered in South Africa. Their exact ages were unclear, but there was faunal evidence that they might be 2 million years old or more. Furthermore, at Swartkrans, it appeared that *Paranthropus robustus* had coexisted with early *Homo*. Similarly, in East Africa's Olduvai Gorge another robust australopithecine species, *Paranthropus boisei*, was known to have coexisted with the newly named *Homo habilis* some 1.75 million years ago. Although all of the various species were clearly hominids, they had some interesting differences. Some had ape-sized brains, while brain size in others showed a clear increase. Some had massive grinding teeth, while others had teeth that looked more like those of modern humans. How did these species relate to one another in evolutionary terms? And then there was the problem of the crude stone tools from the bottom of Olduvai: Exactly who had made and used them? One mystery after another. It was time to break new ground in search of new evidence.

Table 8–1 COMPARISON OF CRANIAL CAPACITY

Species	Range of Cranial Capacity (cc)	Average Cranial Capacity (cc)
Chimpanzees	282–500	383
Gorillas	340–752	505
Australopithecus ramidus	Unknown	Unknown
Australopithecus afarensis	400–500	433
Australopithecus africanus	405–500	445
Paranthropus robustus	Unknown	530
Paranthropus boisei	410–530	487
Paranthropus aethiopicus	Unknown	410
Homo habilis	509–674	612
Homo rudolfensis	752–810	781
Homo erectus	750–1251	988
Modern humans	1,000–2,000	1,330

Note: Measurements of cranial capacity are always given in cubic centimeters (cc; a cubic centimeter equals about 0.06 in³); the size of the brain itself is usually somewhat smaller because the cranial cavity also contains other structures. The above figures are approximate: for the two African apes, they are based on rather small samples; and in the case of the fossil groups, the samples are extremely small and may prove to be misleading (only single complete specimens of *P. robustus* and *P. aethiopicus* are known and measured). For modern humans, rare extremes exceeding even the approximate range given above have been found; the average figure is based on a limited number of samples. Slight variations in these figures will be found in other authors' works.

As a general rule, and within an order, species of animals with larger brains are more intelligent than those with smaller brains, but this does not hold among species of different body sizes. The significance of brain size is considered in Chapter 13. Within a species, variations in brain size are not believed to be related to intelligence among normal individuals. Data from Walker et al. (1987), Tobias (1985), Aiello and Dean (1990), and Brown et al. (1993). Fossils are attributed to *Homo habilis* and *Homo rudolfensis* following Wood (1992). West Turkana fossil KNM-WT 17000 is classified as *P. aethiopicus.*

OMO, TURKANA, HADAR, LAETOLI, AND ARAMIS

The only ways to clear up the mystery were to find more fossils, to date more precisely the ones that had been unearthed, and to dig deeper into time. Toward those ends, an ambitious international expedition was organized in 1967 to look for hominid remains in Ethiopia. The expedition was under the direction of Yves Coppens and Camille Arambourg from France and the American anthropologist F. Clark Howell. Its destination was a remote spot in the southern part of the valley of the Omo River, just north of Lake Turkana (Figures 8–1 and 8–7). Though one of the most desolate places anywhere south of the Sahara and one of the hottest, the area had several attractions. For one thing, it had been visited 35 years before by Arambourg, who had found it rich in animal fossils. For another, it bore a striking resemblance to Olduvai. It, too, is part of the Rift Valley geological complex, a giant crack in the earth that, running north and south through Africa, once was marked by chains of lakes and rivers and now is edged by towering escarpments. Much of the Rift Valley is dry now; its lakes are shrunken, some of its cliffs worn away, and its stones baked in the sun. There is no river at all today in Olduvai Gorge, except during flash floods, although the gorge was made by a river. At Omo, as at Olduvai, deep-cut riverbeds speak of ancient days and long-vanished landscapes. The Omo River still runs down from the Ethiopian highlands and empties into Lake Turkana, just over the border in northern Kenya. Lake Turkana itself has grown and shrunk twice at least in the past 4 million years. Today it is still a sizable lake 185 mi (300 km) long. The brutal, arid lands around it are largely unexplored.

The Rift Valley is an unstable area on the earth's surface where the earth's crust is still moving. It has long been a center of volcanic activity and is pockmarked by cones and craters. Because of neighboring volcanic activity, Olduvai has invaluable layers of datable volcanic ash; so does Omo. Both places supported

FIGURE 8–7   This aerial view of the Omo Valley in southern Ethiopia shows uplifted fossil-bearing deposits of the Shungura formation. The harder layers of rock are the datable volcanic tuffs.

more life in the past than they do now. Laced with rivers, much greener, carrying a far larger animal population than they do today, each provided the lush water-edge environment, the woodland savanna, that the early hominids are believed to have preferred.

But Omo is also different from Olduvai, and the differences are what made it particularly appealing to the 1967 expedition. At Olduvai, the most accurate and useful pages of the volcanic timetable are crowded into an 800,000-year period that is not quite 2 million years old and are contained in layers not totalling much more than 100 ft (30 m) thick. At Omo the strata being investigated are more than 2,000 ft (600 m) thick and span a far longer period of time. Moreover, they contain a great many layers of volcanic ash at varying intervals, some of them only 100,000 years apart, some more widely spaced, and each datable by the potassium-argon method. Together, scientists can use these layers of ash to step backward into time and into the earth, determining an approximate date at each step.

One does not have to dig at Omo to go deeper into time. The strata have been heaved up in the past and now lie at an angle to the earth's surface. One need only walk along to find successively older layers revealing themselves.

The Omo story begins a little over 4 million years ago and continues to about 1.5 million years B.P. This date conveniently overlaps with the fossil deposits at Olduvai, which begin about 1.8 million years B.P., so that the two sites, between them, give us an almost unbroken story for 4 million years.

Omo Hominids (1967–1974)

In this area of great promise, Arambourg, with Coppens, picked the spot he had worked before and knew to be productive. A second group, under Clark Howell's direction, went a short distance up the Omo River to tap a previously unexplored area. A third group, headed by the Leakeys' son Richard, picked another untapped spot, farther north and across the river from Howell. As it turned out, Richard Leakey's choice was the only one that proved somewhat unfruitful. He found plenty of fossil material there, but the strata were not old enough to be of interest to the expedition. He decided to dissociate himself from the project and returned home to Kenya to do some prospecting.

The other members of the expedition persevered where they were. Immediately they began recovering extinct animal fossils of extraordinary richness and variety. The great number of dated layers at Omo made it possible to trace the evolutionary changes that had taken place in some 80 species of mammals: 6 genera and 8 species of extinct pigs laid their secrets bare in the strata; 22 kinds of antelope were discovered; and several extinct saber-toothed cats. Altogether, more than 150 species of fossil animals were found at Omo. These discoveries were so varied and told such a clear story that matching fossils from other places with those from Omo became a distinct possibility.

In addition to all the useful animal fossils found at Omo, traces of hominids began to appear. The French group first found a robust jaw that they felt was sufficiently different from known material to warrant a new name; *Australopithecus aethiopicus*. Both parties found teeth, eventually more than 200 of them; then came other jaw fragments, parts of two skulls, and several arm and leg bones. It has been a spectacular haul and an enormously significant one, for several reasons. First is the age of the oldest specimens, more than 20 teeth: 3.0 million years. These ancient

Australopithecus aethiopicus: original name for the robust australopithecine species now called *Paranthropus aethiopicus*.

teeth are almost certainly those of a small gracile australopithecine whose identity was not clarified until years later (see section on *A. afarensis*). Also of significance was the fact that remains of this small hominid were found along with superrobust fossils similar to, but much older than, *P. boisei* found at Olduvai. Furthermore, robust specimens continued to turn up in various layers, dating right up to 1.5 million years ago. *P. boisei* apparently lived at Omo for almost a million years.

Robust Hominids at Koobi Fora (1969–1976)

Meanwhile, Richard Leakey flew south in a helicopter, across the border into Kenya and along the eastern shore of Lake Turkana, previously called Lake Rudolf (Figures 8–1 and 8–8). Here, Leakey spotted some likely sites from the air and landed to find what has turned out to be one of the richest mines of hominid fossils in the world.

The results of work near Lake Turkana carried out by a large group of scientists directed by Richard Leakey and Glynn Isaac (1937–1985) of the University of California at Berkeley were sensational: at the sites east of the lake, named Ileret and Koobi Fora, they discovered three superb skulls, more than two dozen mandibles or parts of mandibles, some arm- and leg-bone fragments, and isolated teeth, amounting to more than 100 specimens in all. Much of this material is of the

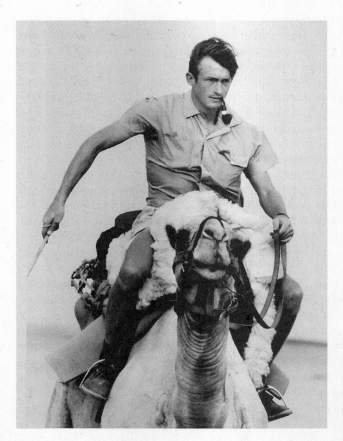

FIGURE 8–8 Richard Leakey's team had astounding success in finding fossil hominids in the desert regions east of Lake Turkana in Kenya. With more than 150 fossil hominids found, his success was unprecedented.

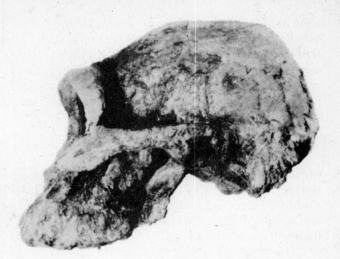

FIGURE 8–9 This skull (museum number KNM-ER 406) of *Paranthropus boisei*, found by Richard Leakey at Koobi Fora, is similar in many ways to that found by his mother at Olduvai (Figure 8–5). This photograph is approximately 30 percent actual size.

superrobust *P. boisei* type and dates from about 2 to 1.3 mya (Figure 8–9). When these East Turkana fossils are combined with the Omo finds, there is enough material in the way of young and old individuals, both males and females, and enough variation in dentition, for the outlines of a variable population of the superrobust *Paranthropus boisei* to begin to reveal itself.

Having a population to study instead of an individual fossil is extremely important. No two people today are exactly alike; no two australopithecines were, either. For that reason, drawing conclusions from a single fossil is risky. Measurements can be taken of a single fossil, and theories can be built up as a result of those measurements, but this information may be misleading because the fossil may not be typical. Only when a large number of specimens is available can variations be taken into account. If visitors from outer space were to describe and name *Homo sapiens* by examining one skeleton—for example, that of a short, heavy-boned Eskimo—they certainly might be excused if they thought they had another species when they discovered a second skeleton, of a 6.5 ft (2 m), slender-boned Watusi tribesman from central Africa.

That is why the *P. boisei* population that is emerging is so valuable. It begins to indicate some of the limits of variability beyond which no members of the species went. Any creature that does exceed those limits significantly can be presumed to be something else. And those limits are now well enough defined to make it quite clear that the gracile *Australopithecus* specimens *are* something else; doubt about the distinctiveness of the two lineages has now evaporated.

P. boisei, on the other hand, is, apart from its size, quite similar to the robust types of South Africa, which also exist in sufficient numbers to constitute a variable population with limits of its own. Like *P. robustus* (Figure 7–8), *P. boisei* had a bony crest along the top of its skull, but its crest is more pronounced, for the anchoring of even bigger muscles to work a more massive jaw containing larger molars. This complex of features indicates a life adapted to eating large amounts of coarse, tough vegetable matter. It is the same adaptation as *P. robustus*, but larger and more highly evolved (Box 8–1).

Because on further analysis the known differences between *P. robustus* and *P. boisei* have proved to be almost entirely differences in size, some workers today consider both groups geographical subspecies of the single species *P. robustus*.

BOX 8–1
CHARACTERISTICS OF THE EAST AFRICAN ROBUST AUSTRALOPITHECINAE[a]

Trait	Paranthropus boisei	Paranthropus aethiopicus
Height	F: 4.1 ft (124 cm) M: 4.5 ft (137 cm) (F is 90% of M)	Unknown
Weight	F: 75–88 lb (34–40 kg) M: 108–176 lb (49–80 kg) (F is 57% of M)	Unknown
Brain size (sexes combined)	487 cc mean (410–530 cc range)	410 cc mean (range unknown)
Cranium	Tall, broad, "dished" face; sagittal crest; low forehead; low-vaulted braincase; some flexure of cranial base	"Dished" face; sagittal crest; low forehead; low-vaulted braincase (compared to P. boisei: unflexed cranial base; shallow jaw joint; extreme facial prognathism; parietal bones flared strongly at the mastoid)
Dentition	Parabolic toothrow; small incisors and canines; huge grinding teeth; lower P3s often have 3+ cusps	Grinding teeth appear to be as large as those of P. boisei
Diet	Hard, tough, fibrous vegetable foods	Unknown
Limbs	Longer arms and shorter legs than modern humans	Unknown
Pelvis	Short, broad ilia; short ischial shafts (?); pelvis wide between hip joints	Unknown
Locomotion	Bipedalism (swaying gait?)	Bipedalism (assumed)
Known dates (million years B.P.)	2.4–1.3	2.6–2.3

[a]Mean values, or range of values, for anatomical measurements may change with additional fossil discoveries.

Whether the remains in fact represent one or two distinct contemporary biological species is something that can be finally determined only when a great deal more fossil evidence is available. For our discussion it is convenient to continue to distinguish them as separate species.

The question of the number of species represented by varied samples of fossils has always been a difficult one. As noted in Chapter 7, paleoanthropologists concerned with these matters are sometimes divided into splitters and lumpers. Splitters divide the spectrum of fossils into groups with small variability, so that many species and genera are recognized. Lumpers accept wide ranges of variability

Table 8–2 ALTERNATIVE CLASSIFICATIONS OF THE HOMINIDAE[a]

Lumper's Classification		Splitter's Classification		Authors' Classification	
Australopithecus	africanus	Australopithecus	aethiopicus	Australopithecus	afarensis
	robustus		afarensis		africanus
			africanus	Paranthropus	robustus
		Plesianthropus	africanus		boisei
		Meganthropus	africanus		aethiopicus
		Paranthropus	robustus		
		Zinjanthropus	boisei		
Homo	erectus	Pithecanthropus	erectus	Homo	habilis
	sapiens	Sinanthropus	pekinensis		rudolfensis
		Atlanthropus	mauritanicus		erectus
		Homo	habilis		sapiens
			heidelbergensis		
			leakeyi		
			neanderthalensis		
			sapiens		
2 genera	4 species	9 genera	15 species	3 genera	9 species

[a]Note: The new species, *Australopithecus ramidus,* has been omitted from this table since it is too early to judge lumpers' and splitters' reaction to the taxon. As shown in Table 7–1 and as described in the text, the authors of this book accept *A. ramidus* provisionally as a valid hominid species.

within groups and so recognize only a few species and genera. In the early days of paleoanthropology, almost every find that varied even the smallest amount from another was given a separate specific or generic name. The result was a splitter's taxonomy with 37 genera and 111 species of Hominidae! Following our present understanding of the variability of modern species, no one today would recognize such a number; nevertheless, there is some divergence of view. Table 8–2 shows two extreme classifications of the family Hominidae, together with the classification used in this book, which lies between the two.

A New Robust Australopithecine from West Turkana (1985)

In 1985 the number of robust australopithecine species increased by one because of discoveries made at the sites of Lomekwi and Kangatukuseo on the west side of Lake Turkana. From deposits dating about 2.6 million years of age, the excavating team, headed by Alan Walker and Richard Leakey, recovered a nearly toothless cranium (museum catalog number KNM-WT 17000, dubbed the Black Skull because of its coloration) and a partial mandible. Although much larger, the mandible is otherwise similar to a jaw found years earlier by French scientists at Omo and named *Australopithecus aethiopicus.* The west Turkana cranium is massively built and quite *prognathic* (Figure 8–10). It features a low forehead and a small braincase (410 cc) and is topped by a sagittal crest that would have anchored large jaw muscles. The zygomatic arches flare widely to the side, and the face is somewhat "dished" (concave) in appearance. The few measurable teeth and tooth roots indicate that the grinding teeth were as large as those of *Paranthropus boisei.*

Naming the west Turkana skull and jaw has proved difficult. In many ways the fossils resemble *P. boisei,* and indeed, many paleoanthropologists view them as

Prognathic: having the lower face and jaws projecting in front of the upper parts of the face.

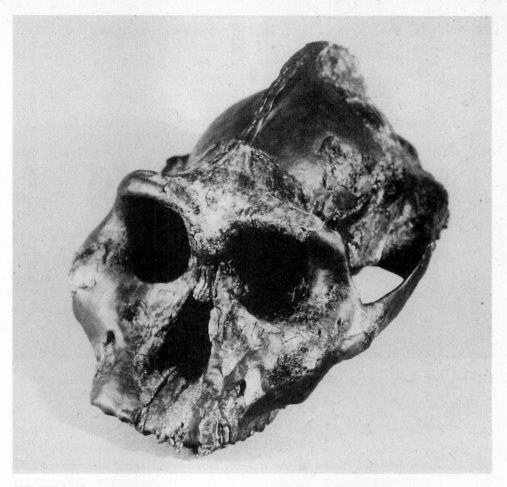

FIGURE 8–10 The Black Skull (museum number KNM-WT 17000) represents a new variety of australopithecine, *Paranthropus aethiopicus*. Although a member of the robust australopithecine clade, it resembles *Australopithecus afarensis* in several traits.

early remains of that species. But in other ways, such as the Black Skull's facial prognathism, its unflexed cranial base, and particulars of the jaw joint, the material resembles the early gracile species *Australopithecus afarensis* (to be discussed shortly). Despite its similarities to *A. afarensis*, however, most workers agree that the west Turkana skull and jaw belong within the robust clade. Following the arguments given at the end of Chapter 7, we agree with F. E. Grine, Bernard Wood, and others in classifying these fossils as a new species, *Paranthropus aethiopicus*—a third variety of robust australopithecine (see Box 8–1). The *A. aethiopicus* jaw discovered earlier at Omo is also included here and thus renamed *Paranthropus*.

Paranthropus aethiopicus: robust australopithecine species that inhabited East Africa 2.6–2.3 mya.

Evidence of *Homo* at Koobi Fora

Early in the work at Koobi Fora, it became clear that the Lake Turkana region contained fossils of hominids other than robust australopithecines. Over time, a number of specimens were recovered of larger-brained, gracile creatures that did not fit well into either *Australopithecus* or *Paranthropus*. One of the finest fossils carries

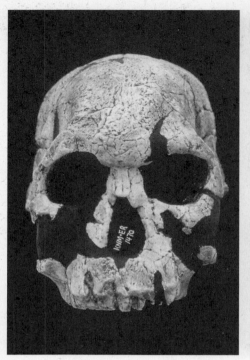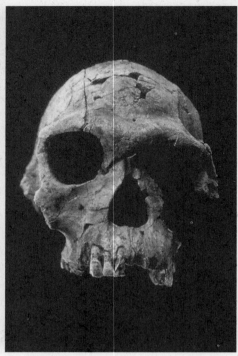

FIGURE 8–11   *Homo rudolfensis* (ER 1470; left) compared with *Homo habilis* (ER 1813; right). Note the differences in size of braincase and brows, as well as the amount of facial prognathism, between the two early *Homo* species.

the museum number KNM-ER 1470, and it is an almost complete cranium and face, but with the skull base and jaw missing (Figure 8–11). ER 1470 combines a large face with strongly built zygomatic arches and relatively large molar teeth (much smaller than in *Paranthropus*, however). The skull is relatively lightly built, and the braincase is considerably larger than any australopithecine's at 775 cc.

As the search for fossils continued at Koobi Fora, several other specimens of relatively large-brained hominids were discovered, including the splendid skull labeled ER-1813 (Figure 8–11). But what to call the nonaustralopithecines from Koobi Fora? Initially, they were lumped with similar specimens from Olduvai Gorge and classified as *Homo habilis*. This is still the position taken by South African anthropologist Phillip Tobias, who prefers a single-species interpretation of all early *Homo* material. Other workers disagree. Bernard Wood in England and American G. P. Rightmire have both argued that there is too much variation in the combined Olduvai and Koobi Fora assemblage to be contained in a single species—even a species with marked sexual dimorphism in body size. It now seems increasingly likely that *Homo habilis*, as traditionally defined, may well actually be at least two species. Wood has proposed the following solution to the problem (a solution that we have adopted for this textbook): Retain the name *Homo habilis* for the Olduvai material and some of the fossils from Koobi Fora (including ER-1813), and classify ER-1470 and certain other Koobi Fora specimens as belonging to a new species, *Homo rudolfensis*.

If the early *Homo* fossils from Olduvai and Koobi Fora are sorted in this way, interesting differences appear between the two resulting species (Box 8–2). *Homo*

BOX 8–2
CHARACTERISTICS OF EARLY *HOMO*[a]

Trait	Homo habilis	Homo rudolfensis
Height (sexes combined)	3.3 ft (100 cm) (?)	4.9 ft (150 cm) (?)
Weight	F: 71 lb (32 kg) M: 82 lb (37 kg) (F about 86% of M)	F: 112 lb (51 kg) M: 132 lb (60 kg) (F about 85% of M)
Brain size (sexes combined)	612 cc mean (509–674 cc range)	781 cc mean (752–810 cc range)
Cranium	Somewhat prognathic face; incipient brow ridge; fore-shortened palate; no sagittal crest; rounded mandibular base	Flat face; no brow ridge; large palate; no sagittal crest; everted mandibular base
Dentition	Narrower lower grinding teeth; mostly single-rooted lower premolars	Broader lower grinding teeth; multirooted lower premolars
Limbs	Longer arms and shorter legs than modern humans; feet retaining adaptations for climbing	Limb proportions unknown; feet more like those of later humans
Locomotion	Bipedalism (modern?)	Bipedalism (modern?)
Known dates (million years B.P.)	2.0–1.6	2.4–1.6

[a]Mean values for anatomical measurements may change with additional fossil discoveries.

habilis (as now narrowly defined) has the more primitive-looking skull, with some prognathism, an incipient brow ridge, and a much smaller brain (although brain size is increased 33 percent over the australopithecine average). Additionally, the postcranial anatomy of the newly defined *Homo habilis* includes small body size, australopithecine-like limb proportions (Figure 8–12) and adaptations of the feet for climbing—features that suggest the continuation of arboreal activities in addition to terrestrial bipedalism. On the progressive side, however, the teeth of *Homo habilis* seem more like those of later hominids than do the teeth of *Homo rudolfensis*. For its part, *Homo rudolfensis* has a larger body, a flatter face and a larger brain than *H. habilis* (showing a 69 percent increase in brain size over the australopithecine average), but these are combined with broad grinding teeth that remind one of *Paranthropus*. And while the limb proportions of *Homo rudolfensis* are currently unknown, certain features of the foot and the thigh are quite similar to those of later *Homo* species. The few pelvic remains of early *Homo* suggest that these hominids may have shown fully modern and well balanced bipedalism, although more fossils are needed to decide this issue conclusively. At any rate, their bipedalism was probably more modern than that of the australopithecines.

These two species of early *Homo* overlapped temporally by 400,000 years or more (Box 8–2), and, at least at Koobi Fora, they overlapped geographically as well. *Homo rudolfensis* was apparently the first to evolve and may have been strictly an East African form. Recent discoveries at the Uraha site west of Lake Malawi have set the earliest date for *Homo rudolfensis* at 2.4 mya. *Homo habilis* (as

Homo rudolfensis: one of the two species of "early *Homo*"; inhabited East Africa 2.4–1.6 million years ago.

FIGURE 8–12 *Homo habilis* as reconstructed primarily from the Olduvai Gorge fossil OH 62, discovered in 1986. Note the relatively long arms and short legs of this species of early *Homo*.

narrowly defined) ranged from Koobi Fora and Omo in the north to Sterkfontein and Swartkrans in the south and shared the latter site with *Paranthropus robustus* (see Chapter 7).

But what are the evolutionary relationships among the various australopithecine and early *Homo* species? We are almost ready to try to sort them out, but before doing so, we must look at two more hominid species, and very special ones at that: the oldest known members of the human family, *Australopithecus afarensis* and *Australopithecus ramidus*.

Discoveries at Hadar (1973–1976)

Five hundred miles (800 km) to the northeast of Koobi Fora, near the Awash River in northern Ethiopia, at a barren and arid place called Hadar (Figures 8–1 and 8–13), extraordinary discoveries have given gracile australopithecines an extremely early date. At Hadar, an international expedition led by Maurice Taieb and Yves Coppens from France and Don Johanson from the United States made several extremely important fossil finds. The story began in 1973, when, during the first season at Hadar, Johanson found a hominid knee joint washed out of a slope. This discovery in itself would not have been so remarkable if the geologists and paleontologists had not assigned it a date of about 3 mya. Furthermore, an examination of its anatomy proved conclusively that the creature to whom the knee belonged had a close-knee stance and walked erect (Figure 8–14). Here was evidence of habitual bipedalism far older than anything known before. Hadar suddenly became the most intriguing prehistoric site on earth.

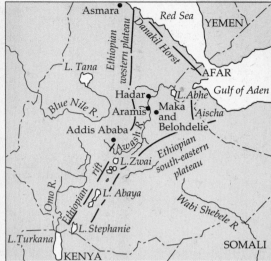

FIGURE 8–13 Important hominid remains have been recovered from the extensive stratified deposits at Hadar (right) in the Afar region. At this site, Donald C. Johanson (at the bottom center) discovered the bones of a skeleton in 1974. After three-and-a-half weeks of mapping, collecting, and sieving, the bones were gathered into one of the most nearly complete early hominids yet found (bottom row, right photograph). "Lucy," as the skeleton is called, lived by a lake about 3 mya; she was only 3.5 to 4 ft (about 1.1 m) tall and died when she was in her early 20s. Based on this and other discoveries, Johanson and his colleagues named a new species, *Australopithecus afarensis*. Also found in this region was a complete palate, dated at around 3.8 million years. In the bottom left photograph it is compared with a cast of a *Homo erectus* palate (right) that is less than 1 million years old. Their similarities suggest that the Afar palate is ancestral to *Homo*.

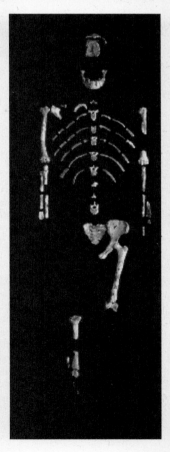

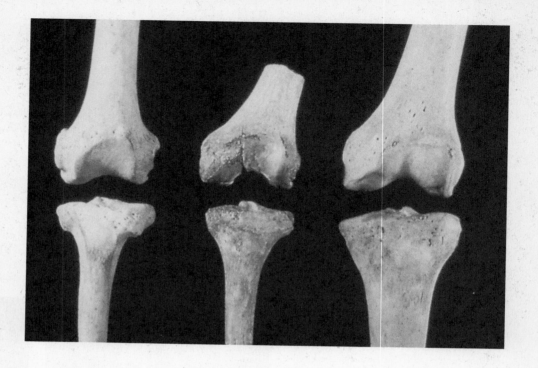

FIGURE 8–14 The interpretation of the *Australopithecus afarensis* knee bones can be understood from this figure. The critical character is the plane of the condyles of the knee joint in relation to the shaft of the femur. The photograph of left knees shows that in the ape (left) the alignment is such that the leg is straight when the knee is extended. In humans (right) and in *A. afarensis* (middle), the alignment is such that the leg is angled at the knee. This is partially a product of the broadening of the pelvis (top drawings). The lower drawings show that the bearing surfaces of the knee condyles are broadened in bipedal species as an adaptation to the greater weight transmitted through the knee.

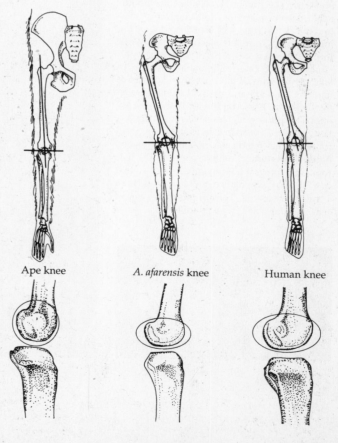

Ape knee   *A. afarensis* knee   Human knee

Johanson and his group returned to Hadar in the fall of 1974, and on November 30 he and his student Tom Gray made a short detour to look in a particular gully that had intrigued him. In it the two men discovered one of the most remarkable finds in all paleoanthropology: the partial skeleton of a hominid about 3 million years of age. Given the name Lucy, the skeleton (from locality 288), which was 40 percent complete, represented a very small gracile *Australopithecus* (Figure 8–13). Although the knee joint and the pelvis again carry the marks of habitual bipedalism, the skull is primitive, as are other features of the skeleton, which is somewhat more apelike than that of *A. africanus* from South Africa.

The 1975 season brought further remarkable discoveries. At a single site (locality 333), one of Johanson's team, Mike Bush, found further hominid fossils, this time a mixed collection of some 200 teeth and bone fragments, representing at least 13 individuals, including males, females, and at least four children. The strange thing about this precious haul was that the hominid bones were all associated and from a single level, not mixed with animal bones as such fossils usually are. They have been called "the first family."

The final field season of 1976 was concerned mainly with stratigraphy and dating. Researchers now believe that this group of fossils probably falls into the time range 2.8–3.3 mya (Figure 8–15). The potassium-argon dates in this section agree with fission-track dates and have been cross-checked by the chemical signatures of the tuffs, while the fauna (in particular, the pig fossils) from the section also support the dates. Figure 8–15 also shows how the paleomagnetism of the section conforms to the paleomagnetic record. In summary, the site is quite well dated, although further dates from below the fossil-bearing strata would help sandwich the lower collection of fossils.

The fossils from Hadar were described by Johanson and his associates. The characteristics of the group have caused Johanson, Coppens, and Tim White to recognize a new, earlier, and more primitive species of *Australopithecus: A. afarensis*. The characteristics of this species are described below and summarized in Box 8–3.

But before describing the traits of *Australopithecus afarensis*, it may be useful to review quickly the anatomical expectations that we have of the first hominids. The biochemical and fossil data together indicate that the Hominidae diverged from the chimpanzee-bonobo lineage quite recently—probably only 5–7 mya. Given this recent evolutionary descent from ape ancestors, we expect the oldest members of the human family to show a clear mixture of ape traits and human traits. Apes have small brains, big canines, and bodies (particularly arms, hands, and feet) adapted for arboreal movement. In contrast, modern humans have huge brains, small canines, and bodies (particularly pelvic girdles, legs, and feet) specialized for bipedal locomotion. If we are correct in concluding that modern humans are descended—via the australopithecines—from a long-extinct species of ape, then our early australopithecine ancestors should be strongly intermediate between the two evolutionary grades.

The body size of *Australopithecus afarensis* varied considerably both within a sex and between sexes (sexual dimorphism), so that females, like Lucy, may have been just over 3 ft (about 1 m) tall, while large males may have been as much as 5 ft (1.5 m) tall. Weight probably varied from 66 to as much as 154 lb (30–70 kg). The individuals, though small, were powerfully built: the bones were thick for their size and carried markings suggesting that they had been well muscled. As we have seen, the evidence of the knee joint makes it clear that, like all other

Australopithecus afarensis: gracile australopithecine species that inhabited East Africa from at least 4.0 to 2.5 mya; if the Lothagam jaw is included in the species, it goes back to 5.6 mya.

FIGURE 8–15 Strati-graphic column at Hadar showing chronometric dates in million years B.P. and probable paleomagnetic match.

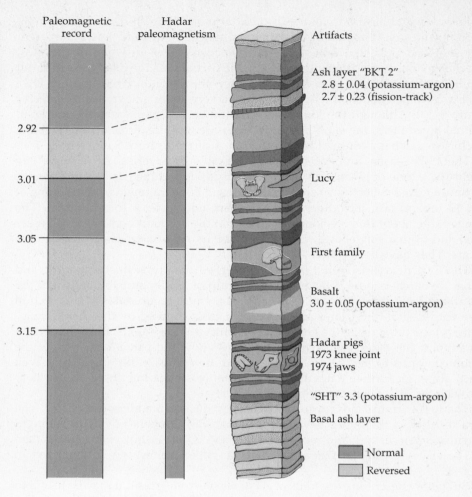

Paleomagnetic record

Hadar paleomagnetism

Artifacts

Ash layer "BKT 2"
2.8 ± 0.04 (potassium-argon)
2.7 ± 0.23 (fission-track)

2.92

3.01 — Lucy

3.05 — First family

Basalt
3.0 ± 0.05 (potassium-argon)

3.15

Hadar pigs
1973 knee joint
1974 jaws

"SHT" 3.3 (potassium-argon)

Basal ash layer

Normal
Reversed

hominids, they were habitually bipedal. A study of footbones, in particular the base of the great toe, shows that this toe was not opposable. All primates except hominids have opposable great toes (just as our thumb is opposable), which enable them to grip branches. The absence of such an opposable toe in *A. afarensis* shows very clearly that while they retained some signs of arboreal activity, they were committed to the hominid, terrestrial way of life.

The pelvis of *A. afarensis* shows unmistakable adaptations for habitual bipedalism (Figure 8–16). First, the iliac blades are short and broad, and deep sci-atic notches indicate the extent of backward expansion and bending. Thus the center of gravity of *A. afarensis* was considerably lower than that of an ape, and as a consequence, bipedal balancing was much more stable and energy-efficient. Second, the iliac blades of *A. afarensis* are curved toward the front of the body, producing a partial pelvic bowl. Third, the anterior inferior iliac spines are well developed and mark the upper attachment of powerful *rectus femoris* muscles that flexed the *A. afarensis* thigh and extended the lower leg during bipedal walk-ing. And finally, the ischial shaft is relatively short compared to the shaft of an ape. In combination with these humanlike features, however, there are clear

Rectus femoris: one of the muscles that flexes the hominid thigh.

BOX 8–3
CHARACTERISTICS OF *AUSTRALOPITHECUS AFARENSIS*[a]

Trait	*Australopithecus afarensis*
Height	F: 3.3–3.4 ft (100–105 cm) M: 5.0 ft (151 cm) (F is 68% of M)
Weight	F: 66 lb (30 kg) M: 99–154 lb (45–70 kg) (F is 52% of M)
Brain size (sexes combined)	433 cc mean (400–500 cc range)
Cranium	Prognathic face; low, flat forehead; low-vaulted braincase; large brows; males with sagittal cresting; unflexed cranial base
Dentition	U-shaped toothrow; relatively large anterior teeth (incisors and canines); moderately large molars; canines that project somewhat; upper jaw diastemata; lower P3s at least semisectorial
Diet	Unknown
Limbs	Long arms relative to legs; curved finger and toe bones; legs and feet that reveal adaptations for arboreal movement; close-knee stance
Pelvis	Short, broad iliac blades; incomplete pelvic bowl; weak iliofemoral ligament; ischial shaft relatively shorter than in apes, but not yet realigned in modern fashion; pelvis wide between hip joints
Locomotion	Bipedalism (swaying gait?) and arboreal climbing
Known dates (million years B.P.)	?5.6–2.5 (without Lothagam, 4.0–2.5)

[a]Mean values, and ranges of values, for anatomical measurements may change with additional fossil discoveries.

pelvic indications that the evolutionary transformation was not complete and that *A. afarensis* probably did not show fully modern bipedal locomotion. These indications include the incomplete pelvic bowl, the lack of modern realignment of the ischial shafts, the extreme width (hip joint to hip joint) of the pelvic girdle, and evidence that the iliofemoral ligaments may have been small and weak. This combination of derived and primitive traits has convinced some anthropologists and anatomists that *Australopithecus afarensis* walked with a swaying gait to balance its body weight as it moved.

The arms of *A. afarensis* were slightly longer and their legs slightly shorter, relative to their trunks (an apelike character), than those of modern humans. Their hands had apelike wrist bones and curved fingers, but the fingers were not long—like those of an ape—but shorter, like our own, with a fully opposable thumb. Their skulls (Figure 8–17; see also the new *A. afarensis* skull in the fossil hominid color essay) were small, almost chimpanzee-like, with a cranial

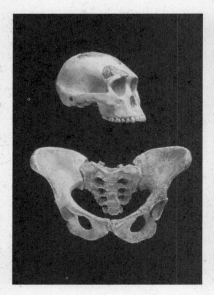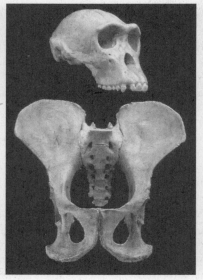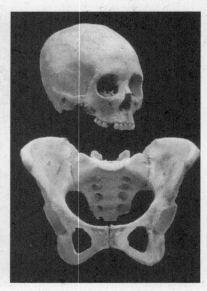

FIGURE 8–16 The restored pelvic girdle of *A. afarensis* (left) compared with that of a modern human (right) and a chimpanzee (center). Note the shorter, broader ilia and more bowllike pelvis of *A. afarensis* compared to that of the ape. Also visible are the deep sciatic notches and extreme pelvic width (hip joint to hip joint) of *A. afarensis*. A typical skull for each species is shown with a pelvis.

capacity of approximately 400–500 cc (Table 8–1)—hardly different from that of chimpanzees.

Finally, the *A. afarensis* dentition is of great importance: it is extremely apelike in many respects. In particular, the canine is somewhat pointed, with a large root, and is reminiscent of that of an ape; it also shows noticeable sexual dimorphism (Figure 8–18). It is associated with a small diastema in the upper jaw. At the same time, the first lower premolar (P3) is also remarkable in lacking or having only a small internal (lingual) secondary cusp; yet the tooth is not truly apelike, for the apes have no second cusp, but only one single large one. It is, as Johanson says, a

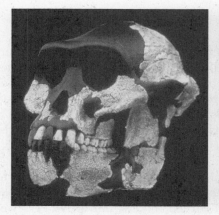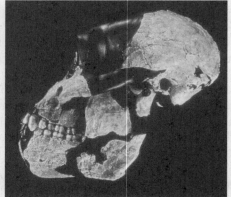

FIGURE 8–17 Composite reconstruction based on *A. afarensis* fossil skull fragments found at Hadar. Reconstruction by Tim White and William Kimbel. The photographs are approximately 25 percent of actual size. See also the new *A. afarensis* skull shown in the fossil hominid color essay.

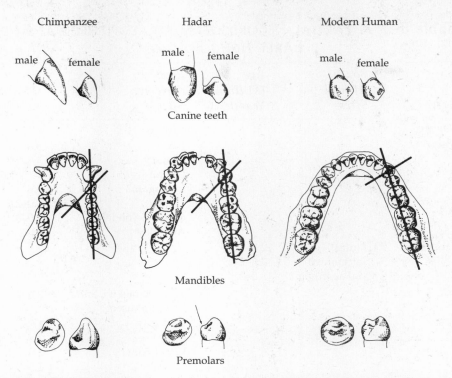

Chimpanzee   Hadar   Modern Human

male   female   male   female   male   female

Canine teeth

Mandibles

Premolars

FIGURE 8–18 Comparison of Hadar (*A. afarensis*) with chimpanzee and modern human dentitions. At the top, a comparison of the male and female canines of each species. Notice the pointed ape canines and the blunt human teeth, together with the considerable sexual dimorphism in the ape and Hadar teeth. Below this, the three mandibles are illustrated. Notice the intermediate traits of the Hadar mandible. The lines show the alignment of the first lower premolar in relation to the molar series as a whole. Below, the first lower premolar is illustrated. The ape premolar is one-cusped; the human premolar two-cusped. The Hadar premolar illustrated has a small lingual cusp (arrow) and is intermediate in form.

tooth in transition. This feature and the form of the canine serve to separate the group from the gracile South African *A. africanus*. The molar teeth show the kind of wear we associate with modern humans, with an indication of the grinding of grit-laden foods. In some specimens the canines show beginning wear from the apex. Finally, the shape of the toothrow is more apelike than human, as is the profile of the face (Figure 8–17).

Altogether the *A. afarensis* fossils show a remarkable set of traits that place them squarely in the family Hominidae, yet reveal many similarities to apes. Two decades' work has made *A. afarensis* one of the best known of all fossil hominid species.

The species *A. afarensis* includes more than the Hadar fossils (see Table 8–3 and Figure 8–1). In addition, there are recently reported 4 million-year-old remains from Allia Bay, east Lake Turkana; more Ethiopian fossils from Middle Awash River sites such as Maka and Belohdelie and from Fejej in the Omo River basin; and the extremely old (5.6 million years B.P.) mandibular fragment from Lothagam, Kenya, that Yale University anthropologist Andrew Hill and his co-workers believe possesses diagnostic features of the species (specialists disagree

Table 8–3 A Partial Record of Australopithecinae and Early *Homo* Fossils

Species	South African Sites	Age (Million Years)[a]	East African Sites	Age (Million Years)[b]
A. ramidus			Aramis	4.4
A. afarensis			Fejej	3.6
			Hadar	3.3–2.8
			Laetoli	3.75–3.6
			Lothagam?	5.6
			Omo	3.0–2.5
			Maka/Belohdelie	4.0–3.4
			Allia Bay	4.0
A. africanus	Taung	2.8–2.6		
	Sterkfontein	2.8–2.5		
	Makapansgat	3.0–2.5		
P. aethiopicus			Omo, Lomekwi, and Kangatukuseo	2.6–2.3
P. boisei			Olduvai	1.75
			Omo	2.4–1.5
			Koobi Fora	2.0–1.3
			Peninj	1.5
P. robustus	Kromdraai	2.0–1.8		
	Swartkrans	1.8–1.0		
H. habilis	Sterkfontein	2.0–1.8	Olduvai	1.9–1.6
	Swartkrans	1.8–1.6	Omo and Koobi Fora	2.0–1.8
H. rudolfensis			Uraha	2.4
			Omo and Koobi Fora	2.0–1.6

[a]Dates attributed to South African sites are based not on potassium-argon analysis, but on comparative analysis of fauna and are not as accurate as potassium-argon dates. Nevertheless, these dates probably do bracket the times of existence of the various fossil species.
[b]Most of the dates for sites in East and northeast Africa are based on potassium-argon analysis and are therefore quite accurate.

on the classification of the Lothagam find; see the conclusions of White et al. in a later section). And finally, *A. afarensis* includes fossils from the site of Laetoli in northern Tanzania.

Discoveries at Laetoli (1974–1977) and the Awash (1981)

In 1974 Mary Leakey returned to Laetoli, a site south of Olduvai (Figure 8–1). The site was first visited by the Leakeys in 1935 and later by the German prehistorian L. Kohl-Larsen. Louis Leakey collected some fossils of Pliocene monkeys, which included some loose teeth, among them a canine tooth. This tooth has recently been reexamined and has turned out to be very similar to those of the species *Australopithecus afarensis;* it is of great interest because its discovery actually predated all the discoveries of Robert Broom in South Africa (Chapter 7). It was in fact the first evidence of an adult *Australopithecus* that was ever recovered.

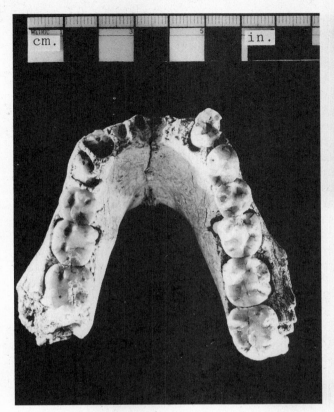

FIGURE 8–19 This hominid jaw from Laetoli was discovered in 1974 and is dated about 3.7 million years B.P. It has been selected as the type specimen of *Australopithecus afarensis*. The left photograph shows the relatively large but damaged canine tooth in the top right-hand corner. The right photograph shows the jaw from the right-hand side.

In 1939 Kohl-Larsen collected a hominid upper jaw fragment with two teeth, which was called *Meganthropus africanus*. We now believe that these finds also belong, with the Hadar fossils, to the species *A. afarensis*.

When Mary Leakey returned to the site she collected more than 20 fragmentary hominid jaws from eroding Pliocene strata in this area (Figure 8–19). They represented eight adults and three children, and they were conveniently sandwiched between two volcanic ash strata dated 3.6 and 3.75 million years B.P. They have a striking affinity with the Hadar fossils, and it is claimed by Johanson and White that they belong to the same species; indeed, these workers selected one of the Laetoli jaws as the *type specimen* of the species *Australopithecus afarensis*. Some workers, however, feel for several reasons that the Laetoli finds may form a taxon (or taxa) distinct from the Hadar fossils. First of all, the Laetoli fossils carry some unique traits, and they have features in common with *A. africanus* and with *Homo habilis* from nearby Olduvai Gorge, though they are much older than either. Second, some researchers, such as anthropologist Sigrid Hartwig-Scherer, are troubled by the extreme degree of sexual dimorphism in body weight attributed to *A. afarensis*. Were there really two species, rather than one species with very large males and very small females? And third, the Hadar and Laetoli sites are just over 1,000 mi (1,600 km) apart—a considerable distance for combining fossil assemblages to produce a single new species.

While many of these issues have yet to be settled, new discoveries and analyses have provided some light. Regarding the issue of sexual dimorphism in body

Type specimen: the fossil specimen that serves as the basis for identifying all other individuals in a species; usually the original specimen to be found.

size, recent fossil discoveries at the Ethiopian site of Maka (just south of Hadar) have shown that a single *A. afarensis* site can produce the same amount of intraspecific variation in tooth and body size as the combined Hadar-Laetoli assemblage. Furthermore, the location of new fossil sites has eased the geographical problems surrounding *A. afarensis*. The sites of Fejej (Ethiopia), Allia Bay (east Turkana Lake, Kenya), and Lothagam (northern Kenya) fall almost exactly halfway between Hadar and Laetoli, and the demonstration of *A. afarensis* material from these localities should put an end to geographical qualms about the species' validity. For now, most anthropologists (including the authors of this book) are following Johanson and White and treating *Australopithecus afarensis* as a single, widespread, and anatomically variable species.

Paul Abell, a geochemist working at Laetoli, made another discovery that was, if possible, more remarkable than the fossil finds. Sandwiched in layers of volcanic ash were the preserved footprints of a whole range of animals, including elephants, rhinoceroses, many types of antelope, three kinds of giraffe, a saber-toothed cat, and many other species, all now extinct. One of these other species was a hominid: clearly impressed in the ash layer, hominid tracks cover a distance of more than 150 ft (45 m). Portions of the tracks are slightly eroded, but several intact prints are preserved (Figure 8–20). The pattern and form of the footprints are like those made in soft sand by modern humans and suggest (like the other evidence) an evolved bipedalism. The smaller and larger footprints (on the basis of modern people's foot size) suggest a stature ranging from about 4 to 5 ft

FIGURE 8–20   At Laetoli has been found a unique record of the footprints of animals dated from about 3.7 million years B.P. The footprints of a large proportion of the fossil species are present, including those of *Australopithecus afarensis* as shown in this photograph and on page 264.

(1.2–1.5 m). This discovery is a most remarkable one, and it is unique in paleontology for the number of mammalian species represented: a large proportion of the Laetoli Pliocene fauna have left their imprint. Above all, it is quite clear that *Australopithecus afarensis* was walking very like a human nearly 4 mya—and perhaps earlier.

Interestingly, adopting bipedalism apparently did not require forsaking the trees completely—at least not initially. *A. afarensis, A. africanus,* and all the *Paranthropus* forms show anatomical evidence of both the derived trait of terrestrial bipedalism and the continuation of some arboreal climbing and suspension. Indeed, australopithecine bipedalism has been described as "facultative" (optional, dependent on conditions), as opposed to the "obligatory" bipedalism of modern humans. And while the australopithecines' hips and feet were evolving relatively quickly in response to conditions favoring bipedalism, other parts of their anatomy were lagging behind. For example, new evidence from CT (computed tomography) images of australopithecine skulls has revealed that these early hominids had *semicircular canal* morphologies like those of apes, not of modern humans. This means that, although routinely bipedal, the australopithecines were not yet perfectly adapted to upright balance and coordination. As is so often the case with evolution, natural selection moved the early hominids toward full bipedalism through a mosaic of adaptive changes.

> **Semicircular canals:** fluid-filled canals of the inner ear that control balance and coordination.

But despite their great age and interesting features, the Hadar and Laetoli materials fall short of giving us a look at the actual *origin* of bipedalism. The Laetoli footprints and the postcranial fossils of *A. afarensis* show clearly that, 3.7 million years ago, members of this species were *already* habitual bipeds, even though their locomotion may not have been quite modern in some ways. One of the few hints the fossils do give about the dawn of bipedalism is to show that our ancestors did not evolve through a knuckle-walking stage: the hands of *A. afarensis* show absolutely no signs of knuckle-walking adaptations. Direct evidence on the actual origin of upright walking has yet to be discovered, but we may have gained important new insights into the problem with the recent discovery of a creature claimed to be the sixth species of australopithecine: *Australopithecus ramidus.*

> ***Australopithecus ramidus:*** species provisionally classified as a hominid; lived in East Africa 4.4 mya.

Oldest Hominid (?) Found at Aramis, Ethiopia (1992–1993)

Between 1992 and 1993, an international team of paleoanthropologists, including American Tim White, Gen Suwa of the University of Tokyo, and Berhane Asfaw of the Ethiopian Ministry of Culture and Sports Affairs, focused its collecting efforts on early Pliocene deposits at the Aramis site in the middle of Ethiopia's Awash River drainage system (Figures 8–1 and 8–13). Suwa made the first Aramis discovery in mid-December 1992 when a glint of sunlight from a fossilized molar tooth caught his eye while he was surface hunting. "I knew immediately that it was a hominid," he said later, "and because we had found other ancient animals that morning, I knew it was one of the oldest hominid teeth ever found." That tooth proved to be just the beginning of a treasure trove of fossils, and over the 1992 and 1993 field seasons, Suwa and his colleagues collected a total of 17 fossil specimens, all of which date back to about 4.4 million years B.P. Among the ancient remains were several teeth, a partial mandible (Figure 8–21), some skull

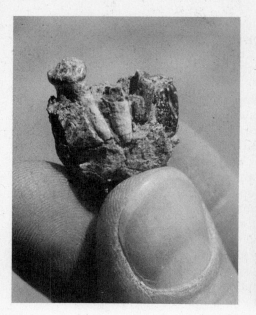 

FIGURE 8–21   (Left) Partial mandible of *Australopithecus ramidus* from Aramis, Ethiopia. (Right) The upper arm bone of *A. ramidus* held here by paleoanthropologist Alemayehu Asfaw. Both photos © 1994 Tim D. White\Brill Atlanta.

fragments, and a few arm bones (including the rare discovery of all three bones from the left arm of a single individual).

After extensive analysis of the Aramis fossils—and comparisons with living and fossil apes, modern humans, and several extinct hominid varieties—White, Suwa, and Asfaw concluded that they had discovered a new, and extremely primitive, species of hominid. Selecting a species name based on the Afar word for "root"—a choice that signifies the belief that the creature belongs at the very base of hominids' evolutionary tree—the researchers dubbed the new form *Australopithecus ramidus*. *A. ramidus* was formally announced and described in the British journal *Nature* in September 1994.

The most important anatomical features of *Australopithecus ramidus* can be summarized as follows (see also Box 8–4): canines shorter and more incisiform than those of apes, but less incisiform and larger (relative to the postcanine teeth) than those of *A. afarensis;* lower anterior premolars (P3s) lacking the honing facet (sectorial functioning) characteristic of apes; enamel on canines and molars that is thin compared to that of *A. afarensis* but approximates the condition in chimpanzees; similar to other australopithecines, but in contrast to apes, a forwardly placed foramen magnum; and, finally, a shape of the head of the humerus (upper arm bone) and the anatomy of the elbow joint resembling that of later hominids, not of apes. One additional characteristic that strongly differentiates *A. ramidus* from *A. afarensis* is the extremely apelike anatomy of the lower first deciduous molar found at Aramis.

White et al. believe that the Aramis fossils show enough derived features to be safely included in the hominid family. They point particularly to hominidlike modifications in the canine–lower-P3 complex, the positioning of the foramen magnum, and the elbow anatomy. To its discoverers, *A. ramidus* fulfills virtually all the theoretical expectations of a species just this side of the ape-hominid split.

BOX 8–4
CHARACTERISTICS OF *AUSTRALOPITHECUS RAMIDUS* (PROVISIONAL)

Trait	Australopithecus ramidus (provisional)
Height	At least 3.3 ft (100 cm; upper height limit and sexual dimorphism unknown)
Weight	At least 66 lb (30 kg; upper weight limit and sexual dimorphism unknown)
Brain size	Unknown
Cranium	Forwardly positioned foramen magnum; small *occipital condyles*; very flat surface of jaw joint
Dentition	Canines shorter and more incisiform than those of apes, but less incisiform and larger (relative to the postcanine teeth) than those of *A. afarensis*; lower anterior premolars (P3s) lacking evidence of sectorial functioning; thin enamel on canines and molars; apelike anatomy of lower first deciduous molar
Diet	Unknown (thin molar enamel may rule out "hard object feeder")
Limbs	Arm bones showing a mosaic of hominid and ape traits; elliptical shape of the head of the humerus and the anatomy of the elbow joint resembling those of later hominids; pelvic and lower limb anatomy unknown
Locomotion	Bipedalism? (classification tentative; knuckle walking can be ruled out)
Known dates (million years B.P.)	4.4

Occipital condyles: pads of bone on the base of the skull that articulate with the uppermost vertebra.

It is much too soon to report a consensus among paleoanthropologists regarding *Australopithecus ramidus.* The few opinions that have been offered so far, however, show that there are both supporters and critics. Bernard Wood agrees enthusiastically with a hominid classification, saying that White et al. "present compelling fossil evidence that they have found the oldest hominid species yet." Wood is less than fully convinced, however, that the Aramis fossils are appropriately classified within the genus *Australopithecus:* in his view, a new genus designation may be justified. Nor is Wood fully comfortable with the view that the Aramis material represents the common ancestor of all later hominids. While conceding that this is the most likely phyletic position for the new fossils, he points out that certain features argue for exclusive ancestry of the *Paranthropus* clade only.

Chris Stringer of the British Museum (Natural History) affirms the importance of the Aramis discoveries, saying they "seem to take us closer to a common ancestor [of apes and hominids]." He is bothered, however, by the thin enamel on the Aramis teeth. Thin enamel is characteristic of the African apes, while all early hominids except *A. ramidus* had thick enamel. To Stringer, thin enamel precludes inclusion of the Aramis materials in the genus *Australopithecus,* but he notes that further fossil discoveries are probably necessary before an appropriate classification can be made. (Adding to the taxonomic uncertainty, in May 1995 White et al. published a correction to their 1994 paper that "made available" a new hominid genus name, *Ardipithecus,* for the Aramis fossils in case *Australopithecus* proves to be inappropriate.)

And finally, Andrew Hill of Yale University voiced a problem that may already have occurred to some readers when he said, "I would be happier if we knew [*A. ramidus*] was a biped." As noted in Chapter 6, habitual bipedalism is *the* primary criterion for inclusion in the family Hominidae. Certain features of the Aramis fossils—especially the anterior placement of the foramen magnum—are quite *suggestive* of some degree of bipedalism, but even White et al. admit that, given the paucity of postcranial material, "Bipedality . . . remains to be demonstrated." According to White, the fossils do allow certain locomotor patterns, such as knuckle walking, to be ruled out. Final resolution of the locomotion question, however, will require finding more fossils.

And so the Aramis fossils present us with a set of dental, cranial, and upper limb traits that are strongly suggestive of hominid status, but the key question of habitual bipedalism remains open. The presence of several features usually correlated with bipedalism helps somewhat, but conclusive proof is lacking at present. Furthermore, there is the uncertainty about whether the Aramis materials should be assigned to *Australopithecus, Paranthropus,* or some other genus (*Ardipithecus?*) altogether. Given all of these considerations, the authors of this textbook have chosen to treat *Australopithecus ramidus* as a *provisional* species within the family Hominidae. Was it an ape with some hominidlike traits, or a hominid so close in time to the family's evolutionary origin that it retained numerous apelike features? We suspect that the latter is true, but further discoveries are needed to settle the taxonomic issues and clarify the true nature of the new species.

Even provisional acceptance of the Aramis fossils as hominids, however, forces two additional important issues. First, how might *A. ramidus* have been related to *A. afarensis?* Given the more primitive (apelike) anatomy of the former, there appears to be no morphological reason to deny an ancestor-descendant relationship. But what about the apparent chronological problem? *Australopithecus ramidus* dates back to 4.4 million years B.P., while *A. afarensis*—if one includes the fossil from Lothagam, Kenya (Table 8–3)—dates back 5.6 million years into the past. Does this disqualify *A. afarensis* as a descendant of the Aramis species? These are murky waters, full of classification and dating problems, but a few observations can be made. White et al. note that Lothagam broadly matches both *A. ramidus* and *A. afarensis* in anatomy. That being the case, it seems only reasonable to put the Lothagam fossil in suspension and to reach a tentative conclusion on the *A. ramidus–A. afarensis* relationship without reference to the Kenyan remains. Suspending Lothagam shortens the time range for *A. afarensis* to 4.0 to 2.5 million years B.P.—comfortably later than the 4.4 mya date established for *A. ramidus.* Thus the removal of ambiguous fossil material allows chronology and anatomy to converge on the likelihood that *A. ramidus* was indeed ancestral to *A. afarensis.*

The second issue has to do with traditional theories about the environmental selection pressures that led to bipedal locomotion in the first place. As will be detailed in Chapter 9, it has long been held that hominid bipedalism originally appeared as an adaptation to life on the African savanna—the implication being that the earliest hominids changed quickly from their ape ancestors' forest-

based existence to terrestrial life in an environment of broad grasslands dotted
with occasional trees. Convincing evidence for this view comes from australopithecine sites in both South and East Africa, including some where *A. afarensis*
remains have been found. The new evidence from *A. ramidus*, however, challenges the traditional scenario with the suggestion that bipedalism may actually
have begun in a closed, wooded environment. Geologists working at Aramis
have reconstructed the environment during the time of *A. ramidus* as relatively
flat, closed woodland because of the occurrence of preserved wood and seeds
and numerous bones of woodland animals like kudus and colobine monkeys.
These remains suggest that the earliest australopithecines were not yet living in
a true savanna environment. But even at Aramis some tracts of open country
may have been present, as indicated by the occasional remains of giraffes and
rhinos. Thus, although *A. ramidus* moves us literally and figuratively closer to
the forest, it certainly does not destroy the hypothesis that bipedalism evolved
in response to a mixed habitat, one that offered foraging and travel opportunities in both wooded and open country. Further information on the locomotor
anatomy of *A. ramidus* and the early Pliocene environment at Aramis will be
eagerly awaited.

(Note: as if to emphasize the dynamic nature of paleoanthropology, new information on *Australopithecus ramidus* has been released just as this textbook goes to
press. The 1994 field season at Aramis resulted in the discovery of some 90 fragments—over 45 percent—of an adult *A. ramidus* skeleton. The new fossil material
includes pieces from the skull, arms, vertebral column, pelvis, and legs. Analysis
of the skeleton is just beginning, but in view of the presence of pelvic and leg fragments, this find should produce critical information about the locomotion—and
therefore, the hominid status—of *A. ramidus*.)

Together, *A. ramidus* and *A. afarensis* strongly support the hypothesis that
hominids evolved from some type of African ape around 5–7 mya. Those apes—
our last common ancestors with chimpanzees and bonobos—were apparently
woodland creatures that engaged in generalized climbing and had few, if any,
locomotor specializations. And although we don't yet know the exact identity of
our last ape ancestors, the recent finds in Ethiopia raise the hope that their remains
will soon be discovered.

Early Stone-Tool Evidence

One of the surprises at Koobi Fora was the presence of stone tools, few and far
between, but possibly as old as those at Olduvai Gorge. Somewhat older tools
have been found by the French-American excavations beside the Omo River.
Here, in beds from 2.3 to 2.4 million years old, we find a recognizable collection of
artifacts made to a regular pattern in undisturbed datable deposits. But these artifacts are not associated with any hominid fossils. A similar date is known from
sites along the Semliki River in the western rift valley. Here, stone-tool assemblages have recently been excavated that may also prove to be 2.3 million years of
age. But work at Hadar has taken the archaeological record back still further. In
the 1976 field season, archaeologists Helene Roche and Jack Harris (from France
and New Zealand) discovered an old land surface with basalt Oldowan tools,
together with elephant molar and bone fragments. The site overlies a tuff (BKT 2)
dated by potassium-argon and fission-track at 2.7 to 2.8 million years B.P., and a
reasonable age for the tools is about 2.4 million years old (Figure 8–22). If the date
can be bracketed by further chronometric estimations from overlying tuffs, we

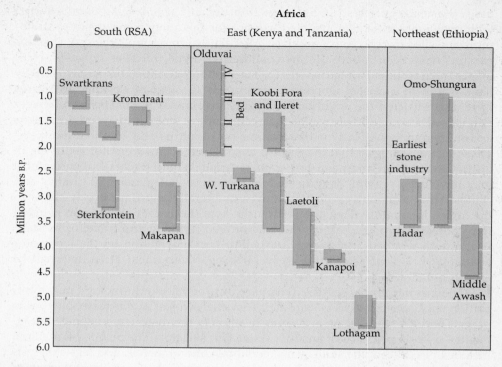

FIGURE 8–22 The approximate time spans of some of the deposits mentioned in the text. The South African dates are generally less reliable than those for East Africa and Ethiopia. The South African deposits usually represent a short time span that falls somewhere in the range of the time indicated. The East African and Ethiopian deposits are deep, and the range indicated is that actually represented by the deposits: fossils are found at many levels.

shall feel secure in attributing stone-tool manufacture of a regular pattern to this early time. Clearly the potential for further work is immense, and we can expect further results from this area in the near future.

Several hominid species are contemporary with early stone-tool use in East Africa: *Paranthropus boisei, P. aethiopicus, Homo habilis,* and *Homo rudolfensis.* The question is: Which one (or several) species made and used these tools? Current wisdom among anthropologists has it that *none* of the australopithecines manufactured stone tools, although, as noted in Chapter 7, analyses of australopithecine hand bones indicate that they were anatomically capable of *stone knapping.* Does the simultaneous appearance of stone tools and early *Homo* around 2.4 mya provide secure evidence that only our own genus engaged in this behavior? What do stone tools tell us about changes in the diet of early hominids? And finally, was stone tool technology important to the survival of hominid species or lineages? At present, we can answer few, if any, of these questions. Much more research is needed.

Stone knapping: stone flaking; generally the production of flake and core tools by striking a stone module with a hammer stone or other object.

LIFESTYLES OF THE EARLY HOMINIDS

Despite a lack of knowledge in many areas, we do know enough at present to make some educated speculations about how the various early hominids lived (Table 8–3 summarizes the early fossil record). For the purpose of such speculations, the australopithecines can be usefully divided into a gracile lineage, containing *Australopithecus afarensis* and *A. africanus,* and a robust lineage, made up of the three *Paranthropus* species (given our limited information about *Australopithecus ramidus,* it is omitted from this discussion). The gracile australopithecines used a variety of habitats, from well-watered and wooded (Hadar and perhaps South Africa) to more open environments (Laetoli). Within those habitats they foraged for a primarily vegetarian diet, although, like today's chimpanzees, they no doubt would have relished the occasional meat meal from small prey animals. They did not make stone tools to assist in their subsistence activities, although the use of perishable tools (again, similar to those of modern chimpanzees) cannot be discounted. While both *A. afarensis* and *A. africanus* were bipeds and spent much time on the ground, their bipedalism was probably not fully modern, and so they are described as moving with a swaying gait. Both species probably also continued to use the arboreal habitat (*A. afarensis* more than *A. africanus*) for foraging and sleeping and as a safe haven from predators. Finally, the moderate-to-extreme sexual dimorphism in body size shown by the gracile australopithecines suggests that they had some sort of polygynous mating system, but whether this involved polygyny with independent harems or occurred within multimale-multifemale groups cannot be determined.

The robust australopithecines (*P. aethiopicus, P. boisei, P. robustus*) also used a variety of habitats; *P. robustus* was adapted to the open grasslands of South Africa (Figure 8–23), while to the north *P. boisei* seems to have preferred well-watered sites such as the gallery forests along rivers. The massive grinding teeth of the robusts suggest that, in contrast to their gracile cousins, they ate large amounts of predominantly tough, fibrous, and/or gritty vegetable foods. That the robusts' vegetable diet may have been supplemented by eating some amount of meat has recently been indicated by the strontium-to-calcium ratio in their bones. Tool use by the robust australopithecines is problematic. They overlapped in time and space with the earliest stone tools (Oldowan choppers and flakes), but because nowhere are they found *exclusively* associated with such tools, they are usually regarded as "nontechnological." Nonetheless, it seems that chimpanzee-type tool use (at least) was well within the capabilities of these hominids. The *Paranthropus* species were all habitual bipeds, although their wide pelvic girdles suggest some lateral swaying for balance. The robusts' long arms and short legs suggest some continuation of arboreal life, and, as in the graciles, moderate-to-marked sexual dimorphism in body size suggests polygynous mating patterns.

Judging by the smallness of their brains and by the brain's presumed proportions, it is likely that none of the australopithecines could talk. But they certainly must have been capable of a number of expressive nonverbal sounds (such as those we find among living monkeys and apes) that others of their kind understood. No doubt they also communicated through various gestures, body movements, and facial expressions. By no standard can the australopithecines be described as "humans" (hominids, yes; humans, no). That term is reserved for more advanced hominids of the genus *Homo.*

By 2.4 mya early *Homo* was present, roaming bipedally across the savannas and through the woodlands of East Africa. Represented by at least two species, *Homo rudolfensis* the older and *H. habilis* the younger, these more advanced hominids apparently lived a life substantially different from that of the australopithecines. Having mastered stone knapping to the point of producing flakes and pebble choppers, these first members of our own genus probably ate considerably

FIGURE 8–23   Reconstruction of a group of robust australopithecines (*Paranthropus robustus*) foraging on the South African grasslands. The use of a digging stick is conjectural.

more meat than did the australopithecines (whether the meat was scavenged or hunted is discussed in Chapter 9). Larger brains no doubt meant more complex communication, although the origins of speech are still uncertain. Similarly uncertain are the social group types and mating patterns of early *Homo*. Interestingly, although early *Homo* apparently showed a more modern type of bipedalism than did the australopithecines, these hominids retained rather apelike limb proportions, suggesting that they may still have made use of the arboreal environment.

Should *Homo rudolfensis* and *H. habilis* be referred to as early "humans"? Now it becomes a matter of taste, with some anthropologists answering "yes" (mainly because of the enlarged brains and technological lifestyle of early *Homo*) and others "no" (because of the apparent simplicity of lifestyle, technology, and communication). Many workers are more comfortable initially applying the label *human* to the next hominid to appear, *Homo erectus*.

EVOLUTIONARY RELATIONSHIPS AMONG THE EARLY HOMINIDS

There are a variety of ways to interpret the evolutionary relationships among the australopithecines and between the australopithecines and the *Homo* lineage. Figure 8–24 illustrates the three predominant views plus two additional evolutionary schemes. The new and provisional species, *Australopithecus ramidus*, has been added tentatively at or near the base of all five trees even though it was unknown when the trees were originally designed (more will be said about *A. ramidus* at the end of this section).

In Hypothesis A, *Australopithecus ramidus* is ancestral to *A. afarensis*. *A. afarensis* then gives rise to *A. africanus,* which in turn serves as the common ancestor of both the robust and *Homo* lineages (note: no attempt is made in Hypotheses A–D to identify the evolutionary relationships either among the robust species or individually for the two species of early *Homo*). In Hypothesis B, the *A. ramidus–A. afarensis* line is still at the base of the hominid evolutionary tree, but now *A. afarensis* gives rise on the one hand to *A. africanus,* which is in turn ancestral to *Paranthropus,* and on the other hand to early *Homo*. And finally, in Hypothesis C, the position of *A. africanus* is switched as the *A. ramidus–A. afarensis* line is seen as directly ancestral to the robust lineage on the one hand and to *A. africanus* on the other, with that species then giving rise to *Homo.*

And as if these three evolutionary hypotheses were not enough, there are other possibilities. Hypothesis D illustrates the view of some workers that *A. afarensis* may not be directly ancestral to *Homo* at all, but that the two forms share an unknown common ancestor (*A. ramidus?*) from the late Miocene or early Pliocene. In this scheme *A. afarensis* gives rise to the robust australopithecines, and *A. africanus* is associated with, but not ancestral to, the *Homo* lineage. And finally, Hypothesis E represents the recently published view of American anthropologists

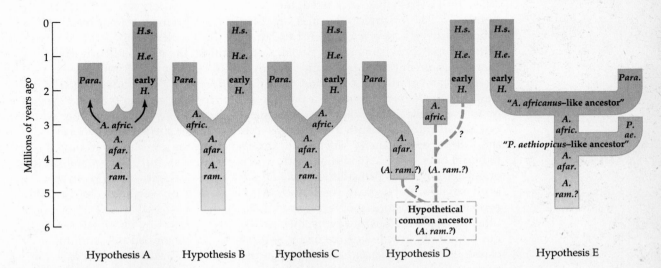

FIGURE 8–24 Five evolutionary trees for hominids. Explanations are in the text. *A. ram.* = *Australopithecus ramidus; A. afar.* = *A. afarensis; A. afric.* = *A. africanus; Para.* = *Paranthropus* (robust lineage); *P. ae.* = *P. aethiopicus;* early *H.* = *Homo rudolfensis* and *H. habilis.*

R. R. Skelton and H. M. McHenry. Here, *P. aethiopicus* is split off early in the evolution of the australopithecines; *A. africanus* is a common ancestor (but not the last such ancestor) of the remaining robusts on the one hand and *Homo* on the other; and several new hypothetical evolutionary ancestors are predicted.

Which (if any) of these phylogenies is correct? Only time and further research will tell. The hominid fossil record has only begun to be discovered, and thus our "family trees" must be flexible enough to accept new evolutionary relatives or revised analyses of old ones. To take a case in point, where should the new (provisional) hominid *Australopithecus ramidus* be located on the family tree? Given the extremely apelike morphology of *A. ramidus,* and its early date, we have simply added the new species at the bottom of phylogenies A–E. However, only time will tell how various specialists will receive and interpret *A. ramidus.* Bernard Wood's brief analysis in the same issue of *Nature* that announced the new species indicated that *A. ramidus* might be either broadly ancestral to all other hominids or ancestral to the *Paranthropus* clade only—a big difference! The evolutionary relationships of *A. ramidus* will be clarified only through additional discoveries and analyses, and there is certain to be a period of controversy over its status. But despite all the confusion, we can be relatively sure of a few things about hominid evolution. First, the fossil and molecular data show clearly that the family Hominidae has been separate from the apes for over 5 million years. Second, some species of gracile australopithecine was directly ancestral to the genus *Homo.* And third, the robust australopithecines were not on the direct evolutionary line to modern humans; indeed, the robust lineage went extinct around 1.0 mya, without leaving any descendants.

SUMMARY

Since the discovery of *Zinjanthropus* (*Paranthropus boisei*) at Olduvai Gorge in 1959, East Africa has produced the remains of a variety of Plio-Pleistocene hominids. The australopithecines are there in abundance, represented by the robust forms *P. aethiopicus* and *P. boisei* and by the smaller forms *Australopithecus afarensis* and (provisionally) *A. ramidus.* In addition, the fossils of early *Homo* are there, announcing the appearance 2.4 mya of the subfamily Homininae—a new evolutionary grade for hominids. In combination with the South African material, the fossils from East Africa provide evidence of two genera and six species of australopithecines and at least two species of early *Homo* (though other workers' classification schemes may produce more or fewer species and genera). With the sole exception of *A. ramidus,* all of these creatures are known to have been habitual bipeds—the main diagnostic trait of hominids—but their habitat preferences and lifestyles probably varied widely. The australopithecines seem to have been small-brained creatures that subsisted mainly on vegetable foods. They probably lacked stone-tool technology. Whether because of that deficiency or for other reasons, the australopithecines had all disappeared by about 1.0 mya, but not before the gracile lineage had given rise to larger-brained descendants now classified as early *Homo.* Early *Homo,* in the form of *H. rudolfensis* and *H. habilis,* apparently made and used the first recognizable stone tools—an advance that many paleoanthropologists feel began to shape both diet and behavior toward the modern human condition.

Those are the bare bones of our beginnings. First appearing over 5 mya, our family initially went through an "australopithecine phase" that gave way to a "*Homo* phase" within the last couple of million years. But much remains to be explained. What selection pressures led to the evolution of bipedalism or to increased brain size or to stone-tool technology? And how did these developments affect hominids' societies, mating systems, and subsistence patterns? It is to these topics that we turn our attention in the next chapter.

REVIEW QUESTIONS

1. Why are the species *boisei, aethiopicus,* and *robustus* classified within the single genus *Paranthropus?* What do these species have in common? How do they differ?

2. Summarize and compare the evidence of bipedalism in *Australopithecus ramidus* and *A. afarensis.*

3. Robust australopithecines overlapped in time and space with early *Homo* for about 1.4 million years. Speculate about relations between these hominid varieties. Do you think competition with *Homo* led to the australopithecines' extinction? If so, why?

4. Today's hominids pride themselves on their huge brains, while taking their adaptations for bipedalism for granted. Discuss the relative contributions of diet, locomotion, and intelligence to the early evolution of hominids.

5. Why is it so difficult for paleoanthropologists to determine how many hominid species and genera they have discovered and how they relate to one another evolutionarily? Discuss the challenges of recognizing species in the fossil record.

POSTSCRIPT

In the savannas and woodlands of Africa, the australopithecines rode the crest of hominid evolution for over 3 million years. The robust lineage (*Paranthropus*)—with its enormous grinding teeth and demanding diet—passed into extinction without issue about a million years ago. In contrast, the gracile lineage (*Australopithecus*) was much luckier. It almost certainly gave rise near the end of the Pliocene to more humanlike hominids of the genus *Homo*. Many of the genes we carry about today were inherited from gracile australopithecine forebears.

But how do scientists decide that "early *Homo*"—*H. habilis* and *H. rudolfensis*—were members of our genus and not simply advanced australopithecines? What derived traits do these species share with later varieties of *Homo* (*H. erectus, H sapiens*) that mark the genus boundary? As it turns out, this is not an easy question, and the answer has become more complex as the fossil record around the Plio-Pleistocene dividing line has become better known. One trait stands out above all others, of course, and that is *Homo*'s increased brain size. A convenient (but arbitrary) dividing line appears to be about 600 cc: *Homo* is above that figure and the australopithecines below. In addition, thanks to modern cladistic analyses, we can expand the defining criteria for *Homo* as follows (Traits 2–9 are taken from B. Wood, 1992):

1. Larger brain (roughly 600 cc and up)

2. Thicker bones of the braincase

3. Reduced postorbital constriction (narrowing of the skull at the temples)

4. Occipital bone's increased contribution to the cranial sagittal arc length

5. Higher cranial vault

6. Foramen magnum farther forward

7. Flatter lower face

8. Narrowed tooth crowns (especially the lower premolars)

9. Shorter molar toothrow

One final trait is ineligible for inclusion in anatomical lists but cannot be dissociated from our image of *Homo*, and that is culture. Modern humans and our immediate ancestors, *Homo erectus*, are characterized by dependence on a cultural lifestyle. The widely accepted view that the Plio-Pleistocene hominids labeled early *Homo* made the simple Oldowan stone tools suggests to many anthropologists that these hominids were taking the first steps toward a cultural way of life and therefore, in addition to their anatomical distinctions, deserve to be included in our genus.

Late-Breaking Discoveries (Summer 1995)

The pace of paleoanthropological discoveries is picking up, as shown by the announcement of yet another new hominid species (the second such in a year) just as this book is receiving its finishing touches. A research team headed by Meave Leakey has recovered the remains of a new type of australopithecine from 4.2 to 3.9 million-year-old strata at Kanapoi and Allia Bay in northern Kenya. Named *Australopithecus anamensis*, the new species may have inhabited bushland, woodland, or gallery forest. It has several traits that differ from *A. afarensis*, including a more apelike dentition with larger canines. *A. anamensis* also seems to differ from *A. ramidus*, with thicker tooth enamel and different dental proportions to the Aramis hominids. Among the later (3.9 mya) *A. anamensis* fossils are leg (tibial) fragments indicating bipedalism.

To our frustration, the announcement of *A. anamensis* comes too late for us to do more than report its discovery. Incorporating the new species into the hominid story must wait for future editions. This is not altogether a bad thing, however, since the delay will allow time for further study and the recovery of more fossils. Although Leakey et al. suggest that the new species may have been ancestral to *A. afarensis* and a sister species to *A. ramidus*, a fully informed interpretation of *A. anamensis* will come only after intensive scrutiny by paleoanthropologists worldwide. One preliminary conclusion from the new fossils seems safe, however: soon after their evolutionary emergence, hominids may have undergone extensive diversification with different species testing the adaptive value of bipedalism in a variety of habitats.

CHAPTER 8 TIMELINE

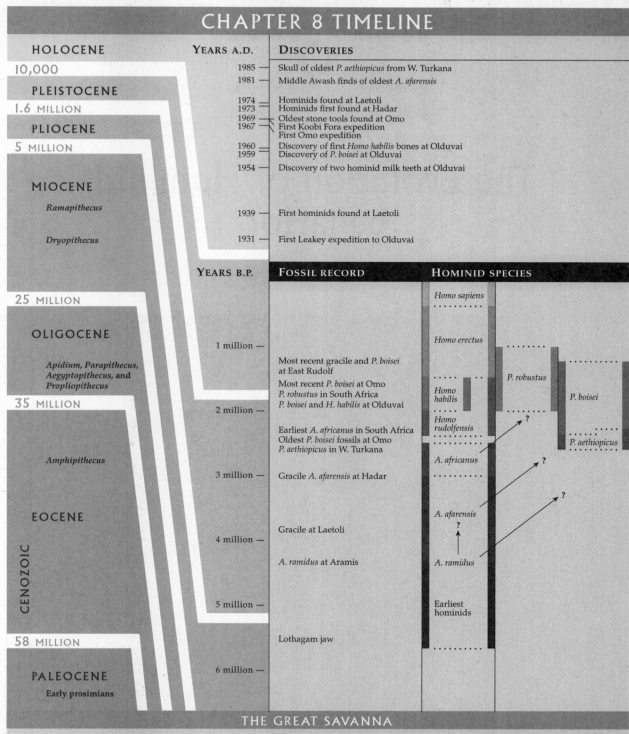

HOLOCENE	YEARS A.D.	DISCOVERIES
10,000	1985 —	Skull of oldest *P. aethiopicus* from W. Turkana
PLEISTOCENE	1981 —	Middle Awash finds of oldest *A. afarensis*
1.6 MILLION	1974 —	Hominids found at Laetoli
	1973 —	Hominids first found at Hadar
PLIOCENE	1969 —	Oldest stone tools found at Omo
	1967 —	First Koobi Fora expedition
		First Omo expedition
5 MILLION	1960 —	Discovery of first *Homo habilis* bones at Olduvai
	1959 —	Discovery of *P. boisei* at Olduvai
MIOCENE	1954 —	Discovery of two hominid milk teeth at Olduvai
Ramapithecus	1939 —	First hominids found at Laetoli
Dryopithecus	1931 —	First Leakey expedition to Olduvai

	YEARS B.P.	FOSSIL RECORD	HOMINID SPECIES
25 MILLION			*Homo sapiens*
OLIGOCENE	1 million —		*Homo erectus*
Apidium, Parapithecus, Aegyptopithecus, and *Propliopithecus*		Most recent gracile and *P. boisei* at East Rudolf	*P. robustus*
		Most recent *P. boisei* at Omo	*Homo habilis*
35 MILLION	2 million —	*P. robustus* in South Africa *P. boisei* and *H. habilis* at Olduvai	*P. boisei*
		Earliest *A. africanus* in South Africa	*Homo rudolfensis*
Amphipithecus		Oldest *P. boisei* fossils at Omo *P. aethiopicus* in W. Turkana	*P. aethiopicus*
	3 million —	Gracile *A. afarensis* at Hadar	*A. africanus* ?
EOCENE			*A. afarensis* ?
	4 million —	Gracile at Laetoli	*A. ramidus*
		A. ramidus at Aramis	
CENOZOIC	5 million —		Earliest hominids
58 MILLION		Lothagam jaw	
PALEOCENE	6 million —		
Early prosimians			

THE GREAT SAVANNA

The story of discoveries in Northeast and East Africa is as exciting as that of South Africa and new discoveries are reported every year. Dating of fossil deposits is far more secure in these areas than in South Africa because there has been much volcanic activity since the early Miocene and potassium-argon dating is therefore possible. Many of the deposits, moreover, are very thick and span a considerable time range.

The Evolution of Hominid Behavior

*A*s unto the bow the cord is,
So unto the man is woman;
Though she bends him, she obeys him,
Though she draws him, yet she follows;
Useless each without the other!
   HENRY WADSWORTH LONGFELLOW, 1807–1882. *The Song of Hiawatha,* x.

OVERVIEW

Working with fossils and artifacts, and with information about the behavior of modern humans and nonhuman primates, anthropologists attempt to reconstruct the evolution of hominids' lifestyles. This chapter describes the current state of such reconstructions and focuses on three primary topics: the selection pressures that favored the evolution of bipedalism; the nature and use of early stone tools; and the likely socioecology of early hominids. With regard to the first topic, several hypotheses are reviewed, including those linking bipedalism with tool and weapon use, energy efficiency, body temperature regulation, and reproductive success. Furthermore, the secondary links between bipedalism and childbirth patterns, and bipedalism and canine tooth morphology are described. The bipedalism sections are followed by a discussion of the nature and probable use of Oldowan choppers and flakes. The chapter ends with current reconstructions of early hominids' ranging and subsistence patterns. Important topics include bipedalism and the various selection pressures that may have favored its evolution; childbirth patterns and canine tooth morphology and how they may be linked to bipedalism; the nature and use of Oldowan tools; and the diets, food procurement patterns, and ranging patterns of early hominids.

HOMINID LOCOMOTION

From the Trees to the Ground

As we have seen, hominid evolution probably began from an unspecialized, arboreal, climbing primate that we would classify as an ape. It was probably somewhat smaller and possibly more general in its food tastes than the chimpanzee of today, and hence more willing to explore a variety of food sources. The world, in short, was wide open to it. It could go in any of several directions.

Imagine hominids' ape ancestor confronting the following ecological possibilities. If in one part of this ape's range there are large forests and an abundance of fig trees, there will be little reason for the animal not to stay in the trees and become increasingly specialized as a fruit eater. In another part of the range, or at another time, however, the environment might be somewhat different: fewer fig trees, but an abundance of seeds, berries, tubers, insects, and other food on the ground. Such a situation may have existed about 5 to 7 million years ago (mya). At that time tropical forest extended through a good part of Central Africa as it does today. Of course, there also existed a comparably large amount of forest edge and open woodland, with opportunities for tree-dwellers to descend to the ground and eat the berries, roots, insects, and other food that abounded in the open. Such a place, where two ecological zones meet, is called an *ecotone*. It presents new opportunities for survival, for if an animal adapts to the ecotone, it can exploit the food found in both zones. Advanced apelike creatures thronged the forests, probably as a number of species, some of which must have lived on the forest edge. Like a good many monkeys and apes today, some of these creatures (among them our ancestors) undoubtedly came to the ground when opportunities for feeding presented themselves.

Opportunity and aptitude went together. No one decision by one ape or one group of apes had any evolutionary meaning whatsoever. But in places that, century after century, provided a better living on the ground for apes able to exploit it, the animals best adapted to living and feeding on the ground were the ones that spent the most time there and whose descendants became still better adapted to this environment and lifestyle.

The apes were not forced out of the trees. It is true that during the Pliocene the forests dried up and retreated, subtracting several million square miles of living space from the possible ranges of tree-dwelling apes. But the process was so gradual that at no time could it have affected the evolving habits of individual animals, and the extent of the forest-edge ecotone was not greatly altered. Variations of climate from one year to the next were all that concerned the animals. If a river goes dry and the trees along it die, the animals that formerly thrived there simply move away, taking their various ways of living with them. They do not abandon living in trees because some trees disappear; they simply find other trees.

Tool Use and Bipedalism

In his *Descent of Man*, Charles Darwin wrote, "The free use of arms and hands, partly the cause and partly the result of man's erect position, appears to have led in an indirect manner to other modifications of structure. . . . As they gradually acquired the habit of using stones, clubs or other weapons, they would use their jaws and teeth less and less. In this case the jaws, together with the teeth, would become reduced in size." Thus Darwin believed that bipedalism led to tool and weapon use and then to smaller jaws and teeth.

In contrast, the American anthropologist Sherwood Washburn suggested that tool using might have preceded walking on two legs; more than that, it probably helped to develop walking. He pointed out that apes, unlike monkeys, were characteristically upright even before they left the trees. Whereas monkeys ran along branches on all fours or jumped about in them, apes climbed hand over hand. They swung from branches, sat upright in them, and sometimes even stood on them. Their arms were well articulated for reaching in all directions, and the important, interrelated development of stereoscopic eyesight, a larger brain, and improved manual dexterity had already evolved. Apes, in short, had the physical equipment and dawning brain potential to use their hands in new and useful ways. That certain of them did so is suggested by the knowledge that chimpanzees, humans' nearest relatives, are simple tool users today. As we have seen, they throw stones and sticks as weapons. They use sticks, rocks, and handfuls of leaves for digging, cracking nuts, wiping themselves, and sopping up water.

Like Darwin, many authors have believed that hominids were bipedal from the time they first stepped away from the trees, and that it was this characteristic that gave them the opportunity to become tool users and toolmakers. If hominids found it technologically advantageous to walk on two legs from the beginning, the argument goes on, then, to make it easier for them to get about in that way, natural selection would inevitably improve their pelvis, leg bones, foot bones, and muscles.

But how much confidence can we have in the tools-and-bipedalism scenario? As we have seen from the fossils and footprints of *Australopithecus afarensis*, habitual bipedalism can be demonstrated clearly from about 4.0 mya (the evidence of earlier bipedalism by *A. ramidus* is too weak to be considered here). With their chimp-sized brains and hands at least as dexterous as those of modern apes, it seems possible that there was some degree of tool use by *A. afarensis*. Modern chimps, however, show us not only that apes can be tool users, but also that it's possible to be an occasional tool user and remain a quadruped. Therefore, chimp-type tool use might or might not have been sufficient to select for habitual bipedalism in the protohominids. A follow-up question then becomes: What about stone-tool manufacture and use? Here the answer seems easier: Because the appearance of *A. afarensis* predates the oldest stone tools by at least 1.6 million years, stone-tool technology can be confidently ruled out as the stimulus for bipedalism in that species. In summary, the tools-and-bipedalism question remains something of a riddle. However, because the earliest hominids do not appear to have exceeded a chimpanzee level of technology, Washburn's argument that tool use was the trigger for locomotor change remains unconvincing.

Energy Efficiency and Bipedalism

There are several other theories about the origin of hominid bipedalism, including the notion that it was favored by selection because it was more energy-efficient than the terrestrial quadrupedalism of our last ape ancestor. The energy efficiency of different locomotor patterns is usually measured by standardized oxygen consumption. Modern humans show the greatest energy efficiency when they are walking at a moderate pace; indeed, our walking bipedalism is slightly more efficient than an average mammal's ambling along quadrupedally at the same speed. (We are not very efficient runners, however, using about twice as much energy as a running quadrupedal mammal of the same body size. This fact suggests that, if energy efficiency played a role, bipedalism probably evolved to allow us to walk, not run.)

But, of course, hominids descended not from an "average quadrupedal mammal," but from a quadrupedal ape, and so comparisons with living apes should provide even more specific clues to the evolution of our bipedalism. Energy studies of chimpanzees have shown that these apes consume oxygen at the same rate whether they are moving bipedally or quadrupedally. Regardless of how they are moving, however, chimps' energy efficiency compares poorly with that of other (equivalently sized) quadrupeds; in fact, chimps use about 150 percent more energy. Therefore, since bipedal humans have a slight energy edge on the average nonprimate quadruped, there is no doubt that human walking is *significantly* more efficient than chimpanzee quadrupedalism.

Results such as these suggest that selection for energy-efficient locomotion was probably an important factor in the evolution of hominid bipedalism. Energy efficiency would have been particularly important if the early hominids were adapting to large home ranges with patchily distributed feeding and sleeping groves. In this case, they would have been faced with long day-ranges as they foraged. Furthermore, since fully upright bipedalism is more energy-efficient than bent-hip, bent-knee walking, the energy model could explain why waddle-and-teeter locomotion gave way to modern striding. It is more difficult, however, to determine whether energy efficiency was *the* selection pressure responsible for bipedalism. A few other candidates must be considered, including body temperature regulation.

Body Temperature and Bipedalism

As noted in Chapter 8, it is a long-held view that hominid bipedalism evolved as an adaptation to life on the African savanna (remember, however, that the evidence from *A. ramidus* may force some modification of this view). One of the most formidable problems facing a diurnal primate living on the savanna is regulating its body temperature. Overexposure to the rays of the equatorial sun can build up a dangerous heat load, and thus we might expect that the early hominids evolved mechanisms to prevent excessive heat buildup and/or to rapidly dissipate body heat once it had accumulated. British researcher Pete Wheeler has looked into this problem, and he is convinced that the solution may provide clues to the evolution of bipedalism.

Two key variables affect the accumulation of heat from direct solar radiation: the amount of body surface a creature has exposed to the sun's rays and the intensity (or heat) of those rays. Using scale models of australopithecines in various postures (Figure 9–1), Wheeler found that, when the sun is near the horizon or about 45 degrees above it (thus emitting cool to moderately warm rays), quadrupeds and bipeds have similar amounts of body surface exposed and accumulate equivalent heat loads. However, at noon, when the sun is directly overhead and its rays are the most intense, the heat load buildup of a biped is 60 percent less than that of a quadruped because of the biped's minimal surface exposure.

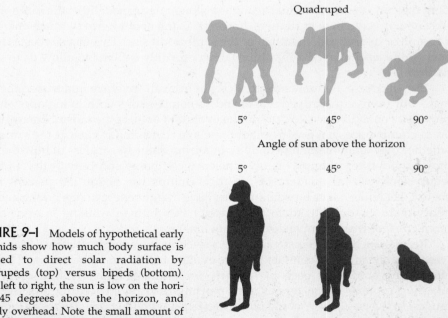

FIGURE 9–1   Models of hypothetical early hominids show how much body surface is exposed to direct solar radiation by quadrupeds (top) versus bipeds (bottom). From left to right, the sun is low on the horizon, 45 degrees above the horizon, and directly overhead. Note the small amount of body surface exposed by a biped at midday.

Wheeler has also calculated that bipedalism would aid in the dissipation of any body heat that did manage to accumulate. Bipeds are farther from the hot ground surface than are quadrupeds, and thus a biped's skin contacts cooler and faster-moving air currents; this contact aids in heat loss through convection. Such convectional cooling would, of course, be enhanced by the loss of thick body hair; the loss would allow an essentially naked surface to be held aloft in the cool breezes. Thus the temperature regulation model may help to explain the reduction of human body hair. Wheeler believes that early hominids might have increased their convectional heat loss by as much as one-third by adopting bipedalism.

The combination of lower heat buildup and easy heat dissipation could have reduced the early hominids' dependence on shade and allowed them to remain active throughout much of the equatorial day and at relatively high temperatures. Furthermore, if heat loss could be accomplished mainly through convectional cooling, rather than by evaporative cooling through sweating, hominids' dependence on water would have been lowered. Wheeler has suggested that early bipeds may have required some 40 percent less water each day than a quadrupedal ape living under the same conditions. If true, this would have freed the early hominids to range widely across the savanna as they foraged.

Reproduction and Bipedalism

Tool use, energy efficiency, and temperature regulation—these are only three of the many explanations that have been offered for bipedalism. Other hypotheses, less popular than those already presented, include the possibilities that bipedalism evolved to allow long-distance surveillance for predators or that bipedal displays fostered social control in early hominid groups. One thing is clear: regardless of what selection pressure(s) led to habitual bipedalism, evolution worked through the enhanced reproductive success of those individuals who were best suited for upright movement. American anthropologist Owen Lovejoy has emphasized the direct effects of bipedalism on hominids' reproductive efficiency. His hypothesis, which is both fascinating and controversial, links bipedalism with the evolution of several unique features of human reproduction (Figure 9–2).

As mentioned briefly in Chapter 5, the reproductive behavior of modern humans differs significantly from that of other primates. Two major changes distinguish humans from the apes: the loss of estrus and strong paternal investment in children. Humans have continued the trend, first seen clearly among the apes, of relaxed hormonal control of sexual behavior. In our species, the ancient estrus cycle of sexual behavior has nearly, if not completely, disappeared. Sex can and does occur throughout the menstrual cycle, and ovulation (the optimal time for conception) is now hidden from both women and men. These changes, and particularly the concealment of ovulation, make it difficult for both sexes to determine the paternity of offspring. Only within exclusive sexual relationships can one be sure that the male mate is the father of the female's children. This is critically important, since kin selection theory predicts that males will invest time, energy, and resources only in youngsters carrying their genes.

Lovejoy, who flatly rejects the energy-efficiency and body-temperature models of bipedalism, focuses his attention on behavior with direct, positive effects on the production and rearing of offspring. Arguing that a primary difference between humans and apes is our greater birthrate (that is, shorter interbirth intervals), he suggests that among the earliest hominids (*A. ramidus?*) some males began to provide for females and young regularly. Such provisioning—locating,

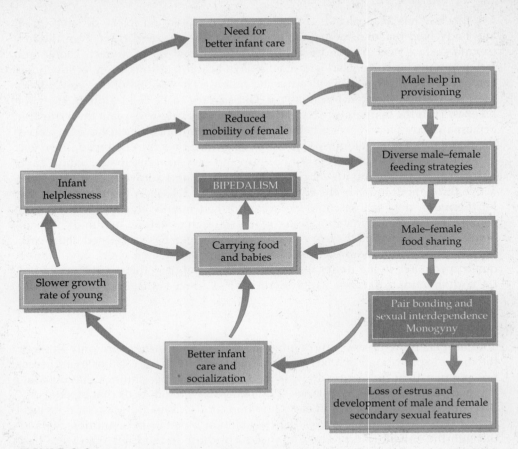

FIGURE 9–2   Pliocene adaptations of early hominids according to Lovejoy, drawn as a feedback system.

collecting, and furnishing food—would have reduced both the amount of parental investment required from females (they would not have been solely responsible for finding food for themselves and their babies) and the mortality risks of females and young (they would not have been ranging as far for food, and thus their risk of predation would be lower). The energy saved by provisioned females would then have been turned into increased reproduction; that is, they could give birth at shorter intervals while staying healthy. But where does bipedalism come in? Lovejoy argues that effective provisioning would have required bipedal locomotion so that males' hands were free to carry food.

So far, so good. Bipedal, provisioning males would have been favored by natural selection over nonprovisioning, quadrupedal males. But of course, this would have occurred only if males were actually investing in *their own young,* and thus Lovejoy speculates that provisioning males must have had a high degree of paternity certainty. He envisions such certainty as being the result of the evolution of monogamous "pair-bonded" nuclear families. Males provisioned only their female mate and her young, and because of the adults' *pair bond* (reinforced by the frequent copulation required for conception now that ovulation was hidden), females remained sexually faithful to their mates during the males' foraging trips.

Pair bond: psychological relationship between mates; thought to be marked by sexual faithfulness.

Lovejoy's scenario, although ingeniously tying together locomotion, reproduction, and family structure, has come under intense criticism. First, it seems male-biased in its explanation of the evolution of bipedalism. As outlined, females' contribution to bipedalism amounted to little more than moving upright while manually carrying helpless infants and mating with bipedal males (both sexes would ultimately have become upright through shared genes for anatomical adaptations to bipedalism). Second, in the days before extensive hominid carnivory and the invention of carrying devices (i.e., perhaps among *A. ramidus* or *A. afarensis*), it is difficult to imagine males hand-carrying enough high-nutrient food to their mates to affect birthrates. Third, the extreme degree of sexual dimorphism in body size that seems to characterize the australopithecines argues strongly in favor of some form of polygynous mating system, not monogamy (or more properly, monogyny). Furthermore, monogamy isn't even characteristic of living humans, who have been described—taking all modern societies into consideration—as "mildly polygynous" (some 85 percent of modern societies allow polygamy). And finally, we agree with anthropologist and sociobiologist Donald Symons that there seems to be no good evidence whatsoever that an evolved pair bond characterizes modern humans. Humans form social and sexual relationships of varying duration, but there is no evidence that we have been shaped by evolution to form long-lasting, exclusive pair bonds of the kind seen in other species such as gibbons. And if modern people lack pair bonds, there is no basis for attributing them to early hominids. For all of these reasons, we have little confidence in the Lovejoy hypothesis.

And so at present there are a number of evolutionary hypotheses that attempt to account for the appearance of habitual bipedalism. Most were devised with a savanna-dwelling hominid in mind, and therefore if bipedalism by the woodland species *A. ramidus* is confirmed, it could force extensive revision or rejection of some hypotheses. While the authors of this book prefer the energy-efficiency and temperature-regulation models, it is important to remember that none of the hypotheses has been falsified unequivocally, and that they all have interesting and attractive features. Indeed, it seems reasonable and probable that some *combination* of selection pressures, rather than a single evolutionary factor, led to habitual uprightness. Additional speculative research and new fossil finds may someday help us to solve the riddle of bipedalism.

The Relationship of Bipedalism to Other Hominid Traits

While habitual bipedalism is *the* distinctive hominid trait, there are others that are almost as diagnostic. Some are anatomical traits, such as short, incisorlike canine teeth and (among *Homo*) big brains. Others are social attributes, such as an evolutionary tendency toward increasingly complex interpersonal relationships and societies. How is bipedalism linked to these important secondary traits? Dealing with the social category, American anthropologist Wenda Trevathan and others have speculated on the possible effects of bipedalism on childbirth and, by extension, on hominid sociality. As shown in the preceding chapters, the evolution of bipedalism involved a good deal of remodeling of the hominid pelvis. In particular, the shape of the *birth canal* changed from the ape's long oval, becoming quite wide transversely (from side to side) but shallow sagittally (from front to back) in

Birth canal: the passage through the mother's pelvis by means of which infants are born.

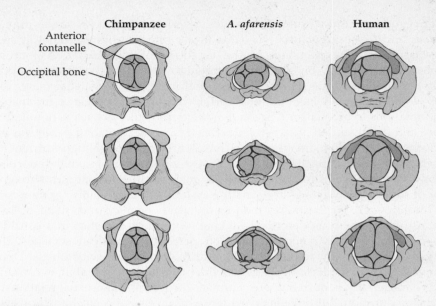

FIGURE 9–3   Three views of the fit between the fetal head and the birth canal in chimpanzees (left), *Australopithecus afarensis* (center), and modern humans (right). The top view shows the orientation of the fetal head at the entrance (inlet) to the birth canal; the middle view is at midcanal; the bottom view is at the exit (outlet). Fetal head size in *Australopithecus* is speculative and controversial.

Australopithecus (Figure 9–3). Later, in *Homo*, the canal regained a relatively long sagittal dimension—particularly at the exit, or outlet—producing a more rounded shape (Figure 9–3). A modern human baby, with its large skull, negotiates the birth canal by entering with the head oriented transversely. It then rotates 90 degrees into a sagittal position before exiting the canal facing the sacrum, that is, with its back toward the mother's face. A human mother is therefore in a bad position to assist in delivery, since her infant is exiting "down and back," away from her helping hands. Furthermore, pulling an emerging human infant up toward the mother's breast would bend it against the normal flexion of its body and would possibly result in injury. Interestingly, the human delivery pattern is very different from that of nonhuman primates, in which there is no fetal rotation (babies are sagittally oriented throughout birth) and newborns exit the canal face-to-face with their mothers. In this pattern, mother monkeys and apes routinely assist in delivery by reaching down and pulling emerging infants up and toward their chests in a curve that matches the normal flexion of the babies' bodies.

Trevathan has speculated that, at some point in human evolution, with the introduction of fetal rotation and down-and-back delivery, hominid mothers would have benefited significantly from the assistance of "birth attendants," and thus the behavior of seeking companionship at birth would have been selected for. In turn, seeking and giving assistance at births is viewed as contributing to the development of empathy, communication, and cooperation among the evolving hominids, that is, to the evolution of social relationships. Although speculative, this all seems logical enough, but a major problem involves determining when the "human birth pattern"—possibly including the first birth attendants—originated. Trevathan thinks this might have occurred early, perhaps among the australopithecines. Other researchers, however, think that australopithecine births were as fast and trouble-free as those of living apes and argue that down-and-back human deliveries, with big-brained babies twisting and turning through a constricted birth canal, are probably the result of strong brain expansion within the genus *Homo*. If the latter view is correct, and it seems most probable, the human birth pattern is probably not much over 2 million years old. Further insights into this interesting issue must await the discovery of additional pertinent fossils.

Discussing the connection between bipedalism and canine anatomy, Sherwood Washburn, champion of the theory that tool use preceded and possibly stimulated bipedalism, called attention to the fact that the australopithecines had relatively small canine teeth that would have been of little value in aggression or defense. In contrast, in all other large, ground-dwelling primates—chimpanzees, gorillas, and, particularly, baboons—the male's canines are enormous teeth, true fangs. Among their uses are self-defense against both conspecifics and the large and dangerous predators that ground-dwelling primates are exposed to. As part of his scenario for early hominid evolution, Washburn argued that the loss of large canines must have been balanced by some other means of self-defense, namely, the use of various objects as weapons.

As noted at the beginning of this chapter, the hypothesis that tool use triggered bipedalism remains to be falsified completely, but the evidence in favor of the proposition is unconvincing. In that case, are there other explanations of canine reduction? If it was not related to tool use, what caused it? Clifford Jolly of New York University's anthropology department has suggested an answer to that question. Jolly proposed that the emergence of the hominid family was marked by a shift from ape-type frugivory to a diet that included a significantly higher proportion of small, hard objects, such as seeds, nuts, and tubers. Such tough, hard-to-chew items would presumably have been plentiful in the woodland-savanna habitat to which the early (and newly terrestrial) hominids were adapting. The evolutionary scenario proposed by Jolly became known as the *seed-eating hypothesis.*

Jolly's hypothesis of hominid canine reduction was based on two types of evidence. First, he presented comparative data from savanna baboons and gelada monkeys that suggested the presence of shorter canines in the more seed-dependent geladas. And second, Jolly argued that long, interlocking canines (such as those shown by apes) limit the range of movement of the lower jaw during chewing (particularly side-to-side grinding movements), and thus long canines would have been *selected against* as early hominids adopted a small-object diet. Finally, according to Jolly, the need for an upright posture during small-object harvesting could have selected for habitual bipedalism. And so, in contrast to Washburn's theories, the seed-eating hypothesis explains the primary hominid characteristics as being the results of a dietary change. In this scenario, tool use followed diet-induced dental and postural changes, rather than serving as the trigger for hominization.

Jolly's theory has been received with a mixture of support and disagreement. A very recent discovery that tends to weaken his model is the evidence that *Australopithecus ramidus*—claimed by its discoverers to be the oldest hominid and to show some anatomical signs of bipedalism—had thin enamel on its canines and molars. As Tim White and his colleagues noted, the thin enamel of *A. ramidus* is hard to reconcile with a "hard-object" diet.

One of Jolly's most vigorous critics is American anthropologist Leonard Greenfield, who feels that flawed assumptions about dental mechanics underlie the seed-eating model. Greenfield has suggested as a substitute his dual-selection hypothesis. This model proposes that two forms of selection shaped canine tooth anatomy: selection for use as a weapon and selection for incisorlike functions. These selective forces tended to move canine anatomy in mutually exclusive directions and therefore can be viewed as "competing" with one another. If the weapon-use function prevailed, the canines would be long, fanglike teeth, but if incisorlike selection was stronger, the canines would be short and would have broader cutting edges. Finally, and of major importance, the dual-selection hypothesis assumes that, if selection for weapon-use functions diminished, canines would *automatically* shift toward an incisorlike anatomy.

Greenfield's model is interesting, and he provides evidence that it applies across all anthropoids. Nonetheless, it leaves unanswered the critical question: Did the canines of early hominids get shorter and broader because they were no longer needed as weapons or because they were *strongly* needed as additional incisorlike teeth? And (to get back to Washburn), if selection for use of the canines as weapons diminished among the first hominids, was it because some sort of biodegradable implements were being used instead?

These questions, like so many others, await definitive answers. There seems little doubt, however, that once hominids had some of the major behavioral and anatomical cards on the table, particularly bipedalism and simple technology, a complex *positive feedback* system could have developed. One such feedback system is shown in Figure 9–4. As explained in earlier sections of this chapter, certain loops in this system are questionable; others, such as those connecting the triangle of technology (toolmaking), subsistence, and intelligence (brain size), were almost certainly of great importance, at least once *Homo* had evolved. While studying Figure 9–4, however, one must keep in mind that this and all speculation-based feedback models are primarily heuristic devices. The danger inherent in model-building is that one may begin to have too much trust in the model as a representation of the real world. Most of the feedback loops shown in the figure await rigorous testing.

Positive feedback: process in which a positive change in one component of a system brings about changes in other components, which in turn bring about further positive changes in the first component.

EARLY TECHNOLOGY

The origin of tools in human evolution must have occurred through trial and error. The nearest we can come to reconstructing that process is to remind ourselves that there was a time when our ancestors could do with fewer tools than chimpanzees can use today. They must have worked their way up from a similar (but not necessarily identical) limited capacity to shape something for a purpose; for example, a grass stem for poking into a termite mound, a chewed-up mouthful of leaves to serve as a sponge, a stick or branch as something to be brandished in an effort to intimidate, or a rock to throw.

A group of not-too-large apes will seem more formidable standing erect because they appear larger; in fact, the erect posture is sometimes used by nonhuman primates as a gesture of threat. The brandishing of sticks or branches enhances that effect and may have been enough, on occasion, to swing the balance to the hominids in a set-to with hyenas over the possession of a kill. The earliest use of objects by our ancestors, ground-dwelling scavengers or hunters, may have received its strongest impetus from its value in threat displays against competing species. For an immensely long time, the found object was the only type of imple-

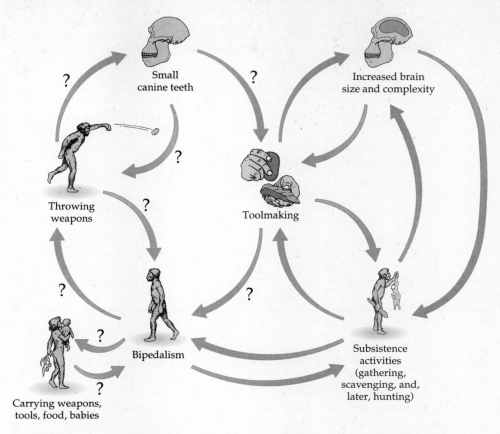

FIGURE 9–4 Numerous feedback systems occur in nature and are often interlocking. Negative feedback maintains stability, and positive feedback brings about major adaptive changes that constitute evolution. Shown here in simplified form is a positive feedback system that may have been important in hominid evolution.

ment, picked up and then thrown away when its immediate use was over. But there must have come a stage at which early hominids began to recognize more and more clearly the usefulness of certain objects and, as a result, tended to hang onto them longer, finally carrying them around much of the time. The great abundance of wood, and the fact that it is softer and easier to work than stone, suggests that the earliest hominids may have used wood a great deal, probably for digging. They may also have used the long bones of some of the larger animals. But the great triumph of our ancestors as creators of culture came much later and is seen most clearly in the legacy they have left us of worked stone. All the oldest surviving artifacts are implements for cutting and chopping, not weapons. We can therefore recognize a clear succession: tool use, tool modification, and toolmaking.

Earliest Stone Industry: The Oldowan

The magnet that drew Louis and Mary Leakey back to Olduvai Gorge year after year was the large numbers of extremely primitive stone implements. Mary Leakey made the study of these objects her special province. Her first monograph on the stone culture at Olduvai covers material taken from the gorge's lowest

Table 9-1 STRATIFIED BEDS AND FOSSILS AT OLDUVAI GORGE

Approximate Age (Years)	Bed	Fossils and Industry
100,000–620,000	Upper beds	*Homo sapiens*
620,000–840,000	Bed IV	Fossils of *Homo erectus* Late Acheulean hand axes and cleavers
840,000–1.2 million	Bed III	No fossils Few artifacts
1.2–1.7 million	Bed II	*Homo erectus* and early Acheulean tools *Homo habilis* and Oldowan tools
1.7–2.2 million	Bed I	*Paranthropus boisei* and *Homo habilis* Oldowan choppers
2.2 million	Volcanic lava	

Note: The ages of the upper beds are still rather uncertain. Bed I fossil sites date 1.7–1.9 mya.

strata, known as Beds I and II, and a time period that extends from 1.2 to 2.2 mya (Table 9–1).

Certain details of the lives of the creatures who lived at Olduvai so long ago have been reconstructed from the hundreds of thousands of bits of material that they left behind—some stone, some bone; some large, some extremely small. No one of these things, alone, would mean much, but when all are analyzed and fitted together like a gigantic three-dimensional jigsaw puzzle, patterns begin to emerge that speak across the gulf of time.

Mary Leakey found that there were two stoneworking traditions at Olduvai. One, the *Acheulean industry,* appears first in Bed II and will be discussed in Chapter 11. The other, the Oldowan, is the older and more primitive and occurs throughout Bed I, as well as at other early African sites. Its signature implements are what anthropologists for a long time called *pebble tools,* but what Mary Leakey prefers to call *choppers.* The word *pebble* suggests something quite small, and her term is an improvement, for many of the chopping tools at Olduvai are of hen's-egg size or larger, some of them 3 or 4 in. (8–10 cm) across. In addition to the choppers, Oldowan sites typically contain numerous stone flakes.

An Oldowan chopper (Figure 9–5) is about the most basic stone implement one can possibly imagine could be recognized on its own by archaeologists. (Even simpler tools, however, such as unmodified cobbles that were used as hammer stones, can often be recognized when they occur in association with a recognizable archaeological assemblage.) The chopper was, typically, made from a cobble, a stone that had been worn smooth by sand and water action. The stone selected was often that of a close-grained, hard, smooth-textured material like quartz, flint, or chert. Many cobbles at Olduvai are of hardened lava that flowed out of the volcanoes in the region.

Oval or pear-shaped, and small enough to fit comfortably in the hand, such a water-rounded stone could be gripped firmly without hurting the palm. What an early toolmaker had to do to turn it into a tool was simply to smash one end down

Acheulean industry: stone tool culture that first appeared about 1.7-1.4 mya in Africa and originated with *Homo erectus.*

Choppers: small, generally ovoid stones with a few flakes removed to produce a partial cutting edge.

FIGURE 9–5 An Oldowan chopper was usually made by striking some flakes from a rounded cobble to give a cutting edge. It is one of the simplest stone implements. Scale is approximately twice actual size.

hard on a nearby boulder, or to balance it on the boulder and give it a good whack with another rock. A large chip would fly off. Another whack would knock off a second chip next to the first, leaving a jagged edge or perhaps a point on one end of the stone. There are large choppers and small ones. The tool was presumably held as one would hold a rock while banging downward, with a direct hammering or chopping motion. The small chips knocked off during the manufacture of choppers are known as *flakes*. Sharper than choppers, they may have been more useful than the core. They undoubtedly became dull very quickly, for although stone is hard, its edges break easily.

Flakes: sharp-edged fragments struck from a stone; the flake may then be used as a tool.

But how were the Oldowan choppers and flakes used? What do they tell us about the lifestyle of their makers? American archaeologists Kathy Schick and Nicholas Toth have made an in-depth study of these questions, and their discoveries are revealing. In order to extract the maximum information from the ancient stone implements, Schick and Toth have used a combination of traditional and innovative techniques. Of course, they have followed traditional archaeological procedures and studied the occurrence and distribution of Oldowan tools at the various African sites, and they have also studied the fossil bone assemblages associated with the tools. In addition, they have conducted numerous field experiments using newly made flakes and choppers to butcher animals that have died naturally and to smash animal long bones for marrow. Finally, they have utilized data from electron microscope studies of cut marks on fossil bones (Figure 9–6) and *microwear* on tool surfaces (the microwear pattern of chips, pits, and polish can provide excellent clues to how a tool was used).

Microwear: the microscopic pattern of scratches, pits, and polish produced during the use of a stone tool.

FIGURE 9–6   Marks on the surfaces of fossil bones, such as those from Olduvai Gorge (left), can be produced in several ways. A study of fossil bones with the scanning electron microscope reveals whether such marks were made by hominids using stone tools. These marks typically contain white parallel striations in the bottom of the groove, as seen on modern bones that have been experimentally cut with stone tools (right). They are easily distinguished from the marks made by the teeth of carnivores. (Scale bar: 0.2 mm.)

Débitage: debris produced during stone tool manufacture.

Manuports: unmodified stones that could not have occurred naturally in an archaeological site and must have been carried there; how manuports were used is unknown.

Based on all of their various analyses, Schick and Toth have concluded that the principal reason for the emergence of stone-tool technology among hominids was for quick and efficient butchering of animal carcasses before eating them on the spot or carrying them elsewhere for later consumption. Flakes were found to be excellent implements for skinning, defleshing, and dismembering animal carcasses (Figure 9–7)—even better than choppers, so often thought of as the premier Oldowan tools (indeed, many "choppers" may be nothing more than *débitage*, or waste cores left after flake manufacture). Using simple flake tools, Schick and Toth were able to skin even an elephant with its inch-thick hide! Choppers were useful for dismembering carcasses and, along with unmodified cobbles, for bone breaking (Figure 9–8). One should not conclude that Oldowan tools were used only for meat processing, however; microwear analyses have identified tools used for cutting soft plants and others used to work wood; hammer stones were no doubt used to crush nuts; and the use, if any, of *manuports* (unmodified stones brought from elsewhere to the site by hominids) is unknown. Nonetheless, based on their work, Schick and Toth believe that the primary message of the oldest stone tools is a significant increase in meat eating by early hominids.

Because progress in the early Stone Age was slow, the beginnings of the Oldowan tool industry were probably far older than would be indicated even by the Hadar site, which dates tools at about 2.4 million years B.P. (Chapter 8). But how much older no one yet has the slightest idea. After 2.4 million B.P., toolmaking and hominid evolution went hand in hand, but the earliest steps are unknown.

As we go back in time, we depend more and more on the ability of archaeologists to identify stone tools reliably; that is, to distinguish between them and naturally occurring rocks. There is no sure way of identifying individual primitive artifacts occurring alone, but if one or more of the following conditions is satisfied, the ancient presence of hominid toolmakers can usually be safely inferred:

1. The tools occur on an ancient land surface in reasonable numbers and conform to a regular and recognizable pattern.

2. The tools are made of a kind of stone that is not present locally and that therefore must have been brought there. The evidence of transport of materials is a very important feature of many stone-tool assemblages. The possibility of

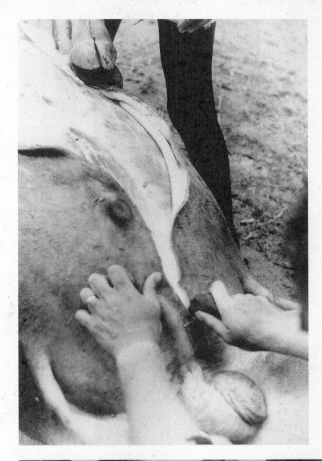

FIGURE 9–7 Experimental archaeologists skinning a wildebeest (who died of natural causes) with a lava flake. Simple, sharp flakes were found to be excellent tools for skinning, defleshing, and dismembering animal carcasses.

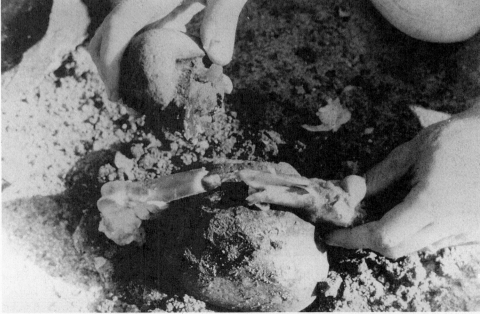

FIGURE 9–8   The use of a stone chopper and an anvil to crack a limb bone in order to expose the marrow.

their arriving in position as a result of being washed by a river or glacier must be ruled out.

3. The tools are associated with bone fragments showing cut marks.

4. The tools occur with other signs of human habitation (e.g., with hearths or the foundations of a shelter).

5. The tools are of such sophisticated manufacture that they could not possibly have been generated naturally.

6. We can expect tools to be made of a rock suitable for bashing or cutting bones or flesh (i.e., not a soft sandstone), usually flint (also called *chert*). Primitive tools might be made of a number of kinds of hard rocks, but the materials from which advanced tools could be made are very much more limited in number.

Given that hominines and australopithecines were contemporary in Africa for 1.4 million years, and given that their remains occasionally occur together at sites that also include stone tools, it is sometimes extremely difficult to know for certain which was the toolmaker. In attempts to make this distinction, the following considerations are taken into account:

1. Where remains of two species are found together with stone implements, the most advanced species (in terms of relative brain size as well as being the most closely related to modern humans) was more likely than the other species to be the toolmaker.

2. There is no way of showing that the less advanced form was not also a toolmaker.

3. Either of these species may have eaten the other. The presence of cut marks made by stone flakes on hominid bones would be very significant.

4. From our knowledge of animal behavior and from the archaeological record, we assume that some of these creatures were scavenging food remains.

5. On the other hand, we rarely know for sure how hominid skeletal remains might have found their way to the site. We have to assume that animal scavengers were also active.

The culture that Mary Leakey's work at Olduvai first revealed was left by a 1.8-million-year-old hominid that most anthropologists think was too small-brained even to talk. Just as the intricacies and subtleties of chimpanzee or baboon society turn out to be much more complex than anyone realized a generation ago, so, too, does the culture of the early bipedal hominids. The Leakeys concluded that the creature responsible for turning out this varied tool kit was of the genus *Homo* and therefore called it *Homo habilis*, because of the elaborateness of the culture Mary Leakey unearthed, not because of the size of the hominid's brain. If it could make tools—particularly stone tools—rather than merely use them, the Leakeys argued, then it was *Homo*.

Occupation Levels at Olduvai Gorge

During their decades of work at Olduvai Gorge, Mary and Louis Leakey and their sons and co-workers laid bare numerous ancient hominid sites (Table 9–1). Sometimes the sites were simply spots where the bones of one or more hominid species were discovered. Often, however, hominid remains were found in association with concentrations of animal fossils, stone tools, and debris. In some places it appeared that the bones and stones had been gently covered without much disturbance by blown dust, encroaching vegetation, rising water, and mud. Other sites, however, revealed signs of disturbance by water and wind. Although many of the sites were originally called *occupation levels*, suggesting that the hominids found there actually camped on the spot, we are now wary of jumping to that conclusion. Only after a team of experts—archaeologists, geologists, paleontologists, paleoanthropologists, and taphonomists—has thoroughly studied a site can its true nature be understood.

Occupation level: land surface occupied by prehistoric hominids.

The oldest sites at Olduvai come from Bed I and date between 1.7 and 1.9 million years old (Table 9–1). Sites at this level have produced Oldowan stone tools in abundance and also (sometimes at the same location) fossils of both the robust australopithecine *Paranthropus boisei* and an ancient representative of our own genus, *Homo habilis.* For many anthropologists, Olduvai Gorge is particularly fascinating because of what we think it tells us about the lifestyle of the latter species. As explained earlier, when the bones of early *Homo* and *Paranthropus* are found together in association with stone tools and other artifacts (as has occurred in both East and South Africa), all tools and artifacts are *assumed* to have been made by *Homo.* This assumption is, however, only the first step in the tricky process of understanding the Olduvai stone and bone assemblages. Other factors that make the interpretation of Bed I difficult include the extreme age and fragmentary nature of these sites from the dawn of culture and, most important, the simple inability to imagine how early *Homo* might have lived nearly 2 million years ago. What living analogues should we use? Should we assume that, although much smaller-brained, *Homo habilis* behaved more-or-less like modern humans? Or should we envision *Homo habilis* as a sort of advanced ape? If we adopt the ape analogy, we risk underinterpreting the Olduvai sites. On the other hand, if we view *Homo habilis* as primitive, long-armed little humans, we risk overinterpretation. It is the latter error that some workers think we have been making for years.

During the 1970s and early 1980s many workers, including Mary Leakey and archaeologist Glynn Isaac, used an analogy from modern hunter-and-gather cultures to interpret the Bed I sites. They concluded that many of the sites were probably camps, often called *home bases*, where group members gathered at the end of the day to prepare and share food, to socialize, to make tools, and to sleep. The circular concentration of stones at the DK-I site (Figure 9–9) was interpreted as the remains of a shelter or windbreak similar to those still made by some African people (Figure 9–10). Other concentrations of bones and stones were thought to be the remains of living sites originally ringed by thorn hedges for defense against predators. Later, other humanlike elements were added to the mix, and early *Homo* was described as showing a sexual division of labor—females gathering plant foods and males hunting for meat—and some of the Olduvai occupation levels were interpreted as butchering sites (Figure 9–11).

Home base: camps where hominid groups gathered at evening for socializing, food sharing, and sleeping.

Views on the lifestyle of early *Homo* began to change in the late 1970s, as many workers became convinced that these hominids had been overly humanized. Taphonomic studies by Pat Shipman and others began to show that early *Homo* shared the Olduvai sites with a variety of large carnivores, thus weakening the idea that these were the safe, social home bases originally envisioned. Furthermore, studies of the bone accumulations suggested that *Homo habilis* was mainly a scavenger—stealing from carnivore kills or using the carcasses of animals that had died naturally—and not a full-fledged hunter. Archaeologist Lewis Binford suggested that the Bed I sites were no more than "scavenging stations" where

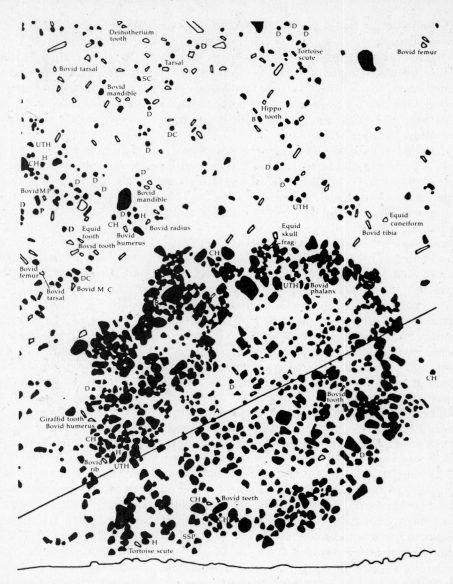

FIGURE 9–9 This plan of an ancient land surface shows the distribution of bones and stones discovered at a site in Bed I of Olduvai Gorge by Louis and Mary Leakey. The dense concentration of rocks suggests to some the remains of a hut or a windbreak; to others it is merely broken lava rocks produced by the roots of an ancient tree. Stones are shown here in black; bones are outlined. Labels for objects other than bones and teeth identify stone tools using the scheme devised by Mary Leakey. Important implement types include choppers (CH), scrapers (SC), hammer stones (H), discoids (DC), heavily utilized material (UTH), and débitage (unmodified flakes, D).

early *Homo* brought portions of large animal carcasses for consumption. Certain sites were regularly used because they allowed easy monitoring of the surrounding area for predators. Sleeping was done elsewhere, away from the remains of the day's meals, which would have attracted hyenas and other dangerous animals.

Richard Potts of the Smithsonian Institution has recently suggested that the Olduvai Bed I sites mainly represent places where raw and worked stone was cached for the handy processing of animal foods obtained nearby. Potts has

FIGURE 9–10   This shelter of branches and grass, built by the Okombambi people of Namibia, is probably little different from those that may have been built for the past 2 million years. The evidence from Olduvai Gorge, Bed I, suggests to some a structure of this type (see Figure 9–9).

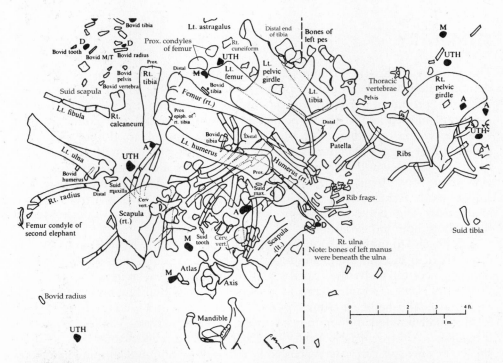

FIGURE 9–11   This plan shows part of the ancient occupation level of a possible butchery site in Bed I of Olduvai Gorge. Stone tools (solid black) are mixed in with almost the entire skeleton of an elephant, together with other food remains. Implement labels are as given in Figure 9–9, with the additional important occurrence of several manuports (unmodified rocks brought from another locality, M).

proposed a resource transport hypothesis that he feels explains the primary subsistence innovation of early *Homo*. Potts believes that Oldowan toolmakers brought raw stone from sources several kilometers away and cached it at a number of locations within the group's territory or range (the original selection of a cache site may have been purely accidental and was very likely related to finding an available carcass on the spot). Stone tools could have been made at the cache sites for use elsewhere, but more frequently portions of carcasses were transported to the toolmaking site for processing. This idea is very similar to Binford's scavenging-station model, with the key addition of cached stone resources. Again, camping and sleeping at the food-processing sites is deemed unlikely by Potts because such locations would have attracted carnivores interested in leftover meat and bones. In this connection, Potts interprets the DK-I "windbreak" as merely a concentration of lava rocks broken up by the roots of an ancient tree, and not as the remains of a shelter at all. Also important is the fact that neither Binford's nor Potts's models necessarily include a sexual division of labor or food sharing (but neither do they preclude such behavior).

Current interpretations of the subsistence, ranging, and tool-using patterns of early *Homo* are therefore much more conservative than they were just 20 years ago. Recently, the Oldowan toolmakers have been dehumanized, and with good reason. Although much more than advanced apes, they still were probably quite different from modern people with regard to their living arrangements, methods and sexual division of food procurement, and the sharing of food. The label *human* has to await the appearance of the next representative of the hominid family: *Homo erectus*.

SUMMARY

The primary hallmark of hominids is bipedalism and yet, as this chapter has demonstrated, we have only an imperfect understanding of the selection pressures that produced our characteristic form of locomotion. Increased energy efficiency (compared to ape quadrupedalism) and body temperature control appear to be the two best explanations for the evolution of bipedalism, although there are several other suggestions that cannot be discounted entirely (such as freeing the hands for tool use and carrying things, and adopting an upright posture to harvest small food items). Furthermore, the connection between bipedalism and canine tooth reduction remains unclear. Undoubtedly, several variables–both anatomical and behavioral—were involved in a complex feedback system throughout hominid evolution.

As described in this chapter, our interpretations of early *Homo* are in a state of rapid change, and our understanding of the beginnings of a modern human way of life is incomplete. It now appears that anthropologists were much too eager to view early *Homo* as a toolmaking, food-sharing, shelter-building hunter-and-gatherer who established base camps on the African plains and who might even have formed pair-bonded monogynous families. Recent analyses challenge most of these ideas. Although *Homo habilis* was clearly more of a meat eater than the australopithecines, we can have no confidence that these hominids hunted game any larger than that taken by chimpanzees. Indeed, all indications are that early *Homo* obtained most of its meat by scavenging on animals that had died of natural causes or from carnivore kills (some archaeologists, such as Lewis Binford, have suggested that hunting as a significant subsistence activity did not appear until the time of *Homo sapiens;* more on this in a later chapter). Likewise, we are speculating virtually without evidence if we attribute the beginnings of a sexual division of labor to early *Homo.* Certainly, at some point in hominid evolution, subsistence activities were partitioned sexually so that women mainly gathered plants and men hunted for animal foods. And equally certainly, the sexual division of labor was linked to the beginnings of significant food sharing. But we are outrunning our data when we attribute these modern behaviors to early *Homo,* whose subsistence patterns may have been entirely unlike those of any living hominoid (anthropologist Nancy Tanner believes that a "female collective" formed the core of early hominid social groups). And who made the Oldowan tools? Believers in the hunting-and-gathering hypothesis and a sexual division of labor have traditionally said that males were the toolmakers, but we have no real proof of this, and indeed, there is evidence that some Oldowan tools were used to process soft plant foods—an activity traditionally viewed as females' work. If true, were females the primary Oldowan toolmakers? Some researchers think maybe so. And finally, home bases with shelters, monogyny, and pair bonds all seem to be much more the products of researchers' active imaginations and the overzealous use of Western human analogues, than conclusions indicated by the data.

In summary, our present knowledge of early *Homo* (*H. habilis* and presumably *H. rudolfensis* as well) limits these hominids to the edge of culture and modern humanity. We know far too little to attempt detailed reconstructions of their lifeways or of the ramifications of lifestyle in such things as differences in male and female anatomy or patterns of reproduction and development. Further fossil discoveries and improved analytical techniques will yield new (and, very likely, unexpected) answers to our questions, but for now, we must be content with a most imperfect picture of the first representatives of the genus *Homo.* In strong contrast, however, we can confidently describe the evolutionary descendants of early *Homo* as living a human lifestyle (i.e., a lifestyle broadly similar to that of modern people). And it is to these ancestors, *Homo erectus,* that we must now turn our attention.

REVIEW QUESTIONS

1. Review the evidence supporting the idea that tool use stimulated the beginnings of habitual bipedalism. If this hypothesis is true, what type and frequency of tool use do you think were involved?

2. Compare the various hypotheses about the origin of hominid bipedalism. Arrange the hypotheses in order from the most to the least likely, and then present evidence to support your ordering system.

3. Owen Lovejoy (and others) have argued that hominids evolved a pair bond and a tendency toward monogyny. Discuss the evidence for and against these propositions.

4. In the nineteenth century it was argued that "the brain led the way" in hominid evolution, that is that brain expansion and elaboration evolved early and other human traits (bipedalism, tool use, language, etc.) followed. Discuss the "brain-first" theory based on your knowledge of the sequence of appearance of distinctive hominid traits.

5. Describe the forms and functions of Oldowan tools. What do these tools suggest about the subsistence patterns of their makers? What conclusions can we reach about the sex(es) of their makers?

6. Which behavioral analogue do you prefer for interpreting the behavior of early *Homo*—chimpanzees or modern humans? Or should some combination of analogues be used? Explain your position.

7. What sort of group structure and mating pattern do you think characterized the australopithecines? What about early *Homo?* Present evidence to support your conclusions.

POSTSCRIPT

In his classic work *On the Origin of Species,* Charles Darwin presented a model of continuous and gradual evolutionary change. In his descriptions of adaptation and speciation, Darwin put particular emphasis on the effects of intra- and interspecific competition (while also noting that organisms struggle with the physical environment) and repeatedly stated his belief that "Natura non facit saltum" ("Nature does not make jumps"). In Darwin's world—following the teachings of the geologist Charles Lyell—organic change was slow and stately.

In contrast to Darwinian slowness and uniformity, some researchers are beginning to present evidence for periods of accelerated tempo in evolution, including the evolution of hominids. A vigorous current supporter of this view is paleontologist Elisabeth Vrba of Yale University, who argues that life's history has been shaped by a process she calls "turnover pulse." According to Vrba, in response to dramatic (and, in the context of geological time, relatively rapid) change in the physical environment, entire communities of organisms may experience spurts (or "pulses") of speciation. And while these pulses do not involve any new or mysterious evolutionary processes, they are triggered primarily by environmental fluctuations that break up ecosystems long in equilibrium.

Vrba's work has identified two turnover-pulse episodes with implications for hominid evolution: one about 5 mya near the Miocene-Pliocene boundary and a second in the late Pliocene about 2.5 mya. Both turnover-pulse events were apparently triggered by drops in global temperatures and increased aridity on the continents—changes that, in turn, were due to continental drifting and altered global air and water circulation. In eastern and southern Africa, the cooling and drying trends resulted in the spread of grasslands and a reduction in bush and tree cover. Vrba has pointed out that the older cooling and drying event coincided with the first proliferation of African antelope species—whose presence clearly proclaimed savanna conditions—and fell *near* the evolutionary appearance of the australopithecines. In her view, therefore, the human family may have originated as part of a broad zoological response to shrinking woodlands and expanding grasslands.

Vrba's second cooling and drying episode—which saw global temperatures plunge some 10°–20° F and the Sahara desert become established in northern Africa—occurred about 2.5 mya. That event witnessed the extinction of numerous older antelope species and the appearance of many modern genera, including several—like *Oryx*—that are strongly adapted to arid environments. Furthermore, many varieties of African animals, including early elephants, pigs, horses, bovids, and rhinos, showed dental changes that indicate an adaptation to diets with more tough and abrasive foodstuffs. And finally, as part of the 2.5-million-year B.P. turnover pulse, hominids experienced an adaptive radiation that resulted in the appearance of *Paranthropus* (with its huge grinding teeth) and early *Homo* (*H. habilis* and *H. rudolfensis*).

Vrba's turnover-pulse hypothesis has much in common with the allopatric speciation model called *punctuated equilibrium*, which hypothesizes that most species experience lengthy periods of stasis (equilibrium), which are occasionally interrupted (punctuated) by rapid evolution and speciation by branching. Together, the punctuated equilibrium and turnover pulse hypotheses provide an important extension to evolutionary theories. Slow, steady Darwinian gradualism occurs under some ecological conditions, but when the physical environment shifts dramatically, individual species and entire communities of organisms may be thrown into pulses of accelerated speciation, extinction, and dispersion, as long-established ecosystems are disrupted. Clearly, hominids are not immune to such turnover pulses. In that light, it is interesting to speculate on the contingent nature of hominid history. Where would we be if the late Pliocene pulse had not occurred?

Punctuated equilibrium: the hypothesis that most species have long periods of stasis, interrupted by episodes of rapid evolutionary change and speciation by branching.

THE EVOLUTION OF HUMANKIND

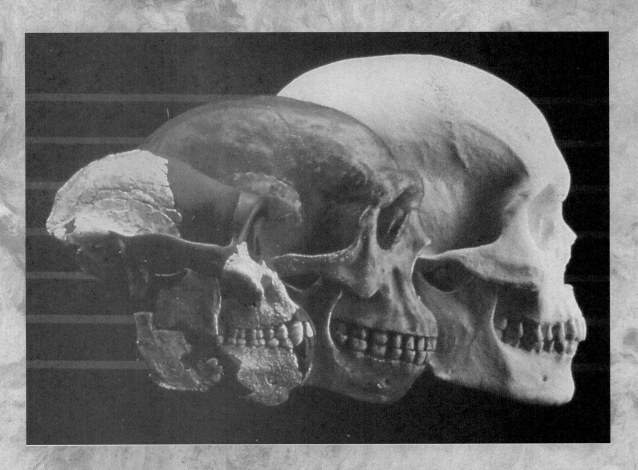

Discovering *Homo erectus*

*T*hen felt I like some watcher of the skies
    When a new planet swims into his ken;
Or like stout Cortez, when with eagle eyes
He stared at the Pacific—and all his men
Looked at each other with a wild surmise—
Silent, upon a peak in Darien.

> JOHN KEATS, 1795–1821.
> "ON FIRST LOOKING INTO CHAPMAN'S HOMER."

OVERVIEW

In 1887, a young Dutchman named Eugene Dubois (Figure 10–1) quit his job as a university professor and sailed to the East Indies in search of the "missing link." Incredibly, within four years he had accomplished his objective with the discovery of *Pithecanthropus erectus* in Java. Although Dubois's claim that *Pithecanthropus* was a "venerable ape-man" was greeted skeptically by the scientific community, it wasn't too many years before confirming fossils were unearthed in China and given the name *Sinanthropus*. Today, *Pithecanthropus* and *Sinanthropus*, along with fossils from Africa and Eurasia, are classified as *Homo erectus*, the species thought by

Homo erectus: extinct human species that lived from about 1.8 million to 300,000 years ago.

FIGURE 10–1 An 1883 photograph shows Eugene Dubois (1858–1940) as a teacher in Amsterdam.

many to be directly ancestral to our own. This chapter tells the story of the various *Homo erectus* discoveries, including the 1984 find of a nearly complete skeleton at the west Turkana site of Nariokotome. In addition, the anatomy of *Homo erectus* is described in some detail, and the evidence for language and speech in this species is reviewed. The chapter ends with a discussion of new dates from the Republic of Georgia and from Java that suggest that *Homo erectus* was present equally early (about 1.8 million years B.P.) in southeastern Europe, Asia, and Africa—dates that raise serious questions about the place of the origin of this species. Important topics and concepts in the chapter include the history of *Homo erectus* discoveries, the anatomical traits that define *H. erectus*, evidence bearing on the question of language and speech, and evidence regarding the origin and spread of *H. erectus*.

WORK OF EUGENE DUBOIS

Nineteenth-Century Background

Because most of what we know about early humans is based on fossil evidence, it is worth mentioning that fossil finds, as far as their influence on knowledge goes, fall into two rough categories. First are the discoveries of previously unknown fossil types, finds that provide brand-new insights into the evolutionary picture; second are those that confirm or enlarge information about a type of fossil already discovered. The first kind—the heart-stopper, the producer of wild surmises—makes newspaper headlines. But the second kind should not be underrated, because, to the scientist, it is at least as important. To get a good idea of the characteristics of dimensions of a species, one must have a series of fragments or skeletons from a number of individuals. Without such a series, a single fossil may be simply a curiosity—a provocative and exciting one, no doubt, but still something that cannot be fitted with any sense of certainty into the overall order of things until a number of like fossils are found and examined. It is the patient, more obscure, and always time-consuming comparative study of later finds, often made years after the original one, that eventually turns the wild surmises into scientific conclusions or destroys their credibility.

In this chapter, we describe the discovery of the fossils that follow *Homo habilis* and *Homo rudolfensis*, fossils that today are seen collectively as representing the species *Homo erectus*. As discussed at the end of Chapter 8, there are several different interpretations of hominids' evolutionary history. Almost all workers agree, however, that the lineage leading to modern humans includes, in succession, *Australopithecus afarensis* (possibly preceded by *A. ramidus* and followed by *A. africanus*), some form of early *Homo*, and *Homo erectus*. Of course, all populations of a species did not usually evolve into its successor species, for some isolated groups may have survived for a while without substantial change, only to become extinct later. Nevertheless, the fossil evidence clearly suggests that the succession of *Australopithecus* to early *Homo* to *Homo erectus*—and the further evolution of *H. erectus* into *H. sapiens*—broadly represents the course of hominid evolution.

To describe the discovery of the fossils of *Homo erectus*, a species that existed in the Old World between about 1.8 and 0.3 million years ago, we will return to the nineteenth century, to a discovery made 35 years earlier than that of *Australopithecus africanus*.

In the mid-1800s the Western world's interest was focused on the present and the future. It was an age of human progress and accomplishment, of prosperity, and of inventions that made life easier and more civilized: running water and lighted streets, iceboxes, sewing machines, elevated railways, lawnmowers, typewriters, and telephones. It is understandable, then, that the new theory about humankind's descent from prehistoric apes provoked doubt and opposition. In this atmosphere of progress and self-approval, the claim that humankind was merely an offshoot of an ape was rejected by much of the public and by many eminent scientists as well. No one had yet found any fossils proving a link between apes and humans. Most of those who doubted our primate origins did so not merely through acceptance of the biblical account of creation, but also because for a long time there was no really convincing fossil evidence to support Darwin.

Some scientists took the lack of any fossils of intermediate humanlike apes as proof that no such creatures had ever existed. At the other extreme, some of Darwin's early supporters rushed forward with fanciful pedigrees for humankind, making up in enthusiasm what they lacked in evidence. Even believers in human evolution were confused by the outpouring of rival experts' family trees for humankind, full of imaginary apish ancestors with scientific-sounding Greek and Latin names.

Eugene Dubois was born in Holland in 1858 and grew up in this atmosphere of often bitter debate over human origins. Although the Dubois family was conventional and religious, the home atmosphere was not one of narrow-minded provincial piety, and the boy's interest in science was encouraged. Dubois went to medical school and then, choosing academic life over medical practice, became an instructor in anatomy at the Royal Normal School in Amsterdam. He was fascinated by the many different family trees that were being published in both learned and popular journals and was much influenced by the work of Ernst Heinrich Haeckel, a German zoologist who had predicted in some detail what *should* be discovered about the course of human evolution (see Figure 10–2). For six years Dubois delivered his lectures and gave no hint of the wild idea that was taking hold in him: to establish the human place in evolution and set the record straight once and for all, by finding a fossil of a primitive creature that was the clear forerunner of humans.

Dubois's Search for the Missing Link

Dubois began to take up his vocation by going over all the clues he could find. One important clue was the first Neandertal fossil, which had been discovered in 1856, two years before Dubois was born (see Chapter 14). For many years the Neandertal remains were the only trace of a nonmodern skeleton in the human closet. Dubois, a firm believer in evolution, considered the Neandertal fossils definitely human, and very ancient. To him they suggested that the search for even more primitive creatures should be carried out in some region of limestone deposits and caves similar to the European habitat of the Neandertal, but they also suggested to him that Europe was not the place to look for a missing link. The creature that provided the evolutionary link between ape and human, Dubois reasoned, must have lived long before the Neandertal, at a time when Europe was far too cold to permit its survival. The forebear he wanted to find must have lived in a tropical part of the world that had been untouched by the glaciers of the ice age.

Other clues as well pointed to the tropics. Darwin had suggested that our tree-dwelling progenitors lived in "some warm, forest-clad land"; Alfred Russel Wallace had also recommended that our forebears be sought in a tropical zone. Wallace had lived in Malaysia for eight years, and he had noticed that the islands of Sumatra and Borneo (Figure 10–3) are the home of both the gibbon, the most

FIGURE 10-2   Ernst Haeckel's work on the ancestry of humankind was one of the first attempts to deal with the specifics of evolution. Although his genealogical chart, which starts with a blob of protoplasm and ends with a Papuan, contains misconceptions and fictitious creatures, it is in some ways surprisingly accurate, considering the dearth of knowledge in his day. The animals illustrated were chosen as representatives of the taxonomic groups to which successive human ancestral species were believed to have belonged.

ancient living ape, and the orangutan, one of the most advanced species of ape. He wrote, "With what interest must every naturalist look forward to the time when the caves of the tropics be thoroughly examined, and the past history and earliest appearance of the great man-like apes be at length made known." Wallace's curiosity about these islands and their caves proved contagious, and Dubois began to think seriously of going to the Dutch East Indies to explore the caves himself. The more he read about the geology and natural history of the region, the more convinced he became that the missing link would be discovered there. The islands once had been part of continental Asia; before the seas had inundated the lower land, turning the mountaintops into islands, animals could have wandered down freely from the north.

At age 29 Eugene Dubois set out to solve the mystery of human origins, to find the fossil of a creature with both apelike and humanlike traits that would prove the relationship between humans and apes. Dubois's planning focused on Sumatra, then under Dutch rule and therefore a practical place for a Dutch citizen to launch a paleontological expedition. In 1886 he told some of his colleagues at the University of Amsterdam that he had reason to believe he would solve the mystery of human origins. They tried to dissuade him, and one even politely suggested that Dubois was slightly mad. His requests for financial backing were turned down flatly by both philanthropists and government bureaucrats. But Dubois was determined to get to Sumatra, and finally he was sent there by the Dutch East Indies Army, in which he enlisted as a doctor.

For the first two years in Sumatra, his investigations of a great many limestone caves and deposits yielded only teeth that were too recent to interest him; they belonged mainly to orangutans. In 1889, following the discovery by a mining engineer of a fossil skull at Wadjak, Java, Dubois persuaded the Dutch East Indies government to transfer him to that neighboring island for further paleontological investigations (Figure 10–3). The colonial government, showing new interest in

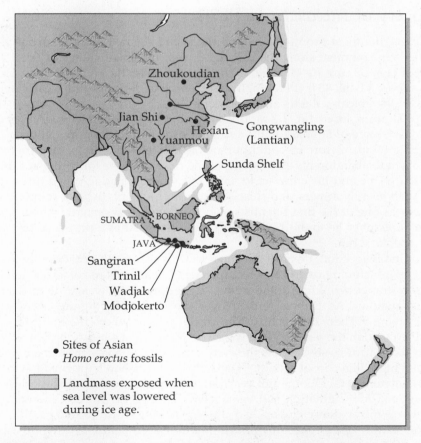

FIGURE 10–3   During glacial periods, when far more water was locked up in the polar ice caps than today, the world sea level fell. During the coldest periods, the maximum lowering of the sea level appears to have been over 300 ft (100 m). This receding would have enlarged considerably the landmasses available for occupation by plant and animal life. Throughout the Pleistocene, the sea level fluctuated extensively.

his work, supplied him with a native crew of convict laborers and two Dutch officers to oversee them. With such backing, excavations began on a grand scale.

Beginning work in the Wadjak region, Dubois's crew had discovered a second—and similar—skull by September 1890. Both were modern in appearance and too recent to have belonged to a missing link. But the region was extraordinarily rich in fossils of many kinds, and Dubois set up several digging parties at different locations. By 1894 he had shipped to the Netherlands 400 cases of fossil bones, including specimens of many extinct and previously unknown animals.

At one site to the north, Dubois's foreman reported an unexpected problem. He had found that for many years natives of the area had been digging up fossils and selling them to Chinese merchants as "dragon bones" to be ground into powder for an ancient and popular Chinese medicine. The local fossil hunters, unwilling to give up a profitable business with the Chinese, would not sell any of their finds to Dubois's party. To make matters worse, the foreman soon discovered that his own workmen were stealing the fossils they unearthed and carrying them off to sell to the local traders. When called on for help, the colonial government issued an order outlawing the sale of any fossils to Chinese merchants in Java.

Dragon bones: the ancient Chinese term for fossils of various sorts that were collected and ground into medicines.

Discovery of *Pithecanthropus* (1891)

To Dubois, the most promising site on the island seemed to be an exposed and stratified embankment along the Solo River, near the small village of Trinil in the center of Java (Figure 10–4). Here, in the months when the river was low, Dubois could survey a bank 45 ft (14 m) high of ancient river deposits with clearly defined layers of fine volcanic debris and sandstone.

In a stratum about 4 ft (1.2 m) thick just above the stream level, Dubois came upon a rich store of animal fossils: a stegodon, an extinct hippopotamus, a small deer, an antelope. Before he could pursue these interesting finds, the rains set in, and he had to abandon his excavations at the river until the following autumn. In August 1891 he and his crew set to work once more, digging down through the strata with hoes, hammers, and chisels—crude implements by later standards, but Dubois was one of the first scientists ever to attempt a systematic search for fossils. In September he found his first recognizable fossil of a primitive primate: a single apelike tooth.

On first inspection, this fossil seemed to Dubois to be the wisdom tooth of an extinct giant chimpanzee. Later, comparing it with molars of other apes, he noticed a strange wrinkling of the crown, suggesting that it was, instead, the tooth of an orangutan. As Dubois mulled over the molar, the digging went on for another month. Then, only 3 ft (0.9 m) to the side of where the tooth had been unearthed, and in the same layer, a workman discovered a heavy, brown rock that looked like a turtle's shell. After the earth was brushed away from the new find, it looked more like part of a skull. "The amazing thing had happened," wrote the English anatomist G. Elliot Smith years later. "Dubois had actually found the fossil his scientific imagination had visualized." Though he did not know it at the time, it was the evidence Dubois had crossed half the world to find.

The skull (Figure 10–5) was unlike any ever seen before. Clearly, it was too low and flat to be the cranium of a modern human. After detailed study of both the skullcap and the tooth, Dubois reported, "That both specimens came from a great manlike ape was at once clear." Despite his expert knowledge of anatomy, he found the skull peculiarly hard to place more precisely than that.

FIGURE 10–4 At this bend in the Solo River at Trinil, Java, Dubois excavated the terraced bank where the Java fossils were found, at a depth of 48 ft (14.6 m).

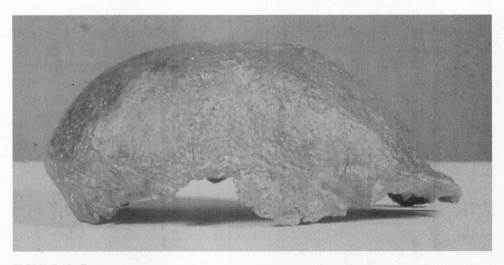

FIGURE 10–5 The skullcap of *Pithecanthropus erectus* was Dubois's greatest find. It was to be nearly 40 years before another skull of this kind was found. This photograph is approximately 60 percent of actual size.

FIGURE 10–6 The first femur that Dubois found appeared very modern and indicated an upright posture. The growth of bone on its inner surface near the top is an unusual pathological condition (probably myositis ossificans) that is also found occasionally in modern humans but has no evolutionary significance. This photograph is just under 25 percent of actual size.

Shortly after these finds were made, the rains came, the river rose, and digging again had to be suspended until the following year. When digging resumed in 1892, Dubois cut a new excavation in the same deposit about 33 ft (10 m) from where the strange cranium had been buried. There, ten months after the apelike skull was found, he discovered another, even more surprising, primate fossil. This one (shown in Figure 10–6) was unmistakable. It was the left femur, or thighbone, of a primate that had walked erect! It resembled a human thighbone in almost every respect, except that it was heavier. Could the curious tooth, the problematic skull, and the unexpected thighbone all have belonged to the same individual? The implications were staggering.

Dubois measured and studied the apelike skull and the humanlike femur from Trinil and in 1892 announced that the skull and femur had belonged to the same creature, which he believed to have been an upright species of chimpanzee that he called *Anthropopithecus erectus*. In 1893, however, he changed his mind and the species' name. After further study of the femur, and after calculating that the fossil skullcap would have held a brain 2.4 times larger than that of an adult chimp, Dubois borrowed the name of Haeckel's hypothetical human ancestor and christened his fossil *Pithecanthropus erectus* (from the Greek *pithekos*, "ape," and *anthropos*, "man"). By appropriating this name for his Java find, Dubois boldly filed his claim to have found, as he cabled his friends in Europe, the "Missing Link of Darwin." He attributed it to a late Pliocene age.

Pithecanthropus: the original genus name given by Eugene Dubois to fossil material from Java now classified as *H. erectus.*

The bones of *Pithecanthropus erectus* were one of the greatest fossil finds ever made, and even though he had only these few incomplete specimens, Dubois fully realized their importance. We now believe that *Pithecanthropus erectus* was actually an early human, a vital link in the chain of human evolution, not the half-ape Dubois had supposed it to be. We also now believe the Trinil skull to date from the middle Pleistocene—perhaps 800,000 to just over a million years B.P.

Java Controversy

Even before Dubois could show his discoveries to colleagues in Europe, his precious fossils became the focus of a raging scientific controversy that embroiled him throughout the rest of his life. His first cabled reports were met with skepticism. Some critics insisted that the fossil bones did not belong together at all and suggested that Dubois had simply made the mistake of mixing the skull and teeth of an ape with the thighbone of a human who had died nearby. One member of the Netherlands Zoological Society, writing in a Dutch newspaper in 1893, ridiculed Dubois's jigsaw-puzzle methods, asking whether more finds at the site in Java might not eventually lead to announcements of an even stranger creature: If another, more human, skull was discovered within 50 ft (15 m) of the other bones, this unfriendly commentator queried, would this mean that *Pithecanthropus* had two skulls, one apelike and one humanlike?

To those unwilling to acknowledge any link with any form of anthropoid ancestor, *Pithecanthropus* was pure insult. Clergy hastened to assure their congregations that Adam, and not the crude half-ape–half-human brute unearthed in Java, was the true human ancestor. Dubois was denounced from pulpit and from podium, for scientists were almost as angry and as skeptical. The combination of apelike head and upright posture ran directly contrary to the belief that the development of a larger, better brain had come first in the separation of the human stock from earlier anthropoids. Scientists expected a being with a human head and an apelike body, not the reverse.

The arrival of the fossils themselves for close inspection did not settle the arguments. Only six weeks after Dubois reached Holland in 1895, he presented *Pithecanthropus* to the Third International Congress of Zoology at Leiden. Almost at once, a great quarrel broke out over where to place this Java "ape-human" in the scheme of evolution. Opinion seemed to harden along national lines: Most German scientists believed that *Pithecanthropus* was an ape that had humanlike characteristics, while most English scientists thought it was a human that had apelike attributes. Only a few scientists were inclined to agree with Dubois that the fossils represented a transitional form, or "missing link," between apes and humans. Among those few supporting voices was the American paleontologist O. C. Marsh and the German evolutionist Ernst Haeckel, whose hypothetical *Pithecanthropus* had been given substance by Dubois.

Dubois gave his colleagues as much detailed knowledge of *Pithecanthropus* as he could. He exhibited the bones at scientific meetings throughout Europe, showed them to any scientists who wanted to examine them, and published detailed descriptions. He had to acquire the skills of a dentist, a photographer, and a sculptor. In order to make accurate brain casts, he spent weeks learning to use a fine dental drill, with which he could clean away minute stone particles inside the skullcap. He invented a special "stereorthoscope" camera, designed to photograph the fossils in various planes without distortion. For the public he sculpted

FIGURE 10–7   Dubois's model of *Pithecanthropus* holds an antler.

a life-sized reconstruction of *Pithecanthropus* (see Figure 10–7), ordering his son to pose for him during a school vacation. He patiently defended his claim for *Pithecanthropus*, carting the bones around in a battered suitcase, and seemed to develop an almost personal attachment to the fossil ancestor whose bones were a constant companion.

In spite of all Dubois's efforts, the attacks on *Pithecanthropus* continued. Dubois took them personally. Deeply hurt by the refusal of other scientists to accept his interpretation of the bones, he withdrew the remains of *Pithecanthropus* from the public realm and refused to allow even scientific colleagues to examine them. He then turned his attention to research on brain evolution.

In 1920 Henry Fairfield Osborn, head of the American Museum of Natural History, appealed to the president of the Dutch Academy of Sciences to help persuade Dubois to once again make his fossils available for study. Soon afterward, in 1923, Dubois opened his strongboxes for Alés Hrdlička of the Smithsonian Institution and thereafter again exhibited *Pithecanthropus* at scientific meetings. He also released a cast of the *Pithecanthropus* skull that indicated a brain of about 850 cc, well above the range of 275–750 cc of the apes and below the 1,000–2,000 cc range of modern humans.

Today there still remain some unanswered questions about Dubois's discovery. Do the bones really belong to the same creature? To suppose that two different primates—an unknown species of ape and an unknown species of human—

had lived in Java at exactly the same time and had died within 35 ft (11 m) of each other at Trinil seemed to Dubois far more improbable than to suppose that the various bones belonged to one creature with both apelike and human characteristics.

It now appears that Dubois was wrong about the association of the Trinil skullcap and femur. Modern studies suggest that they were neither from the same individual nor from the same species. The skull is ancient and undoubtedly from the early human species now called *Homo erectus,* but the femur is probably younger by several hundred thousand years and belonged to *Homo sapiens.* Dubois was right, however, that his "venerable ape-man" was bipedal. Subsequent discoveries of *Homo erectus* postcranial material from sites such as Olduvai Gorge, Zhoukoudian, China (see Figure 10–3), and Nariokotome, Kenya (see Figure 10–16) have verified this point. As regards the Trinil molar tooth, Dubois's initial assessment—that it came from an orangutan—was, in fact, correct.

Because of the great controversy over whether *Pithecanthropus* was a human, an ape, or a true "missing link," Dubois's brilliant detective work in locating the fossils seemed only to add to the mystery of human origins instead of solving it. While anthropologists argued over the Java bones and Dubois withdrew into his home in Holland, the controversy was being settled elsewhere.

TWENTIETH-CENTURY DISCOVERIES

Search for Human Fossils in China

The years following Dubois's discovery saw several important additions to the hominid fossil record: the Mauer mandible (now thought to be early *Homo sapiens*) was discovered near Heidelberg, Germany, in 1907; the fraudulent Piltdown remains were announced in England between 1912 and 1915 (see the Postscript to this chapter); and Dart's baby *Australopithecus africanus* from Taung was described in 1925. None of these finds, however, shed much light on Dubois's *Pithecanthropus erectus* fossils. That light came in 1927 with the discovery of more Asian "missing links" at the Chinese site of Zhoukoudian near Beijing (Peking).

The discovery of "Peking man" in 1927 involved a piece of scientific detective work almost as remarkable as Dubois's exploit in Java. This ancestor was added to the human family tree simply because a small band of scientists had gone to China determined to hunt it down. Even after Dubois's success in Java, the prospect of searching for a primitive human in China could appeal only to people prepared to spend their lives hunting for a needle in one haystack after another. But a Canadian physician, Davidson Black (1884–1934), was sure that he would unearth a human ancestor in China if only he looked long and hard enough. And so in 1919, when he was offered an appointment as professor of anatomy at Peking Union Medical College, which was being set up with funds from the Rockefeller Foundation, he eagerly accepted.

Black's conviction was based both on geologic evidence showing that the ancient climate and geography of China were quite suitable for a primitive human to exist there, and on the theory that patterns of evolution are closely related to climatic conditions. Also supporting his feeling was a single tantalizing piece of fossil evidence that some early primate had once inhabited China. In 1899 a German physician, K. A. Haberer, had chanced on an unusual fossil tooth among some "dragon bones" about to be ground up for medicine in a druggist's shop in Beijing. The tooth was among the more than a hundred bones the doctor had picked up in various Chinese drugstores and sent to paleontologist Max Schlosser. Schlosser identified the tooth as a "left upper third molar, either of a man or a hitherto unknown anthropoid ape" and predicted hopefully that further search might turn up the skeleton of an early human.

Black's hopes of finding time for fossil hunting when he reached China were dissolved by an adviser from the Rockefeller Foundation, who warned him to concentrate on anatomy, not anthropology. It was not until 1921 that the search for early humans in China actually began. That year a group led by John Gunnar Andersson, a Swedish geologist, began to dig at a site 25 mi (40 km) southwest of Beijing, near the village of Zhoukoudian (see Figure 10–3). Excavations were proceeding at a rise called Chicken Bone Hill near an old limestone quarry, when Andersson was told by his workmen that much better fossils could be found on the other side of the village, at Dragon Bone Hill, beside another abandoned quarry.

The Chinese had been digging "dragon bones" out of this spot and others like it for hundreds of years, and no one will ever know how many powdered fossils passed harmlessly through the alimentary canals of dyspeptic Chinese. Whatever the losses may have been to paleoanthropology, some of the limestone caverns in the hillside were still richly packed with interesting material. There were bits of broken quartz among the limestone deposits around an ancient cliffside cave. The quartz would not naturally be associated with limestone, Andersson knew; it must have been brought there—perhaps by some toolmaking peoples of the past.

A great many fossils were dug out of the rock and shipped back to Sweden for study. Twenty different mammals were identified, many of them extinct species. But Andersson's toolmaker was not easily found. A likely tooth turned up, but it was then identified as the molar of an ape. Finally, in 1926, when one of Andersson's associates had given up and returned to Sweden and the digging had stopped, a closer study of this molar and another tooth found later suggested that they might indeed be human. The teeth were sent back to Andersson, who turned them over to Davidson Black for his expert appraisal. Preoccupied though Black was with medicine, he had never lost interest in the Zhoukoudian site. He was certain that the teeth came from a human of great antiquity, and he persuaded the Rockefeller Foundation to support a large-scale excavation of the site.

Sinanthropus Discovered (1927)

Work started up again at Dragon Bone Hill in 1927. At some remote time in the past, water had honeycombed the limestone of the hill with caves and fissures. The caves in turn had filled with the deposits of running water and with the debris of collapsing roofs. By the twentieth century, when modern quarrying had cut away one face of the hill, the former caves appeared only as fossil-bearing rock distinct from the limestone. Digging in this hard, compacted fill material proved difficult; blasting was often necessary. Just as much of a problem was the troubled political condition of China. Antiforeign riots were flaring, and bandits controlled the countryside around Beijing. For weeks at a time they isolated the dig from the city. Nevertheless, work at the dig continued. On October 16, 1927, three days before the first season's work was to end, Birgir Böhlin, field supervisor, found another early human tooth. As he hurried to Beijing to take it to Black, soldiers stopped him several times, without suspecting that he carried a scientific treasure in his pocket.

Black studied the tooth exhaustively. Struck by its size and its cusp pattern, he became convinced that it was a very ancient human molar. Without waiting for any further proof, Black announced the discovery of a new genus and species of prehistoric human: *Sinanthropus pekinensis*, "Chinese man of Peking." Scientists were startled, and although Black traveled around the world to let them examine for themselves the evidence (which he carried on a watch chain in his waistcoat pocket), many refused to recognize *Sinanthropus* as a legitimate ancestor on the evidence of only one tooth.

Sinanthropus pekinensis: the original name given by Davidson Black to ancient fossils from Zhoukoudian. These remains are now classified as *Homo erectus*.

When Black returned to Beijing in 1928, his belief in the humanness of *Sinanthropus* was vindicated. His associates were waiting with fragments of a primitive human jaw they had dug out of the cave. And as tons of earth were excavated from the hillside and sifted for signs of fossil fragments, further teeth and several small fragments of human bone came to light.

Then, in 1929, Pei Wenzhong, a Chinese paleontologist working with Black, turned up the first skull of *Sinanthropus*. Work was about to be closed for the year when Pei opened up two caves at the extreme end of a fissure. On the floor of one was a large accumulation of debris. Pei brushed some of it away, and suddenly, partly surrounded by loose sand and partly embedded in travertine (a water-formed rock), there lay revealed the object of all the searching: a nearly complete skullcap (Figure 10–8). Even at first glance, Pei felt certain that it was a skullcap of *Sinanthropus*. After removing the skull and part of its stone bed from the cave, Pei carefully wrapped it up, set it in the basket of his bicycle, and pedaled the 25 mi (40 km) to Black's laboratory in Beijing. Black showed Pei's discovery to Roy Chapman Andrews, an American scientist. "There it was, the skull of an individual who had lived half a million years ago," Andrews wrote. "It was one of the most important discoveries in the whole history of human evolution. He could not

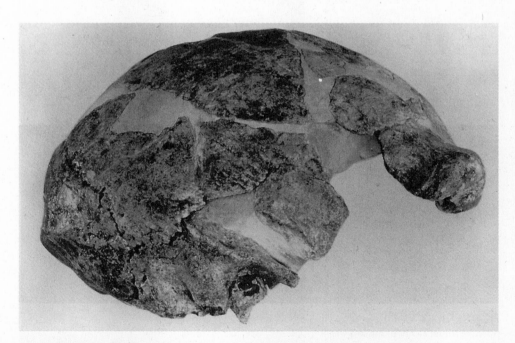

FIGURE 10–8   Although not the first to be discovered, this is one of several skullcaps of "Peking man" (*Homo erectus*) recovered from Zhoukoudian.

have been very impressive when he was alive, but dead and fossilized, he was awe-inspiring."

Black spent the next four months freeing the skullcap from the surrounding stone. When it was entirely clean he separated all the bones, made a cast of each one, and then reassembled the pieces. Black was now able to make a reliable estimate of the brain capacity of *Sinanthropus*. It came to about 1,000 cc, marking its owner as definitely humanlike in this respect.

Intensive Work at Zhoukoudian

The news made headlines around the world. Excavations at Zhoukoudian were reorganized on a broader basis and went on for almost ten more years, finally taking on the proportions of a grand engineering project.

As work advanced, a whole hillside was sliced off, revealing deposits 160 ft (almost 50 m) deep (Figure 10–9). They can be compared with an apartment building about 16 stories tall, each story packed solid with blown-in debris combined with the abandoned rubbish of long-departed tenants. Layer on layer, the caves were filled through the ages with strata of clay, with soil carried in by the wind, with limestone drippings, with rock fallen from the ceiling—all sandwiching layers of human and animal debris. It is clear that large carnivores occupied the caves for long periods of time. Bones of extinct creatures like the cave bear and a giant hyena, together with the remains of animals on which they preyed, occur at cer-

FIGURE 10–9   The excavation of the cave filling at Zhoukoudian was a gigantic undertaking. Work continued at the site from 1927 until 1937.

tain levels. At others, it seems clear that human beings drove the carnivores out and took over the caves for themselves. At first, the animal and human layers alternate fairly regularly, but toward the top, the evidence suggests that humans took over permanently.

A total of 1,873 workdays were devoted to dynamiting and removing some 706,000 cubic feet (20,000 cubic meters) of rock and earth and sorting through this debris for fossils. The findings constituted an encyclopedia of prehistory that has given us a great part of our knowledge of these people. By 1937 parts of more than 40 men, women, and children had been unearthed; these fossils included 5 calvaria (skulls without faces or mandibles), 9 fragmentary skulls, 6 facial fragments, 14 lower jaws, 152 teeth, and numerous skeletal fragments.

Black organized the work, kept detailed records of all the finds, classified them, and made casts, drawings, and photographs of the heavy volume of material pouring into Beijing. Tragically he did not live to savor the full bounty of Zhoukoudian. He died of a heart attack in 1934, but he had seen enough to realize the site's extraordinary significance.

The Rockefeller Foundation sought carefully for a successor and chose Franz Weidenreich (1873–1948), then a visiting professor of anatomy at the University of Chicago (Figure 10–10). Before the Nazis drove him from his native Germany, Weidenreich had completed important studies of the evolutionary changes in the pelvis and the foot that made possible our upright posture. His studies supported

FIGURE 10–10 Franz Weidenreich (left, shown here with an unidentified colleague) succeeded Davidson Black at Peking Union Medical College in 1935 and pursued the excavations at Zhoukoudian with equal fervor.

the contention of Darwin and Huxley that humankind is a descendant of some ancient anthropoid stock.

Assessment of *Sinanthropus*

After Weidenreich's arrival at Zhoukoudian in 1935, only two more seasons of undisturbed digging could be carried out. Fighting between Chinese and Japanese guerrillas broke out nearby, and the archaeologists had to take refuge. With the approach of World War II, Weidenreich concentrated on making accurate drawings and casts of the skulls and published detailed photographs and descriptions of every important fossil. He began a classic series of studies of the fossils: *The Mandibles of Sinanthropus, The Dentition of Sinanthropus, The Extremity Bones of Sinanthropus,* and *The Skull of Sinanthropus.* All four supported Black's conclusion: *Sinanthropus* was not a link between apes and humans but an actual human, though a very primitive one. Weidenreich placed *Sinanthropus* solidly in the human lineage because members of the species undoubtedly could walk upright on two legs. "Apes, like man, have two hands and two feet, but man alone has acquired an upright position and the faculty of using his feet exclusively as locomotor instruments," said Weidenreich. "Unless all signs are deceiving, the claim may even be ventured that the change in locomotion and the corresponding alteration of the organization of the body are the essential specialization in the transformation of the prehuman form into the human form."

The teeth and dental arch of *Sinanthropus* testified further to human status. The canines were not the projecting fangs of the ape, and the dental arch was curved, not oblong. Still more evidence lay in the skull. Weidenreich arranged the skulls of a gorilla, *Sinanthropus,* and a modern human in a row, so that even a glance revealed their striking differences: the extremely low skull of the gorilla, the somewhat higher skull of *Sinanthropus,* and the rounded skull of a modern human (Figure 10–11). The low vault of the gorilla skull houses a brain averaging about 500 cc; the higher dome of *Sinanthropus* held one of about 1,000 cc; and the high cranium of the modern human encloses a brain averaging about 1,330 cc. Because *Sinanthropus*'s brain was so small, some scientists questioned the creature's human status. Weidenreich cautioned that brain size alone is no absolute determinant. One species of whale, he pointed out, has a brain approaching 10,000

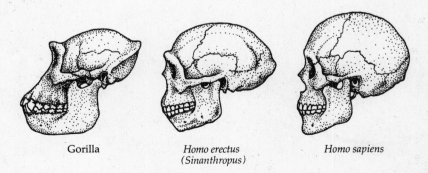

Gorilla

Homo erectus (*Sinanthropus*)

Homo sapiens

FIGURE 10–11   Skulls of a female gorilla, *Sinanthropus,* and a modern Chinese (all equally reduced). Notice the size and form of the braincase in relation to the jaws.

cc, but this amounts to 0.04 oz (1 g) of brain for each 22 lb (10,000 g) of body weight, compared to our ratio of 0.04 oz (1 g) for every 1.6 oz (45 g) of weight. "Neither the absolute nor the relative size of the brain can be used to measure the degree of mental ability in animals or man," he added. "Cultural objects are the only guide as far as spiritual life is concerned. They may be fallacious guides too, but we are completely lost if these objects are missing."

Culture at Zhoukoudian

At Zhoukoudian cultural objects were not missing. The continuing excavations produced thousands of stone tools. Many were simple choppers with only a few chips removed, but they were made to a pattern. In the largest cave that was explored, 100,000 stone tools and fragments, most of quartz, were found. Some of them lay with charred bits of wood and bone. From this it was concluded that *Sinanthropus* had mastered the use of fire.

The bones and antlers of thousands of animals were present in the deposits. Nearly three-quarters of them belonged to deer; there were also bones of giant sheep, zebra, pigs, buffalo, rhinoceros, monkeys, bison, elephant, and even such river-dwellers as the otter. Among these were scattered the bones of predators; bear, hyena, wolves, fox, badger, leopard and other cats, and humans. All these bones came from species that are now extinct.

The possibility that some of the bones and antlers were shaped and used as tools was put forward by the distinguished French prehistorian Abbé Henri Breuil (Figure 10–12). His work has been cited by numerous authors, including Raymond Dart, who used it to support his thesis that there was a somewhat similar "osteodontokeratic" culture at Makapansgat, South Africa. However, as early as 1938 Pei had discussed the effects on bone of predators, rodents, water, soil chemistry, and so on. The fact is that, as Lewis Binford and C. K. Ho have pointed out, the evidence for a bone and horn industry is not by any means conclusive; all the so-called tools of these materials could have been produced naturally, without any human activity. Interpretations of the Zhoukoudian cultural material will be discussed further in Chapter 11.

FIGURE 10–12 Bone and antler fragments were found in abundance at Zhoukoudian. The photograph is approximately one-sixth actual size.

About 20 ft (6 m) below the lowest outer threshold of the big cave, the expedition found what may have been *Sinanthropus*'s garbage dump, a stony amalgam of thousands of scraps of bone, stone chips, and hackberry seeds. All in all, by their handiwork as well as by their bodily structure, the specimens found in China indubitably established their right to a place in the human genus. Recent Chinese research places the human occupation of the cave between 230,000 and 500,000 years B.P.

Relationship of *Pithecanthropus* and *Sinanthropus*

Weidenreich's assessment corroborated Black's earlier conclusion that *Sinanthropus* was humanlike. In 1929 Black had compared his Zhoukoudian skull with Dubois's detailed description of *Pithecanthropus*. He concluded that the skulls were two specimens of the same type of creature. In each, the bones of the skull were thick, the forehead was low and sloping, and massive brow ridges jutted out over the eye sockets.

In 1931, on an upper terrace of the same Solo River whose banks had harbored the bones of Dubois's *Pithecanthropus*, fragments of 11 somewhat more recent skulls were excavated by Dutch geologists. This discovery encouraged G. H. R. von Koenigswald (1902–1983), a German paleontologist (Figure 10–13), to keep

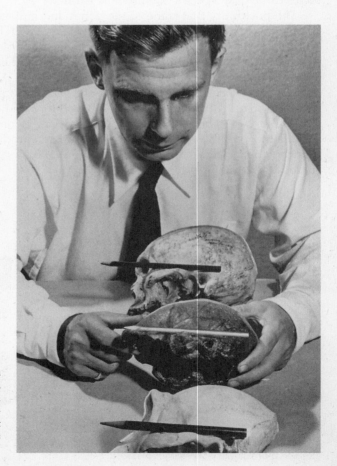

FIGURE 10–13 G. H. R von Koenigswald worked in Java in the 1930s and managed to find more specimens of *Pithecanthropus*. He helped establish that *Sinanthropus* and *Pithecanthropus* were of the same genus.

searching for more specimens of *Pithecanthropus*. Eventually, in 1937, in a region to the west called Sangiran, he found pieces of three more skulls, definitely human and definitely very old—and presumably remains of the same *Pithecanthropus* that Dubois had found 40 years before. When the most complete skull was assembled, it scarcely could have been more like Dubois's fossil. "It was a little eerie," said von Koenigswald, "to come upon two skulls . . . which resembled each other as much as two eggs." In 1936 von Koenigswald had excavated a child's skull at Modjokerto, Java, which later proved to be that of a 6-year-old *Pithecanthropus*.

In 1939 a historic meeting of *Sinanthropus* and *Pithecanthropus* took place in Weidenreich's laboratory, when von Koenigswald paid a visit and brought his Java fossils along to compare them with the Zhoukoudian finds. The two scientists concluded that *Pithecanthropus* and *Sinanthropus* were indeed close relations. "In its general form and size [the Peking man skull] agrees with the Java skull to such an extent that it identifies *Pithecanthropus* too, as true man, and a creature far above the stage of an ape," said Weidenreich, upsetting the judgment of Dubois that *Pithecanthropus* had come long before the first humans.

The assessment of von Koenigswald and Weidenreich was later corroborated by Wilfred Le Gros Clark. *Pithecanthropus*, Le Gros Clark said, appeared slightly more primitive, with a brain of about 900 cc and a slightly heavier jaw. In addition, the animals associated with *Pithecanthropus* were a little older than those found at Zhoukoudian, and no tools were found with *Pithecanthropus*. Despite these differences, the two ancient beings were strikingly alike.

Von Koenigswald and Weidenreich had agreed that *Pithecanthropus* and *Sinanthropus* differed little more than "two different races of present mankind," and Le Gros Clark came to the same conclusion. He proposed dropping the *Sinanthropus* classification, which implied a separate genus, for it was doubtful that the two formed even separate species. He suggested that both should be identified as *Pithecanthropus* and distinguished only by their specific names, *Pithecanthropus erectus* for the Java finds and *Pithecanthropus pekinensis* for the Chinese discoveries.

The aging Eugene Dubois bitterly opposed Le Gros Clark's conclusion, continuing to insist that his own find was quite distinct from all others. But von Koenigswald and Weidenreich were little disturbed by his protests. More upsetting was the rumble of war.

Fate of the Java and Beijing Fossils

In Java, von Koenigswald knew that it was only a matter of time until the island would be seized. He quietly gave some of his most valuable fossils for safekeeping to a Swiss geologist and a Swedish journalist, neutrals in the conflict between Allies and Axis. (The journalist put the teeth in milk bottles and buried them one night in his garden.) When the Japanese occupied Java in 1942, they demanded that von Koenigswald give up his fossils. He surrendered a few, but he substituted plaster casts for some of the originals.

At the end of the war, von Koenigswald tracked down and reassembled all the fossils. "My happiness was complete," he said, "when I learned that my precious specimens had been saved. Large parts of my collections, many of my books, and all of my clothes had been stolen, but Early Man had survived the disaster." Von Koenigswald later exhibited *Pithecanthropus* in New York and then took the bones to the Netherlands and on to Frankfurt, Germany, where they now remain.

The Beijing fossils were not so fortunate as the Java fossils. By the autumn of 1941, the scientists working at Zhoukoudian were more immediately threatened than they had been before the war. After some debate about what to do with the fossils, the Chinese scientists appealed to the president of the Peking Union Medical College to have the irreplaceable Beijing fossils taken to safety. It was arranged to send the collection to the United States. The boxes of fossils were entrusted to a detachment of U.S. Marines who were evacuating Beijing. The marines, with their baggage and the fossils, were scheduled to leave China on the steamship *President Harrison* on December 8.

But the rendezvous was never kept, for on December 7 Japanese bombs were dropped on Pearl Harbor, and total war came violently to the Pacific. The U.S. Marines and their precious cargo were captured by the invading Japanese, and somehow, in the chaos of war, the fossils of *Pithecanthropus pekinensis* were lost, never to reappear. Luckily, Weidenreich had overseen the preparation of a superb series of fossil casts, and these did survive. The casts, along with Weidenreich's excellent descriptions and photographs, preserve much information about the original Zhoukoudian fossils.

During the 1940s it became increasingly clear that *Pithecanthropus* showed strong anatomical resemblances to modern humans, *Homo sapiens*. As a result, in

FIGURE 10–14   The reconstruction of the skull and jaw of *Homo erectus* is based on numerous fossil finds. The general form of the face can also be reconstructed with reasonable accuracy, but we have no evidence of such important features as nostrils, lips, and hair.

1951, as part of a general taxonomic house-cleaning, *Pithecanthropus*, in all of its Asian forms, was formally sunk into the single species *Homo erectus* (Figure 10–14). And no sooner had the new species been established than it proved to have some surprises up its sleeve. Discoveries over the following 40-plus years have shown that *Homo erectus* is much older than the initial 800,000-year estimate and was much more widely spread across the Old World.

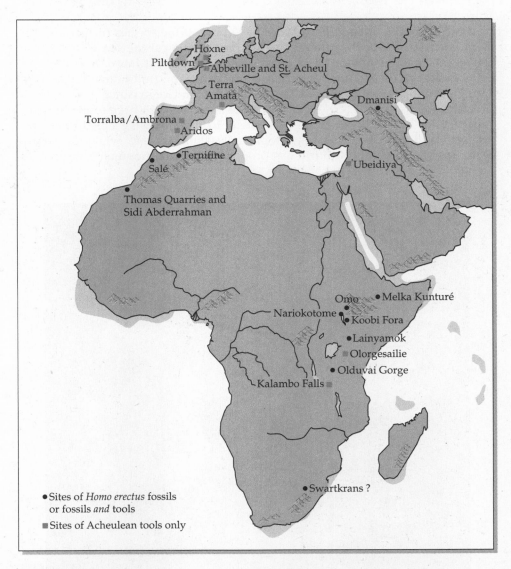

FIGURE 10–15   Since the earliest discoveries in East Asia, a number of sites in Europe and Africa have yielded fossil remains of *Homo erectus* and/or Acheulean tools. On this map the coastline is shown as it might have been during a period of glaciation when the sea level fell. The site of the Piltdown "discovery" has been added, together with important archaeological sites mentioned in the text.

HOMO ERECTUS FOSSILS FROM AFRICA AND EUROPE

Since the 1950s the continent of Africa has yielded numerous fossils of *Homo erectus* from a variety of locations (Figure 10–15). In 1954 *Homo erectus* mandibles dating 600,000–700,000 years B.P. were discovered at the northwest African site of Ternifine, Algeria. The next year another jaw was recovered from slightly younger deposits at the coastal Moroccan site of Sidi Abderrahman, and in 1971 cranial fragments of late *Homo erectus* (ca. 400,000 years B.P.?) were reported from Salé, Morocco.

Fossils from South and East Africa have pushed the species further and further into the past. The Swartkrans site has produced a partial jaw (SK 15) dating between 1.0 and 0.5 million years of age that *may* represent *Homo erectus*. In 1960 Louis Leakey recovered undoubted *Homo erectus* remains (museum number OH9) dating 1.2 million years B.P. from Tanzania's Olduvai Gorge (since then, younger *H. erectus* fossils, ca. 600,000–700,000 years of age, have also been found at Olduvai). Just north of Olduvai, the Kenyan site of Lainyamok has yielded *Homo erectus* teeth and limb bones dating around 600,000 years B.P., while the central Ethiopian site of Melka Kunturé has produced a cranial fragment that may go

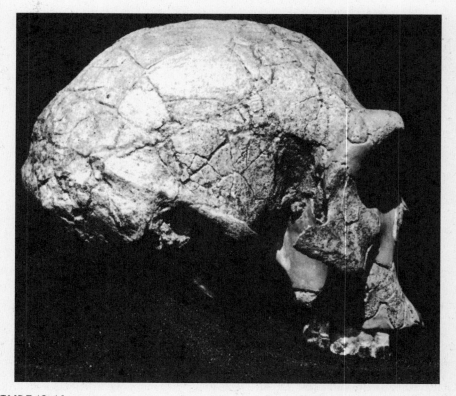

FIGURE 10–16   This skull from Koobi Fora in Kenya is one of the best-preserved skulls that belongs to the species *Homo erectus*. The present evidence suggests it may be 1.7 million years old. This photograph is approximately one-third actual size.

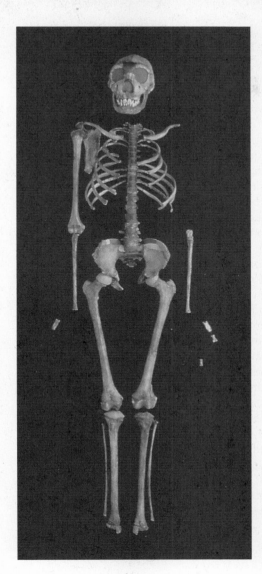

FIGURE 10–17 The most complete early hominid skeleton ever found was discovered at Nariokotome, west of Lake Turkana, Kenya, in 1984 and was excavated from sediments that are dated close to 1.5 mya. The skeleton, known as KNM-WT 15000, belongs to a 12-year-old *Homo erectus* boy who would have grown into an adult over 6 ft (1.8 m) in height.

back 900,000 years. The distinction of producing the most ancient remains of African *Homo erectus*, however, belongs to the Omo region of extreme southwestern Ethiopia and the east and west shores of Lake Turkana in Kenya. Relevant Omo fossils date to 1.4 million years ago (mya), while discoveries in east Turkana's Koobi Fora region carry *Homo erectus* all the way back to 1.8 million years B.P. Among the Koobi Fora fossils is a superb skull, designated KNM ER-3733, whose owner boasted a cranial capacity of 850 cc some 1.7 mya (Figure 10–16).

But of all the African specimens, the *Homo erectus* boy from the west Turkana site of Nariokotome is perhaps the most exciting. Initially discovered in 1984 by the veteran fossil hunter Kamoya Kimeu, the specimen consists of a nearly complete skeleton (Figure 10–17) that lacks only the left humerus (upper arm bone), both radii (lower arm bones), and most of the bones of the hands and feet. Dated to 1.5 million years B.P., the Nariokotome boy was about 12 years old when he died (perhaps from the septicemia of a gum infection after the loss of a lower milk molar) and came to lie in a shallow swamp that was probably replenished seasonally by the floodwaters of the Omo River. After death, the body lay relatively undisturbed in the quiet water as it gradually decomposed. Small portions of the body were very likely eaten by scavenging catfish, and the skeleton was dispersed and damaged somewhat as large wading animals trampled and kicked the bones. Most of the skeleton, however, settled quietly into the mud and began the long wait until its discovery a million and a half years later.

The nearly complete nature of the Nariokotome skeleton has allowed detailed studies of *Homo erectus* anatomy never before possible. The boy was about 5.3 ft (160 cm) tall at death and would very likely have grown to be a big man of about 6.1 ft (185 cm) and 150 lb (68 kg). His boyhood cranial capacity of 880 cc would probably have expanded to about 909 cc when he became an adult (68 percent of the modern human average). He had long arms and legs and a slender torso—bodily proportions identical to those of modern people who are adapted to hot, dry climates. His estimated adult pelvic dimensions, if characteristic of the species, suggest that *Homo erectus* newborns had relatively small brains (perhaps about 200 cc) and that, as in modern humans, rapid brain growth then continued for the first part of an infant's life. And finally, details of his thoracic (rib cage) vertebrae suggest that *Homo erectus* may have lacked the fine muscular control over breathing that is required for speech (more on this in a later section).

One last fossil remains to be mentioned, and that is the tantalizing specimen from the Caucasus site of Dmanisi in Georgia (Figure 10–15). In 1991 a lower jaw was discovered at this extreme southeastern European site that has been identified as the only *Homo erectus* fossil known from that continent. That distinction would be sufficiently interesting by itself, but, in addition, the fossil is extremely old, apparently dating between 1.6 and 1.8 million years of age! These dates provide a strong challenge to the traditional theory that *Homo erectus* dispersed from Africa about 1 million years ago. As noted below, that theory is also being challenged by new *H. erectus* dates from Java.

THE ANATOMY OF *HOMO ERECTUS*

Homo ergaster: this name is given by some specialists to certain African fossils regarded by most workers as being *Homo erectus.* The authors of this text side with the majority.

Fossils attributed to *Homo erectus* cover an enormous time span (1.8 to 0.3 million years B.P.) and geographic range (South Africa to southeast Asia). As a consequence of its longevity and geographic spread, *Homo erectus* displays a good deal of anatomical variability (Figure 10–18).

Indeed, some researchers think the variability justifies placing the early African representatives from Lake Turkana (including KNM ER-3733 and the Nariokotome boy) in a separate species from Asian *Homo erectus* (Louis Leakey's 1.2-million-year-old fossil from Olduvai Gorge would be retained in the latter group). The ancient African fossils would then be classified as *Homo ergaster.* Supporters of this new scheme, including British researcher Bernard Wood, view *Homo ergaster* as more closely related (and more likely to be ancestral) to modern humans than was Asian *Homo erectus.* Other workers disagree with the new taxonomy, however, and chief among the dissenters is American anthropologist G. Philip Rightmire, who has made *Homo erectus* something of a research specialty. In

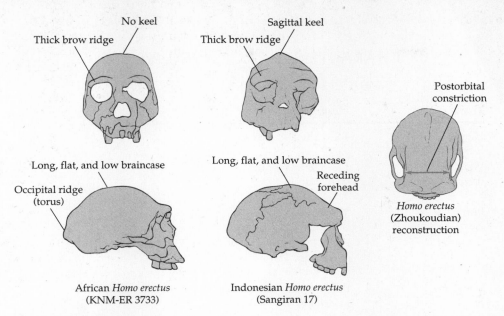

No keel

Thick brow ridge

Sagittal keel

Thick brow ridge

Postorbital constriction

Long, flat, and low braincase

Occipital ridge (torus)

Long, flat, and low braincase

Receding forehead

Homo erectus (Zhoukoudian) reconstruction

African *Homo erectus* (KNM-ER 3733)

Indonesian *Homo erectus* (Sangiran 17)

FIGURE 10–18 *Homo erectus* skulls from Africa (left) and Asia (center) are compared. Shared traits include the platycephalic braincase, large brows, an angled occipital region, and an occipital torus. In contrast to the African specimens, Asian *H. erectus* skulls are often topped with a sagittal keel. A superior view of the skull of *H. erectus* (right) reveals a marked postorbital constriction (specimen from Zhoukoudian).

our opinion, the issue cannot be settled at present and depends on future fossil discoveries and additional analyses. That being the case, we have opted to retain the traditional classification scheme and to place all mid-Pleistocene hominids in one variable and widespread species: *Homo erectus*.

In many important ways, *Homo erectus* had reached anatomical modernity. On average, these mid-Pleistocene people were as tall and as heavy as modern humans (see Box 10–1; modern humans average 5.3–5.7 ft, or 161–175 cm, in height and 119–143 lb, or 54–65 kg, in weight). In addition, the limb proportions of *Homo erectus* were similar to those of modern humans, in contrast to the long arms and short legs of early *Homo* (Box 8–2). There can be no doubt that these people stood and moved in a fully modern, upright fashion.

Despite their modern postcranial skeletons, however, *Homo erectus* individuals differed greatly from modern people in their brain size and cranial anatomy. The average brain size for *Homo erectus* was 988 cc (range 750–1,251; Table 8–1)— some 27 to 61 percent bigger than early *Homo* (Box 8–2), but still only two-thirds the modern average. But because brain expansion in *Homo erectus* was matched by increased body size, the species' relative brain size (brain size controlling for body weight) was not significantly greater than that of early *Homo* (see Chapter 13). Furthermore, the enlarged *Homo erectus* brain was still encased in a primitive-looking container (Figures 10–16 and 10–18). The skull of *Homo erectus* was constructed of thick cranial bones, and it was long, low-vaulted, and widest at the base, a combination of traits labeled *platycephalic*.

The front of the cranium was topped with huge brow ridges, and behind those brows the skull showed a distinct postorbital constriction at the temples. Often,

Platycephalic: a term describing a skull that is long, low-vaulted, and wide.

BOX 10-1
CHARACTERISTICS OF *HOMO ERECTUS*

Trait	*Homo erectus*
Height (sexes combined)	4.8–6.1 ft (145–185 cm)
Weight (sexes combined)	123–128 lb average (56–58 kg) (range up to 150 lb, or 68 kg)
Brain size (sexes combined)	988 cc mean (750–1,251 cc range)
Cranium	Long, low-vaulted ("platycephalic") braincase, widest at the base; large brow ridges; sagittal keeling of frontal bone; thick skull bones; unflexed cranial base; *occipital torus*
Dentition	Both anterior and posterior teeth smaller than those in early *Homo*
Limbs	Arm and leg proportions within modern human range of variation
Locomotion	Bipedalism
Distribution	Africa, Asia, Europe (Dmanisi, Georgia)
Known dates (millions of years B.P.)	1.8–0.3

Occipital torus: a ridge running side-to-side across the occipital bore.

Sagittal keel: a slightly raised ridge running down the center of a skull; smaller than a sagittal crest.

particularly in the Asian specimens, the top of the skull showed a distinct *sagittal keel*. And finally, at the back the skull of *Homo erectus* was ridged and angled sharply toward the cranial base (Figure 10–18), and the cranial base itself tended to be rather flat and unflexed, lacking the arched configuration characteristic of modern humans (see Chapter 13).

Several researchers have attempted to determine whether *Homo erectus* showed any significant evolutionary changes in anatomy during its long period of existence, and here again opinions differ. Milford Wolpoff of the University of Michigan has argued that brain size did show such an increase, but Rightmire and others disagree. In the latest statement on the subject, David Begun and Alan Walker present evidence that little, if any, expansion of the brain occurred from early to late *Homo erectus* (Figure 10–19). Similarly, Walker and various co-workers have argued that *Homo erectus* showed no significant temporal changes in stature, dental dimensions, or skull shape. Thus the weight of the evidence at present seems to indicate that *Homo erectus* experienced a rather long period of anatomical stasis. Its characteristic anatomy remained essentially stable for over a million years, and then disappeared only upon the evolution of *Homo sapiens*.

Anatomical Evidence of Speech and Language

A crucial question that so far has defied our attempts at an answer concerns the beginnings of those uniquely human traits, speech and language (see Chapter 4

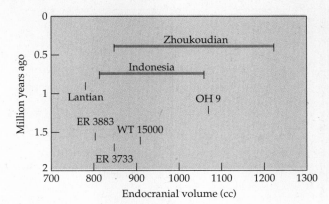

FIGURE 10–19   A comparison of brain sizes from African and Asian *Homo erectus* specimens (most, but not all mentioned in the text). Some researchers think the fossils reveal little, if any, increase in brain size during the species' period of existence. Others disagree, but small sample sizes prevent a firm conclusion. Note that the dates for Indonesian *Homo erectus* are currently being revised.

for definitions). The australopithecines all seemed too small-brained and behaviorally primitive to have had language and speech. Early representatives of *Homo* showed a strong increase in brain size and the beginnings of stone-tool technology, but most workers hesitate to regard them as linguistic creatures. But what about *Homo erectus*? Surely, with all we know about the anatomy of this species, we can draw some clear conclusions about its linguistic capacities.

Unfortunately it seems that when it comes to speech and language evolution, additional anatomical knowledge has exacerbated the problem rather than reducing it. Certainly *Homo erectus* had an absolutely larger brain than its evolutionary predecessors, but this only increases the *likelihood* that they produced spoken language rather than proving it conclusively. An examination of the brain's so-called language areas (see Chapter 13) is also inconclusive. Although *Broca's area* in the inferior frontal lobe is well developed in *Homo erectus,* recent research on modern humans has shown that this cortical region supports both the hierarchical organization of grammar and the manual combination of objects, including tool use. Whether the manual coordination involved in tool manufacture and use, or the production of hierarchically organized speech, or both, were associated with Broca's area development in *Homo erectus* is unknown. Furthermore, *Wernicke's area* in the temporal lobe appears to be extremely difficult to assess for most ancient skulls—including those of *Homo erectus*—because of distortion during fossilization. And finally, *hemispherical asymmetry* in the cerebrum—demonstrable in the Nariokotome boy and very likely associated in that specimen with right-handedness—cannot be trusted as a guide to language abilities since asymmetry (including left-hemisphere dominance for vocalizations) has been documented for monkeys and apes.

Two negative bits of anatomical evidence argue against spoken language in *Homo erectus*. First, although there is some variation among specimens, the cranial base is generally flat and unflexed. As detailed in Chapter 13, this suggests a short pharynx and an inability to produce the full range of modern vowel sounds. Second, analyses of the vertebral canals of the Nariokotome boy have revealed dimensions similar to those of monkeys and apes in the thoracic (rib cage) region (Figure 10–20). In contrast, modern humans have enlarged canals in their thoracic vertebrae, possibly to accommodate increased nerve connections with the rib cage muscles that control this part of the breathing apparatus. The small thoracic canals

Broca's area: part of the human cerebral cortex involved with the hierarchical organization of grammar and the manual combination of objects.

Wernicke's area: part of the human cerebral cortex essential in comprehending and producing meaningful speech.

Hemispheral asymmetry: the condition in which the two cerebral hemispheres differ in one or more dimensions. In most modern humans, the left hemisphere is somewhat larger than the right.

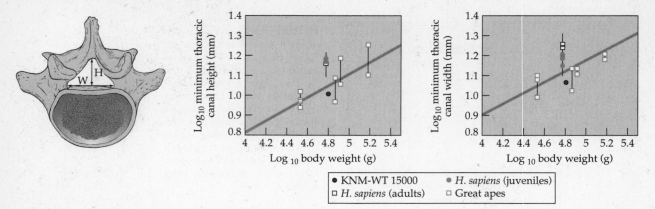

FIGURE 10–20   A representative human vertebra (left) showing the vertebral canal and how it can be measured. The Nariokotome boy (KNM-WT 15000) had smaller thoracic canal measurements than both adult and juvenile modern humans (center and right). The KNM-WT 15000 dimensions are roughly comparable to those of some apes.

found in *Homo erectus* suggest to Alan Walker and others that this species lacked the fine control of breathing that is essential for speech.

So, could *Homo erectus* talk? The best answer from anatomy is a rather unsatisfying "maybe." After a thorough review of the evidence, Walker thinks that speech and language probably appeared rather late in hominid evolution and that archaeology may be a better guide to these capacities than is anatomy. This is an important point to keep in mind when we examine the archaeological evidence gathered from *Homo erectus* sites (Chapter 11).

HOMO ERECTUS MIGRATIONS AND NEW DATES FROM JAVA

Until quite recently, anthropologists enjoyed widespread agreement on the origin and spread of *Homo erectus* (the evolutionary fate of the species is considerably more controversial, as we will see in Chapter 14). *Homo erectus* has traditionally been viewed as a species that evolved in Africa about 1.8 mya (Figure 10–21) from an early *Homo* ancestor (either *H. habilis* or *H. rudolfensis*) and then, about 1 mya, as a result of increased intelligence and cultural complexity, was able to expand its geographic range out of Africa and into Europe and Asia, reaching Java no later than 800,000 to 900,000 years B.P. In the past two years, however, this scenario of an African origin and subsequent migration by *Homo erectus* has been challenged strongly by new discoveries and dates. First, as we have seen, in 1991 a *Homo erectus* mandible was found at Dmanisi in the Caucasus. This fossil has now been dated by Georgian scientists L. Gabunia and A. Vekua at 1.6 to 1.8 million years of age. Although these dates fall short of disproving an African origin for *H. erectus*, they do argue persuasively that the species existed outside of that continent much earlier than traditionally believed. If *H. erectus* people did spread outward from an African homeland, their migration began well over a million and a half years ago.

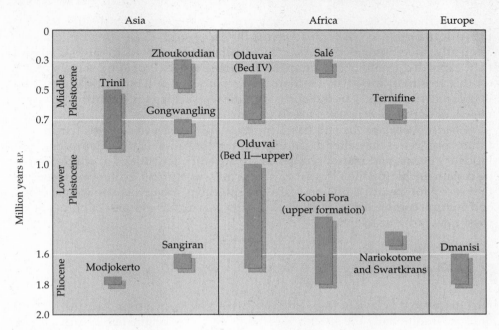

FIGURE 10–21   This chart shows the approximate ranges of time of the deposits that contained the fossils of *Homo erectus* mentioned in this chapter.

The possibility of an earlier migration has recently been strongly supported by the work of an American and Indonesian research team headed by geochronologists Carl Swisher and Garniss Curtis. Using an argon–argon dating technique (^{40}Ar/^{39}Ar dating), Swisher et al. determined in 1994 that *Homo erectus* inhabited the Sangiran region of Java over 1.66 million years ago and the Modjokerto region as early as 1.81 million years B.P.! Thus it appears that *Homo erectus* may have reached extreme southeast Asia fully a million years earlier than was traditionally believed. If these new dates are valid—and like all scientific findings, they require verification—then *Homo erectus* is equally old in Asia and Africa (Figure 10–21) and old views on the species' origin and migration may have to be revised substantially.

Do the new dates from Dmanisi and Java falsify the hypothesis of an African origin for *Homo erectus?* Not necessarily. If the species evolved just slightly earlier than the oldest African fossils—say, 1.9–2.0 mya—and then immediately began its geographic spread, it could have reached Europe and Asia fairly quickly. For example, an African origin of 1.9 million years B.P. would have allowed a leisurely spread of about 1 mi (1.6 km) every 10 years to get to Java 100,000 years later. As detailed in the next chapter, however, there is one major problem with scenarios involving departure dates earlier than about 1.4 to 1.7 million years B.P., and that is simply that they involve geographic spread before the cultural developments that are supposed to have made it possible. On the other hand, as Chapter 11 will make clear, an early migration could go far toward explaining technological differences between western and eastern *Homo erectus* populations that have long baffled anthropologists.

Of course, the early Georgian and Javanese dates do open the door to other, nontraditional scenarios concerning hominids' arrival in Asia. Instead of *Homo erectus,* perhaps some earlier form of hominid (early *Homo?*) was the first to leave the African birthplace and spread across the Old World. *Homo erectus* might subsequently have originated in Asia (or anywhere between Africa and Asia) and then expanded to fill its known mid-Pleistocene range. Providing some support for this possibility are yet-to-be-confirmed reports of 2-million-year-old Oldowan pebble tools from Pakistan and northern India. Weakening the scenario is the complete lack of pre–*Homo erectus* fossils outside Africa.

Clearly, *Homo erectus* still has some tricks up its sleeve for researchers, and future discoveries may alter drastically our interpretation of mid-Pleistocene evolutionary events and migrations. But there are still a few things of which we can be certain, including the fact that *Homo erectus* was a grand evolutionary success that lasted for about 1.5 million years and showed a strong increase in behavioral and cultural complexity over its predecessors. It is to that complex culture that we must now turn our attention.

SUMMARY

First discovered in Java in 1891, *Homo erectus* is now known from Asia, Africa, and Europe. Traditionally the species was thought to have originated in Africa about 1.8 mya and then to have spread to other parts of the Old World. This interpretation has recently been called into question, however, by reports of very ancient fossils from Georgia and Java. Compared to its evolutionary predecessors, *Homo erectus* had achieved considerable modernity in its anatomy. These people were as tall and as heavy as modern humans, and they showed modern limb proportions. Average brain size had increased to nearly 1,000 cc, but these big brains were still contained in rather primitive-looking skulls that were long, low-vaulted, and widest at the base. Despite their large brains, however, there seems to be little anatomical evidence that *Homo erectus* had spoken language. Their unflexed cranial base suggests an inability to produce the full range of vowel sounds, and details of the thoracic vertebral canals may indicate that they lacked the breathing control needed for speech.

Some researchers believe that the anatomical variability of *Homo erectus* justifies splitting the taxon into two species: the name *Homo erectus* would be retained for specimens from Olduvai Gorge and Asia, while the name *Homo ergaster* would be introduced for early African specimens from the Lake Turkana region. We do not feel that such a step is warranted at present and thus have treated *Homo erectus* as a single, anatomically variable, widely spread species.

REVIEW QUESTIONS

1. Summarize the anatomical differences between *Homo erectus* and early *Homo.* How did *Homo erectus* differ anatomically from modern humans?

2. Discuss the reasoning that led Eugene Dubois to search for the "missing link" in Java. How do modern paleoanthropologists decide where to search for fossils?

3. There are few indications from anatomy—other than gross brain size—that *Homo erectus* had language. Discuss how a hominid species might have lived

successfully for over a million years and spread out of the tropics and into the colder regions of the Old World *without* language.

4. Discuss the suggestion that *Homo erectus* should be split into two species: *H. erectus* for Asian and later African specimens and *H. ergaster* for earlier African specimens. How much anatomical difference do you think is needed to justify naming a new species?

5. Discuss the implications of dating the Dmanisi jaw and the oldest Javanese *Homo erectus* fossils to 1.8 million years B.P. for our interpretations of the origin and spread of this species.

POSTSCRIPT

From the story of human evolution told thus far, one could get the impression that anthropologists' first reaction to new fossil finds is skepticism and rejection. Dubois's *Pithecanthropus* was taken by most turn-of-the-century experts as either an incredibly apelike human or a somewhat humanlike ape; very few of Dubois's colleagues agreed with him that it was a creature intermediate between humans and apes. Similarly, Raymond Dart's claim in 1925 that *Australopithecus africanus* was an evolutionary relative of humans was widely rejected by the scientific community. Why were these apparently reasonable—and subsequently verified— claims so unsuccessful when they were first made? What kept anthropologists and anatomists from recognizing these fossils for what we now know them to be? The answers to those questions are actually rather complex. But if we limit our attention to the British scientific community, two primary explanations appear that together teach a lesson about how science should be conducted. First, neither *Pithecanthropus* nor *Australopithecus* fit the theoretical expectations of the senior English scientists, and second, after 1912 there was a much more acceptable candidate for the role of "missing link": Piltdown man (Figure 10–22).

To address the issues in order, Grafton Elliot Smith was a major force in British anatomy and anthropology in the first half of the twentieth century. He was an acknowledged expert on primate brains, and he believed strongly that in human evolution "the brain had led the way." In other words, Elliot Smith held the view that expansion and elaboration of the human brain had preceded all other major evolutionary events—particularly dental changes and bipedalism—and, indeed, had made them possible. The unexpected combination in *Pithecanthropus* of fully developed bipedalism and modern teeth with a small (850 cc) brain did not sit well with Elliot Smith. And if *Pithecanthropus* was a bitter pill, *Australopithecus africanus*, with its ape-sized brain (445 cc), humanlike teeth, and Dart's claim of bipedalism, was a horror! For Elliot Smith, both fossils challenged a theoretical position that he had laboriously constructed and in which he was strongly invested, and not surprisingly, he greeted them with skepticism.

And after 1912, agreeing that the brain had "led the way" was quite easy for British scientists because a wonderful fossil that matched their theoretical expectations to the letter had been discovered right on English soil: Piltdown man. The Piltdown fossils were brought to public attention by amateur archaeologist Charles Dawson and paleontologist Arthur Smith Woodward. Dawson had made the original discovery of apparently ancient skull fragments in a gravel pit near Piltdown Common in 1911. With Smith Woodward's help, additional remains were recovered

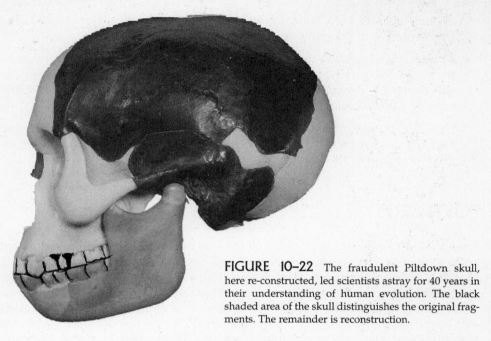

FIGURE 10–22 The fraudulent Piltdown skull, here re-constructed, led scientists astray for 40 years in their understanding of human evolution. The black shaded area of the skull distinguishes the original fragments. The remainder is reconstruction.

in 1912, and in 1913 Teilhard de Chardin retrieved a lower canine tooth from the Piltdown gravels. When the pieces were reconstructed, they produced a very large (almost 1,500 cc) and high-vaulted braincase with an apelike jaw and lower canines. Elliot Smith's theories seemed to be verified: Piltdown man combined a modern-sized brain with a primitive dentition. Furthermore, it was thought that *Eoanthropus dawsoni* ("Dawson's dawn man"), as the Piltdown specimen had been officially dubbed, was quite old—probably Pliocene in age and fully as ancient as *Pithecanthropus*. And so Dubois's and Dart's fossils, with their theoretically unpopular mixtures of traits, were pushed aside in favor of Piltdown.

For 40 years Piltdown man influenced researchers' interpretations of human evolution. Unfortunately, with each new find, Piltdown became more and more of an oddity. The accumulating collection of australopithecine fossils and the remains from Zhoukoudian and elsewhere all seemed to proclaim that the legs and the teeth had led the way, not the brain. Finally, in the early 1950s, scientists at Oxford University and the British Museum of Natural History initiated a series of new analyses to test the unspeakable possibility that the Piltdown fossil was a fraud. To their dismay, the tests proved beyond a doubt that a hoax had been perpetrated. Bones had been stained and broken, and teeth had been filed flat in order to make it appear that the skull and the jaw belonged to the same ancient creature. In reality, an ape's jaw had been combined with a human skull, and the best scientific minds in the world had been hoodwinked!

To this day, no one is sure who was responsible for the Piltdown hoax. Some think Dawson, the original discoverer; others believe that Teilhard de Chardin or Arthur Keith was the joker. In all likelihood, we will never know the identity of the guilty person(s). And ironically, over the years Piltdown has changed from an embarrassment to anthropology to a useful reminder not to become overly invested in the truth of a particular theory or to put unqualified trust in new discoveries that fit one's expectations. *Eoanthropus* now serves to remind us that science makes progress only through a healthy mix of hard work, insight, skepticism, data sharing, and verification or falsification of results.

CHAPTER 10 TIMELINE

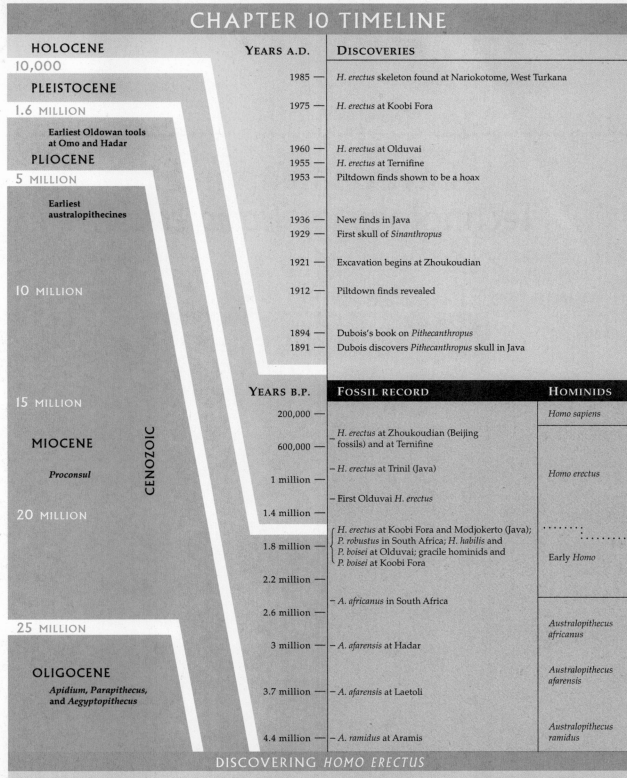

HOLOCENE		
10,000		
PLEISTOCENE		
1.6 MILLION		
Earliest Oldowan tools at Omo and Hadar		
PLIOCENE		
5 MILLION		
Earliest australopithecines		
10 MILLION		
15 MILLION		
MIOCENE		
Proconsul		
20 MILLION		
25 MILLION		
OLIGOCENE		
Apidium, Parapithecus, and *Aegyptopithecus*		

CENOZOIC

YEARS A.D.	DISCOVERIES
1985 —	*H. erectus* skeleton found at Nariokotome, West Turkana
1975 —	*H. erectus* at Koobi Fora
1960 —	*H. erectus* at Olduvai
1955 —	*H. erectus* at Ternifine
1953 —	Piltdown finds shown to be a hoax
1936 —	New finds in Java
1929 —	First skull of *Sinanthropus*
1921 —	Excavation begins at Zhoukoudian
1912 —	Piltdown finds revealed
1894 —	Dubois's book on *Pithecanthropus*
1891 —	Dubois discovers *Pithecanthropus* skull in Java

YEARS B.P.	FOSSIL RECORD	HOMINIDS
200,000 —		*Homo sapiens*
600,000 —	*H. erectus* at Zhoukoudian (Beijing fossils) and at Ternifine	
1 million —	*H. erectus* at Trinil (Java)	*Homo erectus*
1.4 million —	First Olduvai *H. erectus*	
1.8 million —	*H. erectus* at Koobi Fora and Modjokerto (Java); *P. robustus* in South Africa; *H. habilis* and *P. boisei* at Olduvai; gracile hominids and *P. boisei* at Koobi Fora	Early *Homo*
2.2 million —		
2.6 million —	*A. africanus* in South Africa	
3 million —	*A. afarensis* at Hadar	*Australopithecus africanus*
3.7 million —	*A. afarensis* at Laetoli	*Australopithecus afarensis*
4.4 million —	*A. ramidus* at Aramis	*Australopithecus ramidus*

DISCOVERING *HOMO ERECTUS*

Discoveries of *Homo erectus* have been made throughout the Old World since the first Java finds in 1891. *Homo erectus*'s pre-decessors, early *Homo*, were intermediates between the ancestral *Australopithecus* and themselves.

CHAPTER
11

Environment and
Technology of *Homo erectus*

*M*an *is a tool-making animal.*

BENJAMIN FRANKLIN, 1706–1790.

OVERVIEW

As currently known, the fossil record indicates that prior to the appearance of *Homo erectus*, hominids' geographic range was limited to Africa. All that changed with the evolution of *H. erectus*, however, and by 1.8 million years B.P. these early humans were spread from Africa to extreme southeast Asia and were beginning a period of existence that would last 1.5 million years. But what allowed such phenomenal geographic spread and species longevity? This chapter examines several cultural innovations and behavioral changes that might have contributed to the success of *H. erectus*: stone-knapping advances that resulted in Acheulean bifacial tools; the beginnings of shelter construction and the control and use of fire; and increased dependence on hunting. Important topics and concepts include Ice Age climatic conditions; the manufacture and use of Acheulean tools; artifactual evidence for *Homo erectus*'s presence in central and western Europe; the absence of Acheulean tools in the Far East and the possible use of bamboo tools in that area; evidence for the construction of shelters and the control and use of fire; and, finally, evidence for the appearance of hunting-and-gathering as a way of life.

HOMO ERECTUS: NEW QUESTIONS ABOUT AN OLD SPECIES

For over a quarter of a century, the story of *Homo erectus*—including time and place of origin, cultural development, geographic spread, and role in human evolution—has seemed straightforward. Anthropologists seemed to have many more answers about the species than questions (or, at least, many of the major problems appeared to have been solved). Now all of that has changed. With the recent announcements of *Homo erectus* fossils from the Caucasus and from Java that are fully as old as African representatives of the species—we face more questions than answers. Certainly *Homo erectus* can still claim the distinction of being the first hominid species known to exist outside Africa, and in our view, it still seems reasonable to assume an African origin for the species since all pre–*H. erectus* hominid fossils are from that continent. Furthermore, *Homo erectus* enjoyed impressive longevity as a species and great geographic spread, lasting for 1.5 million years and inhabiting the Old World from Southeast Asia to the Caucasus and south to the tip of Africa. Nonetheless, many traditional scenarios about connections between cultural (particularly technological) developments and geographic spread must be reexamined. It is time to stop and take stock of what we know and don't know about these early humans and their lifeways, and it is to that end that this chapter is dedicated.

As described in Chapter 10, the anatomy of *Homo erectus* seems quite modern in many ways. For example, it appears that these mid-Pleistocene people were about as tall and as heavy as modern humans and that they had modern limb proportions (Figure 11–1A). Certain important differences quickly become apparent,

FIGURE 11–1A Although imaginative, these reconstructions probably give a reasonable approximation of the posture and form of early *Homo* and *Homo erectus*. The main differences between them probably lie in the size and robustness of the body and in the size of the brain.

Early *Homo*   *Homo erectus*

FIGURE 11–1B Though stockily built, *Homo erectus* was becoming very modern in most features and distinct from early *Homo;* the differences in the skull are the most striking. In addition, *Homo erectus* probably had longer legs and shorter arms than their ancestors. Stature is a very variable characteristic, and some living populations of *Homo sapiens* are smaller than the average *Homo erectus* and no bigger than the skeleton of early *Homo* shown here. The bones known from the right side of the body are colored.

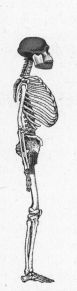

Early *Homo*   *Homo erectus*   *Homo sapiens*

however. First, *Homo erectus* possessed a brain that was only about two-thirds modern size, and furthermore, as we have seen that brain was packaged in a rather primitive-looking skull. The thick-boned cranium of *Homo erectus* was long, low-vaulted, and wide at the base. Additionally, the face was more prognathic than that of modern humans, sticking out in front of the braincase rather than being tucked underneath the frontal portion of the cranium (Figure 11–1B), and the cranial base was flat and unflexed. Studies of the surface anatomy of the *Homo erectus* brain, combined with other aspects of anatomy, fail to provide compelling evidence for spoken language.

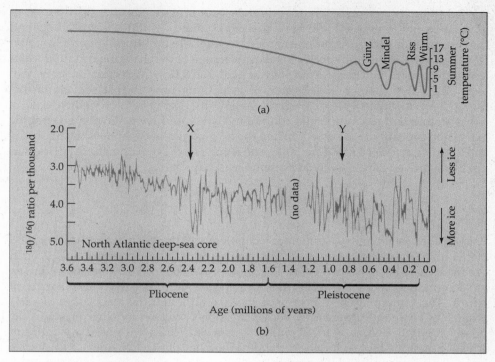

FIGURE 11–2　Plio-Pleistocene glacial and interglacial cycles now extend much further into the past than originally believed based on evidence from the European Alps (a). Oxygen isotope measurements from deep-sea cores (b) show evidence for Northern Hemisphere glaciations starting about 2.4 million years ago (Point X) with an intensification following the mid-Pleistocene (Point Y).

What sort of world did these early people with their smallish brains and primitive skulls inhabit? Clearly, the answer to that question varies from one *Homo erectus* population to another, since the species lived a long time and was spread from the tropics to the cold-temperate zones. Traditionally, we might have said that they preceded and then overlapped the beginnings of the "Ice Age." It is now known, however, that the Ice Age began much further back in time and involved a more complex pattern of glacial advances and retreats than thought originally (Figure 11–2). The first important Plio-Pleistocene glaciation occurred around 2.4 million years ago, and there were additional important pulses on both sides of the 2.0-million-year B.P. mark. Granted, there was an intensification of the climatic swings in the mid-Pleistocene that resulted in a series of very strong glacial advances, but it is no longer accurate to describe the Ice Age simply in terms of the traditional four-stage Alpine glaciation series (Günz, Mindel, Riss, and Würm; indeed, some specialists have suggested that this outmoded terminology should be discarded entirely). During periods of glaciation, worldwide temperatures would have fallen significantly, and parts of the Northern Hemisphere would have been bitterly cold. Rainfall patterns would have been altered, probably producing more extensive grasslands in North Africa and other parts of the Old World. In addition, with so much water locked up in the glaciers, ocean levels would have dropped some 330 ft (100 m) or more, exposing continental shelves and creating land bridges between locations now separated by the sea (Figures 10–3 and 10–15).

All these factors—temperature, rainfall, land bridges, and the distribution of grasslands and forests—would have affected hominids' abilities to spread beyond the continent of Africa. As noted earlier, we prefer the traditional assumption that *Homo erectus* was the first species to take advantage of the changing conditions and extend its geographic range. And starting with the following section on stone-tool technology, this chapter is dedicated to examining how cultural developments might have facilitated *Homo erectus*'s geographic expansion. Nonetheless, it is worth noting that environmental conditions that would have allowed geographic expansion probably also existed during the time period of early *Homo* (at about 2.4 and 2.0 million years B.P.; Figure 11–2), and a pre–*H. erectus* exodus from Africa cannot be disproved conclusively at present (see Chapter 10).

STONE TOOLS

As described in Chapter 9, stone-tool technology got its start with early *Homo*, and by the time *Homo erectus* appeared, Oldowan choppers and flake tools had been in use for at least half a million years. For another 100,000 to 400,000 years, Oldowan tools continued to be the top-of-the-line implements for early *Homo erectus* in Africa. The same may have been true in Asia, although the association of early Asian (i.e., Javanese) *Homo erectus* with stone tools of *any sort* remains questionable. In any event, between 1.4 to 1.7 million years B.P., Africa witnessed a significant advance in stone-tool technology: the development of the Acheulean industry of bifacially flaked tools and its premier implement, the *hand ax*. Named after a much later French site at St. Acheul, where hand axes were found in abundance, the Acheulean tool kit included not only bifacial hand axes, picks, and cleavers (Figure 11–3), but also an assortment of Oldowan-type choppers and flakes, suggesting that the more primitive implements continued to serve important functions.

In order to understand the nature of this advance in *lithic technology*, we need to take a closer look at how stone tools are made. First of all, not all stones are suitable for use in tool production. Rocks of a coarse, granular composition, like granite, are almost useless for making chipped tools; they do not fracture along smooth, clean edges but tend to crumble. Certain other rocks, like common feldspar, tend to break only along certain fracture lines and hence cannot be controlled by the toolmaker. The ideal stone from the point of view of the toolmaker is one like flint or chert: hard, tough, and of a smooth, fine-grained consistency. Stone of this type behaves somewhat like glass; it fractures rather than crumbles,

Hand ax: a bifacially flaked stone implement that characterized the Acheulean industry.

Lithic technology: stone-tool technology.

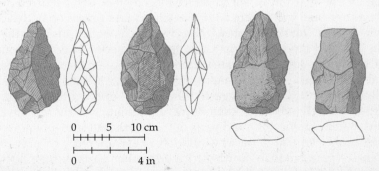

```
0      5     10 cm
|++++++|—————|

0         |         4 in
|————|————|
```

FIGURE 11–3   These early Acheulean artifacts are from Olduvai Gorge and date to approximately 1.5 million years B.P. From left to right, three hand axes (the right one is quite crude in its chipping) and a cleaver are shown. Note the cleaver's straight bit.

and cone-shaped flakes can be knocked off it that are razor-sharp. Flint was the most common of the desirable tool stones in western Europe, and the typical Acheulean implement there was a flint hand ax. In Africa, Acheulean tools were often fashioned from large lava flakes.

Combining various kinds of stone with various ways of working them produces a surprising variety of results. The finer-grained the stone, the flatter and more leaflike the flakes that can be chipped loose from it. The size and shape of these flakes can be further controlled by how they are separated from the original stone. They may be knocked loose by a hammer or pried loose by a pointed stick or bone. The angle at which the hammer blow is struck can be changed to produce either a small, thick flake or a large, thin one. Also, different kinds of hammers produce different kinds of flakes. Relatively soft hammers of wood or bone produce one kind, hard stone hammers produce another, and a wooden point pressed against the edge of the stone will produce still a different kind. Even the way a tool is held while it is being made will affect the kind of flake that can be struck from it: when it is held in the hand, the results are not the same as when it is balanced on a rock.

Every toolmaker must have had a good deal of skill, based on necessity, on years of practice, and on an intimate knowledge of the nature of different stones. For each stone has its own qualities, which vary further depending on whether the stone is hot or cold, wet or dry. But the basic principles of toolmaking are fairly simple. If you decide to try it, you may be surprised at how hard a blow it takes to crack or flake a stone, but if you do it right, the stone will behave in a predictable way.

Core and Flake Tools

Despite all these variations in techniques and materials, there are still only two basic categories of tools: *core tools* and *flake tools*. To make a core tool, take a lump of stone and knock chips from it until it has the desired size and shape; the core of stone that remains is the tool (Figures 11–4 and 11–5). A flake tool, as its name implies, is a chip struck from a core. It may be large or small, and its shape may vary, depending on the shape of the core from which it was struck. It may be used as it is, or it may itself be further flaked or chipped, somewhat in the matter of a core tool. In any event, the flake itself, and not the core from which it was struck, is the tool.

Core tool: implement shaped from the core of a rock nodule.

Flake tool: implement made from a flake struck from a stone.

In the earliest days of toolmaking, flake tools were very simple. Whatever happened to fly off a core would be put to use if it had a sharp edge. In general, flakes were used as cutters, because their edges were sharper than the edges that could be produced on core choppers, which were more useful for heavy hacking. As time went on, more and more skills were developed in the manufacture of flakes, and eventually it became a much more sophisticated method of toolmaking than the simple core technique.

The Acheulean industry is noted for its use of a prepared core in the production of its characteristic implement, the biface, a tool whose cutting edge has been flaked more carefully on both sides to make it straighter and sharper than the primitive Oldowan chopper. This may seem like an awfully small improvement, but it was a fundamental one and made possible much more efficient tools. The purpose of the two-sided, or bifacial, technique was to change the shape of the core from essentially round to flattish, for only with a flat stone can one get a decent cutting edge. The first step in making an Acheulean hand ax was to rough out the core until it had somewhat the shape of a turtle shell, thickest in the

FIGURE 11-4 Stone toolmaking is not simple; it requires skill and much practice. Most people, however, can learn how to make simple tools. These photographs show Francois Bordes making a chopping tool (bottom right).

middle and thinning to a coarse edge all around. This edge could then be trimmed with more delicate little scallops of flaking (Figure 11–6). The cutting surfaces thus produced were longer, straighter, and considerably keener than those of any Oldowan chopper.

One technological improvement that permitted the more controlled working required to shape an Acheulean hand ax was the gradual implementation, during the Acheulean period, of different kinds of hammers. In earlier times, it appears, the toolmaker knocked flakes from the stone core with another piece of stone. The hard shock of rock on rock tended to leave deep, irregular scars and wavy cutting edges. But a wood or bone hammer, being softer, gave its user much greater control over flaking. Such implements left shallower, cleaner scars on the core and produced sharper and straighter cutting edges. In time, the use of stone was pretty

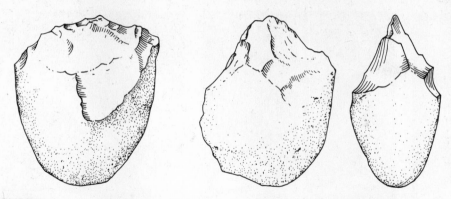

FIGURE 11–5 It is not difficult to see how a simple chopper (left) developed into a very primitive biface or hand ax (right). These tools are from Olduvai.

much restricted to the preliminary rough shaping of a hand ax, and all the fine work around the edges was done with wood and bone (Figure 11–6).

Acheulean hand axes were usually pear-shaped or pointed and were somewhat larger than chopping tools. Some have been recovered that were more than 2 ft (0.6 m) long and weighed more than 25 lb (11 kg). Obviously these were far too heavy and cumbersome to have been used for the kind of cutting and scraping that the smaller ones were designed for. One suggestion is that they may have been fitted to traps, set to fall and split the skulls of animals that triggered them.

Another type of implement that appears for the first time in the Acheulean industry is the *cleaver*. A cleaver had a straight cutting edge at one end and actually looked much more like a modern ax head than the pointed hand axes did. It was probably used for heavy chopping or for hacking through the joints of large animals (Figure 11–3).

As noted earlier, Acheulean tools originated in Africa between 1.4 and 1.7 mya. They were then produced continuously (along with a few Oldowan choppers and flakes) throughout *Homo erectus*'s long African residency and beyond, finally disappearing about 200,000 years B.P. Acheulean tools were being made in the Middle East by 1 mya, as shown by the site of 'Ubeidiya in Israel, and they were present in Europe as early as 500,000 to 780,000 years B.P. and in northeastern Pakistan by 400,000 to 730,000 years B.P. Several later sites in Africa and Europe show that the Acheulean tradition survived *Homo erectus* in some areas and was continued for a time by early *Homo sapiens*. Generally, Acheulean tools from sites clearly older than 400,000 to 500,000 years B.P. are attributed to *Homo erectus*, even in the absence of confirming fossils. At several important Acheulean sites, however, the toolmakers' species identity remains ambiguous because the sites lack hominid fossils and they date to a period when *Homo erectus* and early *Homo sapiens* overlapped in time. Examples of Acheulean assemblages that could have been produced by either late *H. erectus* or early *H. sapiens* include Africa's Kalambo Falls; Torralba and Ambrona in Spain; Abbeville, St. Acheul, and Terra Amata in France; and Hoxne in England (Figure 10–15).

Wherever they are found, Acheulean hand axes and cleavers are generally interpreted as being implements for processing animal carcasses (Figure 11–7). True, the cleavers could have been used to chop and shape wood, but according

Cleaver: an Acheulean stone implement with a straight cutting edge at one end; probably used for butchering animal carcasses.

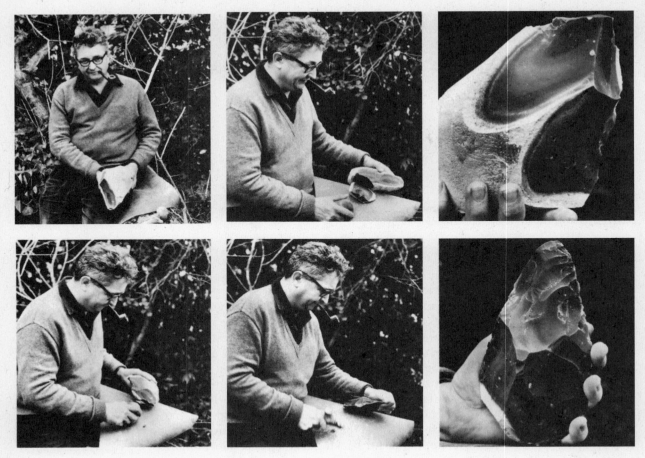

FIGURE 11–6 Making a hand ax is more difficult than making a chopping tool, as these photographs of Francois Bordes illustrate. Having knocked the end off a large flint nodule, Bordes has prepared a striking platform (upper left). Using a hammer stone, he proceeds to strike off several large flakes, roughing out the general shape (upper center, upper right, and lower left). He then switches to an antler hammer, working both sides of the tool to thin out and retouch the edge (lower center). The final product, with long, straight, sharp edges, is one of the tools used for hundreds of years by *Homo erectus* and early *Homo sapiens* (lower right).

to archaeologists Kathy Schick and Nicholas Toth, the wear pattern on cleaver bits is more suggestive of use on soft material, such as hides and meat. Schick and Toth believe that Acheulean tools represent an adaptation for "habitual and systematic butchery, [and] especially the dismembering of large animal carcasses," as *Homo erectus* experienced a strong dietary shift toward more meat consumption. Schick and Toth leave unanswered the question of whether meat was obtained primarily by scavenging or by hunting.

By now careful readers will have noticed that no sites in China or Southeast Asia are included in the inventory of Acheulean locales. In fact, there is strong evidence that Acheulean tools were never produced in much of the Far East. As first pointed out in 1948 by Hallam Movius (then of Harvard University), Acheulean sites are common in Africa, the Middle East, Europe, and much of western Asia, but they are strangely absent in far eastern and southeastern Asia. The line divid-

FIGURE 11–7 Held in the palm of the hand, an Acheulean hand ax would have been an excellent tool for dismembering and butchering animal carcasses.

ing the Old World into Acheulean and non-Acheulean regions became known as the *Movius line* (Figure 11–8A). Hand-ax cultures flourished to the west and south of the line, but in the east, only choppers and flake tools were found (Figure 11–8B). (Today we know the actual situation wasn't quite as clear as first described. There are a few examples of crude hand axes from sites in South Korea and China, but nothing that is clearly Acheulean. Also, there are some African and European sites contemporaneous with the Acheulean that produced only chopper and flake assemblages. Nonetheless, the "Movius line" remains a useful heuristic device for archaeologists.)

But why were there no Acheulean hand-ax cultures in the eastern extremes of Asia? Traditionally this has been a hard question to answer, since researchers believed until quite recently that *Homo erectus*'s departure from Africa postdated the invention of Acheulean tools by some 400,000 years. If *Homo erectus* left Africa with Acheulean technology, why didn't the tradition arrive in eastern Asia? Was it discarded or forgotten along the way? The new dates from Java help solve this riddle somewhat, since they place *Homo erectus* in Southeast Asia at least 100,000 years *before* the advent of the Acheulean in Africa. It thus appears that even if *Homo erectus* turns out to be a native African species that spread to Asia (thanks to the new Javanese dates, this is now in some doubt), its initial migration certainly predated the development of Acheulean tools. Thus a chronological barrier might have prevented the introduction of Acheulean technology to eastern Asia.

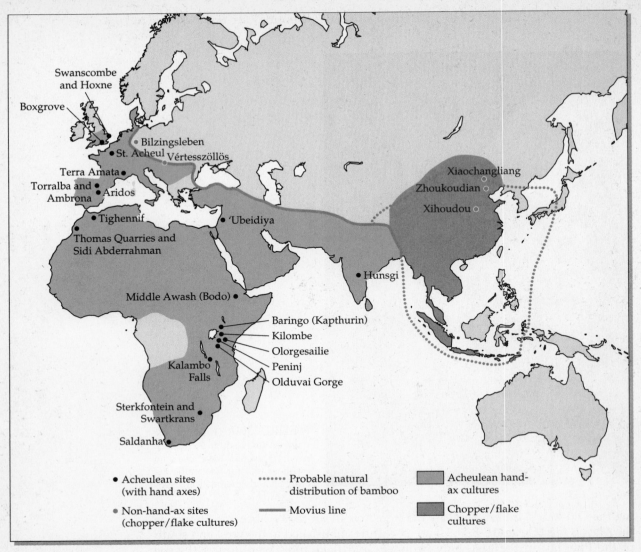

FIGURE 11–8A The "Movius line" divides the world of *Homo erectus* and early *Homo sapiens* into Acheulean hand-ax cultures to the west and chopper-flake cultures to the east. Note that in east and Southeast Asia the absence of hand-ax cultures coincides closely with the presence of bamboo.

Legend:
- Acheulean sites (with hand axes)
- Non-hand-ax sites (chopper/flake cultures)
- ⋯⋯⋯ Probable natural distribution of bamboo
- ─── Movius line
- Acheulean hand-ax cultures
- Chopper/flake cultures

Map labels: Swanscombe and Hoxne, Boxgrove, Bilzingsleben, St. Acheul, Vértesszöllös, Terra Amata, Torralba and Ambrona, Aridos, Tighennif, 'Ubeidiya, Thomas Quarries and Sidi Abderrahman, Middle Awash (Bodo), Baringo (Kapthurin), Kilombe, Olorgesailie, Peninj, Olduvai Gorge, Kalambo Falls, Sterkfontein and Swartkrans, Saldanha, Hunsgi, Xiaochangliang, Zhoukoudian, Xihoudou

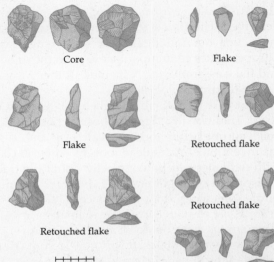

Core, Flake, Flake, Retouched flake, Retouched flake, Retouched flake, Notch

CM

FIGURE 11–8B Assemblages of choppers and flake tools such as these characterize the early Stone Age of east Asia.

Schick and Toth have listed several other explanations for the absence of the Acheulean tradition from eastern Asia. Perhaps it was due to a paucity of suitable raw stone; coarse quartz is common in the East, but fine-grained flints, cherts, and lavas are rare. This distribution of raw materials would lend itself to the production of Oldowan choppers, but not to bifacial hand axes requiring extensive chipping. Alternatively, the absence of the Acheulean tools may be related to different functional requirements in Asia compared to the West. If the Acheulean developed as an adaptation for meat processing by African hunters-and-gathers operating in open country, it may have been distinctly less useful in the closed and forested habitats of Asia, where large prey animals were probably less common and vegetable foods easier to harvest.

Certainly the most intriguing of the explanations for the "missing Acheulean" is the suggestion by anthropologist Geoffrey Pope and others that, in far eastern and southeastern Asia, bamboo tools were used in place of stone implements to perform a variety of tasks. To quote Pope, "There are few useful tools that cannot be constructed from bamboo. Cooking and storage containers, knives, spears, heavy and light projectile points, elaborate traps, rope, fasteners [and] clothing . . . can be manufactured from bamboo." When a bamboo stalk is split, it produces razor-sharp "stick knives" that can be used to butcher animals or perform other hacking and scraping jobs. Such bamboo utensils are still used in some parts of the world today (Figure 11–9), and as Pope has pointed out, the natural distribution of bamboo coincides closely with those Asian areas that lack Acheulean tools (Figure 11–8A).

We can conclude, therefore, that, while the Acheulean tradition, with its hand axes and cleavers, was an important lithic advance by *Homo erectus* over older technologies, it constituted only one of several adaptive patterns used by the species. Clever and behaviorally flexible, *Homo erectus* was capable of adjusting its

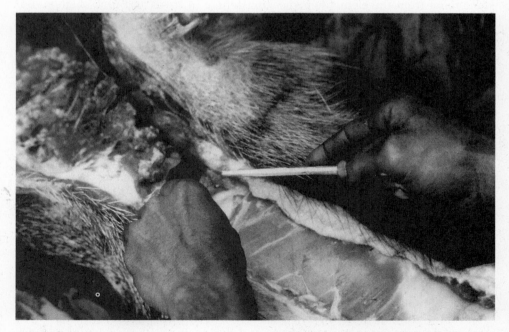

FIGURE 11–9 Split bamboo has razor-sharp edges and can be used as a "stick knife." Here a bamboo knife is used to butcher a pig in New Guinea.

material culture to the local resources and functional requirements. Nonetheless, the Acheulean tradition clearly reflected significant cognitive progress by *Homo erectus* people over their evolutionary predecessors. As American anthropologist A. J. Jelinek has remarked, Acheulean tools were the first "fully conceived implements whose final form is regularly patterned and in no way suggested by the shape or exterior texture of the stone from which they were made. This is certainly a significant step in conceptualization." Interestingly, once in existence, the Acheulean tradition showed very little overall change during perhaps 1.5 million years. Harvard's William Howells has referred to this lack of change as a "general stagnation" in material culture, and he has attributed it to a long period of stasis in intelligence and communication skills—a stasis that was apparently interrupted only by the evolution of *Homo sapiens*.

SHELTER AND FIRE

As noted earlier, Plio-Pleistocene glaciations would have produced a variety of environmental changes, but most important, they would have caused a strong drop in global temperatures. The cold would have been worst, of course, for populations living near the glaciers (as in Europe) or in the higher latitudes (as at Zhoukoudian). But what enabled *Homo erectus* to inhabit and thrive in so many parts of the Old World, including such environmentally challenging regions as northern China and periglacial Europe? True, from the beginning *Homo erectus* people were toolmakers, and as described in the last section, by no later than 1.4 mya their lithic technology had made a strong advance with the development of the Acheulean tradition. It is equally certain that *Homo erectus* would have gained some relief from the elements by seeking refuge in caves and rock shelters. But would this behavior have been enough? For years, scientists have searched for—and argued about—evidence that *Homo erectus* had gained additional control over its environment through the construction of shelters and the control and use of fire. The evidence is sparse and difficult to interpret, but a review of it should prove instructive.

Let's begin with the evidence for "domestic architectural features" (shelters and huts). At the site of Soleihac in southeastern France, *Homo erectus* apparently left a collection of choppers and flakes (no hand axes) just over 900,000 years ago. Also from Soleihac comes a rather mysterious line of basalt blocks 66 ft (20 m) long. It is difficult to know what to make of the line of stones. Are they all that's left of a shelter, or are they a natural feature of the site? Some researchers, such as paleoanthropologist Richard Klein, are clearly skeptical. Says Klein, "[The basalt line] may represent the oldest structural remnant in Europe, *if it is truly of human origin*" (italics added).

For the next, and considerably more impressive, evidence of shelter construction, we must jump forward a half million years to the 300,000 to 400,000-year-old French site of Terra Amata (located under the modern city of Nice). Excavated in the 1960s by Henry de Lumley, the site revealed evidence in the form of ancient postholes and concentrated artifacts of several huts measuring 20–49 ft (6–15 m) long by 13–20 ft (4–6 m) wide. De Lumley concluded that the hut roofs had been supported by two or more large posts, and that the walls were made of saplings and branches (Figure 11–10). He also estimated that each hut was large enough to hold up to 15 people. Shelters very similar in size and construction to those envi-

FIGURE 11–10 The drawing at right reconstructs the kind of huts that Henry de Lumley excavated at Terra Amata in France. The hut has been cut away to show the method of construction. The exact form of the roof is uncertain, but this type of construction is common today in Africa, as can be seen in the photograph of a San hut in the northern Kalahari. The drawing shows some worked stones in the center. The oval of rocks and the central postholes were the main clues to the size and form of construction.

sioned by de Lumley have been documented among some modern hunter-and-gatherer groups (Figure 11–10).

In addition to the remains of ancient shelters, Terra Amata also produced evidence of the control and use of fire. In the center of each hut was a hearth, a fairly compact area of baked and discolored sand, and some hearths were ringed by a windscreen of stones, suggesting that the shelters were rather drafty (Figure 11–11). Little evidence was found for cooking food, although de Lumley believes that the Terra Amata people may have heated stones in order to boil food in wooden containers. Rather, the fires were apparently kept burning for warmth. Around one hearth there were impressions on the floor that were apparently made by animal skins, suggesting that the inhabitants slept by the fire at night.

The problematic aspect of Terra Amata is not the evidence of shelters and fire—that is clear and convincing; rather, it is our inability to determine accurately the hominid species responsible for the site. Terra Amata has produced no fossil remains of its inhabitants that would allow their identification. Couple that fact with the young age of the site—perhaps 300,000 years B.P.—and it becomes clear that either late *Homo erectus* or early *Homo sapiens* might have been the builders and firemakers of Terra Amata.

In summary, there appears to be no convincing evidence that *Homo erectus* regularly constructed huts, windbreaks, or any other sort of shelter during the bulk of its long period of existence. Shelter construction apparently developed late in the species' life span, if at all, and therefore cannot be used as an explanation of *Homo erectus*'s capacity for geographic expansion (which was displayed very early). As Richard Klein has noted, "The argument for *H. erectus* as builder remains hypothetical."

As it turns out, proving the use of fire by *Homo erectus* is almost equally problematic, although we have more evidence. The oldest evidence of fire use comes from Koobi Fora and other Kenyan sites and dates about 1.4 to 1.6 million years B.P. Some researchers, such as Randy Bellomo of the University of South Florida, feel that a strong case can be made for hominids (presumably *Homo erectus*) using

FIGURE 11–11   On one of the Terra Amata hut floors, a windscreen of stones still shields a shallow hearth (left).

controlled fire at this time for protection against predators and for heat and light. Other workers are not so sure. The problem is that the baked earth found at these sites could have been produced as easily by natural fires as by fires started—or at least controlled—by *Homo erectus*. Ash alone, or baked earth alone, does not necessarily prove hominid involvement. Something more must be present: other artifacts or some degree of spatial arrangement, such as the hearths at Terra Amata.

Better evidence of the use of fire comes from sites that date near the end of *Homo erectus*'s existence as a species. The French site of Menez-Dregan has produced evidence of a hearth dating 380,000 to 465,000 years B.P., but unfortunately the identity of the responsible hominids is unclear. Furthermore, from the 400,000-year-old sites of Torralba and Ambrona in Spain come animal bones (including those of elephants, horses, deer, and rhinos), as well as Acheulean tools and scattered bits of charcoal. Initial interpretations of the sites proposed that *Homo erectus* hunters had used fire to drive animals into marshy areas where they finished them off. Reanalysis of the sites in the 1980s, however, indicated that natural deaths of most of the animals (followed perhaps by hominid scavenging) and natural causes of the charcoal (e.g., brush fires) were more likely explanations than hominid activity.

At another 400,000-year-old site—Zhoukoudian, China, renowned as the home of "Peking man"—ash is (apparently) present in abundance, along with chopper and flake tools and the fossilized remains of late *Homo erectus*. Chinese workers and others have long claimed that, at Zhoukoudian, *Homo erectus* people kept fires burning more-or-less continuously to warm their cave homes, to keep away predators, and to cook their food. One typical illustration shows a *Homo erectus* woman feeding the fire as a man chips a stone tool and a second man hauls in a deer for dinner (Figure 11–12). But how accurate is this cozy domestic scene, even for late *Homo erectus*? While acknowledging some evidence of fire use at Zhoukoudian, archaeologist Lewis Binford and his co-workers have challenged the notion that fire played a regular or important role in the daily life of these early humans. Binford reexamined the evidence from Zhoukoudian and found that many of the extensive "ash" layers reported from the site may in fact be the results of the decalcification of massive organic deposits (including bird droppings, bat guano, and hyena feces) and not evidence of fire at all. Or, he suggested, if fires had occurred, they may have involved the accidental ignition of the organic mate-

FIGURE 11–12 This painting by English artist Maurice Wilson dates from 1950 and shows a typical "home-hearth-and-hunting" interpretation of *Homo erectus*.

rial, which then slowly smoldered for some time. Binford found no evidence of hearths, nor any clear and recurring associations between "ash," stone tools, and *Homo erectus* fossils. In other words, all the ingredients of the traditional cozy scene were present, but they were simply not connected. As for cooking food, Binford found some support for the practice, but precious little. A few burnt bones were recovered, including evidence of at least two episodes of roasting horses' heads. Some other burnt bones, however, had clearly been dry (meatless) when burned, a fact suggesting that they may have been caught up in smoldering organic material. Binford and his colleagues concluded that *Homo erectus* shared the Zhoukoudian site with hyenas, and that hyena—not hominid—activity probably accounted for most of the accumulated materials in the cave.

Finally, as described above, both the use and control of fire can be documented at the site of Terra Amata, but some doubt remains about whether *Homo erectus* or early *Homo sapiens* people were responsible. In all, the evidence for the control and use of fire by *Homo erectus* is very slim, and what little there is occurs very late in the species' life span. The evidence at present suggests that fire was not the key to either the geographic spread or the longevity of these early humans.

SUBSISTENCE PATTERNS AND DIET

Early discoveries of *Homo erectus* fossils in association with stone tools and animal bones readily lent themselves to the interpretation of a hunting-and-gathering way of life—an interpretation that anthropologists eagerly embraced. The *Homo erectus* inhabitants of Zhoukoudian in China were described as deer hunters who consumed (cooked?) meals that combined venison with local plant products such as hackberries (Figure 11–12); at Torralba and Ambrona in Spain, the archaeological evidence—primarily the presence of Acheulean tools—was believed to indicate that *Homo erectus* hunters had systematically dispatched and butchered elephants on the spot, possibly after driving them into a marshy area by using fire; and in Africa, the Olorgesailie site was interpreted as showing that *Homo erectus* hunters occasionally preyed on fellow primates, including giant gelada baboons. All of these bits of data were then spun into an elaborate picture of the society and lifestyle of *Homo erectus* that generally tended to portray these Plio-Pleistocene hominids as a watered-down version of modern human hunters-and-gatherers (see Chapter 12).

Recently, several of the original studies describing *Homo erectus* as a hunter-and-gatherer have come under intense criticism. For example, Lewis Binford and his colleagues have reexamined the material from the late–*H. erectus* site of Zhoukoudian and concluded that there is very little *conclusive* evidence of systematic hunting. Comparisons of the Zhoukoudian animal bones with faunal remains from both carnivore (especially hyena) dens and undoubted hunting sites (such as the 105,000-year-old European site of Combe Grenal) convinced Binford that the Chinese assemblage was *primarily* the result of animal activity rather than hunting-and-gathering. A few of the deer and horse bones at Zhoukoudian showed cut marks from stone tools that *overlay* gnaw marks by carnivores, suggesting that *Homo erectus* was not above scavenging parts of a carnivore kill. While acknowledging that *Homo erectus* certainly used the Zhoukoudian cave site, Binford and his co-workers were forced to conclude that at Zhoukoudian "all the positive evidence is consistent with what is believed to be evidence for hominid scavenging [and] there are *no positive indicators* of hunting in the available data" (italics in the original). In a similar fashion, archaeologist Richard Klein has shown that the bone and stone assemblages at Torralba and Ambrona fail to provide conclusive proof of *Homo erectus* hunting. Both sites could be nothing more than lakeside or streamside assemblages produced by regular animal use for feeding and drinking, predation by carnivores, and scavenging by Acheulean people. At both sites, the evidence for scavenging by hominids is much more convincing than is that for actual hunting.

But do these reanalyses of some classic *Homo erectus* sites provide the last word on the question of hunting by these people? Must one conclude that hunting-and-gathering as a primary way of obtaining food appeared only at the level of *Homo sapiens*, where unequivocal proof can be presented at last? We think not. We believe that there are at least two sorts of evidence that show that *Homo erectus* people were consuming so much more meat than their evolutionary predecessors that hunting was almost certainly a regular subsistence pattern. First, there is the matter of their advance in stone-tool technology. As noted earlier, archaeologists Kathy Schick and Nicholas Toth, among others, have concluded that Acheulean hand axes and cleavers were used primarily for dismembering and butchering large animal carcasses. This conclusion is based on studies of the artifacts' design and wear patterns, as well as on experimental studies of how they could have been used most effectively. It appears, therefore, that the development of the Acheulean tradition is a clear indicator of a distinct shift toward greater reliance on meat by *Homo erectus*. The absence of Acheulean tools in eastern and southeastern Asia may well be related to the presence of fewer game animals in tropical forests than in open grasslands, although, as discussed above, other explanations may apply as well.

The second bit of evidence in favor of hunting by *Homo erectus* involves the size of these early people. Alan Walker has concluded that *Homo erectus* people were quite big—comparable to the top 17 percent of modern human populations with regard to height and well within the modern range with regard to weight—and that early African *Homo erectus* differed little in body size from late Asian representatives of the species. Compared to early *Homo* (*H. habilis* and *H. rudolfensis*), *Homo erectus* showed an increase in body size of about one-third (compare Boxes 8–2 and 10–1). To us, it seems a little difficult to explain this significant jump in body size simply as the result of increased scavenging activities. Although the evidence is admittedly shaky, we prefer to think that *Homo erectus* people evolved to modern size because they were not only scavengers but active hunters who regularly ate an extremely rich source of nutrients: meat. The key point here, of course, is not that *Homo erectus* people were the first hominid hunters, but that they depended on meat for a much larger portion of their diet than had any previous hominid species. As noted in earlier chapters, occasional hunting is seen among nonhuman primates and cannot be conclusively denied to the australopithecines. But apparently for *Homo erectus* hunting took on unprecedented importance, and in doing so it must have played a major role in shaping both material culture and society.

SUMMARY

Homo erectus evolved sometime in the late Pliocene. If the new dates from Java are to be trusted—and clearly, the authors of this text accept them provisionally—the species was spread from extreme southeastern Asia to eastern Africa by 1.8 mya. What enabled this phenomenal geographic spread? Was it increased intelligence? Certainly this must have played a part, as *Homo erectus* showed a significant jump in overall brain size compared to early *Homo*. But precisely how increased intelligence aided the species' spread and longevity is unclear. Was it spoken language? Maybe, but the indicators are mixed. *Homo erectus* probably had a large enough brain for language, but the proportions of its throat probably did not allow the modern range of vowel sounds, and it may not have had the fine control of breathing that modern speech requires. If these people produced spoken language, it probably was not as rich in sounds nor as rapid and complex as that of modern humans.

But what of culture? Surely there were key cultural advances that set *Homo erectus* apart from early *Homo* and enabled its success. Again, the only possible answer is "maybe." Admittedly, this is not very satisfying, but for a couple of reasons it is the best we can do at present. First, we are limited primarily to statements about the *material culture* of *H. erectus*, that is, their tools and other artifacts. Social and behavioral traits, such as group composition, level of social organization, territoriality, and cooperation in (and/or division of) subsistence activities, do not fossilize and can only be inferred (see Chapter 12). And unless we give in to unbridled speculations, inferred cultural advances must be described only as hypotheses for investigation, not as reliable explanations of other phenomena. Thus we can draw solid conclusions only about a greatly impoverished version of culture—but that's the nature of the archaeological data currently available.

Table 11–1 A DISTRIBUTION OF THE TECHNOLOGICAL AND SUBSISTENCE INNOVATIONS OF *HOMO ERECTUS* TO EARLY, MIDDLE, AND LATE STAGES OF THE SPECIES' SPAN[a]

Stage	Bracketing Dates (Million Years B.P.)	Technological or Subsistence Innovation
Early *Homo erectus*	1.8–1.3	Acheulean industry (Oldowan continues as well). Hunting-and-gathering lifestyle likely (more meat).
Middle *Homo erectus*	1.3–0.8	No clear innovations. Acheulean continues west of Movius line, Oldowan to the east.
Late *Homo erectus*	0.8–0.3	Shelters (possibly). Control and use of fire (possibly).

[a] Stages were arbitrarily defined as 500,000-year periods.

Second, although the innovations in material culture are there, in most cases the timing is wrong, at least with regard to *Homo erectus*'s initial geographic spread. As summarized in Table 11–1, only one technological advance can be attributed undeniably to *Homo erectus*, and that is the early development of the Acheulean lithic tradition, with its bifacial tools, particularly hand axes and cleavers. As discussed above, this innovation in stone-tool technology probably signaled a shift from scavenging-and-gathering to hunting-and-gathering—an extremely important change in subsistence patterns that helped catapult *Homo erectus* to the top of the Plio-Pleistocene food chain and enabled the exploitation of energy and nutrient-rich animal products with an entirely new intensity. Other cultural innovations frequently attributed to *Homo erectus*, such as shelter construction and the control and use of fire, probably came so near the end of the species' life span that many researchers feel they are better assigned to early *Homo sapiens*. Unfortunately—at least for our understanding of the Old World–wide spread of *Homo erectus*—even the appearance of Acheulean tools and hunting-and-gathering as a way of life postdate the hypothesized exodus from Africa. The very earliest dates given for Acheulean technology are 1.7 mya, and many archaeologists prefer 1.4–1.5 mya. Since *Homo erectus* people (or their ancestors?) *had* to have left Africa before 1.8 million years B.P., the conclusion seems inescapable that they did so as *scavengers* and gatherers, and with tools no more complex than Oldowan choppers and flakes. Their successful colonization of Eurasia is all the more impressive.

As noted by William Howells, *Homo erectus* was a very stable species once its basic adaptive niche had taken shape. After inventing Acheulean tools and adopting a hunting-and-gathering lifestyle, *Homo erectus* showed little if any cultural change for over a million years! In the next chapter, we will investigate further the behavioral and societal implications of hunting-and-gathering for these early humans.

REVIEW QUESTIONS

1. Describe the innovations in material culture attributed to *Homo erectus*. Which ones are we sure of, and which are we not? Where do these innovations fall within the species' time span?

2. Speculate about why *Homo erectus* apparently stagnated with regard to material culture. What anatomical or environmental factors might have contributed to this stasis?

3. There seems to be little direct evidence that *Homo erectus* could talk. If this is true, how do you think the species communicated? How would a lack of spoken language have affected the species' potential for geographic spread?

4. How do you feel about referring to *Homo erectus* individuals as "people" and "early humans"? What criteria do you think must be met before a hominid is labeled a "human"?

5. Why have so few Acheulean hand axes been found in eastern and southeastern Asia? Give as many explanations as you can for their absence.

POSTSCRIPT

For paleoanthropologists and archaeologists, interpreting the fossils and artifacts that they discover is both the bane of their existence and the spice of life. How can we ever know what prehistoric tools were used for or how the toolmakers organized and lived their lives? These are difficult questions precisely because there are few established principles regarding how interpretations of ancient bones and stones should be carried out. Some headway is surely being made, and as shown by the reanalyses of Zhoukoudian by Lewis Binford and of Torralba and Ambrona by Richard Klein, researchers are becoming increasingly cautious and conservative in their interpretations of prehistoric sites. Modern researchers are much less prone to hasty speculations than their predecessors were, preferring to force recovered bone and stone assemblages to *prove* the existence of particular behavioral patterns. Thus both Binford and Klein question the regular use of fire by *Homo erectus*. Nonetheless, guidelines for interpretations are few and far between, and therefore disagreements among specialists are legion. Consider the problem of analogue models.

Two sources of information are commonly used to interpret the behavior of prehistoric hominids: data from modern people still practicing hunting-and-gathering and data from nonhuman primates (usually apes; Figure 11–13). Conclusions about extinct hominid types are then reached by a process of triangulation; that is, nonmodern hominids are described as behaviorally intermediate between modern hunters-and-gatherers and apes, with humanlike traits predominating in relatively recent species and apelike traits predominating in very ancient hominid types. Thus *Homo erectus* has been described traditionally as a sort of primitive human, while the australopithecines have been interpreted as more like apes.

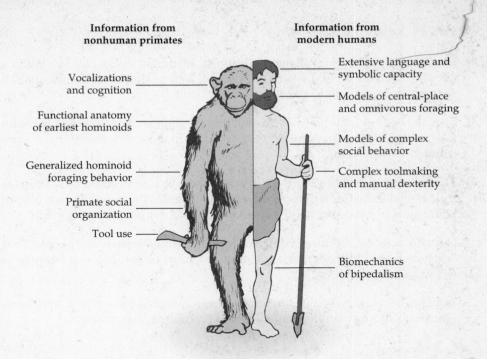

**Information from
nonhuman primates**

**Information from
modern humans**

Vocalizations
and cognition

Functional anatomy
of earliest hominoids

Generalized hominoid
foraging behavior

Primate social
organization

Tool use

Extensive language and
symbolic capacity

Models of central-place
and omnivorous foraging

Models of complex
social behavior

Complex toolmaking
and manual dexterity

Biomechanics
of bipedalism

FIGURE 11–13   This figure shows some of the sorts of information researchers can derive from non-human primates and living humans that aid in the interpretation of extinct hominids.

In principle, there is nothing wrong with this sort of triangulation. Problems arise, however, in determining which analogue model—modern hunters-and-gatherers or apes—is most appropriate in each case and (perhaps more important) because reliance on these two established models sometimes seems to limit our imagination and prevent us from considering the possibility of adaptive systems unlike those known in any living primate. Leaving some room for imaginative interpretations (always tentative and constructed as testable hypotheses) is quite important, since comparative information from apes is limited by the small number of living species and since comparative data from modern hunters-and-gatherers, almost all of whom live in marginal habitats, may not be representative of the past, when hunting-and-gathering people had access to richer environments. And finally, it must be remembered that arguing from living systems to systems that are extinct is a multistep process that involves data gathering at several levels, rather than a simple transference from the present to the past (Figure 11–14).

Now, with these heavyweight considerations in mind, let's take a look at a distinctly lightweight question: Did *Homo erectus* people make and use bolas? The bola, of course, is the throwing implement of the gauchos and other people of the Argentine pampas and consists of spherical stones tied together by leather thongs in groups of two or three. It is used by hunters to entangle and trip up game. Interestingly, *Homo erectus* sites regularly produce rounded, battered pieces of stone that are usually labeled simply as *spheroids*. Furthermore, because of the physical

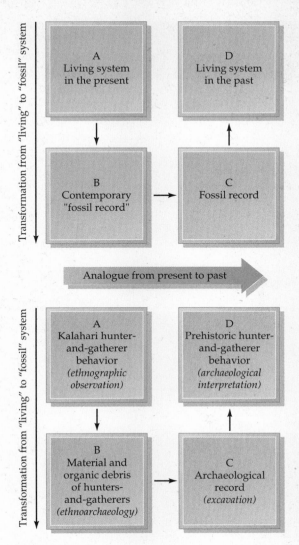

FIGURE 11-14 Making inferences using analogue models is a multistep process. The top set of boxes shows the route of inference making. The bottom set gives an example by ethnographic analogy.

similarity between spheroids and true bola stones, some anthropologists have made the simple transference from living people to the past and have concluded that *Homo erectus* hunters also used the bola. But how much confidence can we have in this conclusion? Very little, according to recent results from experimental archaeologists Kathy Schick and Nicholas Toth. After considerable rock pounding, Schick and Toth found that initially angular stones—particularly chunks of quartz—that were used as hammers for several hours always ended up with a spherical shape *"without any necessary intent or predetermination"* (italics in original). Since *Homo erectus* people presumably used hammer stones a lot—to shape other stones, smash bones for marrow, and so on—Schick and Toth feel it is best to regard *Homo erectus* spheroids simply as well-used hammers rather than as bola stones. The moral of this little story is clear: Analogies from the present to the past must be made with extreme care and, if at all possible, must be subject to testing.

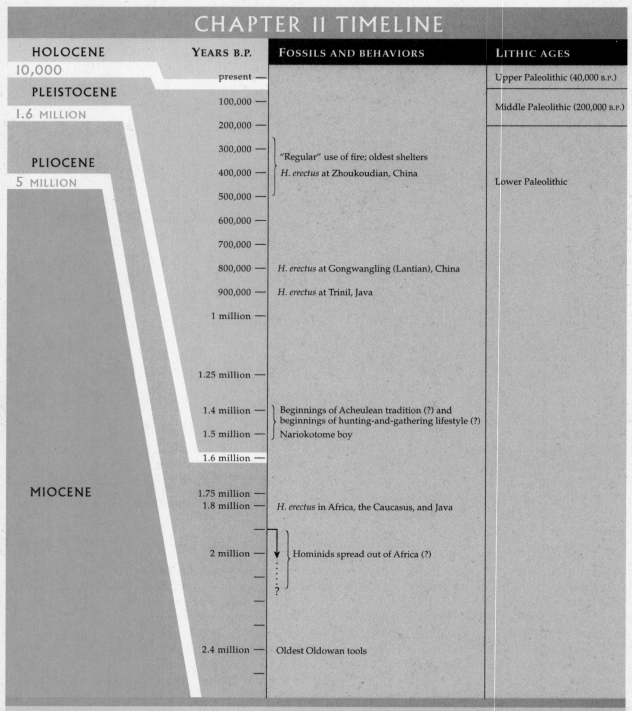

CHAPTER 11 TIMELINE

HOLOCENE	YEARS B.P.	FOSSILS AND BEHAVIORS	LITHIC AGES
10,000	present —		Upper Paleolithic (40,000 B.P.)
PLEISTOCENE	100,000 —		Middle Paleolithic (200,000 B.P.)
1.6 MILLION	200,000 —		
	300,000 —	⎫ "Regular" use of fire; oldest shelters	
PLIOCENE	400,000 —	⎪ *H. erectus* at Zhoukoudian, China	Lower Paleolithic
5 MILLION	500,000 —	⎭	
	600,000 —		
	700,000 —		
	800,000 —	*H. erectus* at Gongwangling (Lantian), China	
	900,000 —	*H. erectus* at Trinil, Java	
	1 million —		
	1.25 million —		
	1.4 million —	⎫ Beginnings of Acheulean tradition (?) and	
		⎬ beginnings of hunting-and-gathering lifestyle (?)	
	1.5 million —	⎭ Nariokotome boy	
	1.6 million —		
MIOCENE	1.75 million —		
	1.8 million —	*H. erectus* in Africa, the Caucasus, and Java	
	2 million —	⎬ Hominids spread out of Africa (?)	
		?	
	2.4 million —	Oldest Oldowan tools	

Developing the Acheulean stone tool tradition seems to have been the primary technological innovation of *Homo erectus*.   Researchers disagree whether these early humans used fire and built shelters.

CHAPTER

12

Hunting, Gathering, and the Evolution of Society

347

*It is far from easy to determine whether Nature has proved a kind
parent to man or a merciless stepmother.*
                    PLINY THE ELDER, 23–79. *Natural History*, BOOK VII, 1.

OVERVIEW

Most anthropologists are comfortable referring to *Homo erectus* as a species of
early "humans." This is so because we think these people had evolved a culturally dependent lifestyle similar to that of modern hunters-and-gatherers. The present chapter is devoted to a discussion of what we think the *Homo erectus* lifestyle
may have been like. When we use living hunting-and-gathering people as our
analogue model (see the Postscript to Chapter 11), several informed speculations
about the behavior, subsistence patterns, and societies of *H. erectus* may be presented. Important topics and concepts include evidence of hunting-and-gathering; the nutritional benefits of such a lifestyle; the hunting techniques possibly
used by *H. erectus;* the evolution of male and female social roles; the evolution of
the family; likely *H. erectus* mating patterns; the development of the "home base";
and evidence of aggression and possibly cannibalism by *Homo erectus.*

BEHAVIORAL SPECULATIONS

Humankind and human society are so closely interwoven that it makes no sense to
talk of human evolution without considering human society. Indeed, our social life
is the area in which our humanity is most strikingly expressed. That society
evolved, as did humankind, is not in question. But because we are the bearers of
symbolic culture, the evolution of human society is not another biological phenomenon such as the evolution of ant or bee society. Although human social evolution rides on the back of human biological evolution, the mechanism of change is
different. The use of the word *evolution* is justified by reference to its original meaning: an "unfolding." The unfolding or development of human society, though it
bears many resemblances to the evolution of organisms, was and is distinct, and the
two should be not confused. Evidence for social evolution is provided by archaeologists, and in this chapter we shall consider some of that evidence in more detail.

Before we begin, however, a brief caveat is warranted. Much of the material
that follows is based on our conclusion that *Homo erectus* people subsisted primarily by hunting-and-gathering. From this postulate we will speculate, sometimes
rather freely, about how their societies and interpersonal relationships *might* have
been structured. But as you know from Chapter 11, anthropologists are actually in
a state of considerable disagreement about the specifics of the *Homo erectus* subsistence patterns. Some specialists, like Lewis Binford, prefer to view these early
humans as *scavengers* and gatherers, not as hunters. Furthermore, it is unclear how
much of the behavior, role differentiation, social structure, and so on of modern
hunters-and-gatherers can be projected safely back into the past and can be read
into the archaeological record of *Homo erectus.* It is unlikely that these early people,
with their smaller brains and (probably) limited communication skills, behaved

just like modern humans, but how similar were they? Can we avoid the tendency to overmodernize *Homo erectus* people as we reconstruct their behavior patterns?

Despite the obvious dangers involved in behavioral reconstructions, we believe the effort is worthwhile so long as *all speculations are viewed only as hypotheses that must be formally tested and supported before we can have any real confidence in them.* Undoubtedly hunting-and-gathering evolved as a primary human way of life sometime within the past million years or so. How might such a lifestyle have affected the behavior of *Homo erectus*? Although fully aware that our conclusions will be tentative, let's try to answer that question.

THE ARCHAEOLOGY OF THE HUNTERS

The interpretation of archaeological sites is not always as straightforward as it may appear. Many of the sites in Olduvai Gorge excavated by the Leakeys have probably been correctly interpreted; they include ancient land surfaces preserved more or less as they were left by early hominids. It often happens, however, that some movement occurs in such deposits, and in more extreme cases the archaeological remains may be washed out by heavy rains or river action and redeposited in another place. Such deposits are called *secondary sites.* In many instances the stones and bones may be sorted by the moving waters of a river and deposited in very dense accumulations that have the superficial appearance of being the result of human activity.

Secondary sites: archaeological sites in which the artifacts have been disturbed by natural forces and then redeposited.

The distinction between primary and secondary sites in archaeology is an important one. In the past, investigators have sometimes been misled into believing that bones or stone tools scattered on an ancient riverbank represented an original living floor. In many cases microscopic analysis of the material is required, which will reveal if the bone or stone has been battered or "rolled" in the flowing river or still remains in an uneroded condition.

Such a site is Olorgesailie in southwestern Kenya, where for many years it was thought by some archaeologists that there was definite evidence of hunting and butchery. Here, at one site, in an area only 40 by 50 ft (12 by 15 ms), Glynn Isaac unearthed bones and teeth of at least 14 adult and 76 juvenile monkeys of the now extinct species *Theropithecus oswaldi*. Mixed with them was more than a ton of hand axes and cobbles (altogether 4,751 artifacts). The date is estimated at about 650,000 years B.P. It seemed to some that a massive organized slaughter had been conducted on the site, followed by a tremendous amount of butchery. A band of hominids appeared to have ambushed and killed a big troop of these formidable animals (the males almost the size of the hunters). The density of bones and stone tools was most unusual.

Theropithecus oswaldi: an extinct species of gelada baboon.

Glynn Isaac, however, believed it most likely that the stone tools and bones had been washed down the river, sorted, concentrated, and deposited in distinct areas on its banks. Taphonomic studies have shown that such a hypothesis is a possible explanation of these dense accumulations of material. The site contains an enormous hoard of heavy stone tools, and the evidence suggests that *Homo erectus* was systematically butchering these giant gelada monkeys and perhaps even hunting them, upstream of the actual site, and that this probably continued over a considerable period of time.

We must bear the difficulties of archaeological interpretation in mind as we turn to look at the question of evidence of the hunting prowess of *Homo erectus*.

Hunter's Diet

As discussed in Chapters 8 and 9, the archaeological evidence suggests that early *Homo* groups consumed a wide variety of animals, some of which they possibly caught, but many of which they scavenged. The picture changes with *Homo erectus*. Although they undoubtedly continued to rely heavily on plants for nourishment—as do practically all modern humans—they surely possessed both the intellect and the equipment necessary to assure themselves more regularly of meat.

Like all evolutionary change, this development was a slow matter of advantage and capacity reinforcing each other. Humans did not become hunters because some individuals decided they liked meat. Instead, a creature able to catch, eat, and digest meat was favored, at a particular time and place, in the competition for survival. Hunting makes available to humans far more food per square mile of the African savanna than plant life can provide. As vegetarians, humans can make use of only a limited number of the things that grow on the ground: mainly roots, nuts, fruits, berries, and some tender shoots. The most abundant plants—the grasses of the savanna and the leaves of the forest trees—contain a high proportion of cellulose, which cannot be digested by the human stomach. But the animals that live on the things that humans cannot digest may themselves be both edible and nourishing. Through hunting, previously inedible vegetation, converted to edible meat, became available as a food source for humans.

Hunting not only increased the amount of food available but also provided better food. Meat is a much more concentrated form of nourishment, a more efficient source of energy, than wild vegetables, fruits, and berries. Venison, for instance, yields 572 calories (calories measure the energy available in food) per 3.5 oz (100 g) of weight, whereas the same weight of most fruits and vegetables yields well under 100 calories. One medium-sized animal would have provided, in a compact, easily carried form, the same amount of energy as the results of a whole day's foraging for vegetables. (Nuts yield more calories than most meats and were undoubtedly a vital part of early humans' diet when and where nuts could be found, but nuts grow only in certain localities, and most of them are at least roughly seasonal, whereas game is widely available throughout the year.) Finally, the high protein content of meat is a very important dietary factor.

Another very important factor in the development of hunting and the evolution of *Homo erectus* is the seasonality of vegetable food in the temperate regions. In tropical savanna regions, with their annual wet and dry seasons, the supply of vegetable foods is more-or-less continuous—barring a prolonged drought—as the success of the vegetarian savanna monkeys demonstrates. In northern temperate zones, however, there is a real dearth of vegetable foods after the nuts and berries have been consumed in the fall. In the winter and early spring, meat, we can suppose, may have been a major part of the diet of *Homo erectus* groups that had expanded into the temperate zones. Hunting was surely an essential adaptation for any groups that were to succeed in the bitter winters of northern Eurasia.

Skin Adaptation

One major physical change that had possibly occurred by the time of *Homo erectus* was adaptation of the skin. When hominids started diverging from the African apes, they probably were just as hairy as those animals are now. In time, their hair must have grown less dense and the sweat glands in their skin more numerous.

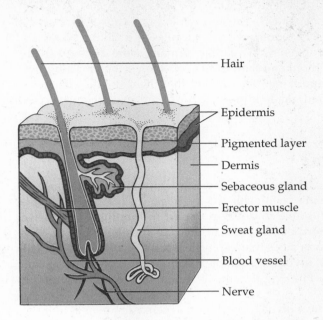

Hair

Epidermis

Pigmented layer

Dermis

Sebaceous gland

Erector muscle

Sweat gland

Blood vessel

Nerve

FIGURE 12–1 The skin is an organ of astonishing complexity. It is the barrier between the relatively closed system of a human body and its external environment; it is strong, elastic, waterproof, protective, and self-repairing. Beyond this, it serves as a sense organ, an excretory organ, a heat control mechanism (involving hair and sweat glands), and the organ of individual identification. It responds to environmental stress, both directly (suntanning and healing) and indirectly (sweating).

By the time of *Homo erectus,* if not before, the skin probably had become relatively hairless and had developed a greater number of sweat glands (Figure 12–1). This change sharply differentiates humans from other primates. Today, though we still have as many hair roots as apes, our hair is generally much shorter and finer, and over large areas of our bodies it is almost invisible. Conversely, we have from 2 to 5 million sweat glands, more than are found in any other primate, and are far more productive of sweat.

Scientists are not sure why this change in body hair took place, but it seems to have been connected with an increasing ability to sustain strenuous physical exertion. As we have seen, most meat-eating animals hunt at night. As hominids ancestral to humans moved from the protective forests onto the open savanna and became *daytime* scavengers, they faced a new problem. They generated a great deal of body heat (metabolic heat), just at the time of day when the temperature of the air was high, so that the cooling effect of the air was low. To maintain a constant body temperature, essential to any mammal, a very efficient cooling mechanism was required. A logical evolutionary adaptation to this biological need was the increased number of sweat glands, producing far more sweat per gland, and the reduction of hair cover. During heavy exertion or in hot weather, the sweat glands bathe the body in moisture. Evaporation of this moisture cools the surface of the skin and the blood just below it. Dense hair would inhibit evaporation and would get matted and clogged by dried sweat. Hence, the theory goes, the marked decrease in hair density.

There are, of course, other savanna animals that sweat heavily during strenuous exertion and yet retain a full coat of hair; zebras are an example. But their metabolic rate is noticeably lower than that of humans, and their dependence on grazing allows them to lead a much less active life. Strenuous exertion is rare and occurs mostly during the cooler night, when predators are active.

Sweating is not an unmitigated blessing to humans. As biologist William Montagna pointed out, sweating represents a major biological blunder in some ways, for it drains the body of enormous amounts of moisture, requiring fairly constant replenishment, and depletes the system of sodium and other essential elements. But higher primates all require regular supplies of drinking water, and so this requirement was nothing new. Sweating humans were certainly better equipped than their ape and monkey relatives to exert themselves for long periods in the tropical sunlight, and it can be assumed that the dramatic changes in the skin, however they occurred, made it possible for humans to engage successfully in their new way of life.

Hunting and Intelligence

It seems likely that many of the important physical adaptations that equipped humans for hunting had already been achieved by *Homo erectus*'s predecessors. What, then, made *Homo erectus* able to develop the art of hunting? The answer almost certainly lies in the enormous increase in the size and the adaptive capabilities of the brain. Hunting was more than a physical activity; it helped to create a new way of life, probably involving complex communication, culture, and improved social organization. Hunting became as much a matter of the mind as of the body.

We have seen that one indication of *Homo erectus*'s increasing mental ability is the refinement and improvement of their technology. Their stone tools and weapons were improvements over those of their predecessors, and they may also have had wooden spears, which would have made hunting safer and more effective. Even if they only jabbed with the spear rather than throwing it, they could still attack an animal without getting within immediate reach of its claws and teeth. And a spear embedded almost anywhere in an animal's body is likely to disable the animal; a stone, to be equally effective, must be thrown accurately to hit a vulnerable spot.

Perhaps as important as any improvement in weapons technology was a change in tactics. We can suppose that with a bigger brain *Homo erectus* had a greater attention and memory span. By being able to remember information from their own and their fellows' past experiences, they could amass knowledge of animal behavior, plan ahead, work out strategies, and roam farther afield than their forebears without getting lost. Furthermore, they could cooperate more subtly with other band members, increasing their chances of making a kill.

BEGINNINGS OF HUNTING

Homo erectus's success must have depended to a large extent on their guile and their understanding of animal behavior. If so, just how did they hunt? Some methods are perhaps documented in the remains found in excavated sites; others can be inferred by examining hunting techniques employed in modern times by hunters-and-gatherers—by ethnographic analogy.

They were clever enough to have looked carefully for the weaknesses of the animals they hunted, big or small. African hares are quick but vulnerable, and they, too, must have figured as part of *Homo erectus*'s diet. How easily they can be caught by an intelligent (and agile) human was demonstrated by Louis Leakey, who ran them down and captured them with his bare hands. The technique is simple. The hunter, on spotting a hare, need only watch its long ears. When the hare is about to dodge, it lays its ears all the way back. Seeing this telltale sign, the hunter veers immediately either to the left or to the right, which gives a 50/50 chance of picking the way the hare is going to go. If the hunter has guessed correctly and is quick, the animal will be caught. If the hunter misses, the hare will usually run for cover and freeze there. The hunter, with the advantage of the primates' highly developed color vision, will see through the animal's camouflage and simply go over and pick up the prey.

Persistence Hunting

Because *Homo erectus* would not have been fast enough to run down larger quarry, they might have used a technique that anthropologist Grover S. Krantz has called *persistence hunting*. Development of this method, too, would have required insight into the behavior of animals, such as the tendency of antelopes and gazelles to move in an arc when trying to escape from a pursuer, giving the intelligent hunter the opportunity to cut them off. But the key to persistence hunting is persistence: never allowing the animal to rest, but keeping it constantly in motion until it grows so tired it can go no farther; when it slumps from exhaustion, it can be killed easily. *Homo erectus* may have had to keep up the chase for hours on end. The Tarahumara Indians of Mexico have been known to pursue a deer for as long as two days. Although the hunters may at times lose sight of their quarry, they never lose track of its spoor—hoofprints, droppings, and other signs of its passage—and relentlessly continue the pursuit until the deer collapses.

Persistence hunting: hunting by chasing the prey until it stops, exhausted, when it can be killed.

Stalking, Driving, and Ambush

In addition to persistence hunting, one can speculate that *Homo erectus* people may have practiced stalking, driving, and ambush as hunting techniques. All three are risky procedures since they can bring hunters into close proximity to formidable creatures that are fresh and dangerous, not exhausted after hours of pursuit. And just how *Homo erectus* hunters may have dispatched prey at close range is difficult to tell from the archaeological record. Perhaps they used fire-hardened wooden spears for throwing or jabbing. Such implements could have been quite effective, especially if the tips were smeared with poison, as seen among Pygmy elephant hunters today (no hard evidence of poison use by *Homo erectus* exists, however). Or perhaps *Homo erectus* simply stoned to death animals that had wandered—or had been intentionally driven by humans—into marshes and had become immobilized in the mud. As noted in Chapter 11, the Spanish sites of Torralba and Ambrona were originally interpreted as yielding evidence of *Homo erectus* hunters driving elephants into bogs, finishing them off, and then butchering them (Figure 12–2). More recent analyses, however, by Richard Klein and taphonomist Pat Shipman have shown that, while hominids (either *Homo erectus* or early *Homo sapiens*) used some of the carcasses at these sites (as shown by cut marks) and at a third elephant-butchering site called Aridos near Madrid, no conclusive evidence of actual hunting exists. The hominids may simply have been scavenging the remains of animals that had died naturally or had been killed by carnivores. Incontrovertible evidence of hunting by deliberately driving animals probably postdates *Homo erectus*. At the site of La Cotte de St. Brelade on the British Channel Island of Jersey, archaeologists have unearthed evidence of elephant and

FIGURE 12–2   Workers clear the floor of the Spanish site of Ambrona, where elephant bones (in the foreground) showing cut marks made by stone tools were found.

rhinoceros drives dating from 125,000 to 240,000 years B.P. But at this date, the hunters were very likely representatives of *Homo sapiens*.

Because they were hunters and gatherers (and occasional scavengers), it seems very probable that the nomadic lifestyle imposed on *Homo erectus* by their wandering and migratory prey must have affected them enormously. It forced them to cover new ground and exposed them to varied new experiences and sensations. All primates are curious, and doubtless *Homo erectus* explored the diverse features of their enlarging world with interest. They must have had to solve new problems, such as how to transport food and water as they moved from one hunting ground to the next. No direct evidence has been discovered so far to show that they had receptacles of any sort, but it seems reasonable to conclude that they at least had crude skin bags made of animal hides or perhaps containers made of wood, leaves, or even clay. Material for toolmaking was certainly transported, at least in small quantities, and tools were often made at the butchery site. As they extended their range northward, the cooler climates could have stimulated the control and use of fire and the construction of clothing of some sort. Both these behaviors can be related to meat eating. The cold, harsh winters of the north deprived *Homo erectus* of a year-round supply of vegetable food and put an even higher premium on meat. Clothing could have been made from the pelts of animals; impressions in the ground at Terra Amata and elsewhere suggest to some researchers that *Homo erectus* may have used hides for some purposes (but see Chapter 11 on the problematic nature of Terra Amata).

NEW SOCIAL DEVELOPMENTS

The records left by *Homo erectus* at Zhoukoudian, Aridos, (possibly) Terra Amata, Olduvai Gorge, and other sites may not seem like much for their million-year tenure. And yet in successfully adopting meat eating as a way of life, humans had taken a major step toward setting themselves apart from their animal ancestors and establishing the genus *Homo* as supreme among the creatures of the earth. The dependence on meat and the expansion into temperate regions of the Old World must have profoundly influenced human social organization.

The expansion into temperate zones was perhaps the high adventure of those million years during which *Homo erectus* people established themselves as nature's dominant species. Before the great expansion, their immediate ancestors had been evolving by the dictates of natural selection in much the same way as other animals had: adapting imperceptibly to their environment; living, as other higher primates, in loose social groups; depending on a generally benign environment for food and warmth; and having very little awareness of the past or thought for the future. But when *Homo erectus* spread into the world's previously unpeopled regions, their relationship to natural selection began to alter. *Homo erectus* prevailed over the obstacles of new environments not because they developed new bodily equipment but because they had a better brain. At least by the time of late *Homo erectus*, they were meeting the challenges of changing conditions with solutions of their own making, rather than waiting until evolution created solutions for them. For the first time, hominids were taking an active part in their own adaptation and evolution. Humans' "cultural environment" was beginning to take shape.

The Evolution of Male and Female Roles

As discussed in Chapter 9, it is very difficult to speculate about the behavior and social relations of early *Homo* (*H. habilis* and *H. rudolfensis*) because of a paucity of information about anatomy and subsistence patterns, and because these hominids were probably on the fringe of "humanness" with regard to intelligence. But with *Homo erectus* it's an entirely different story. Thanks to the discovery of critical postcranial material at Nariokotome and elsewhere, and because we believe these hominids were the first to live a hunting-and-gathering lifestyle, we can sketch a much more complete picture of their lives.

Let's begin with the implications of *Homo erectus*'s pattern of brain growth. Among modern humans, because of constraints on women's pelvic dimensions related to efficient bipedal locomotion, babies are born with brains that are only about 25 percent of adult size (in comparison, a chimpanzee infant has accomplished 45 percent of total brain growth at birth). As we all know, modern babies are *altricial* or helpless at birth and completely dependent on adult care. Ours is a particular kind of helplessness, however, that is called *secondary altriciality* because it affects mainly the motor skills and not the senses. Although their sensory systems quickly become functional, modern babies' motor skills take a long time to develop. But our babies are accomplishing something vital during their period of

Altricial: the state of being born helpless and requiring parental care.

Secondary altriciality: the phenomenon of an infant's motor skills requiring a lengthy period of postnatal development, as opposed to its sensory systems, which are functional at birth or soon after; characteristic of *H. erectus* and *H. sapiens* (see *altricial*).

motor helplessness: they are undergoing very rapid postnatal brain growth that will carry them to about 70 percent of adult brain size by 1 year of age. Thus, modern babies play catch-up in brain growth during their first year of life, but only at the cost of requiring full-time care. And, of course, since humans are mammals, the responsibility for the care and feeding of dependent infants falls primarily on their mothers, producing an immediate distinction between women and men that has had far-reaching effects on their respective roles in many cultures.

The pelvis of the *Homo erectus* boy from Nariokotome has been studied by Alan Walker and Christopher Ruff. From the adolescent's pelvis, Walker and Ruff have calculated the probable pelvic dimensions of *Homo erectus* adults and have concluded that this species resembled modern humans in producing secondarily altricial infants. Among *Homo erectus* people, infants' brains were probably about 22 percent of adult size at birth but grew rapidly (more than doubling in size) during the immediate postnatal period, when the infants were almost certainly totally dependent on adult care. The strong implication of this finding is that, as among modern humans, *Homo erectus* women were cast in the role of primary caretakers for extremely helpless infants and very likely experienced some behavioral limitations as a result.

FIGURE 12–3 *Homo erectus* probably evolved a pattern of division of labor similar to that of these present-day !Kung San. While the men search for meat, the women gather and dig vegetable foods.

As noted in the last chapter, the large body size of *Homo erectus* people and their development of effective butchering tools suggest to us that they were becoming increasingly dependent on meat as a dietary staple, and that they were obtaining animal resources primarily by hunting, although scavenging would have continued as well. Since *Homo erectus* women would have had the primary responsibility for slow-developing, dependent children, it seems likely that these early humans had a sexual division of subsistence activities—women doing *most* of the gathering and men doing *most* of the hunting (Figure 12–3). We are emphasizing the word *most* here because among modern hunters-and-gatherers the sexual division of subsistence activities is often less than clear-cut. Indeed, in a few living hunter-and-gatherer societies, women make a major contribution to the hunting effort, while in all such cultures, men may do some gathering of vegetable foods. There is nothing about their respective anatomies that *strictly* limits the sexes to different subsistence roles.

Together *Homo erectus* women and men no doubt made an effective economic team. Based on studies of modern hunters-and-gatherers, it can be estimated that vegetable foods gathered mostly by women made up 60 to 80 percent of the diet, the remaining 20 to 40 percent consisting of meat usually obtained by male hunters (Figure 12–4). Not only did gathering make the largest contribution to the *Homo erectus* diet, but it is important to note that it also represented an entirely new subsistence pattern for hominoids. Occasional hunting of small game followed by food sharing can be documented among apes, and it almost certainly characterized the australopithecines and early *Homo* as well. But gathering, along with the subsequent sharing of vegetable foods, was a novel and important development not found among apes. Undoubtedly, when *Homo erectus* women assumed the primary role as gatherers of vegetable foods, it had significant effects on social relations. Furthermore, gathering almost certainly provided important

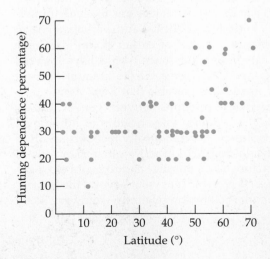

FIGURE 12–4 Among living hunters-and-gatherers, the percentage of food obtained through hunting varies strongly with latitude. In tropical and subtropical areas, hunting generally contributes 10 to 40 percent of the total food, while in higher latitudes (as among certain Eskimo groups) the bulk of the diet may come from meat.

selection pressures for the development of material culture. Of primary importance would have been the invention of containers, such as woven sacks or wooden bowls, that would have enabled the gatherers to bring home a substantial load each day. And finally, gathering, along with hunting, no doubt contributed to the development of a migratory lifestyle, as *Homo erectus* bands moved seasonally within their home ranges or territories in search of fluctuating vegetable and animal resources.

Families and Bands

As mentioned above, a sexual division of subsistence activities strongly implies food sharing, and it seems quite safe to conclude that this practice existed among *Homo erectus* people. Women and men shared the fruits (often, literally) of their labors, and judging from their body size, the combined diet must have been quite nutritious. But with whom would these people have shared their food? Certainly mothers would have shared with their children, but what of sharing between men and women and between men and children? As suggested some years ago by Owen Lovejoy, it seems reasonable that adults would have shared frequently with their mates, and that women would have focused their sexual activity on supportive males. Men would then have been selected to share with the offspring of their mates since, presumably, these were also their own children in most cases. Combining a degree of paternity certainty with dietary interdependence might have been among the first steps toward the development of that human institution, the *family*, although it seems doubtful that, among *Homo erectus* hunters-and-gatherers, families were monogynous (if families existed, they more likely polygynous, judging from modern cultures). Whether mating and child-rearing partnerships were formalized in some way—marking the beginnings of the institution of marriage—must go forever unknown.

Homo erectus bands probably averaged around 25 members, although some may have been twice that large. Each band very likely moved within a large home range (or a territory, if it was defended). Among modern hunters-and-gatherers, population density ranges from 1 or less to about 6 persons per square mile (0.4–2.3 persons per km²). Within the *Homo erectus* band, it seems likely that interdependence of males and females, of children and adults, and perhaps even of adult males was being intensified compared to that of earlier hominids. Some anthropologists think that increased male interdependence would have fostered male-male cooperation during hunting and thus increased the amount of meat coming into a band (Figure 12–5). And finally, it is possible that *Homo erectus* people were beginning to recognize and formalize relations between genetic kin. As discussed in Chapter 5, kinship affects the behavior and societies of nonhuman primates, although it is clearly not consciously or symbolically recognized. Monkeys and apes tend to behave altruistically toward kin more often than toward nonkin (such altruistic behavior may include food sharing) and to avoid close kin in mating. Thus food sharing by *Homo erectus* people that went beyond the bounds of the immediate family was probably patterned by kin relations—and very likely the same was true of mate selection.

Family: in human society, generally a unit marked by subsistence interdependence, sexual relationships among adults, and parent-offspring relationships.

FIGURE 12–5 Two !Kung brothers and their wives go out in the morning to find food. The men carry springhare poles, bows, and quivers of arrows for hunting; the women, one carrying two children, will gather plant foods.

Incest Taboo

As family patterns developed within *Homo erectus* society, avoidance of inbreeding (sexual relations between closely related individuals) very likely became an established pattern. Inbreeding inhibitions have been found in several species of monkeys and apes. Among rhesus and Japanese macaques, for instance, there is apparently some sort of restraint against sex between mother and son; in chimpanzees this inhibition is usually extended to brother and sister, although in other ways the sex lives of chimpanzees are promiscuous. In modern humans an *incest* taboo is found in all societies (though a few societies have carefully defined exceptions). At some time during human evolution, then, the partial inhibition became a hard-and-fast taboo. It seems fair to suggest that, as *Homo erectus* grew more aware of kinship structures within the community, a sanction against sex within the family became more pronounced. Perhaps familiarity inhibited sexual interest. This change may have functioned to retain stability in the family and the broader social structure. Bonds within the family may certainly be threatened by incest, and development of bonding between descent groups (discussed below) would have depended on extending the incest taboo to a widening group of kin. That extensive inbreeding can be genetically undesirable was surely not known to these people, yet in this respect also a taboo would be an advantageous behavior pattern.

Incest: legally prohibited sexual relations between kin. How closely related individuals must be for mating to be considered incestuous differs from culture to culture.

Exogamy

Homo erectus people may have shown an increasing tendency to look around widely for mates until, eventually, they reached beyond their own band to select partners from neighboring groups. Among modern humans this practice is called *exogamy*, and it involves the exchange of marriage partners (incipient exogamy, like that envisioned for *H. erectus*, probably did not include formal marriages). The beginnings of exogamy would certainly have had advantages for *Homo erectus* people, including the development of blood ties between groups that would have encouraged intergroup harmony. If competition for game among neighboring bands was a potential problem at the time, this development could have been of great social importance. When bands with adjoining hunting ranges are related, sharing develops; when game and other foods become scarce, the bands can hunt freely over one another's ranges. By bringing in mates strange to the group, exogamy would have made family ties and band identity even more important. Rules of exogamy—which today cause individuals to marry outside their social group and may even specify the outside group into which they must marry—are characteristic of all existing traditional human societies and are undoubtedly an ancient custom, and certainly one of extraordinary importance.

Exogamy: among modern humans, the pattern of marrying (and mating) between individuals from different social groups; incipient exogamy, like that envisioned for *Homo erectus*, need not have included formal marriages.

Home Base

With developing family ties and individualization, *Homo erectus* may have shown another cultural development vital to society's growth: the idea of a home base. In a society more complex than that of most primates, subgroups of hunters or foragers are likely to be isolated from the main group for a time. Certainly, constant association as a group would not have been possible for *Homo erectus*, whose hunters ranged far and whose young were becoming increasingly dependent. The solution was a place, however temporary, where the children could be looked after, where the women could stockpile the fruits of their gathering, and where the men could bring their supplies of meat after a day or two on the hunt.

Interestingly, evidence of a home base is lacking until late *Homo erectus* times, perhaps 400,000 to 500,000 years ago. As discussed in Chapter 11, the best evidence comes from the Chinese site of Zhoukoudian, which was used by *Homo erectus* (and also local carnivores) for many millennia and has yielded some evidence of the control and use of fire. In addition, the French site of Terra Amata may reflect shelter construction by late *Homo erectus* at an annually used home base near the sea, but some researchers feel that the site is better attributed to early *Homo sapiens*.

With a home base, humankind had a new social blueprint and one unique among primates. For one thing, the existence of a home meant that the sick or infirm no longer faced abandonment along the way; now they had a place where they could rest and mend in comparative safety. "For a wild primate," Sherwood Washburn and Irven DeVore write, "a fatal sickness is one that separates it from the troop, but for man it is one from which he cannot recover even while protected and fed at the home base. . . . It is the home base that changes sprained ankles and fevers from fatal diseases to minor ailments."

Thus development of the home could have affected the normal life span. Still, only a few *Homo erectus* individuals are believed to have attained the age of 40, and anyone who survived to 50 would have reached a ripe old age indeed. Most died much earlier, as shown by the evidence from the cave at Zhoukoudian: 50 percent of the human bones found there belonged to children under 14.

For the long-range development of human society, the real importance of the home base was that it provided a medium for cultural growth. Within its safe circle could grow a fellowship, a self-awareness and trust, and a sense of community that was new on earth. There people could begin to learn more than simply how to survive; they could improve their tools and weapons, fashion a language, and look not only to the past but to the future.

INTRASPECIES AGGRESSION

Theories of Aggression

The home, for all it contributed to human growth, could also be involved in another, and much less desirable, hallmark of human society—one that some observers think they can trace to *Homo erectus* and before. That is the human's unhappy tendency to do violence to other humans.

Author Robert Ardrey hypothesized that people instinctively guard whatever territory they consider their own, such as that of a home base, and will defend it, violently if necessary, against all intruders. He suggested that an inborn drive for aggression carried over from animal forebears explains all humans' violent behavior, from wars to riots to throwing dishes in a domestic quarrel. Konrad Lorenz, an Austrian authority on animal behavior, argued that this innate drive will express itself in one way or another; if it is not channeled productively, in society's terms, it will burst out destructively—sooner or later, but inevitably.

Most anthropologists and ethnologists today disagree with Lorenz's and Ardrey's hypotheses. They believe that humans have no specific innate drive for aggression but merely the potential for this kind of behavior, and that this potential is shaped by society. When people are threatened or think they are threatened by another, their response may just as well be to flee the threat as to fight the provoker. All vertebrate animals are provided with a dual innate response to danger of "fight or flight." Thus all species have the possibility of peaceful coexistence. Among humans, culture and experience determine which response they make.

Aggression Among *Homo erectus*

The possibility of conflict within or between bands of *Homo erectus* cannot be entirely eliminated. Much that we know portrays *Homo erectus* as solid and industrious social humans, sharing the burdens of a primitive existence. Yet among the fossils unearthed on the cave floor at Zhoukoudian were human skulls that were faceless and had been opened at the base. This evidence can be explained in many ways; some archaeologists conclude that the first humans practiced cannibalism and ate the brains of the dead. Savage as this act is now considered, it does not necessarily make *Homo erectus* less human. In fact, it could be taken as evidence of a step toward modern humanity.

Among the tribal peoples that have been known to practice cannibalism in recent times, the act is nearly always carried out not for the sake of food, but as a

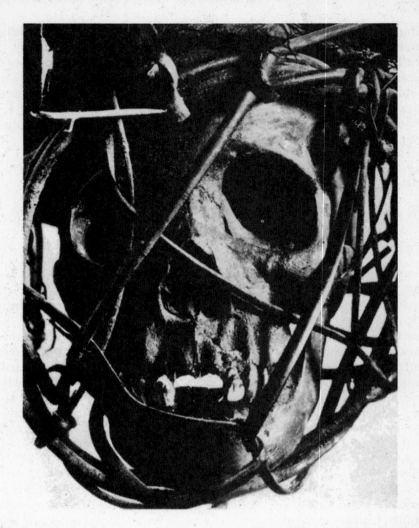

FIGURE 12–6   Bornean headhunters usually keep the skull of the man they have killed as a trophy. The base of the skull is always damaged; the foramen magnum has been enlarged and the brain removed. It is normally eaten, an example of ritual cannibalism.

ritual (Figure 12–6). The distinction between dietary and ritual cannibalism is important; it is extremely rare for people to eat other people merely for food. Writing of some present-day headhunters, G. H. R. von Koenigswald explained, "The head hunter is not content merely to possess the skull, but opens it and takes out the brain, which he eats in order by this means to acquire the wisdom and skill of his foe." The very evidence suggesting that the first humans ate each other and each other's brains, then, may suggest that they had some spiritual notion that cannibalism could increase their powers.

On the other hand, some archaeologists, including Lewis Binford, have criticized this traditional interpretation of the deposits and human bones at Zhoukoudian. Binford points out that the bones of *H. erectus* are found in deposits that also contain a wide range of other bone fragments, together with remains of numerous predators, including the Chinese hyena. The removal of the faces of the human skulls and the destruction of the skull base are exactly what happens when gnawing predators or scavengers chew out the face of their prey. But earlier investigators also believed that the way in which the human long bones were broken at Zhoukoudian indicated cannibalism: the breaks were distinctive and even diagnostic of human activity. Yet it was already known as early as 1939 that hyenas chewed and split long bones in this way. So it seems clear that, while it is entirely possible that early humans occasionally practiced cannibalism, the archaeological evidence at this site is not irrefutable.

Looking at the issue from a broader perspective, Binford also makes the point (which applies equally to some other sites) that, because human beings did at certain times undoubtedly occupy the cave, the assumption was made that everything in the cave during those periods was therefore a product of human activity—not just the tools, but all the bone fragments and ash layers. And this assumption was made despite the clear and extensive evidence of the presence of numerous predators. The assumption is clearly unjustified.

Whatever the correct explanation, conflicts between bands, if they occurred, must have been rare in an uncrowded world such as that of *Homo erectus*. No doubt true warfare was a later (and dubious) achievement that probably came after humans settled down on the land, became a more numerous species, and forged cultures that encouraged individual and group pride in possessions, territories, and beliefs, even as they fostered art, science, and literature.

These are today's problems, of course, and there is little reason to think they afflicted *Homo erectus*. They were confronting their own challenges and, with perseverance and imagination, solved them remarkably well. To their success we owe many of our flaws and triumphs.

SUMMARY

Within limits, a reasonable—although certainly speculative—picture can be drawn of the subsistence activities and society of *Homo erectus*. As sketched in this chapter, we believe *Homo erectus* to have been a species of far-ranging hunters-and-gatherers that very likely lived in bands of about 25 people. Evidence for hunting-and-gathering includes the development of Acheulean tools and the attainment of large body size. Significantly more dependent on animal resources than their evolutionary predecessors, *Homo erectus* people probably practiced a sexual division of labor with regard to subsistence, with women responsible mainly for the collection of plant foods (which made up the bulk of the diet) and men responsible mainly for hunting. Hunting techniques may have included persistence hunting, stalking, and ambush. Evidence that *Homo erectus* hunters ever "drove" animals into kill sites is unconvincing. Undoubtedly, *Homo erectus* people would have continued to scavenge meat whenever possible.

With regard to social developments, it seems likely that *Homo erectus* women gave birth to secondarily altricial infants who were completely dependent on adult caretakers (primarily their mothers) for a prolonged period. No doubt this development was linked to the sexual division of subsistence activities described above. Food sharing between female gatherers and male hunters, coupled with increasing paternity certainty, may have contributed to the development of the family. Along with the family may have come increased recognition of kin relationships, and these, in turn, may have led to the development of incest taboos and exogamy.

And finally, the evidence that *Homo erectus* showed two other interesting human behaviors—the idea of a home base and cannibalism—is equivocal. If *Homo erectus* people centered their activities and movements on a home base, it was not until very late in their life span as a species. Regarding claims of cannibalism, all such evidence (mostly faceless skulls that have been opened at the base) is probably better attributed to the actions of scavenging carnivores.

REVIEW QUESTIONS

1. Review the evidence regarding the question of whether *Homo erectus* people were hunters. What sort of archaeological or anatomical evidence is needed to settle the matter conclusively?

2. Explain how the production of secondarily altricial infants may have been linked to a sexual division of labor among *Homo erectus*. Can you envision a child care system that would not have restricted the ranging and activities of *Homo erectus* women?

3. If *Homo erectus* women gathered and men hunted, what are the implications about who made and used the various types of Acheulean tools?

4. As noted in earlier chapters, there is no overwhelming anatomical evidence that *Homo erectus* people had spoken language. What conclusions do you think can be drawn from their artifacts and (hypothesized) social behavior?

5. What form do you think the first human families took? Monogynous? Polygynous? Review the factors that may have contributed to the evolution of the family.

POSTSCRIPT

A Chinese proverb says that a picture is worth a thousand words. The same can be true, of course, of a name, a descriptive term, or a slogan. All can conjure up entire gestalts, complex units composed of associated elements that collectively go far beyond the literal meaning of the name, term, or slogan. Take, for example, *hunting-and-gathering*.

As used in this chapter to describe the subsistence activities of *Homo erectus*, the term *hunting-and-gathering* simply identifies the two main ways we think these early humans obtained food. The term itself says nothing about amounts of food obtained by hunting versus gathering, nor the identities of the hunters and the gatherers, nor the value placed by the culture on hunted versus gathered food items. Read literally, the term says that *Homo erectus* people hunted some and gathered some. Period. But things are not so simple. In anthropological circles, *hunting-and-gathering* is a loaded label. Ever since the development during the mid-twentieth century of the "hunting hypothesis" (described by Matt Cartmill in *A View to a Death in the Morning*), the term *hunting-and-gathering* has carried a long train of implied elements, including sexual division of subsistence activities, with men hunting and women gathering; the greater value (either nutritional or symbolic) of meat over vegetable foods, with men thus making a more important dietary contribution than women; men as far-ranging providers and protectors and women as stay-at-home dependents; men as strong and aggressive and women as weak and passive; men as the creators and users of technology and women as nontechnological creatures; men as dominant and women as subordinate; and finally, men as the "movers and shakers" of human evolution, with women riding men's evolutionary coattails.

No wonder many researchers, and especially feminist anthropologists, fulminate against the term! In hindsight, the traditional "hunting-and-gathering" gestalt is clearly sex-biased in its overemphasis on men and its deemphasis on the role of women. And besides, it's just plain wrong. First, as discussed in this chapter, although among living hunters-and-gatherers men do *most* of the hunting and women do *most* of the gathering, the subsistence activities of the sexes may overlap significantly, and in some cultures women hunt a good deal. Second, although there is much variation from culture to culture, meat obtained by hunting usually makes up a considerably smaller portion of the diet than plant foods obtained by gathering. Thus, if the term were intended as a literal description of dietary proportions, with the larger portion listed first, it should read "gathering-and-hunting" (many anthropologists prefer to use it this way). And furthermore, if one sex had to be identified as the primary dietary providers, it would be women. Third, the hunting-gathering dichotomy has few clear technological implications. Both forms of subsistence activities would have been enhanced by the use of implements: stone picks, digging sticks, and wooden or fabric containers for gathering; wooden spears and stone tools for killing animals; and stone or bamboo implements for butchering. Surely there were plenty of opportunities (and selection pressures) for both sexes to make technological contributions. And finally, it simply makes no sense to talk of one sex leading the way in evolution, with the other following in its wake. The physical traits and behavior (including subsistence behavior) of each sex have evolved *in the context of the opposite sex*. In other words, females have "enabled" males' traits, and males have "enabled" females' traits. It takes two to tango (or, in this case, evolve).

We have chosen to use the term *hunting-and-gathering* in its traditional form simply because we want to emphasize the increased importance of hunting among *Homo erectus* people. Our usage is certainly not intended to elevate or demean the cultural or evolutionary contributions of either sex. Over the last 2 million years, humans have become extremely omnivorous in their diet—gathering, scavenging, catching, killing (and long after *Homo erectus*, growing) a wide variety of foodstuffs. Both women and men have contributed in important ways to this development, and in turn, dietary diversity has played a major role in the evolutionary success of humankind.

CHAPTER

13

The Evolution of Language and the Brain

He gave man speech, and speech created thought, Which is the measure of the universe.
PERCY BYSSHE SHELLEY, 1792–1822. *Prometheus Unbound*, II, IV, 72–73.

Speech was given to man to disguise his thoughts.

ATTRIBUTED TO CHARLES MAURICE DE TALLEYRAND, 1754–1838.

OVERVIEW

Of all of the various traits of living humans, spoken language appears to be unique. At first glance, language and speech seem to separate us rather cleanly from all other living organisms, and virtually all theories of human origins include spoken language as a key evolutionary milestone in our history. But how wide is the "language gap" between humans and other animals, when did it first appear, and how closely is it related to differences in brain anatomy? This chapter addresses these and other questions as it describes the anatomical specializations (brain size and organization, and throat and mouth anatomy) that enable humans to talk. The chapter also compares human language to the communication patterns of wild monkeys and apes, discusses apes' abilities to learn gestural and computer-based language systems in the laboratory, and reviews the hominid fossil record for evidence of the beginnings of spoken language. Important topics and concepts include early theories of language development; primate communication in the wild (including the production of "vocal symbols"); laboratory studies of apes' capacity for language; "language areas" of the human brain; contributions of the pharynx to speech; and, finally, brain enlargement among primates and its implications for "theories of mind" and language.

WAYS OF COMMUNICATING

As the social life of humans grew more complex, the ability to communicate must also have developed. Spoken *language*, we can now see, was humankind's passport to a totally new level of social relationship, organization, and thought; it was the tool that allowed humans to vary expressions to meet changing conditions instead of being limited by less flexible patterns of communication, as other primates are.

Language: the cognitive aspect of human communication, involving symbolic thinking structured by grammar.

Early Theories on the Origins of Speech

When did hominids begin to speak? How did they start? What did their first words sound like? Investigators have been seeking answers to these questions for thousands of years. In ancient Egypt the pharaoh Psammetichus ordered two infants reared where they could hear no human voice. He hoped that when at last they spoke, uninfluenced by the sound of the Egyptian tongue, they would resort to their earliest ancestors' language, which he confidently assumed lurked within them. One child finally uttered something that sounded like *bekos*, or "bread" in the language of Phrygia, an ancient nation of central Asia Minor. Phrygian, said Psammetichus triumphantly, was obviously humankind's original tongue.

Many centuries later King James IV of Scotland tried a similar experiment with two babies. The result, he let it be known, was that his experimental subjects spoke passable Hebrew. This report must have pleased biblical scholars of the day, for they had contended all along that Adam and Eve had conversed in Hebrew. A Swede of the late seventeenth century believed otherwise: he announced that in the Garden of Eden, God had used Swedish, Adam Danish, and the serpent French.

As time went on, all sorts of theories sprang up about the origins of *speech*. The eighteenth-century French philosopher Jean-Jacques Rousseau envisioned a group of tongue-tied human beings getting together and stammering out more-or-less overnight a language they could use. Why they felt the need for one, and how they had communicated with each other before they had invented the words to communicate with, Rousseau failed to mention. His contemporary, the German romantic historian Johann Gottfried Herder, also espoused the notion that language was humanmade, not God-instilled, as most people believed. Anything so illogical, so imperfect as language could hardly be attributed to a divinity, Herder argued. But he would have none of Rousseau's ideas, either. Instead, he saw language springing from the innermost nature of humans, in response to an impulse to speak. Just how language took shape Herder could not say, but he imagined that it had started when humans began imitating the sounds of the creatures around them, using eventually the imitative sounds as the words for the animals themselves. This theory, known today among those who disagree with it as the "bow-wow thesis," was followed by a number of others, similarly named and ridiculed, ranging from the whistle-and-grunt thesis to the ouch-ouch, which claimed that language had arisen from exclamations of pain, pleasure, fear, surprise, and so on.

Darwin's concept of human evolution provided a new way of approaching the problem of the origin of spoken language. Scientists are now beginning to develop some theories about how we came to speak. Studies of animals, particularly monkeys and apes, both in the laboratory and in the wild, have given us an understanding of the foundation on which language is based; they have shown that there is considerably more of the ape in talkative humans than most people think. Examination of that foundation is necessary, because understanding what communication was like before there were words helps make clear why and how spoken language evolved and emphasizes the tremendous biological and cultural changes that it made possible.

Communication Among Animals

Nonhuman vertebrates and insects have some intriguing ways of communicating. Honeybees perform a kind of dance on the honeycomb; the dance accurately transmits information about the direction, distance, and nature of a food source. Dogs and wolves use scents to communicate in addition to barks, howls, and growls; they also use a system of visual signals that includes not only facial expression and body movement but also the position of the tail.

Communications get more complex as the social organizations of animals do, and next to ourselves the nonhuman primates have the most intricate systems of all. Far from depending only on vocalizations, nonhuman primates seem to rely

---

Speech: the oral expression of language, or "spoken language" (other expressions include gestural or written language).

FIGURE 13-1 Facial expression is one of the most important modes of nonverbal communication in both chimpanzees and people. The functions of such expressions in the two species are quite closely related.

heavily on combinations of gestures, facial expressions, and postures as well as scents and sounds (Figure 13–1). They apparently are able to lend many shades of meaning to this body language vocabulary. Often they use sounds as a means of calling attention to their other signals. On some important occasions, however, only sounds will do. On discovering something good to eat, a monkey or ape will let out a cry of pleasure that brings the rest of the troop running; sensing danger, it will give a shriek that causes its companions to seek shelter frantically.

This wordless communication system serves the nonhuman primates extremely well. As social animals living in troops, they use it to keep in touch with one another at all times. More important, it allows individuals to display their feelings and to recognize at a glance the intentions and moods of others, enabling them to react appropriately. Many of the signals express the established hierarchy of dominance and submission within the group (see Figure 13–2). A subordinate male chimpanzee, seeing signs of aggression directed at him by a male of superior rank, backs up to the other and presents his rump in a gesture of appeasement— unless he intends to challenge the other male. Different signals, vocal and visual, help individuals stay in contact when moving through the community territory.

FIGURE 13–2   A dominant male chimpanzee reassures a young male that is presenting his rump in appeasement. As a result, the younger male now feels able to turn and face his superior.

Still other signals promote mating behavior or foster good mother-infant relations. A mother chimpanzee has been observed to calm her disturbed youngster simply by touching its fingers lightly with hers (Figure 13–3). So complex and so delicate is this language of gesture in the chimpanzee that it cannot be said to be less evolved than our own. It serves to maintain an extremely complex social system.

Yet for all its complexity, and however well suited it may be to the chimpanzees' needs, such a communication system falls far short of human language. As far as is known, nonhuman primates in the wild are limited in the ways they can refer to specific things in their environment and cannot communicate thought through the complex phonetic codes called words that are used by humans. Nor do they seem able to refer easily to the past or future with the aid of their signals. For them, what is out of sight is usually out of mind. The signal system narrowly circumscribes what can be communicated, and vocalizations and facial expressions are not under voluntary control.

This is not to say that the nonhuman primates' vocal signals are entirely unspecific. Some apes indicate the desirability of the food they are eating by the intensity of their food calls. During normal feeding, chimpanzees emit food grunts, but for a favorite food they give the more excited food bark. They still cannot say "banana," of course, but they communicate something more than simply "food." Even more specialized is the danger-call system of the African vervet monkeys, which have three alarm calls for three kinds of predator and a fourth for baboons. The vervets use a chitter for snakes (Figure 13–4), a chirp for ground-dwelling carnivores, and a *r-raup* sound to warn of birds of prey. When tape recordings of their alarm calls are played back to them, a chirp is enough to send the vervets scrambling to the tips of branches, well out of reach of ground animals, whereas a *r-raup* launches them from the trees into the thickets below, where birds cannot get at them. As the young mature, they are able to make finer distinctions between the different alarm calls. A cry of "Watch out—eagle!" is beyond their capabilities, but it is also beyond their needs. They do not have to know whether

FIGURE 13–3 Among chimpanzees, as among humans, physical contact is a most important means of communication between individuals. Even a touch is reassuring. This photograph is of wild chimpanzees in Tanzania.

it is an eagle or a hawk diving on them; what matters is that they get the message that the danger is from above, so that they can flee in the right direction.

Young vervets sometimes make mistakes in giving alarm calls, and as they grow up they improve their performance. The calls can also be adapted and modified for different circumstances. This evidence suggests that the alarm calls are learned or are reinforced by learning rather than being simply innate.

In addition to vervets' predator-specific alarm calls, a few other species of nonhuman primates are also capable of conveying specific environmental information by using vocalizations. For example, rhesus macaques have five acoustically different scream vocalizations that they can give when threatened or attacked. These screams are essentially recruitment devices (cries for help), and primatologists Sarah and Harold Gouzoules and Peter Marler have found that the particular scream an animal gives depends on the identity of its opponent (kin or nonkin, dominant or subordinate) and the severity of the fight. Group mates are clearly able to "screen" the various calls for help, and their responses match the caller's level of danger.

Distinct alarm calls like those of vervet monkeys or foe-specific screams like rhesus monkeys' may be more widespread than we know. However, based on current knowledge the vocalizations which are most typical of the higher primates, such as grunts and barks, and which have been well studied in a number of

FIGURE 13–4 Vervets (*Cerco-pithecus aethiops*) are here photographed responding to the presence of a python. The appropriate snake alarm call caused the monkeys to run to the nearby acacia trees.

species, especially chimpanzees, are quite distinct and do not indicate a particular feature of the environment so much as an inner state of excitement.

Limbic and Nonlimbic Communication

In their function, as well as in their causation, the vocal and visual signals used by nonhuman primates can be divided into two kinds. The majority of these signals, probably most of the vocal signals, as we have seen, express inner emotional and physiological states and involuntarily accompany such states. They allow all members of the troop to monitor the emotional status of all other members. All signals of this sort are generated by a group of structures in the brain known collectively as the *limbic system* (the "emotional brain"). These signals come from below the level of conscious awareness, just as the human scream is generated. (We will take a closer look at the limbic system later in this chapter.)

In contrast to these signals, some gestures appear to communicate conscious will or intent. A chimpanzee holds out its hand as a gesture of submissive greeting or raises it in threat. A young baboon anxiously presents to a superior male, backing rump first toward him. A mother chimpanzee uses her hand to beckon to her infant or repel its approach. These conscious gestures, which are normal, vol-

Limbic system: the emotional brain; a group of structures in the brain important in regulating such behavior as eating, drinking, aggression, sexual activity and expressions of emotion. Proportionately smaller in humans than in other primates, it operates below the level of consciousness.

untary movements, have taken on a role in communication. Because of the intentions and wishes they symbolize, they fall into a category very different from the expressions of emotion we have considered above. They are generated not by the limbic system but by the higher centers of the brain, just as human language is. It is for this reason that chimpanzees are excellent gestural mimics and, as we shall see, can learn sign language.

Ronald Myers and his colleagues at the University of California have clearly demonstrated the dichotomy. In humans both the face and the voice are activated by two quite distinct brain mechanisms: the limbic system and the cortex. In the rhesus monkey Myers and his colleagues have shown that the vocal apparatus and facial musculature are activated by the limbic system alone and are poorly accessible to voluntary control by the motor cortex of the brain (labeled *motor output* in Figure 13–13).

Both kinds of communication are seen in our own behavior. We, too, have a repertory of wordless signals that universally express emotions: a person has only to smile to demonstrate friendly intentions; clenched fists and jaws, scowls, and frowns are unmistakable signs of anger or disappointment; and the laugh, the cry, and the scream are direct expressions of inner psychological and physiological states. Humans even have acquired an involuntary signal other primates do not have: the blush, over which most people have little or no control, but which sends a clear message about what is going on inside the brain. And when humans are most excited, they often show it by speechlessness. Such basic signals are in a different category from the many other body motions humans use, such as shaking and nodding the head, shrugging the shoulders, and clapping the hands; these are really abbreviated substitutes for spoken language and vary in meaning from one place to another. Nonverbal communication is still an essential component in modern human relationships (see Figure 13–1).

In this context the observations made of vervet monkeys by Robert Seyfarth and Dorothy Cheney are of the greatest interest. Alarm calls, which appear to benefit kin (kin selection) as well as the alarmist itself (as a result of reciprocal altruism) are made by many social species of birds and mammals. Among primates, vervets have received the most detailed study. It is clear that their calls, described above, refer to objects in the vervets' environment and are not merely expressions of emotion (no support for the "ouch-ouch" hypothesis). Thus they are described as *semantic* rather than *affective:* they are words, not vocalized emotions. The sounds are arbitrary and do not resemble in any way the objects to which they refer (no support for the "bow-wow" hypothesis). However, it must be added that there is certainly an affective component of emphasis, such as volume, length, or rate of delivery, just as there is in human language.

To students of language evolution the vervets are fascinating. The research suggests that vervets have evolved the ability to use vocalizations which are not generated by the limbic system but which are probably learned and therefore generated in the cortex. These symbols, as we may correctly call them, have many of the characteristics of human language and show us that the higher primates do have the capability of developing such symbols, which indicate how language may have first made its appearance in our own evolution. It remains to be seen whether the great apes also carry such intimations of linguistic ability.

Signals generated by the limbic system are less important to humans than they are to other animals, for they make up a smaller part of humans' total communication system. Much of the information necessary for social interaction among humans is conveyed vocally; a blind human can communicate satisfactorily. But deafness from birth probably has a greater impact on communication; because babies born deaf cannot hear and imitate spoken words, they can learn to speak only with great difficulty. Fortunately they can use sign language—a real language, although nonvocal.

Nature of Language

Spoken language provides a magnificently efficient and versatile means of communication. It is a complex system of chains of symbols to which meanings have been assigned by cultural convention. The number of meanings that can be so assigned is, in practice, infinite. Its coded series of sounds conveys conscious thought at least ten times faster than any other method of signaling can—faster than hand signs, moving pictures, or even other kinds of vocalizations. Through language humans can step outside themselves and give things and people names, reflect about others and themselves, and refer to the past and the future. Most important of all, language gives people the capacity to share their thoughts. As Sherwood Washburn and Shirley Strum write, "It is the communication of thought, rather than thought itself, that is unique to man, makes human cultures possible, that is the primary factor in separating man and beast." Discussion, complex bargaining, and democratic processes became a possibility for the first time.

Whenever spoken language evolved—and the last chapter suggested that this development probably postdated *Homo erectus*, despite that species' worldwide spread—it was the new and extraordinarily efficient means by which humans acquired and passed on from one generation to the next the flexible network of learned, rather than genetically inherited, behavior patterns and the knowledge that allowed them to alter their environment and adapt to new ones. Once language had evolved, culture had a symbolic form that changed its whole nature. From this point in human evolution, culture and its medium—language—were necessary for survival.

ABILITY TO SPEAK

Though it has long been clear that this watershed in evolution occurred largely because of the ability to use words to communicate symbolic meaning, it was not at all clear until recently why humans alone, and not their intelligent close relatives among the apes, are capable of speech. After all, apes have much of the vocal apparatus—lips, a tongue, and a larynx or voice box with vocal cords—that humans have.

Talking Apes?

An eighteenth-century French physician and philosopher, Julien Offroy de la Mettrie, imagined that apes were on about the same intellectual level as retarded humans and that all they needed to turn them into "perfect little gentlemen" was speech training. Not until early in the twentieth century, however, were any scientific attempts made to teach apes to talk. One couple worked with a chimpanzee called Viki, and only after six years of the most painstaking effort on their part and a great deal of frustration on hers did she manage to say, on cue, what sounded like "Mama," "Papa," "up," and "cup." It was clear that, although accomplished gestural mimics, chimpanzees cannot mimic vocally, as humans can.

A more recent experiment made by Beatrice and Robert Gardner produced a more startling result. A chimpanzee named Washoe learned by age 5 to understand more than 350 hand signals of the standard American Sign Language (ASL) of the deaf, and to use at least 150 of them correctly (see Figure 13–5). With these, she learned to name things and express her wants and needs by using those names. Another chimpanzee, Sarah, learned to communicate with her keepers by selecting from a number of plastic signs that carried particular meanings, which she placed on a magnetic board. A third chimpanzee, Lana, learned to communicate by pressing buttons on a computer keyboard. A gorilla, Koko, trained in ASL, by Penny Patterson of Stanford, has learned a vocabulary of over 350 hand signals and understands many more. Others are teaching the orangutan. Constant training by humans enables these apes to associate visual symbols not only with concrete objects, but also with such abstracts as adjectives, verbs, and even prepositions. With these symbols it is claimed that they can construct simple sentences, which they use to express their desires. It is said that they can also lie, abuse their trainers, and invent new expressions. Examples of the latter include "water bird"

FIGURE 13–5 One of the most impressive projects for teaching a chimpanzee sign language was run by Columbia University psychologist Herbert Terrace. In this photograph his subject, Nim Chimpsky, is signing "give" to his teacher and companion, Laura Petitto. Nim gained a firm command of about 125 signs, understood many more, and produced thousands of combinations of two or more signs.

for swan (Washoe) and "white tiger" for zebra and "eye hat" for mask (Koko). Koko has also combined signs to make entirely new words.

But of all the ape subjects used thus far in language studies, perhaps the most accomplished is Kanzi, a male bonobo under observation at Georgia State University. Psychobiologist Sue Savage-Rumbaugh has worked with Kanzi since his infancy. Kanzi showed early an outstanding—and spontaneous—ability to master the meaning of lexigrams (word symbols or icons) on a computer keyboard, and after learning a number of lexigrams, he began to combine them to produce the occasional multiword message (such as "Matata group room tickle," in which he requested that his mother, Matata, be allowed to join in a tickling session in the group room). But even more impressive, as a youngster Kanzi began to comprehend a certain amount of spoken English, and by age 5 he was able to respond correctly to Savage-Rumbaugh's spoken requests and directives (Kanzi has even shown the ability to respond appropriately to some novel sentences *the first time he heard them*). Furthermore, it appears that as part of his spontaneous development of speech comprehension, Kanzi may have picked up a bit of English *syntax*. According to Sue Savage-Rumbaugh, Kanzi's lexigram-encoded messages to his human companions often have "a primitive English word order."

It is difficult to know precisely what to make of the linguistic feats of Kanzi and the other "ape language" subjects. Clearly these apes have a certain capacity for symbol comprehension and use, but their best efforts still do not exceed those of a 2- to 3-year-old human child. These studies show that, with exposure to humans (and usually after considerable instruction), apes can learn symbols and use a symbolic means of communication, but in all cases they produce messages only by gesture or icon manipulation, and not by means of their vocal apparatus. Furthermore, their messages show only a very rudimentary syntactic structure (at best) and no development of phrases or other linguistic subunits. Nonetheless, Kanzi, Koko, Lana, Washoe, and the others have certainly narrowed the "language gap" between apes and humans. As Kathleen Gibson of the University of Texas and other researchers have argued, these results strongly suggest that a *quantitative* rather than *qualitative* gap in communication capacities separates humans from their ape relations. It remains true, however, that "ape language" certainly does not amount to human language in the most complete sense.

Syntax: the rules of structure in language.

The Pharynx

Viki's frustration and Washoe's success have led to a clearer understanding of what is involved in human speech. Spoken language requires equipment, both physical and mental, that apes and monkeys simply do not have (see Figure 13–6). The adult human tongue, for example, is thicker than that of monkeys and apes, and unlike theirs, it bends in a sharp angle into the throat. In addition, the human larynx, with its vocal cords, lies farther down the throat than the ape larynx. The part of the throat above the larynx, the pharynx, is proportionately much longer in humans than in any other primates.

The pharynx serves as a combined opening for the windpipe (trachea), which goes to the lungs, and the gullet (esophagus), which leads to the stomach. The anchor for the base of the tongue, it also plays a fundamental part in producing speech, and this is where the longer human pharynx becomes important. It is the pharynx that modifies the sounds made by the vocal cords and gives them the

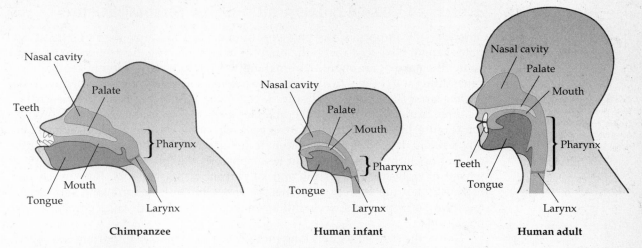

Chimpanzee   **Human infant**   **Human adult**

FIGURE 13–6 Insights into the speaking ability of early hominids have come from comparisons of the vocal apparatus of modern human adults and babies with that of a chimpanzee. To form words, sounds must be modulated by the pharynx, which lies above the larynx. The human newborn baby resembles the chimpanzee with its high larynx and short pharynx. By the age of 3, the child's larynx has descended from the level of the fourth cervical vertebra to that of the seventh, and the long human pharynx is complete.

varying tones that language requires. To provide this control, the muscles of the pharynx walls and the base of the tongue move continuously during speech, constantly and precisely varying the dimensions of the pharynx; the greatest width of the pharynx is at least ten times its narrowest. These dimensional changes produce much the same effect on sounds that an organ achieves with its dozens of pipes of different lengths and diameters, each making a particular tone. The pharynx is extremely important to speech; it is quite possible to speak intelligibly without the larynx or the tip of the tongue as long as the pharynx and the base of the tongue are intact.

Monkeys and apes, lacking the human vocal equipment, vary the shape of only their mouths when they vocalize; there is practically no movement of the pharynx, the musculature of which is rudimentary. The oral cavity of the mouth is large, and the tongue is incapable of forming the consonants of speech. They can produce only a limited number of distinct sounds—10 to 15 in most cases—and because of limitations of the brain's cortex, they cannot combine them at will to form words.

The same limitation restricts the vocalization of human babies, who at birth are unable to make the vowel sounds typical of human speech. For at least six weeks a baby's tongue remains immobile during its cries. It rests almost entirely within the mouth, as in nonhuman primates, and the larynx sits high in the throat. This arrangement permits babies as well as all other primates to swallow and breathe at the same time without danger of choking. By the time they reach the babbling stage, at around 3 months, the base of the tongue and the larynx have begun to descend into the throat, enlarging the pharyngeal region. Not until this development is complete during the third year are humans physically equipped to make all of the speech sounds that distinguish them from their simian relatives.

Centers of Vocal Communication: The Cerebral Cortex

Cerebral cortex: gray, wrinkled, outer layer of the brain; largely responsible for memory and, in humans, reasoned behavior and abstract thought. (Also referred to as the *neocortex*.)

Other equally important reasons why humans can talk and the nonhuman primates cannot have to do with the brain. When people use their voices to communicate, they are doing more than making noise. They are codifying thought and transmitting it to others in a string of connected sounds. The coding begins in the *cerebral cortex*, the convoluted outer layer of the brain. The cortex (or neocortex) has three primary areas and several lesser areas of importance in speech production (Figure 13–7). All primary areas typically occur on one cerebral hemisphere only, usually described as the dominant hemisphere, because speech is so important in human life. The dominant hemisphere is the left hemisphere in about 95 percent of right-handed people and 70 percent of left-handers. But speech production is not an entirely asymmetrical matter. The nondominant hemisphere does play some part in speech, influencing such things as rhythm, emphasis, and intonation.

One of the cortical regions long thought to be of primary importance in speech production is called *Broca's area* and is located in the inferior frontal lobe of the dominant hemisphere. Traditionally, Broca's area has been understood as the region that sends codes for the succession of phonemes (speech sounds) to an adjacent part of the brain (the motor cortex, just anterior to the central sulcus; Figure 13–7) that controls the muscles of the face, jaw, tongue, pharynx, and larynx; thus it helps set the speech apparatus in operation. Damage *in the vicinity* of Broca's area has been linked to a form of aphasia (loss or impairment of speech) in which articulation is slow and labored. While much of this traditional view may still be correct, very recent work has raised questions about precisely how Broca's area is involved in speech. In this work, researchers using PET (positron emission tomography) technology have measured the patterns of cranial blood flow in normal, conscious humans involved in language and speech tasks and other activities. The PET results have convinced some workers that much of Broca's area is

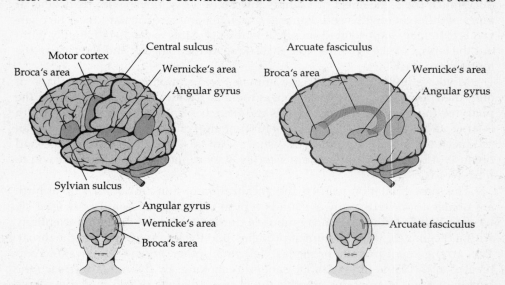

FIGURE 13–7   Areas of the brain cortex (surface layer) involved in speech production are shown in the left drawing. The drawing at the right shows the arcuate fasciculus, which links Wernicke's to Broca's areas deep within the brain. Wernicke's area and the angular gyrus are also involved in the decoding of speech.

involved either with the hierarchical organization of manual object combination or with higher-level coordination of oral movements and that only part of the area is involved specifically in speech. This idea is supported by evidence that lesions limited strictly to Broca's area frequently fail to produce full-blown Broca's aphasia. The PET studies have found other areas more directly related to speech just anterior to Broca's area or deep within the Sylvian sulcus (Figure 13–7; the latter areas do not show on the surface of the cerebral cortex). Based on the PET results, some researchers are beginning to distrust evidence of an enlarged Broca's area on fossil endocasts as a clear indicator of speech.

The second primary region is *Wernicke's area,* located farther back in the dominant hemisphere, in the temporal lobe; it is vital to the process of comprehension. Damage to Wernicke's area usually produces another form of aphasia: speech that is fluent but meaningless. A bundle of nerve fibers (the arcuate fasciculus), transmits signals from Wernicke's area to Broca's, making possible the vocal repetition of a heard and memorized word.

The third primary region, adjacent to Wernicke's area, is the *angular gyrus.* It occupies a key position at the juncture of the portions of the cerebral cortex connected with vision, hearing, and touch—the parts of the brain that receive detailed information from the world outside the body. Linked to these sensory receivers by bundles of nerve fibers, the angular gyrus operates as a kind of connecting station, permitting one type of incoming signal to be associated with others. For example, the angular gyrus makes it possible for the brain to link a visual stimulus produced by the sight of a cup with the auditory stimulus produced by a voice saying "cup" and with the tactile stimulus produced when the hand picks up the cup. The importance of these associations is clear when we think of the way children learn the words for things: when children ask, "what's that?" and are told by their parents, they match the image of the seen object with the sound of the spoken word and thus absorb the name for the object, automatically filing the sound for that association in their memory bank. This process of association and memorization is the first and most basic step in the acquisition of language.

Angular gyrus: part of the human cerebral cortex that allows information received from different senses to be associated.

It is important to note, however, that the human brain is an elaboration on an older pattern found in many nonhuman primates. Anthropologist Dean Falk of the State University of New York at Albany has conducted numerous studies of the comparative anatomy of anthropoid brains, and she has this to say: "There are frontal lobe and temporal/parietal regions in the brains of monkeys and apes that appear to be in (somewhat) similar positions and to have similar arrangements of cells as Broca's and Wernicke's areas do in [modern] human brains. There is also some evidence that the left hemisphere differentially processes socially meaningful vocalizations in nonhuman higher primates. It therefore appears that . . . human language areas are an elaboration on the basic primate pattern" (a development that Falk limits to the genus *Homo*). Kathleen Gibson is in basic agreement with Falk's elaboration theory and argues that human language is the result of quantitative increases in brain size and information-processing capacities, not the appearance of entirely new cortical areas.

Limbic System

And so the brains of monkeys and apes are broadly similar to humans' brains but are significantly less developed in some important areas. An ape's angular gyrus is small, and there is limited association between information signals coming from

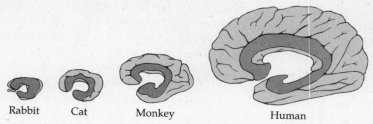

Rabbit   Cat   Monkey   Human

FIGURE 13–8 These drawings of the brain in partial section show the relative size of the limbic regions in different species (dark shading, approximately to scale). The limbic system is the "emotional brain" in all mammals, including humans. It is connected with the expression and decoding of much of the nonverbal communication that plays such a big part in the social life of mammals. Though still large and important in humans, it is no longer the largest component of the brain, as it is in other mammals. The limbic system lies beneath the neocortex, which is distinctive of mammals and reaches its greatest development among primates.

different senses. Apparently, incoming signals are routed mainly to another part of the brain altogether: the limbic system (see Figure 13–8). All mammals, including humans, have this evolutionarily ancient region lying near the core of the brain, a kind of netherworld of neurological activity. Among other things, it activates the physical responses that go with hunger, fear, rage, and sexual activity, and it triggers the feelings that accompany these responses (Figure 13–9). If a monkey sees a predator, the visual signal feeds into the limbic system and produces a physical reaction—the sounding of the danger call with its accompanying facial expression, perhaps—and also makes the animal feel fear. Similarly, sexual signals sent out by a female chimpanzee go to the limbic system of a male, causing him to feel sexually stimulated and prompting a sexual response. Humans are no different.

In other words, information channeled to the limbic system from the outside produces an instantaneous, unthinking, adaptive response. As anthropologist Jane Lancaster writes, the limbic system "makes the animal want to do what it has to do to survive and reproduce."

As we have seen, among the responses that are directed by the limbic system are facial expressions and vocal signals—cries of fear or pleasure, for example—that are quite distinct from language. That communication through signals like these is controlled by this part of the brain can be demonstrated by laboratory experiment. When electrodes are planted in the limbic system and related structures of a monkey, and its brain is stimulated electrically, the animal responds with its repertory of cries, even though the situations that normally stimulate those sounds (aggressive behavior by a dominant animal, food, enemies) are not present. Furthermore, other monkeys of the same species in the laboratory react to these sounds (by cringing, searching for food, taking an alert stance) just as though they were bona fide signals. Similar experiments have been performed on human subjects during brain surgery, and they react in a similar way. When certain parts of the human limbic system are stimulated, the patient responds with sounds.

The sounds produced through the limbic system in both ape and human are not the sounds of speech. In apes, both vocal and facial expressions are under limbic, not voluntary, control. They reflect emotion, not volition. This suggests that

FIGURE 13-9   Chimpanzees have a complex repertoire of facial expressions, as varied as our own. Most facial expressions are components of the multimodal communication system generated by the limbic system.

primate vocalization did not evolve into spoken language, which is clearly a volitional act. Instead, language is an entirely novel development in our evolution. For that distinctive emblem of humanness it was necessary for other parts of the brain, specifically the angular gyrus and Wernicke's and Broca's areas of the cortex, to develop fully. It was through this development and the evolution of the speech apparatus that emerging humans began to speak and left the inarticulate apes far behind.

In the cortex evolved the means of producing complex vocal sounds that could be used to communicate intent, will, and desire, as could the gestures discussed earlier used by nonhuman primates. Spoken language is a learned symbolic communicatory system that is cortical in origin. It can be used to refer to all kinds of objects, processes, and concepts, and indeed it is practically unlimited in its value to human society. It was probably the most important development in human evolution, because it made possible our extraordinary recent cultural adaptations.

EVOLUTION OF SPEECH

It is obviously impossible to pinpoint when hominids began to use language: the development of speech and other human characteristics was infinitely gradual.

The process may have begun when they started making and using tools. If early hominids at first depended on gestures to communicate, such hand signals would no doubt have eventually become inadequate; the hominids might literally have had their hands full, carrying tools or food. Thus the ability to use sounds voluntarily to attract attention and to make meaning clear would have proved a great advantage.

But for the process of naming things to start, the vocal apparatus had to be modified, and the brain had to evolve. This development must have taken hundreds of thousands of years. Some small mutations may have enabled *Australopithecus* to make a few voluntary sounds, providing an edge in the competition for survival. The ability to signal one another through a more extensive repertoire of phonemes would have been a definite advantage to the australopithecines' descendants. And then, as the number of phonemes grew, brain development could have permitted more precise differentiation between them and new combinations of them, so that primitive words may have taken shape. All the while, the brain and the vocal apparatus would have been involved in a feedback relationship with each other, changes in one fostering development of the other: the success of the cortex in forming a rudimentary sound code would have affected the vocal apparatus, and this, in turn, would have helped enlarge the speech centers of the brain, and so on, until the rudiments of language appeared. Then hominids were ready to begin combining a few separate sounds, or words, representing specific elements of terrain, the hunt, the family, and seasonal changes, into simple combinations that conveyed a great deal of information.

Phonation: Lieberman and Crelin

What this first speech sounded like depended on how far the dual development of vocal apparatus and cortical brain equipment had progressed. Linguist Philip Lieberman's analysis of the character of modern speech emphasizes the importance of the human vocal equipment. He points out that the pharynx is essential for producing the vowel sounds *a* ("ah"), *i* ("ee"), and *u* ("oo"), which are crucial to all modern languages, from English to Kirghiz. Virtually all meaningful segments of human speech contain one or more of these sounds. Combining these vowel sounds with a wide assortment of consonants, the human vocal apparatus not only can produce an infinite number of variations but also, and more important, can connect them with great rapidity in the coded series of sounds that is spoken language.

This involves the putting together of separate phonetic segments into a sound that can be understood as one word. A person saying *bat*, for instance, does not articulate the fragments of sound represented by the letters *b, a,* and *t* but combines these elements into one syllable. This ability to combine sounds gives the voice the ability to put together and transmit more than 30 phonetic segments a second.

The key to human phonation lies in the position of the larynx. As we have seen, during modern human growth the pharynx lengthens and the larynx descends in the neck, so that by the age of 3 the low larynx separates humans from all other primates. Edmund S. Crelin and Jeffrey Laitman have shown that this movement is associated with the appearance of flexion in the base of the skull (the basicranium). A skull with a flat base is associated with a high larynx, and this is found in all primates and in newborn babies. In contrast, a flexed cranial base is found in all modern humans after the early years of life and is associated with a low larynx. Researchers have examined the cranial base of various hominid fossils and report that the angle in *Australopithecus* was the same as that of extant apes. Similarly, although there is some variation, the cranial base in *Homo erectus* is essentially unflexed. Thus the crucial restructuring of the upper respiratory tract may not have begun until after *H. erectus*. Full basicranial flexion similar to that seen in modern humans is first found among certain early members of the species *H. sapiens* some 300,000 to 400,000 years ago.

Articulation: Linda Duchin

But basicranial flexion is not the end of the story, as other studies have shown. The pharyngeal cavity and the larynx together generate the vowel sounds, but it is the tongue and lips that produce articulation of these sounds by interspersing the vowels with consonants. Research by Linda Duchin of the University of Washington, Seattle, has shown how very different the tongue musculature and oral cavity of the chimpanzee are from those of humans. The production of consonants has not been reported in chimpanzee vocalizations, evidently because the palate and the mandible create a much longer oral cavity than in humans, and the muscles that support and move the tongue (its extrinsic muscles) lie in slightly different places and are set at different angles from those of humans. The *hyoid* bone, to which some of these muscles are attached, lies in a different position in apes: higher and farther back than in humans. Altogether, these differences mean that control of the tongue in apes is less efficient than in humans. Furthermore, because of the larger oral cavity in apes, the tongue cannot reach all the necessary contact points needed to create consonants during phonation. In humans the position of the anchorage of the tongue muscles and the smaller oral cavity mean that the tongue can move very rapidly from point to point in the mouth to create the fast-changing consonants of speech. Notice the extraordinary speed and accuracy of your tongue movements during speech. No wonder slow and slurred speech is one of the first signs of inebriation!

Hyoid: a bone of the throat positioned just above the larynx and just below the mandible. The hyoid provides attachment for one of the muscles of the tongue and for certain muscles of the front of the neck.

Measurements of the oral cavities of Neandertal and *Homo erectus* fossil skulls fall close to or into the human range and distinguish them clearly from the chimpanzee. This would appear to imply that these fossil hominids may have had some potential for articulate speech. (The Neandertals are discussed in the next chapter.)

Speech is therefore a product of both phonation (made possible by a low larynx and an adjustable pharynx) and articulation (made possible by an efficiently controlled tongue in a small oral cavity). Phonation and articulation are unique to humans and arose as a result of changes in the balance of the head on the vertebral column and the reduction of the jaws.

While this research is by no means conclusive, it does give us some useful insight into the evolution of the speech apparatus and thus into the evolution of speech.

Krantz: The Brain of *Homo erectus*

Anthropologist Grover Krantz confronted a problem that has puzzled anthropologists for a long time: Why did the quality of *Homo erectus*'s stone tools remain static for so long? Over many thousands of years, no matter where found, they show little sign of improvement. Why did they not become sophisticated more quickly? Krantz poses an ingenious explanation that may shed light on the acquisition of language by the first humans. Assuming that *Homo erectus* produced some sort of spoken language, Krantz suggests that among these early people the brain was not well enough developed to allow them to begin to speak as early in their lives as a child does today. Because *Homo erectus* people were short-lived, they therefore had a shorter period in which to use language in order to acquire and augment the skills necessary for toolmaking.

Although this argument may have value, it is important to realize that brain size alone does not make speech possible. The complexity of the brain structure and, above all, the brain's internal organization are the primary factors in the evolution of language. At the same time, a great deal of learning, including toolmaking, can occur without language skills.

The Importance of Rudimentary Speech

While all of these various considerations are enlightening, they still fail to tell us precisely when and in which hominid species language first evolved. Perhaps we will never have conclusive answers to those questions. Nonetheless, as we wrestle with these issues, it is important to keep in mind that spoken language need not have been fully developed in order to be useful to ancestral hominids. Even rudimentary speech would have allowed *Homo erectus* people, for example, to communicate a great deal about themselves and the world around them. It is necessary only to listen to very young children to see how effective language can be, even in its simplest form. Between the ages of 18 and 24 months, only half a year or so after children first speak, they begin to use two-word sentences. The sentences are neither copies of grown-up speech nor reductions of it, but the children's own inventions, conforming to what would seem to be native, universal rules of grammar. They are made up of so-called "open words," words that can be said by themselves and still mean something (such as the nouns *blanket, milk,* and *baby*), and "pivot words," often prepositions, adjectives, or verbs (such as *on* and *hot*). At this age, children put words together to describe the world or to get people to act ("pajama on"), but they are not used to express emotion.

Only when the children are 3 or 4 do they begin to put feelings into words. Before then they rely, as nonhuman primates must, on the workings of the limbic system to call attention to their needs. Rather than say, "I'm angry," or "I'm afraid," they demonstrate physically how angry or afraid they are. They find temper tantrums, whimpering, or crying a much easier way to communicate; that is, they find emotions easier to express than to explain. As any parent knows, children have little difficulty in making themselves understood. Perhaps *Homo erectus,* speaking the simplest of sentences reinforced by gestures and hand signals, communicated just as well with some early version of human speech.

Whatever it sounded like, and at whatever age they began to use it, once our ancestors developed language it became a tool used in its own right—a tool to drive like a wedge into the environment, hurrying the split from nature that marked their development and foreshadowed ours. For the first time in human history, cultural evolution, because of speech, began to outpace biological evolution, as instinct and emotion were counterbalanced by symbol and custom.

THE BRAIN

Humans Among Mammals

For many researchers the most striking evidence of the evolution of language is the increase in size of the hominid brain. Evidence of this increase is the expanding cranial capacity that we see in successive hominid fossil skulls. As we saw in Chapter 8, the cranial capacity trebled during the past 3 million years, certainly a very rapid rate of evolution. But to see this figure in perspective, we need to relate it to body size, for a simple increase in body size itself (accompanied by an appropriate increase in brain size) can occur rapidly in evolution and is not an unusual occurrence. To relate brain size to body size, we need to calculate how large a brain a typical ape would have if it were to have a body the same size as ours. The answer reveals that the present human brain is 3.1 times larger than we would expect in a primate of our build. It appears, then, that our brain's trebling in size occurred despite only a moderate increase in our body size. This is perhaps the most significant anatomical fact about the species *Homo sapiens*.

This characteristic is perhaps even more striking when we remember that monkeys and apes have the biggest brains in relation to body weight of any land animal. California psychiatrist Harry Jerison has introduced the *encephalization quotient* (EQ) to compare relative brain sizes. The EQ is calculated by relating the brain size of each species to the size expected for an average mammal of the same body weight. By definition, an average mammal has an EQ of 1.0. If the relative brain size is smaller than average, then the EQ has a value of less than 1.0; if the relative brain size is larger than average, then the EQ ranges above 1.0. Figure 13–10 very briefly summarizes Jerison's results. Insectivores and rodents are in

Encephalization quotient: in mammals, a number expressing observed brain size in a particular species relative to expected brain size calculated from body weight.

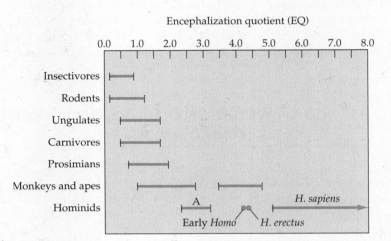

FIGURE 13–10   The encephalization quotient (EQ) is shown here for several groups of mammals including a number of hominids. For most groups, a range of EQ values is shown by a horizontal line; for two hominid species, small sample sizes allow only EQ means (shown by dots). The upper range of values for monkeys and apes is generated by certain small and distinctive New World monkeys. Hominid types include the australopithecines (A), early *Homo*, *Homo erectus*, and *Homo sapiens*. The EQ range for modern humans extends to a high value of about 10.6. Average EQ for modern people is about 7.2. (Data from H. J. Jerison, *Evolution of the Brain and Intelligence*, Academic Press, 1973.)

one group, with EQs generally below 1.0. Ungulates (hoofed mammals), carnivores, and prosimians make a second group, with EQs slightly over 1.0. Monkeys and apes are quite distinct from these other groups, with EQs ranging between 1.0 and 5.0. Modern humans have an average EQ of about 7.2. Here again we see that humans are absolutely distinctive in the size of their brains.

If we relate brain weight to body weight and generate a simple ratio, we get further remarkable results (Table 13–1). Here, surprisingly, humans do not fall at the top of the list; the highest positions are occupied by two small New World monkeys. It was in fact these monkeys that occupied the top section of the monkey and ape histogram in Figure 13–10. This anomalous state of affairs can be understood as a product of a higher primate with relatively small body size, for another fact of brain development is that small animals in any particular order have relatively larger brains than large species. For the same reason, large animals (within any particular order) have relatively smaller brains. Thus, as Table 13–1 shows, the elephant and the whale, which have the largest brains of any animals (of about 4,000 cc and 6,000 cc, respectively), have relatively small brains within their respective orders. The most surprising figure in Table 13–1 is that for the porpoise. Although good data on the brain and body sizes of porpoises are very limited, it does appear that this group of marine animals has exceptionally large brains, and this ratio is particularly striking in the smaller species. The dolphin brain is famed not only for its size but for the extent of its convolutions, which implies a relatively immense neocortex. The explanation for this remarkable-looking brain is still one of the great mysteries of modern biology.

If primate brains are relatively large, we may then ask if the proportions of the different parts separate them from those of other orders of mammals. We have seen (Figure 13–8) that the development of the neocortex is distinctive in mammals and especially in primates, a characteristic that becomes clear in dissection and measurement. The jackal, a large-brained carnivore, has a brain of about 2 oz (64 g), the same size as that of the macaque monkey. In the jackal the cerebral hemispheres form 60 percent of the brain, but in the monkey they constitute 78 percent of the brain.

Within the order Primates, however, the story is different. It has been claimed that the human brain is preeminent in the development of the neocortex, espe-

Table 13–1 RATIO OF WEIGHT OF BRAIN TO WEIGHT OF BODY IN CERTAIN MAMMALS

Mammals	Brain-Body Ratio
New World, squirrel monkey	1:12
New World, tamarin, a marmoset	1:19
Porpoise (dolphin)	1:38
Higher primates	
Humankind	1:45
Australopithecus afarensis (estimated)	1:100
Old World monkey (*Macaca*)	1:170
Gorilla	1:200
Elephant	1:600
Sperm whale	1:10,000

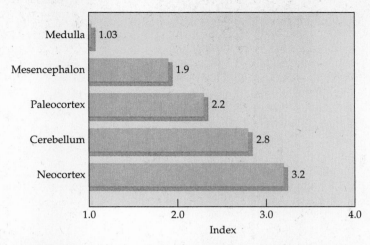

FIGURE 13–11 Indices comparing the size of parts of the human brain with values predicted for a primate of the same body weight. The index is the actual value of the weight of the part in humans divided by the predicted value. Notice that not only the neocortex but other parts, particularly the cerebellum, show considerable development. Certain of the parts are labeled in Figure 13–13.

cially the prefrontal and association areas. According to British psychologist Richard Passingham, however, the evidence for these claims is still flimsy, and they cannot be substantiated at present. He demonstrates convincingly, though, that in the human brain the relative proportions of the main subdivisions of the brain, including the neocortex, do indeed differ from those which might be expected in monkeys and apes of similar body weight (Figure 13–11). He points out, however, that this difference is in fact predictable from higher primate data, and that if the brain proportions are related to brain size and not body size, they can be predicted in a brain of human size (Figure 13–12). We have known for some time that the functional areas of the brains of apes and humans are comparable (Figure 13–13); now we can conclude from evidence currently available that the human brain is indeed a standard higher primate brain that has simply been increased in size by a factor of 3.1. No new structures appear to have been introduced at this gross level of measurement.

When we come to consider the more detailed structure of the neocortex, of the neurons, and of their interconnecting pathways, we may be forgiven for expecting something distinctively human. Ralph Holloway of Columbia University summarizes the evidence that human brains have larger and more complex neurons (individual brain cells) and many more interconnections among them than other primate brains. He shows, too, that the brain cells are less densely packed than in other primates. It appears, however, that one rule governs the density of brain cells in all mammals, varying in size from elephant to mouse. The human brain, surprisingly, obeys that rule. In fact, the human brain has the same number of neurons in a radial section of the cortex as any other mammal, for although the cells are less dense, the cortex is thicker. Thus, in both its microscopic and macroscopic structure, the human brain is a standard, though large, primate brain.

We can therefore conclude that the unique human potential has been made possible by our large brain. Expansion of a standard primate brain has provided us with behavioral possibilities undreamed of in other, even closely related,

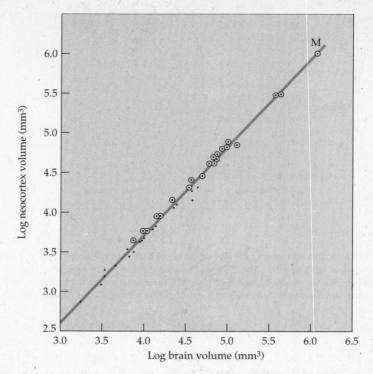

FIGURE 13–12   When we plot the volume of the neocortex (in cubic millimeters) as a function of the volume of the brain, we find that the relationship is the same throughout the primates. The slope of the line is steeper than 45 degrees because the neocortex is relatively larger in larger brains by a constant proportion: dot, prosimians; circled dot, monkeys and apes; M, humans.

species. This brain, absolutely as well as relatively large, with its absolutely large number of neurons (about 10^{10}) and its unbelievably large number of dendritic interconnections (about 10^{12}), gives us the human potential for making tools, talking, planning, dreaming of the future, and creating an entirely new environment for ourselves. The primate laws of relative brain growth have been followed in all respects, both macroscopically and microscopically, except in one factor: the brain-body ratio. That factor 3.1 has lifted humans far above their animal cousins into a new order of organic life.

The size of the brain, therefore, crudely measured in cubic centimeters, tells us something very profound about human nature. Our brain is not so much different from other brains as it is bigger. We are not a unique evolutionary experiment, but a superprimate. Quantitative changes in the evolving hominid brain, however, produced extraordinary qualitative changes in behavior.

Brains, Minds, and Radiators

Three supremely important aspects of that qualitative change may be listed. First, as described in this chapter, humans' communication skills were greatly enhanced by brain enlargement (culminating in the evolution of language). In turn, enhanced communication skills presumably carried enormous survival and reproductive benefits for our hominid ancestors. Second, brain enlargement undoubtedly contributed to the evolution of a theory of mind among hominids.

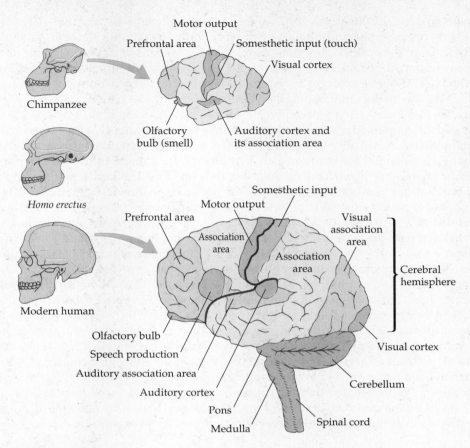

FIGURE 13–13   Comparison of ape and human brains shows that the human brain is not only bigger but more deeply folded. The form of the brain of *Homo erectus* can be guessed at only by the shape and size of the endocranial cast.

According to psychologists David Premack and G. Woodruff, having a theory of mind involves being able to attribute beliefs, knowledge, and emotions to oneself and to others. In species that possess a theory of mind, individuals benefit by using these attributed mental states to manipulate others (for example, by sharing or denying information or through deception). Although more evidence is needed, it appears that by the time apes reach adolescence, they *may* possess something like a theory of mind, judging from examples of deception and from the fact that they seem to have some self-awareness. Monkeys, on the other hand, apparently lack such a theory completely (see Chapter 4). Precisely when during hominid evolution a theory of mind developed is unclear, but some psychologists, such as the Russian scientist L. Vygotskii, believe that modern people *learn* a theory of mind through the medium of language. And finally, brain enlargement certainly brought enhanced abilities for information processing. Such an increase in "general intelligence" would presumably have been strongly favored by natural selection.

Communication, mind, and general intelligence—all of these things should have been prime movers of brain evolution within the human family, but it may have been a fairly simple development in the brain's cooling system that made them possible. Paleoneurologist Dean Falk has developed what she calls the radiator theory of brain evolution. According to Falk, in response to their evolving bipedalism, the australopithecines developed new means of draining blood from their (elevated) braincases. *Paranthropus* (and, in Falk's opinion, the Hadar hominids as well) evolved a system in which an enlarged occipital-marginal (O/M) sinus delivered blood to the vertebral plexus at the base of the skull (Figure 13–14). This system worked well enough as long as the brain was not overheated and remained relatively small, and thus Falk concludes that the robust australopithecines probably lived mainly in forests rather than on the savanna, and that their potential for brain growth was limited. In contrast to the robust (plus Hadar) hominids, however, Falk describes the gracile australopithecines and their *Homo* descendants as evolving a "radiator" system that allowed both savanna living *and* continued expansion of the brain. The graciles' radiators worked like this. Instead of an enlarged O/M sinus, they evolved a two-way system of emissary veins that pass through the bones of the skull via small openings called foramina (Figure 13–14). The emissary veins were capable of draining blood *from* the braincase to the vertebral plexus when the individual was at or below normal body temperature, and of pumping blood *into* the braincase when the individual was overheated. This two-way system allowed evaporation-cooled blood from the skin to be shunted to overheated brains in hominids who were working up a sweat during their gathering and scavenging (and later, hunting) on the tropical savanna. And the radiator system was wonderfully modifiable. Over time, the gracile australopithecine-*Homo* lineage evolved more and more emissary veins that allowed better and better temperature regulation. To quote Falk; "[The cranial radiator system] released thermal constraints that had previously kept brain size in check." Hominids' cranial radiators thus allowed them to combine diurnal exploitation of the tropical savanna with continued brain expansion.

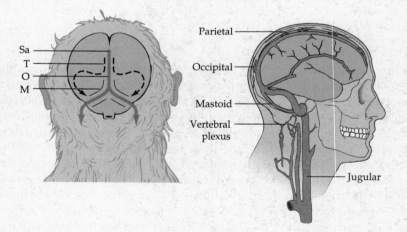

FIGURE 13–14   Blood flow from the cranium of a robust australopithecine is shown at left (rear view of skull). In addition to exiting the skull via the superior sagittal sinus (Sa), blood drained out through the enlarged occipital sinus (O) and marginal sinus (M). The transverse sinus (T) was of relatively little importance in these hominids. In contrast, in the gracile australopithecine/*Homo* lineage, a radiator network of emissary veins evolved for cranial drainage and brain cooling. The side view of a modern human skull at right shows the parietal, occipital, and mastoid emissary veins and their drainage target, the vertebral plexus.

Interestingly, according to the EQ data presented in Figure 13–10, brain expansion within the gracile australopithecine-*Homo* line was not smoothly continuous. Rather, after early *Homo*'s significant increase in relative brain size over that of the australopithecines, brain expansion seems to have entered a prolonged period of stasis. The Jerison EQ value for early *Homo* is 4.3; that for *Homo erectus* is about the same at 4.4. Thus it appears that *Homo erectus*'s increase in brain size was matched by a proportionate enlargement in body size, and that *Homo erectus* was no brainier, *relatively speaking*, than early *Homo* (*H. habilis* and *H. rudolfensis* considered collectively). The EQ stasis came to an end in *Homo sapiens* when a strong enlargement of the brain went unmatched by increased body size. This trend carried humans to the modern average EQ value of 7.2.

SUMMARY

Language is perhaps the most remarkable and distinctive characteristic of humans. In its spoken form, it combines a variety of features: the arbitrary form of speech units (sounds, words) with regard to their referents, the combination of units following elaborate rules of syntax, the ability to refer to things not physically present and to the past and future, and the openness of the system to the invention of new units. *In their entirety* these features differentiate us quite cleanly from the rest of the animal world, even though apes have been shown to possess rudimentary language capacities. Combined with culture, spoken language must have provided a strong stimulus to human evolution and contributed significantly to our modern way of life. It is this central importance of language that makes our inability to pinpoint its evolutionary beginnings so extremely frustrating. But at present those beginnings are still shrouded in mystery.

The evolution of language and speech apparently involved several interconnected anatomical developments. First, there was an increase in overall brain size. This would have provided enlarged cortical areas for sensory input, association, memory, coding, and motor output. Second, there was the elaboration of the "language-speech areas" in the hominid cerebral cortex. Broca's area, Wernicke's area, and the angular gyrus are the three main cortical regions that have been implicated in language and speech production. Third, before modern speech was possible, the proportions of the throat and the oral cavity had to change, and certain of these modifications—in particular, the lengthening of the pharynx—were related to flexure of the cranial base. And finally, fine control of breathing was achieved through increased innervation of the intercostal muscles of the rib cage.

Using these anatomical points, we can evaluate the likelihood of language and speech among the hominid species described thus far. First, beginning with the oldest members of the human family, the australopithecines appear to be very poor candidates for language and speech. Their brains were small (ape-sized) and showed little if any humanlike development of the language-speech areas. Furthermore, although the robust forms (*Paranthropus*) showed some flexure of the cranial base—and thus presumably some lengthening of the pharynx—this feature was absent in the gracile forms (*Australopithecus*). Second, early *Homo* appears to be a better candidate for language and speech, but the evidence is equivocal. Arguing against language and speech is evidence that *Homo habilis* and *Homo rudolfensis* possessed brains that were still only about one-half modern size and, in addition, apparently lacked cranial base flexure. Furthermore, the stone tools produced by early *Homo* are quite simple, and their reconstructed lifestyle seems to have been very different from that of modern humans. On the other hand, some researchers, such as South Africa's Phillip Tobias, believe that early *Homo* had significantly enlarged Broca's and Wernicke's areas, and therefore that spoken language might have been possible. On balance, it appears reasonable to deny language and speech to early *Homo* until more positive indicators are forthcoming.

With regard to *Homo erectus,* the question of language and speech is particularly difficult since they were much more like us—physically and behaviorally—than were any of the earlier hominids. But despite their large brains (74 percent of the modern average), which included some development in the speech-language cortical areas, it seems safest to conclude that *Homo erectus* people either lacked spoken language entirely or, at best, had an extremely rudimentary form of speech that fell short of a fully articulated language. We base this conclusion on the following considerations: their cranial bases generally lacked flexure, suggesting a short pharynx and a limited ability to produce speech sounds; analyses of the thoracic vertebrae suggest that innervation of the rib cage was insufficient for the fine control of breathing required by speech; an exclusive link between an enlarged Broca's area and speech has been challenged by recent studies; and finally, with the exception of the invention of Acheulean stone tools, the material culture of *Homo erectus* apparently remained very simple until quite late in its existence as a species (see Table 11–1).

For all of these reasons, the safest conclusion, *given the evidence now available,* seems to be that only one species in the history of the earth has been fully linguistic: *Homo sapiens.* And it is to the evolutionary appearance of that species that we must now turn our attention.

REVIEW QUESTIONS

1. Compare the communication systems of humans and animals. How are animals limited in their communication compared to people?

2. Discuss the importance of a theory of mind for the evolution of language.

3. How do the following brain regions affect communication among modern humans:—Broca's area, Wernicke's area, and the limbic system?

4. Compare the brains of apes and modern humans with regard to absolute size, EQ, and the development of the language-speech areas.

5. Describe the "radiator theory" of hominid brain enlargement.

6. Discuss the evidence for and against the appearance of language and speech in the various fossil hominid species. When do *you* think speech and language evolved, and under what circumstances?

7. If, as suggested in this chapter, all hominids before *Homo sapiens* lacked complex spoken language, how did they communicate? Can you imagine a communication system intermediate between that of apes and modern humans?

POSTSCRIPT

Although Alfred Russel Wallace shared with Charles Darwin a deep understanding of natural selection and of its potential in the evolutionary process, he had one major problem in coming to terms with human evolution. This difficulty still constitutes a stumbling block for many people seriously interested in the origin of humanity.

Wallace believed, with Darwin, that variation and natural selection were responsible for organic evolution, but he identified three points at which, he concluded, some other (spiritual or perhaps divine) factor had operated: (1) the origin of life, (2) the origin of consciousness, and (3) the origin of the modern human brain. It is with the third that we are concerned here. Wallace could not see how the advanced moral and intellectual nature of humanity could possibly have evolved as a product of natural selection, and he took issue with Darwin over this problem. To restate his case in modern terms: How could our brain, extraordinarily capable in art, language, music, mathematics, science, and ethics, have evolved so long ago? How could this brain, evolved to hunt and gather, design a computer or build a vehicle to travel to the moon? Wallace replied, "We can only find an adequate cause in the unseen universe of spirit." He is not the only one who has attributed the creation of the human mind to a divine hand.

Darwin's answer was first of all one of horror! "I hope you have not murdered too completely your own and my child," he wrote. His considered reply may be translated into modern terms: The ancient brain was in fact already adept at handling complex socialization, emotional expression, language, natural history, hunting techniques, and simple technology, together with much else besides. Such capabilities already required a large and complex brain which, like a computer (though vastly more complex), can be turned to different uses depending on the program installed. A computer originally bought as a word processor can also be used for a vast array of functions if correctly programmed. The hard-wiring is almost infinitely versatile if the design is appropriate. Referring to the human brain, Stephen Jay Gould has written that "the additional capacities are ineluctable consequences of structural design, not necessarily direct adaptations." Our large brains were selected in evolution for flexibility and intelligence, but they contain "a terrifying array of additional capacities including, I suspect, most of what makes us human." This is a profound comment on the nature of humankind.

For Alfred Russel Wallace, a divine touch was necessary for the production of the human brain. Charles Darwin, in contrast, was convinced by his studies of the continuities of animal and human behavior that the human brain was not a special and unique gift from God, but, no less miraculous, an astounding product of variation and natural selection.

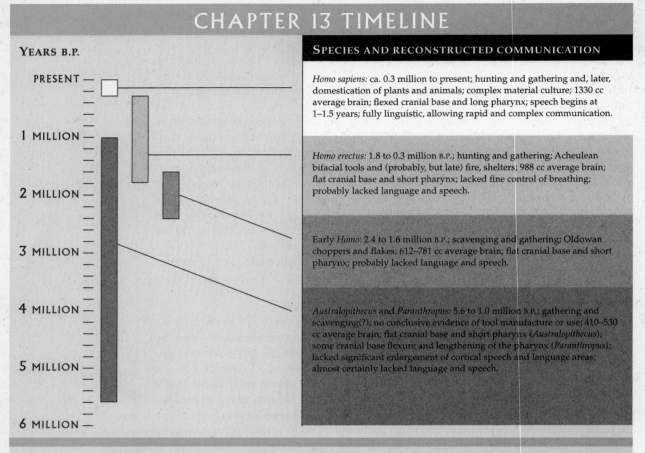

CHAPTER 13 TIMELINE

YEARS B.P.

PRESENT —

1 MILLION —

2 MILLION —

3 MILLION —

4 MILLION —

5 MILLION —

6 MILLION —

SPECIES AND RECONSTRUCTED COMMUNICATION

Homo sapiens: ca. 0.3 million to present; hunting and gathering and, later, domestication of plants and animals; complex material culture; 1330 cc average brain; flexed cranial base and long pharynx; speech begins at 1–1.5 years; fully linguistic, allowing rapid and complex communication.

Homo erectus: 1.8 to 0.3 million B.P.; hunting and gathering; Acheulean bifacial tools and (probably, but late) fire, shelters; 988 cc average brain; flat cranial base and short pharynx; lacked fine control of breathing; probably lacked language and speech.

Early *Homo:* 2.4 to 1.6 million B.P.; scavenging and gathering; Oldowan choppers and flakes; 612–781 cc average brain; flat cranial base and short pharynx; probably lacked language and speech.

Australopithecus and *Paranthropus:* 5.6 to 1.0 million B.P.; gathering and scavenging(?); no conclusive evidence of tool manufacture or use; 410–530 cc average brain; flat cranial base and short pharynx (*Australopithecus*); some cranial base flexure and lengthening of the pharynx (*Paranthropus*); lacked significant enlargement of cortical speech and language areas; almost certainly lacked language and speech.

As hominids' brains increased in size, so did the likelihood of linguistic communication. Anthropologists are fully confident of spoken language only among *Homo sapiens.*

IV
MODERN HUMANITY

CHAPTER

14

Discovery of Neandertals and Their Contemporaries

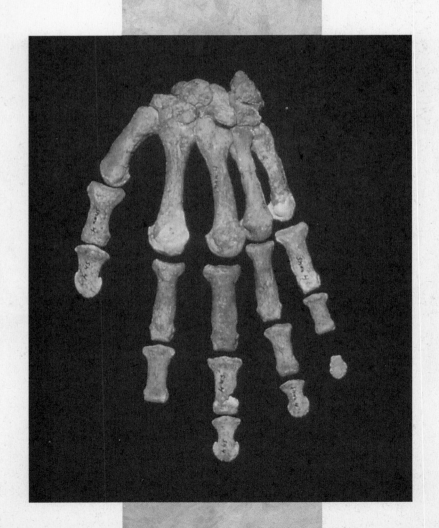

*T*he savage . . . breathes only peace and liberty; he desires only to
live and be free from labour.

JEAN-JACQUES ROUSSEAU, 1712–1778. *A Discourse on the Origin
of Inequality.*

*A*nd the life of man, solitary, poore, nasty, brutish, and short.

THOMAS HOBBES, 1588–1679. *Leviathan*, PT. 1, CH. 13.

OVERVIEW

About 400,000 years ago a new species of humans split off from *Homo erectus* stock. Broadly classified as "archaic *Homo sapiens*" (and therefore the first representatives of the species that includes living humans), these people had considerably larger brains than their *H. erectus* ancestors, although they retained several rather primitive cranial traits. Fossils of archaic *Homo sapiens*, or *archaic humans*, were first discovered in western Europe, but representatives are now known from Africa and Asia as well, and the species' point of origin remains unknown. This chapter tells the story of the discoveries of archaic *Homo sapiens*, including those fascinating Middle Eastern and European archaics, the Neandertals. A summary account of archaic *H. sapiens* anatomy is also presented, as well as a justification for including all archaic populations in a single, highly variable species. Important topics and concepts in the chapter include the various fossil discoveries; Marcellin Boule's "misanalysis" of the Neandertals; the anatomy of archaic *Homo sapiens* and its variability; and, finally, the question of whether to classify the archaics into one species or several.

Archaic humans: early members of the species *Homo sapiens* who preceded anatomically modern people.

FIRST VIEW OF NEANDERTALS

Of all the kinds of prehistoric peoples, certainly those who project the clearest image are the *Neandertals*. For many they are *the* Stone Age humans, shambling, beetle-browed louts who prowled the earth during the time of the glaciers. The Neandertals got such a poor reputation among the general public because they were grievously misjudged by the experts. Previously, many paleoanthropologists regarded Neandertals as a brutish breed that at best represented an insignificant side branch of the human family tree. Only recently has this misjudgment been remedied: although there is disagreement, many paleoanthropologists believe that Neandertals may have been members of our own species. From perhaps as early as 300,000 years ago to about 35,000 years ago, they and their contemporaries greatly expanded the regions occupied by humans, devised ingenious stone tools to exploit nature, developed a relatively complex society, and possibly opened the door to the world of the supernatural. Clearly they were people of great accomplishments.

Why did the experts misjudge the Neandertals? Many reasons could be given: the scarcity of fossils, errors in reconstructing bone fragments, and other technical difficulties. But perhaps more important, these problems were compounded by an accident of timing. To tell the story of the Neandertals, we have to return again to

Neandertals: (often spelled *Neanderthal*) were a variety of archaic *Homo sapiens* that lived in Europe and the Middle East between 300,000 and 35,000 years ago. In this text, they are classified as *Homo sapiens neanderthalensis*.

the previous century—to a time even before the publication of Darwin's *On the Origin of Species*, when almost no one believed that humankind had ever had a primitive ancestor.

The first fossil skull ever to be positively identified as belonging to an ancient human was that of a Neandertal. No one was prepared for the sight of a primitive-looking skeleton in the human closet, and when such a skeleton was found in 1856, it brought on a crippling case of ancestor-blindness. Having nothing with which to compare the first Neandertal skull except the skull of a modern human, scientists of the time were struck more by the differences between the two than by their similarities. Today the reverse is true. Compared to their predecessors, *Homo erectus*, Neandertals showed considerable evolutionary advancement. They may have been a little shorter than the average modern European, and considerably heavier-featured, squatter, and more muscular than most, but they were well on their way toward modernity.

First Discovery (1856)

The first Neandertal to be recognized as a primitive human was discovered in 1856, not far from the city of Düsseldorf, Germany, where a tributary stream of the Rhine flows through a steep-sided gorge known as the Neander Valley, *Neanderthal* in 19th-century German (see Figure 14–6). In 1856 the flanks of the gorge were being quarried for limestone. During the summer, workers blasted open a small cave about 60 ft (18 m) above the stream. As they dug their pickaxes into the floor of the cave, they uncovered a number of ancient bones. But the quarriers were intent on limestone; they did not pay much attention to the bones, and most of what was probably a complete skeleton of a Neandertal was lost. Only the skullcap (Figure 14–1), ribs, part of the pelvis, and some limb bones were saved.

The owner of the quarry thought these fragments belonged to a bear, and he presented them to the local science teacher, J. K. Fuhlrott, who was known to be interested in such things. Fuhlrott had enough knowledge of anatomy to realize that the skeletal remains came not from a bear but from a most extraordinary human with thick limb bones and a heavy, slanted brow. The bones seemed very ancient to him. To account for the apparent antiquity and odd location of the relics, he concluded that they belonged to some poor mortal who had been washed into the cave by Noah's flood.

Knowing that this judgment was bound to be disputed, Fuhlrott called in an expert, Hermann Schaffhausen, professor of anatomy at the University of Bonn. Schaffhausen agreed that the bones represented one of the "most ancient races of man." He had in mind an age of no more than a few thousand years; the fossil fragments could have come, he suggested, from some barbarian who had lived in northern Europe before the Celtic and Germanic tribes arrived.

Missing Links in the Chain of Being

Schaffhausen can hardly be criticized for missing the truth about the bones from the Neander Valley: the scientific community of 1856 did not realize that humankind had been on earth for a substantial length of time, and no respectable scientist believed that humans had ever existed in any form other than that of the modern human. Such a notion would have been directly contrary to the belief in Genesis and in what was known as the Chain of Being, a grandly conceived hier-

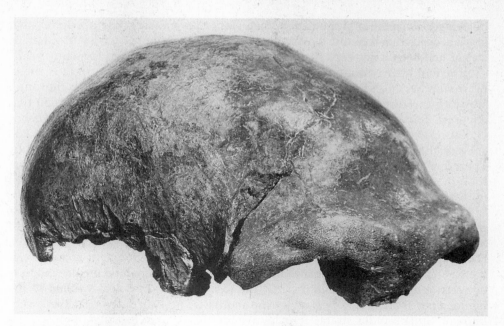

FIGURE 14–1   The skullcap from the Neandertal is possibly the most famous fossil discovery ever made. Following its discovery in 1856, it was thought by many to be the skull of some pathological idiot. Today we know that it belonged to an early, but by no means primitive, member of our own species, *Homo sapiens.* This photograph is just over one-half actual size.

archy of all living things. The separate links of the Chain of Being were thought by most scientists to have been fixed forever at the Creation; species never changed and certainly never evolved from the lowlier forms.

As we have seen (Chapter 1) this orderly scheme still held in 1856, but it was being shaken both by changing ideas about the age of the earth and by the appearance of animal bones unlike those of any living creature, suggesting to some dissenting thinkers that the Chain of Being did not tell the full story of life. But extinct animals were not the only threat to the established scheme. Records exist of a few primitive-looking human fossils that were found as early as the year 1700, and many finds probably went unrecorded before (and after) that. Remains that are now also known to be Neandertal had been uncovered in Belgium in 1829 and on the north face of Gibralter in 1848. Unlike the bones from the Neander Valley, however, these finds received no publicity, and science was not forced to grapple with their significance. But when Darwin's *On the Origin of Species* was published in 1859, the way was open to the recognition of fossilized human ancestors of not completely human form.

Homo neanderthalensis?

Experts familiar with human skeletons and skull structure could see some very peculiar things about this Neandertal skull (see Figure 14–1). It was clearly humanlike, yet it had strongly developed eyebrow ridges and a retreating forehead, and it was much flatter on top and more bulging in the back than is typical of the skull of a modern human. At the time, it was easier to regard the skull as a deformed specimen of a modern human skull than to accept the possibility that human ancestors actually looked like that. That opinion of the skull—that its owner had been a not very ancient pathological idiot—prevailed for many years.

Darwin heard about these remarkable bones but never investigated them. However, his friend and supporter Thomas H. Huxley undertook a thorough study of the unprecedented skull. In the condition in which it had been discovered, Huxley determined that the cranium could hold 63 cubic inches (1,030 cc) of water; complete, it would have contained 75 cubic inches (1,230 cc), which is not far from the average cranial volume of many modern people. Therefore the brain must have been of modern size, too, and the limb bones, though on the bulky side, Huxley found to be "quite those of an European of middle stature."

"Under whatever aspect we view this cranium," wrote Huxley in 1863, "we meet with ape-like characteristics, stamping it as the most pithecoid [apelike] of human crania yet discovered." In view of the large cranial capacity, however, Huxley did not see Neandertal as an ancestral form. He wrote, "In no sense can the Neanderthal bones be regarded as the remains of a human being intermediate between men and apes." Noting that the fossils were more nearly allied to the higher apes than these apes are to the monkeys, he concluded that they were human. "In still older strata," Huxley wondered, "do the fossilized bones of an Ape more anthropoid, or a Man more pithecoid, than any yet known await the researches of some unborn palaeontologist?"

Meanwhile, a second skull had been brought to England from the Natural History Society collections in Gibralter, where it had been discovered in a cave in 1848. When it was exhibited at the meetings of the British Association for the Advancement of Science in 1864, it was seen quite clearly to be a second example of a human with the hitherto unique but recognizable shape of the Neandertal skull.

William King, professor of anatomy at Queen's College in Galway, Ireland, accepted the German fossil as an extinct form of humanity. In 1864 King suggested that the specimen be placed in a separate species, *Homo neanderthalensis.* In giving the fossil the genus name *Homo,* King was acknowledging a general similarity to humankind, but he felt that he could not add the species name for modern humans, *sapiens,* because, as he wrote, "The Neanderthal skull is so eminently simian . . . I am constrained to believe that the thoughts and desires which once dwelt within it never soared beyond those of the brute."

King's assessment was closer to being correct than anyone else's, but he changed his thinking when he heard what the German pathologist Rudolf Virchow had to say. In a closely reasoned paper, Virchow stated that the man from the Neander Valley was not ancient at all, but a modern man who had suffered from *rickets* in childhood and arthritis in old age; at some time during his life, he had also received several stupendous blows on the head. This pronouncement, coming from a highly respected source, effectively silenced all further speculation.

How could authorities such as Rudolph Virchow conclude that the Neandertal bones were modern? The incompleteness of the fossil was one factor: because the skull lacked a face and a jaw, it was hard to tell what the original owner had looked like. Also, no one could say for certain that the Neandertal bones were really old, for no stone tools or bones of extinct animals had accompanied the fossil, and no reliable methods of dating existed. Without proof of great age, it was thought best to err on the side of caution and presume a date not too remote from the present. It would not be fair to indict the cautious scientists of the day for inclining toward the safest position. Those who accepted the theories of Darwin

Homo neanderthalensis: species designation suggested in 1864 for the Neandertal fossils. This name is not used in this text, as all Neandertal remains are included in "archaic *H. sapiens.*"

Rickets: pathological condition involving curvature of the bones; caused by insufficient vitamin D.

were open-minded by any standard, but it took a large measure of intellectual courage to surrender the accepted wisdom of centuries for Darwin's brave new world of evolution.

The Darwinians, to their great credit, were actively interested in discovering a primitive human ancestor from the moment *On the Origin of Species* appeared. But they had no way of knowing where to look. Huxley, a bold and brilliant man, believed that there was little hope of finding fossils that would reveal human evolutionary history. Some of the evolutionists did not even think that it was necessary to peer into the past. They believed that the present offered examples of humans who were intermediate between the evolutionists themselves and some primitive ancestral form. One presumed authority pointed to mental institutions: "I do not hesitate to uphold . . . that microcephali and born idiots present as perfect a series from man to ape as may be wished for." Although such surmises received only slight approval, they do suggest one reason for failure to understand the evolutionary significance of Neandertal. Scientists evidently did not expect evolutionary intermediates to turn up in a cave, and so they never really gave the evidence a fair chance.

As soon as Virchow had announced that the odd appearance of the bones from the Neander Valley was the result of disease rather than antiquity, the fossil ceased to disturb anatomists. They simply forgot about it. Prehistorians, however, were still very interested in finding an ancient fossil ancestor of *Homo sapiens*—as long as the fossil looked like a modern human; anything that resembled an animal ancestor, or an ape or a monkey, would surely be rejected automatically.

Discoveries at Spy (1886)

In 1886, additional primitive-looking fossils appeared. A cave near a town called Spy in Belgium (see Figure 14–6) yielded two skeletons. One skull, probably from a female, was reminiscent of the original fossil from the Neander Valley, although the cranium was higher and the forehead somewhat less slanted. The other skull was virtually identical to the German find (see Figure 14–2). Coincidence? Yes, said Rudolf Virchow, dismissing the Spy skeletons as further diseased specimens of modern humans. But this explanation began to sound hollow. Not only was such a coincidence of pathological deformity most unlikely, but these fossils were

FIGURE   14–2 The skull of Spy I, though incomplete, shows clearly the long head and the large brow ridges typical of Neandertals. This photograph is approximately 40 percent actual size.

definitely very old: along with them were found primitive stone tools and remains of extinct animals. Most scientists were obliged to admit that an archaic people, distinct from modern humans, had indeed lived in Europe during some bygone era.

The fossil skeletons found at Spy lacked some parts, but they were complete enough to serve as models for a rough sketch of the Neandertal race. These people were short and thickset. Their heads were long and low, with large brow ridges. Their faces were massive and protruding, with a heavy jaw but a receding chin. Could these have been our ancestors? Nearly all scientists said no. They were willing to give Neandertal a place on the human family tree, but not on any branch shared by modern humanity. Some authorities felt that the Neandertals might represent an offshoot from the main evolutionary line; if they were related to humans at all, they were poor and distant relatives.

By this time the initial shocked reaction to Darwin's theory of evolution was over, and the disturbing idea that humans had been around for tens or hundreds of thousands of years was becoming accepted. The fossils from Spy indicated that the Neandertals were ancient people, not modern ones deformed by disease. And Dubois's discovery of small-brained *Pithecanthropus* (Chapter 10) helped put the Neandertals in perspective. Although most experts were not yet willing to trace our lineage through a Neandertal stage of evolution, their belief that humankind could never have looked so primitive as Neandertal was now recognized as perhaps a subjective feeling, and thus open to debate. At this time, when the riddle of human ancestry was already confusing, new evidence appeared that complicated the problem further.

La Chapelle-aux-Saints (1908) and Other Finds

In the first decade of the twentieth century, archaeologists were at work in the Dordogne region of southwestern France (see Figure 14–6). From the 1860s on, countless stone tools had been found in southwestern France, proof that the Dordogne had been a population center in ancient times. Beginning in 1908 a magnificent series of Neandertal fossils were also discovered. One of the first to turn up was the skeleton of an old man in a cave near the village of La Chapelle-aux-Saints (Figure 14–3). A nearby cave at Le Moustier, from which quantities of stone implements had been excavated earlier, yielded the skeleton of a Neandertal youth. A rock shelter at La Ferrassie produced adult male and female Neandertals and later the remains of several children (see Figure 14–4). Another rock shelter at La Quina held parts of several Neandertal skeletons.

The great value of this material was its completeness. The bones from Spy had given a rough portrait of the Neandertal people, but as long as the fossil record remained essentially fragmentary, venturesome scholars could leap to extremes and see them as either *Homo sapiens* or gorilloid. The wealth of skeletal material from southwestern France now seemed to promise enough data to set the most vivid anthropological imagination to rest. Now scientists would be able to reconstruct what a Neandertal looked like and study the physical resemblances—or lack of them—between Neandertals and modern humans.

Boule's Reconstruction (1911–1913)

The man from La Chapelle-aux-Saints was selected for a detailed reconstruction of what was thought to be a typical Neandertal. The task of rebuilding the skele-

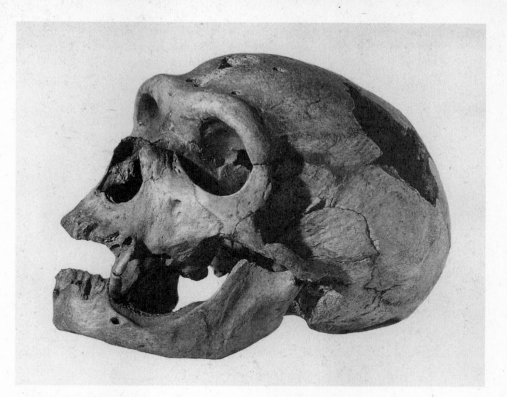

FIGURE 14–3 The skull of the old man of La Chapelle-aux-Saints shows he lost many teeth during life. He was less than 5 (1.5 m) tall and bent by arthritis, but he had a large cranial capacity of about 1,600 cc. The average modern human capacity is 1,330 cc. The photograph is approximately 40 percent actual size.

ton fell to a French paleontologist named Marcellin Boule, of the French National Museum of Natural History. On this project, Boule had an unusually fine set of bones to work with. The materials were well preserved, and although some of the bones were broken, almost everything of importance was available except some teeth and vertebrae. Despite the completeness and good condition of the bones, Boule proceeded to commit an astonishing series of errors—and they were not corrected for decades. Boule's mistakes—due in equal parts to his theoretical leanings, his habit of ignoring important work by others when it suited him, and the fact that human paleontology was in its infancy—combined to make the reconstructed skeleton appear almost apelike from head to toe (see Figure 14–5). He mistakenly arranged the foot bones so that the big toe diverged from the other toes like an opposable thumb, which implied that Neandertals walked on the outer part of their feet, like apes. Boule's interpretation of the knee joint was equally incorrect: he declared that Neandertals could not fully extend their legs, a fact that would have resulted in the bent-knee gait that observers could readily see the skeleton would adopt if it could walk. In every respect, the posture of Boule's reconstruction seemed nonhuman. Unfortunately, photographs of Boule's reconstruction appeared in many textbooks during the first half of the century.

The most devastating conclusion of Boule's study was on the intelligence of the man from La Chapelle-aux-Saints. Boule ignored the fossil's large cranial capacity. He looked only at the long, low skull—and perceived severe mental

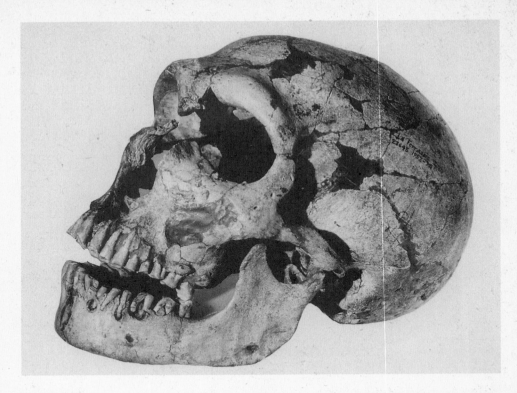

FIGURE 14–4   The male skeleton from La Ferrassie, buried with five others, had an even larger cranial capacity than La Chappelle: 1,640 cc. His front teeth show a rare type of extreme wear that is found today among some Eskimo tribes and other hunting people. It may have been caused by chewing animal skins to soften them for clothing. This photograph is just over 40 percent actual size.

retardation. He cited the interior of the skull as support for this judgment; measuring the space behind the retreating forehead, the paleontologist determined to his satisfaction that there was not much room for the frontal portion of the brain, which was then thought (incorrectly) to be the center of higher intelligence. And so Boule ranked the fossil man's brainpower somewhere between that of apes and modern humans, but closer to that of the apes.

Boule wrote disparagingly of the "brutish appearance of this muscular and clumsy body, and of the heavy-jawed skull that declares the predominance of a purely vegetative or bestial kind over the functions of the mind. . . . What a contrast with the men of the next period, the men who had a more elegant body, a finer head, an upright and spacious brow, and who were the first to merit the glorious title of *Homo sapiens!*" Boule was willing to grant the Neandertals the honor of the genus *Homo*, but he relegated them to *Homo neaderthalensis*—in his view a separate, aberrant species that had died out long ago.

Marcellin Boule was a man of excellent reputation and formidable diligence, virtues that made his errors all the more serious. Between 1911 and 1913, he published his conclusions in three exhaustive volumes. Packed with detail and ringing with confidence, these monographs had tremendous influence on scientists and the public alike. Although a few prehistorians stuck to their view that Neandertals were respectable ancestors of modern humans, practically everyone now felt that such a lineage had been proved impossible.

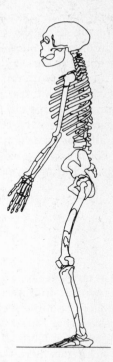

FIGURE 14–5 Marcellin Boule made a series of errors when he reconstructed the skeleton from La Chapelle-aux-Saints and so implied that all Neandertal people walked with stooping gait and bent knees.

The sheer force of Boule's work was not the only reason for its acceptance. Some circumstantial evidence pointed toward an evolutionary gap between the Neandertals and the later Cro-Magnons, those "elegant men of the next period" to whom Boule referred, who by this time were acknowledged to be the immediate ancestors of present-day Europeans. (The Cro-Magnons are discussed in Chapters 16 and 17.) Even if the Neandertals were not quite as debased as Boule supposed, they definitely looked different from the anatomically modern Cro-Magnons, and no one had come across a fossil that indicated an evolutionary transition between the two. Without an intermediate fossil, it was only prudent to assume that the Cro-Magnons derived from stock that had been occupying Europe or some other part of the world during or possibly before the era of the Neandertals, thus granting the Neandertals no significance in human evolution.

Archaeologists believed that there was no cultural connection between the Neandertal and the Cro-Magnon peoples. The stone tools of the Cro-Magnons seemed markedly more sophisticated than Neandertal implements. And when archaeologists dug down through successive layers in caves, they sometimes found sterile layers between the Neandertal deposits and the deposits left by Cro-Magnons, indicating that no one had occupied the cave for a time. These layers containing no sign of human occupation were interpreted as proof that the Neandertals had become extinct without having given rise to their successors in western Europe.

Today, both the classification of the Neandertals and their place in hominid evolution are still in dispute. Some paleoanthropologists, such as Chris Stringer of the British Museum (Natural History), prefer to follow William King's lead of

1864 and put the Neandertals in their own species: *Homo neanderthalensis*. Other workers, including the authors of this textbook, prefer to place the Neandertals within a wider group of fossils informally called archaic *Homo sapiens*—a group that, broadly considered, represents the descendants of *Homo erectus* and the immediate ancestors of modern humans. With regard to formal classification, we consider the Neandertals to have been a subspecies of *Homo sapiens*, namely *H. sapiens neanderthalensis* (the rationale for this classification is given later in this chapter). Whether or not the Neandertals in particular made a genetic contribution to modern humanity is a matter of great controversy and will be treated in more detail later in this chapter. For now, however, let's take a look at a few more of the archaic *Homo sapiens* fossils, including several from outside Europe.

DISCOVERY OF ARCHAIC *HOMO SAPIENS* BEYOND EUROPE

Boule had depicted Neandertals as creatures that might have had a hard time surviving, much less thriving, in the world. But if territorial range is any measure of success, these "uncouth and repellent" people seem to have done quite well. As the years passed, Neandertal fossils were found all over Europe, from Romania and the Crimea in the east to the western lands of Spain and the Channel Island of Jersey (see Figure 14–6). Still, as long as there was no evidence of them outside Europe, they could be written off as a localized evolutionary aberration. Prehistorians could safely claim that the main line of human evolution belonged elsewhere, in a still-unlocated Eden.

African Fossils

In 1921 some laborers mining lead and zinc ore in Zambia (previously Northern Rhodesia), thousands of miles from Europe, uncovered a skull and other human bones that somewhat resembled Neandertals. The fossil fragments came from a cave in a knoll called Broken Hill, which rose above plateau country just north of the Zambesi River, at a place called Kabwe (see Figure 14–7). The presence of stone tools and extinct animal bones indicated considerable age, and indeed the skull is currently dated at 130,000 to 250,000 years B.P.

This fossil human from Kabwe had a large, heavy skull (1,280 cc) and a receding forehead like the European Neandertals. The heavy bar of bone over the eyes was even more pronounced than any yet seen. But there were also anatomical differences: the limb bones were straighter and slenderer than those of the European Neandertals.

The newly discovered fossil (Figure 14–8) was called *Rhodesian Man*. Where did it fit into human evolution? Its age was uncertain initially. Some scholars, echoing Virchow, proclaimed that the Rhodesian was a modern-day mortal deformed by disease. A British expert entrusted with the job of describing the bones for his fellow scientists went to the opposite extreme. Following Boule's example, he declared that the formation of the pelvis "leaves no doubt that the gait of Rhodesian Man was simian, and that he walked with a stoop." He considered the creature "nearer to the Chimpanzee and Gorilla than was Neandertal Man." We now know that this analysis was completely erroneous.

FIGURE 14–6 The first Neandertal discoveries were made in western Europe, especially in southwestern France. During the last ice age, when Neandertals flourished, the sea level was lower than today (see shading), and vast areas of fertile grassland and woodland were added to the present lands that border the Atlantic Ocean. This map also shows the sites of certain other fossils discussed in this chapter.

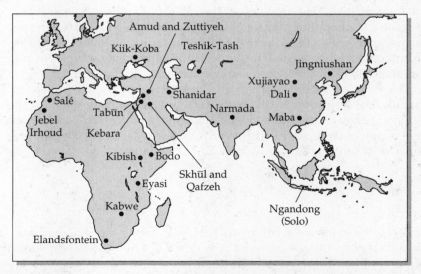

FIGURE 14–7 During the first half of the twentieth century, archaic *Homo sapiens* people somewhat similar to the west European Neandertals were discovered at many sites outside Europe. Although they show some variation in skull shape, they bear many characteristics that seem to unite them genetically. Not all known sites are shown.

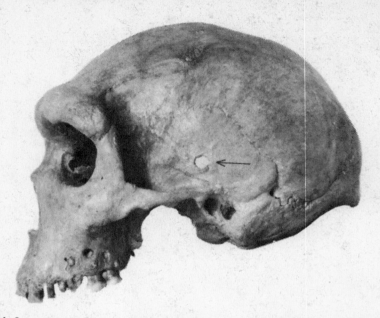

FIGURE 14–8 Archaic *Homo sapiens* people somewhat similar to the European Neandertals flourished during the same period in Africa. This skull from Kabwe, in Zambia, is exceptionally powerfully built. The hole in the temporal bone (arrow) was probably caused during life by a small tumor. (This photograph is approximately 40 percent actual size.)

Since then further discoveries have followed: a cranium found at Elandsfontein, South Africa, in 1953 on an open site near Saldanha Bay has turned out to be very similar to the Kabwe skull, though less complete. It is probably of about the same age, though it may be older, possibly dating to 300,000 years B.P. Somewhat more recently (1973), a crushed human skull was found near Lake Ndutu in Tanzania, which has turned out to be of the same general type but may be even older (400,000 to 200,000 years B.P.) (see Table 16–1).

These are all very robustly built skulls, which, although superficially somewhat like the European Neandertals, turn out not to carry many of their typical features. Although the brow ridges are heavily buttressed and the skulls thick, these people were clearly distinct from the Neandertal people. All are currently classified as "archaic *Homo sapiens*."

Asian Fossils

Many scientists, however, originally believed that Rhodesian Man was simply an African version of the Neandertal type. They began to wonder if some members of the breed had lived in Asia. An apparently positive answer came from fossils discovered decades earlier. During 1931 and 1932, fragments of 11 individuals were dug from the banks of the Solo River at Ngandong (see Figure 14–7) in Java. The fossils, collectively named *Solo man*, consisted of several calvaria (skulls that lacked their bases and faces) and other bones that were badly shattered. There were enough fragments to suggest a kinship with the Neandertals, although the thickness and low dome of the skulls suggested an even earlier evolutionary level and a close genetic link with *Homo erectus*.

The geographic gap between Java and Europe was filled in 1938 by a find in the desolate Bajsun-Tau Mountains of Uzbekistan, about 78 mi (125 km) south of Samarkand. A cave in a cliff called Teshik-Tash (the Pitted Rock) (see Figure 14–7) yielded the fossilized remains of a boy with clear similarities to the Neandertals of Europe.

More recently an important discovery was made in India. In the Narmada Valley, near Hoshangabad in central India, the Indian paleontologist Arun Sonakia made the first discovery of a Pleistocene hominid from the subcontinent. In 1982 Sonakia unearthed a heavy skullcap (without a jaw) from alluvial river deposits of the late Middle Pleistocene epoch—probably in the region of 150,000 years B.P. The skull is heavily built and reminiscent of the Beijing *Homo erectus* fossils; it also bears some resemblances to European forms. Though it still remains to be described in detail, it is undoubtedly an archaic member of the species *Homo sapiens*. It is associated with hand axes, cleavers, and scrapers of quartzite, together with some small flint artifacts. Its considerable importance lies in the way it links Europe and China both geographically and anatomically.

And finally, China itself has produced several fossils of archaic *Homo sapiens*, including some with impressively early dates (see Figure 14–7). From the site of Dali in north China, a nearly complete skull dating 230,000 to 180,000 years B.P. was discovered in 1978. Sharing features with both *Homo erectus* and modern humans, the Dali skull (with its cranial capacity of 1,120 cc) seems best placed in the archaic *Homo sapiens* category. Similar classification appears appropriate for fossil remains from the sites of Xujiayao (125,000 to 100,000 years B.P.), Maba (140,000 to 119,000 years B.P.), and Jingniushan. The last-named site has yielded an archaic skull with a cranial capacity of 1,390 cc that dates from about 260,000 years B.P.

Discoveries from Israel

During the early 1930s a joint Anglo-American expedition was looking for fossils in what is now Israel, then called Palestine. The expedition had extraordinary good luck in two caves on the slopes of Mount Carmel, overlooking the Mediterranean near Haifa (see Figure 14–7). The first find, at Mugharet et-Tabūn (Cave of the Oven), was a female skeleton, definitely Neandertal-like but possessing a skull slightly higher-domed than usual and with a more vertical forehead. A second Mount Carmel site, Mugharet es-Skhūl (Cave of the Kids), yielded remains of ten individuals. Some resembled Neandertals in a few features, others looked more advanced, and one approached the appearance of modern humans (Figure 14–9). This last individual displayed only a trace of the Neandertal brow ridge, but the forehead was steeper, the jaw more delicate, the chin more pronounced, and the shape of the cranium distinctly modern. Today we have further important discoveries from Israel: undoubted Neandertal skeletons from Amud (north of the Sea of Galilee) and Kebara and several more of the

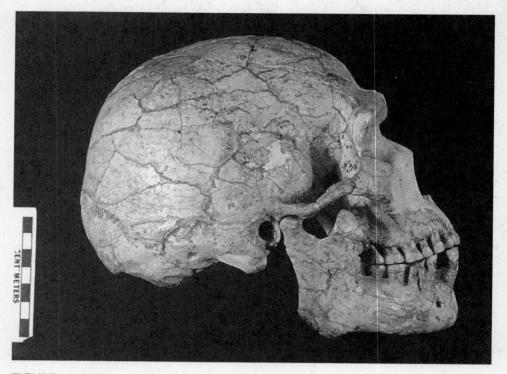

FIGURE 14–9 Shown here is the skull of a man from the cave of Skhūl on the slopes of Mount Carmel. This skull shows several modern features, including a chin and a relatively steep forehead. The photograph is about 45 percent actual size.

modern-looking skeletons from Qafzeh (south of Nazareth). The variation exhibited is striking. The sites from this region appear to span a period from about 120,000 to 40,000 years B.P.

The initial impression left by these people was that they occupied an evolutionary middle ground between the Neandertals and modern humans. They were certainly extremely variable in form. But the assumption that all Neandertals belonged to a dead-end species was, by the 1930s, so deeply entrenched that most experts could not believe that the Mount Carmel specimens might be direct ancestors of people living today. Some paleoanthropologists concluded that the fossil people from Palestine were hybrids: products of interbreeding between Neandertals and modern-type people. Louis Leakey even suggested that any mating between Neandertals and people of modern type might well have produced sterile offspring, like a mule born of a horse and a donkey.

The latest dates for the Middle Eastern cave-dwellers are surprising and have necessitated considerable revision in our understanding of human occupation in that region. Although scientists originally believed that more modern-looking people succeeded the Neandertals, new dates based on uranium analyses, thermoluminescence, and electron spin resonance (see Figure 1–16) indicate that Neandertals and "early moderns" may have been approximate contemporaries in the Middle East for thousands of years. The Neandertal remains from Tabūn are now known to date to approximately 110,000 years B.P., while the "early moderns" from Qafzeh and Skhūl date to 120,000 to 100,000 and 100,000 to 80,000 years B.P., respectively. Neandertals continued to use the region until at least 45,000 years ago, based on the dates from Amud, but by 37,000 years ago modern people were probably back in exclusive possession of the Middle East. We will attempt to interpret this rather confusing sequence of dates later in this chapter.

Pre-Neandertal Archaics from Europe: Swanscombe and Steinheim Skulls (1933–1936)

Interesting skull fragments pertinent to the origins of modern humans and Neandertals were discovered in the mid-1930s in some gravel deposits in the Thames Valley, near the village of Swanscombe, England (see Figure 14–6). Detailed geological knowledge about that part of England and the animal fossils found above and below the skull in a number of ancient terraces along the river enabled scientists to assign the Swanscombe fossil an approximate date of 200,000 to 300,000 years B.P. The skull, as finally known, consisted of only three bones: both parietals and the occipital. When first studied, these bones appeared to fall within the range of variation of modern *Homo sapiens:* their size, their proportions, and particularly their curves seemed much the same as a modern human's (Figure 14–10), and they definitely were not those of *Homo erectus* or Neandertal.

Inasmuch as science for many years regarded Neandertals as much more primitive than ourselves, the modern-looking yet ancient Swanscombe fragments were obviously a gift for those who saw all the Neandertal fossils as representing a separate branch of hominid evolution. A fascinating alternative solution begins to suggest itself if we now turn to another skull, which had been discovered at Steinheim, in Germany, in 1933. This, too, has been dated with great care, and its age appears to be approximately the same as the Swanscombe fossil's. The shape of the back of its head is also more-or-less similar. What the Steinheim fossil adds to the picture is a face, for the front of the skull has been preserved. It is not modern. It has quite heavy brow ridges and a low forehead that are neither primitive enough to fall within the range of variation of *Homo erectus* nor advanced enough to fall within the range of variation of modern *Homo sapiens.* Clearly Steinheim is an intermediate type. If, as seems likely, the Swanscombe and Steinheim skulls

Swanscombe   Modern *Homo sapiens*   Steinheim

FIGURE 14–10 The Swanscombe and Steinheim skulls compared with the skull of a modern human being. The form of the back of the skull is quite comparable; the differences lie in the face. (This drawing is just under 25 percent actual size.)

represent the same sort of hominid, both could be considered archaic *Homo sapiens* and either ancestors or near-relatives of the Neandertals.

Other European Archaics

In addition to Swanscombe and Steinheim, several other European sites excavated since the turn of the century have produced fossils of archaic *Homo sapiens*, including some that clearly predate the Neandertals. In 1907 quarry workers found a primitive-looking mandible at the site of Mauer near Heidelberg, Germany. The fossil is between 700,000 and 400,000 years old and shows similarities to both *Homo erectus* (in its overall robusticity) and *Homo sapiens* (in its molar size). Interestingly, it shows few traits that anticipate the Neandertals. Along with the approximately 280,000-year-old fossils from a second German site at Bilzingsleben, the Mauer jaw is believed by some paleoanthropologists to be evidence of *Homo erectus* in Europe. We prefer, however, to emphasize the Mauer jaw's modern dental proportions and the Bilzingsleben fossils' late date and to classify both as archaic members of our own species.

The oldest hominid fossil known from England was excavated very recently (1993) at the site of Boxgrove in West Sussex (Figure 14–6). The fossil is a fragment of a massive left tibia, or shinbone, and is between 524,000 and 478,000 years old (roughly the same age as Mauer). Analyses of the bone suggest possible assignment to archaic *Homo sapiens*. Besides being the earliest evidence of hominid occupancy of the British Isles, the Boxgrove tibia is exciting because it is accompanied by Acheulean stone tools. As noted in Chapter 11, a critical absence of hominid fossils leaves the identity of the toolmakers uncertain at several Acheulean sites in Europe; particularly sites that fall within the period of *Homo erectus*–archaic *Homo sapiens* overlap. At Boxgrove, however, it seems likely that a half million years ago archaic *Homo sapiens* people made and used Acheulean tools, and this discovery will no doubt have implications for interpreting other sites.

In 1960 the Greek site of Petralona (Figure 14–6) produced a large-brained (1,230 cc) skull that may be archaic *Homo sapiens*. Dating approximately to 500,000 years B.P., the Petralona skull shares some features with its *Homo erectus* ancestors and others with the more modern specimen from Kabwe in Africa. Certain features of the Petralona face and braincase suggest links to the later Neandertals. Also resembling *Homo erectus* to some extent, but with a projected brain size that is too large and a date (210,000 to 160,000 years B.P.) that is too late, are some scrappy dental and cranial remains from Vértesszöllös in Hungary (Figure 14–6).

In 1971 a new discovery was made of fossil humans from approximately the period of the Swanscombe and Steinheim fossils. Henry and Marie-Antoinette de Lumley excavated a cave at Arago near Tautavel in the Pyrenees (see Figure 14–6). Along with stone implements, the de Lumleys found the partial skull of a man about 20 years old (see Figure 14–11) and two partial jaws of other individuals. The man had a forward-jutting face, heavy brow ridges, a slanting forehead, and a braincase somewhat smaller than the modern average. The two jaws were massive and somewhat resembled the Mauer jaw of much greater antiquity; they seemed well suited to chewing coarse food. Altogether classified here as archaic *Homo sapiens*, the fragments appear to be more primitive in form—that is, closer to *Homo erectus*—than Swanscombe and Steinheim.

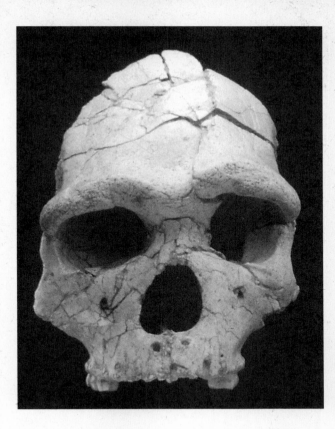

FIGURE 14–11   The skull from Arago is much more robust than those from Swanscombe and Steinheim. This photograph is approximately 60 percent actual size.

Finally, there is the very interesting and important assemblage of fossils from the Sima de los Huesos (Pit of Bones) site in the Sierra de Atapuerca of northern Spain (Figure 14–12). At Atapuerca, over 700 fossils from at least 24 people have been recovered from deposits that are over 300,000 years old. These archaic fossils share many traits with *Homo erectus* and others with modern *Homo sapiens*. The majority of their anatomical characteristics, however, are shared with later Neandertals, prompting some anthropologists to recognize them as the earliest representatives of that hominid type. The message of Atapuerca is clear: Although many details remain to be worked out, the Neandertals were evolving in Europe by about 300,000 years ago.

AN ASSESSMENT OF ARCHAIC *HOMO SAPIENS*

Our survey of the pertinent fossils has shown that, by at least 400,000 years ago, *Homo erectus* had given rise to a more modern-looking type of hominid who, for lack of a better term, scientists call archaic *Homo sapiens*. Spread over much of the Old World and including such distinctive varieties as the Neandertals, archaic *Homo sapiens* people were essentially modern in body size, limb proportions, and locomotion (the Neandertals were probably more stocky than other archaic populations; Box 14–1). The average "archaic" brain size (1,390 cc) was probably just a bit larger than that of modern people, primarily because the Neandertals had exceptionally

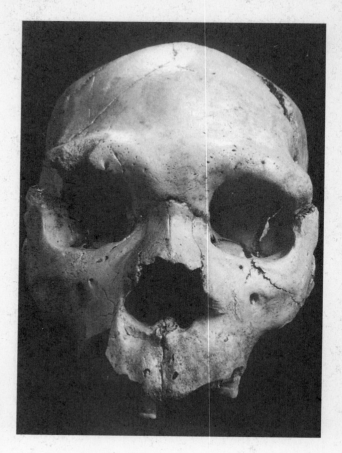

FIGURE 14–12 This skull from the Spanish site of Sima de los Huesos in the Sierra Atapuerca displays several evolving Neandertal traits, including large brows and midfacial prognathism.

Suprainiac fossa: a characteristic depression on the occipital bone of Neandertals.

large brains (the Neandertal average was about 1,520 cc). Those big brains were housed, however, in a rather primitive-looking head, and archaic *Homo sapiens* generally showed a lower cranial vault, bigger brows, and a more prognathic face than modern humans. The Neandertals in particular showed several distinctive cranial traits, including strong midfacial prognathism, big noses, and a characteristic depression, the *suprainiac fossa*, just above the occipital torus. Archaic *Homo sapiens* people were present in some form or other somewhere in the Old World until as recently as 30,000 years ago. After that date, only fully modern humans (*Homo sapiens sapiens*) remained to represent the hominid family.

But this list of specifications leaves several critical questions unanswered, chief among them: Where did archaic *Homo sapiens* first evolve? Unfortunately, this key question remains beyond our grasp at present. Soon after the appearance of the earliest *Homo sapiens* people some 400,000 years ago, representatives of the species were living in Africa and Europe and, shortly thereafter, in Asia. Anthropologists are currently deeply divided over how, when, and where the first archaic *Homo sapiens* (and later, the first fully modern humans) evolved. (We will discuss this issue at some length in Chapter 16.) But despite the controversies and unanswered questions, we are making progress. New discoveries and analyses enable us to understand archaic *Homo sapiens* in the context of our modern definition of biological species, and furthermore, many of the old misconceptions about the Neandertals are being dispelled.

BOX 14–1
CHARACTERISTICS OF ARCHAIC *HOMO SAPIENS* AND NEANDERTALS[a]

Trait	Archaic *Homo sapiens*	*H. sapiens neanderthalensis*
Height (sexes combined)	Essentially modern? 4.9–6.1 ft (150–185 cm)?	4.9–5.6 ft (150–170 cm)
Weight (sexes combined)	Essentially modern? 110–165 lb (50–75 kg)?	110–143 lb (50–65 kg)
Brain size (sexes combined)	1,390 cc mean (1,100–1,750 cc range)	1,520 cc mean (1,200–1,750 cc range)
Cranium	Compared to *Homo erectus*: smaller brows; higher cranial vault; less prognathic face; incipient chin on some specimens; variability in degree of cranial base flexure	Occipital depression (*suprainiac fossa*); occipital torus; large nose; midfacial prognathism; variability in degree of cranial base flexure; modern hyoid bone
Dentition	Similar to *Homo erectus*, but with smaller teeth overall	Large incisors; retromolar gap behind lower M3
Limbs	Modern arm and leg proportions	Robust, stocky physique as adaptation to cold
Locomotion	Bipedalism	Bipedalism
Distribution	Africa, Asia, and Europe	Middle East and Europe
Known dates (thousand yrs)	400,000–30,000 years B.P.	300,000–35,000 years B.P.

[a]Mean values for anatomical measurements are sometimes based on small samples and may change with additional fossil discoveries.

To treat these issues in reverse order, the old prejudices regarding the Neandertals began to evaporate in 1955, when several scientists suggested that Boule may have been in error in describing the posture of the Neandertal from La Chapelle-aux-Saints as slumped. Even children learning to walk, it was pointed out, or apes standing on their hind legs, have a fully upright trunk. The major turnabout came in 1957, when two anatomists, William Strauss and A. J. E. Cave, took a second, closer look at the fossil from La Chapelle-aux-Saints. The fossil was supposed to be typical. Strauss and Cave, however, emphasized a deformation of some of its bone joints, indicating that this Neandertal had suffered from arthritis, which affected the formation of the vertebrae and the jaw. Strauss and Cave spotted many other mistakes in Boule's reconstructions. The big toe was not opposable; the foot was definitely not a "prehensile organ," as Boule had said. The neck vertebrae did not resemble those of a chimpanzee, nor was the pelvis apelike in structure. All in all, Strauss and Cave found Neandertal to be quite modern in shape. They wrote, "If he could be reincarnated and placed in a New York subway—provided that he were bathed, shaved and dressed in modern

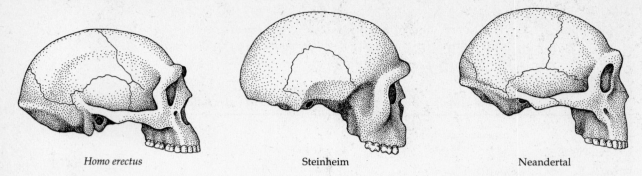

Homo erectus   Steinheim   Neandertal

FIGURE 14-13   Compared to *Homo erectus*, archaic *Homo sapiens*, represented here by the Steinheim fossil and a Neandertal skull, showed a much larger brain and more modern cranial anatomy, although they often retained such primitive traits as relatively large brows. The drawing is approximately one-quarter actual size.

clothing—it is doubtful whether he would attract any more attention than some of its other denizens" (see Figure 14–13).

As noted earlier, Boule was not misled so much by the diseases of this aged skeleton as by his prejudices in seeing only the archaic, even the "simian," aspects of the Neandertal skeleton (which he believed could in no way be ancestral to ourselves), and by his failure to recognize just how much variation does occur in any human population. There is no doubt that to some extent each generation sees in these hominid fossils both what it hopes and expects. No doubt our present interpretations reflect our current beliefs and prejudices.

By removing the taint of apishness that had been associated with Neandertals for so long, Strauss, Cave, and others have revived Neandertals' candidacy as possible ancestors of modern humans. It is still true, of course, that the fossil from La Chapelle-aux-Saints does not look much like Cro-Magnon or most humans of today, and many paleoanthropologists continue to deny an ancestral relationship to the western European specimens. Some of the skeletons uncovered at Mount Carmel, however, definitely cannot be dismissed from the human lineage on the basis of looks. And some anthropologists continue to argue that the Neandertals made at least a minor genetic contribution to modern human beings.

Species and Speciation

These considerations cause us to face the problem of the definition of species and subspecies. Studies have shown that the ranges of variation of many characteristics of archaic *Homo sapiens* and modern humans overlap. Indeed, the more we learn about fossils of this period, the greater the overlap appears to be. This similarity eventually forces a critical question: Were they, and was Neandertal in particular, really so different from modern *Homo sapiens* as to merit being considered another species? Fifty years ago anybody rash enough to raise such a question would have been laughed out of the room. Today, with the overthrow of prejudices of the sort Boule displayed and with the clarified status of Swanscombe, Atapuerca, and other fossils, most paleoanthropologists agree that the Neandertals and their contemporaries were sufficiently human in mind and body to have been members of our species, *Homo sapiens.* On the end of this title is tacked the subspecies name *neanderthalensis,* denoting some difference from fully modern people. But *sapiens* places them all squarely in the human fold.

This placement does not mean that there are not differences between the subspecies; there are plenty. To understand and evaluate both the differences and the similarities, though, it will be necessary to reconsider for a moment how speciation takes place and what makes a species.

The classic definition of a species is, as we have seen, one or more groups of individual organisms, the members of which interbreed with one another in nature or are enough alike in structure and behavior so that, if they had access to one another, they could interbreed and produce fertile offspring. They are genetically isolated from other species. This concept recognizes that all breeding populations within a species are not always in contact with one another. If geographic separation goes on for a long time, the different populations may become so changed through evolution that if they should come together again they might no longer interbreed. In this case it would be correct to say that the original single species had split into two species.

This is an extremely simplified statement of a very complex and subtle process. For one thing, separation is often behavioral: if one animal acts in a way that makes it impossible for it to breed with another, the separation between the two is as real as if they were kept apart by a mountain range. Consider the races of song sparrows that inhabit North America (see Figure 14–14). Some song sparrows habitually migrate north to Alaska every year; others remain in Mexico during the breeding season. Theoretically these two populations could interbreed, but their habits as migrants do not give them a chance to. What tends to hold them together as a species is the existence of a large number of sparrows that breed between the extreme northern and extreme southern breeding areas. Through these intermediary birds, the individuals on the northern and southern fringes keep in genetic touch through gene flow, discussed in Chapter 3. Their genes are distributed inward from the edges of an enormous pool of genes that represents all the traits of the species; at the same time, they keep receiving genes that are passed out toward them from the center of the pool. This mingling reduces any tendency toward extreme differentiation along the edges. In other words, genetic contact with the main body of birds tends to ensure that the outlying members of the species will continue to look and act pretty much as all the others do. As long as the contact is maintained, the species remains intact. Two opposing influences determine the course of speciation in any group of organisms: one is environmental and selective, tending to create differences (through mutation, differential natural selection, and isolation); the other is genetic and connective, tending to distribute the same traits through a population (through gene flow).

If we were collecting sparrow fossils and had only a couple of Alaskan specimens and half a dozen from Mexico, how would we relate them, particularly if we had no knowledge of any sparrows living anywhere else? Would we recognize the obvious differences between them and assign them to different species, or would we still consider them the same kind of bird? It is that problem which continually confronts paleoanthropologists. Their sample of human specimens is often so small that it is next to impossible for them to learn enough about the distribution

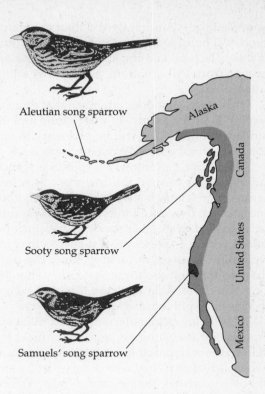

FIGURE 14–14 At present there are 34 subspecies of the song sparrow (*Passarella melodia*) in North America; 3 are shown here. Their approximate breeding ranges are indicated and those of 14 other subspecies along the West Coast are shown by medium shading (from the West Coast to the Midwest of the United States are the breeding ranges of 5 other subspecies). The subspecies vary greatly in color and size, but if we look at representatives of all 34, we find a continuous, gradual series.

of the people they are studying to tell whether their samples are from opposite fringes of one, rather varied, population or whether they are truly separate and different species.

Current species theory emphasizes whole populations, not individuals. It deals with the entire gene pool of the species. It recognizes that differences exist among individuals or groups of individuals, and that such differences continue to have a chance, through interbreeding, to be reabsorbed into the whole gene pool and in this way continue to be expressed as part of the species' genetic makeup. One can visualize a species as a tangle of interlocking strands that separate and join again in no orderly pattern. How they join is not so important as that they do join. These constant joinings represent the individual matings of countless members of the species and the fate of numerous small populations. If a population drifts away from the main body to such an extent that these rejoinings no longer take place, then it will have a separate gene pool and will eventually, perhaps, become a separate species.

Species Model of Archaic *Homo sapiens*

This flexible model of a species fits rather neatly with what we know about *Homo erectus.* It emphasizes the broad similarities that exist among the various known specimens, and it acknowledges their differences by assuming that a good deal of variety will inevitably manifest itself in any widely distributed species. Their successors present us with a similar situation, but compared with *Homo erectus* fossils, their remains are numerous. The difficulty is not so much with rarity as it is with how to interpret a rather embarrassing and perplexing abundance and variability.

Although the issue is complex and many of our colleagues may disagree, the authors of this text prefer to extend the model of a single widely spread and anatomically variable species to the first representatives of *Homo sapiens*. Thus we lump all of the immediate successors to *Homo erectus* into the broad category of archaic *Homo sapiens*. Populations of archaic *Homo sapiens* from different parts of the Old World showed considerable anatomical variability, the most extreme specializations occurring in Europe and the Middle East among the Neandertals (see Box 14–1). Particularly during their "classic" phase, from 90,000 to 35,000 years ago, the western European Neandertals showed a distinctive suite of features, including large brains housed in long and rather low-vaulted skulls; midfacial prognathism; large noses; large (and, usually, strongly worn) incisors; well-developed brows; and relatively short, muscular bodies with slightly curved limb bones (Figure 14–15). Many of these features, and particularly the stocky body build and the short limbs, probably originated as heat-conserving adaptations to an extremely cold climate (see the discussions of Bergmann's and Allen's rules in Chapter 18). Furthermore, such Neandertal specializations may have been facilitated by reduced gene flow in and out of periglacial Europe. In comparison, archaic people from warmer climates in Africa and elsewhere were less massive

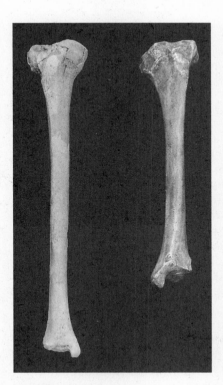

FIGURE 14–15   The short and strong tibia (shinbone) on the near left is from the Neandertal site of Spy. It is noticeably different from the less robust, longer, non-European tibia on the far left, which is from Skhūl. The plaster case of a Neandertal footprint from an Italian cave suggests a broad, short foot. (Both photographs are approximately one-fifth actual size.)

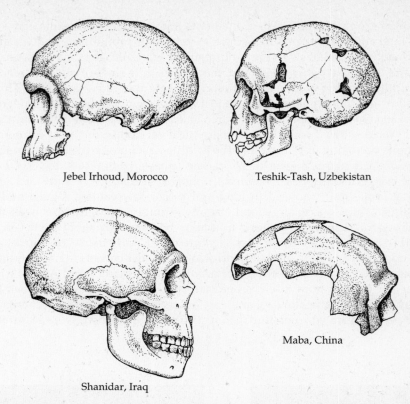

Jebel Irhoud, Morocco

Teshik-Tash, Uzbekistan

Maba, China

Shanidar, Iraq

FIGURE 14–16   The wide distribution and variability of archaic *Homo sapiens* is suggested by these four examples. The Shanidar and Teshik-Tash skulls are morphologically close to the Neandertals of western Europe. (The skulls face different directions so that their most nearly complete side will show.)

in their body build, were somewhat taller (Figure 14–15), and had more lofty skulls and slightly smaller faces (Figure 14–16).

Despite their differences, however, all regional populations of archaic humans shared a sufficient number of traits among themselves and with modern people to warrant inclusion in a single species, *Homo sapiens*. (Note that this classification opens the way for gene flow between archaic populations or between archaics—including the Neandertals—and any anatomically modern contemporaries. This subject is discussed in detail in Chapter 16.) Like the North American song sparrows, archaic humans were widespread and anatomically variable, but their shared traits far outweighed their differences. Precisely when and where they descended from *Homo erectus* is still unclear; a traditional branching model of allopatric speciation suggests that such a split occurred once and in a particular location (see Chapter 3). Some specialists, however, argue that the *H. erectus*-to-*H. sapiens* transition occurred gradually across the entire Old World. This controversy, as well as the equally thorny problem of the final archaic-to-modern human transition, will be addressed in detail in later chapters. For now, however, let us turn our attention to the cultural advances of archaic *Homo sapiens*. As the next chapter will show, these ancient people were beginning not only to look like, but also to act like, modern humans.

SUMMARY

In the century and a half since the first Neandertal discoveries, the remains of these ancient people and their contemporaries have been found at dozens of sites in Asia, Africa, the Middle East, and Europe. Although authorities disagree about how the various fossils should be grouped and classified, it is clear that they broadly represent the transition from *Homo erectus* to modern humans and fall generally within the time range of 400,000 to 30,000 years B.P. (a few appear to be older). Following what we believe to be the majority opinion among paleoanthropologists, the authors of this text include all of these transitional forms in the category archaic *Homo sapiens*.

The archaic *Homo sapiens* populations showed strong regional differences in anatomy. In western Europe, the Neandertal people were short and stocky, possibly in response to their periglacial environment. Further east in Asia, and south in Africa, archaic people were taller and more slender in body build. Wherever they were found, archaic *Homo sapiens* people showed an essentially modern-sized brain.

At present, the details of the *Homo erectus*-to-*Homo sapiens* transition are unclear and controversial. Equally controversial are the contributions of the various archaic populations to the ancestry of fully modern people. Without doubt, archaic *Homo sapiens* bridged the gap between *Homo erectus* and modern people, but whether one, a few, or all of the regional populations bestowed their genes on modern humans is still in doubt.

REVIEW QUESTIONS

1. Summarize the anatomical features that distinguish archaic *Homo sapiens* from *Homo erectus*. How did the Neandertals differ anatomically from other archaics?

2. Marcellin Boule was a competent anatomist and a well-respected scientist of his day. Nonetheless, he made a number of glaring errors in his interpretation of Neandertal anatomy and behavior. Summarize the problems in Boule's 1911–1913 Neandertal studies, and speculate on the factors that may have contributed to his errors.

3. In contrast to the position taken in this text, some modern paleoanthropologists prefer to classify the Neandertals within their own species: *Homo neanderthalensis*. Present the arguments for and against creating a separate species for the Neandertals.

4. Explain how the regional populations of archaic *Homo sapiens* could show so much anatomical variability and still be grouped in the same species.

POSTSCRIPT

Following their origin from *Homo erectus* stock some 400,000 years ago, archaic *Homo sapiens* people fairly quickly replaced their evolutionary ancestors and became the dominant hominid form throughout the entire Old World. By combining biological adaptations with cultural advances (see the next chapter), these ancient hunters-and-gatherers were able to exploit not only tropical and temperate habitats, but also rigorous periglacial environments. But many issues remain undecided, and chief among them are the now-familiar questions concerning speech and language. Did archaic *Homo sapiens* people, including Neandertals, have language, and could they talk?

The answer on both counts appears to be "yes." Archaic *Homo sapiens* people had a modern-sized brain (Box 14–1), strong development of the "speech-language areas" of the cerebral hemispheres, and—*at least in some specimens*—modern development of the basicranium and vocal tract. Furthermore, as will be discussed in Chapter 15, archaic *Homo sapiens* people showed several significant cultural advances over their predecessors. Based on this evidence, most anthropologists concede linguistic abilities to the archaics. Specialists start to quibble, however, when they discuss *degrees* of linguistic sophistication among the various archaic populations. For example, some adult Neandertal skulls show little flexion of the cranial base, suggesting a nonmodern vocal tract. Based on this and other bits of evidence, Neandertal specialists Chris Stringer and Clive Gamble conclude that Neandertals in particular may have had "a rudimentary form of language, but that it was probably simple in construction and restricted in its range of expression." Other experts, however, including Dean Falk, argue that Neandertal cultural complexity strongly implies fully modern speech.

In an extensive review of the evidence for the evolution of speech and language, paleoanthropologist Lynn Schepartz of the University of Michigan recently addressed the problem of variation in the archaics' vocal anatomy. As part of her argument that language has a long history within the genus *Homo*, Schepartz points out that, although there are some anatomical indications of restricted speech among the Neandertals, "*other archaic* sapiens . . . *specimens* [appear to have been] *capable of modern human speech*" (italics in the original). The Kabwe (Rhodesian Man) and Steinheim specimens, for example, appear to have been considerably more modern in their vocal anatomy than some Neandertals. On balance, therefore, it seems undeniable that archaic *Homo sapiens* had language and were talking, although some populations perhaps better than others.

Schepartz makes an important point in her review when she notes that modern people (anthropologists included) have a strong tendency to be "linguicentric," that is, to view speech and language not only as variables that separate us from all other living species, but also as traits that therefore must have separated anatomically modern humans from all fossil predecessors. If we can no longer uniquely define ourselves as toolmakers or hunters, perhaps we can hold the line at "Humans the Talkers"! But, of course, such "lines in the sand" have a way of crumbling under the weight of further discoveries (studies of chimpanzees forced the abandonment of labels such as Man the Toolmaker and Man the Hunter), and thus, as Schepartz correctly points out, such centristic approaches should be rigorously avoided if we are ever to attain a true understanding of hominid evolution. It is important to remember that language capability probably evolved slowly like most biological traits and that in evolving lineages, sharp lines of demarcation are impossible to draw.

CHAPTER 14 TIMELINE

HOLOCENE

- 10,000

- 100,000   "Classic" Neandertals
             Skhūl, Qafzeh, Maba
             Swanscombe, Steinheim,
               and Kabwe
- 200,000   Dali

- 300,000   Atapuerca

             Mauer, Elandsfontein

             Beijing finds
- 500,000   Petralona

PLEISTOCENE

- 1 MILLION *Paranthropus* extinct

             Earliest Acheulean tools
- 1.6 MILLION

             H. habilis at Olduvai

             H. erectus in Africa,
               the Caucasus, and Java

- 2 MILLION

PLIOCENE

             H. rudolfensis
             Earliest Oldowan tools
- 2.5 MILLION

YEARS A.D.	DISCOVERIES		PUBLICATIONS
1992 —	Atapuerca Neandertals		
1971 —	At Arago		
1965 —	At Hortus	1964 —	Swanscombe report
1961 —	At Amud		
1957 —	At Shanidar	1957 —	La Chapelle reconsidered by Strauss and Cave
1939 —	At Monte Circeo	1939 —	Full publication of finds at Tabūn and Skhūl
1938 —	At Teshik-Tash		
1935 —	First Swanscombe discoveries		
1933 —	First Qafzeh discoveries; at Steinheim		
1931 —	At Solo, Skhūl, and Tabūn		
1926 —	Gibraltar child	1928 —	Monograph on Rhodesian finds
1924 —	At Kiik-Koba		
1921 —	At Kabwe (Broken Hill)		
1914 —	At Ehringsdorf	1913 —	Boule's monograph on La Chapelle finds
1909 —	At La Ferrassie		
1908 —	At La Chapelle, Le Moustier, and La Quina		
1886 —	At Spy		
		1864 —	King creates species *Homo neanderthalensis*
		1863 —	Huxley's report on the Neandertal skullcap
		1859 —	Darwin's *On the Origin of Species*
1856 —	In Neander Valley		
1848 —	In Gibraltar		

DISCOVERY OF NEANDERTALS AND THEIR CONTEMPORARIES

The greatest period of archaic *Homo sapiens* discoveries was betweeen 1900 and 1940, and most finds came from Europe and the Near East. Finds from Africa and China are relatively rare. Today more research effort is being put into the earlier periods that preceded Neandertals and their contemporaries.

CHAPTER
15

Archaic *Homo sapiens*
Culture and Environments

*M*an is no more than a reed, the weakest in nature. But he is a
thinking reed.

BLAISE PASCAL, 1623–1662. *Pensées*, VI, 347.

OVERVIEW

Archaic *Homo sapiens* people differed from their *Homo erectus* forebears in a number of significant ways. Not only were they considerably brainier, but in addition—and perhaps as a consequence—they showed a number of important cultural advances. This chapter describes the cultural innovations that allowed archaic *Homo sapiens* to inhabit not only the hospitable tropics and subtropics of the Old World, but also the considerably more challenging periglacial northern regions. Important topics and concepts in the chapter include lithic innovations, such as the Levallois and disk-core techniques, and the beginnings of blade technology; the challenges—biological and cultural—imposed by periglacial conditions; the intelligence of archaic humans; cultural variation among archaic populations; evidence of rituals, art, and burial practices; and evidence of violence—possibly including cannibalism—among archaic people.

RANGE AND ADAPTATIONS OF ARCHAIC *HOMO SAPIENS*

Two hundred and fifty thousand years ago the human population was probably less than 3 million. But this unimpressive total is deceptive, for even then humankind occupied far more of the earth's surface than any other mammalian species. Most of Europe was then woodland, frequently interrupted by lush meadows, with temperatures so warm that water buffalo thrived in central Germany and monkeys chattered in dense woodlands along the northern Mediterranean coast. Most of Asia was less hospitable, and human bands apparently avoided the heartland of that continent because of the harsh winters and dry, blistering summers. But human groups scattered around the entire southern perimeter of Asia, from the Middle East to Java and northward into central China. In all probability the most densely populated continent was Africa. This sprawling landmass may have contained more people than the rest of the world put together.

The sorts of lands settled by these various people reveal much about their ability to deal with nature. They almost invariably lived in grasslands, savannas, or partially wooded country. There was a very good reason for this preference: These regions supported the herds of grazing animals that provided much of the meat in the human diet. Even though vegetable foods probably still provided the bulk of a group's diet, wherever animals were lacking, humans stayed away. The unoccupied areas included the deserts, the rain forests, and the dense evergreen woods of the north—a very substantial portion of the earth's surface. A few herbivorous animal species did exist in the forests of north and south, but they tended to wander alone or in small groups, for the scantiness of forage and the difficulty of moving through the thick growth of a forest made herd life impractical. To find and kill solitary browsers and grazers was so difficult at this stage of human development that it seems probable human groups were not attracted to these regions.

Another environment that resisted human invasion for a long time was the *tundra* of the far north. Here, obtaining meat was not the problem. Enormous herds of reindeer, bison, and other large, vulnerable animals found ready forage in the mosses, lichens, grasses, and shrubs of the nearly treeless tundra country. People, however, could not yet cope with the extreme cold of the region. Consequently archaic *Homo sapiens* stuck primarily to the same lands that had supported their *Homo erectus* ancestors: the savannas and open thorn woodlands of the tropics and the grasslands and open deciduous woodlands found in the temperate latitudes.

Tundra: treeless, low-vegetation arctic or subarctic plain, swampy in summer, with permanently frozen soil just beneath the surface.

Evidence of Adaptations

It is remarkable that paleoanthropologists have been able to learn as much as they have; many materials are highly perishable. Foods, hides, sinews, wood, plant fibers, and even bone last no time at all except under the rarest conditions. The few scraps of organic materials such as these that have survived often seem more tantalizing than informative. Take a sharpened piece of yew wood, thought to be about 300,000 years old, found at Clacton-on-Sea in England (the wood was preserved because the site was waterlogged). This wooden point may have come from a spear: having been dried over flames, it was hard enough to penetrate the hides of animals. It may have served some entirely different purpose, however, such as digging up edible roots.

Yet such seemingly ambiguous clues can be interpreted. In a case like that of the yew fragment, common sense helps. Certainly humans were using both spears and digging sticks well before this artifact was made, but a person would probably be more likely to take the trouble to harden a spear point than a digging implement. Similarly, we have every reason to believe that people who lived in cool climates wore some sort of clothing many hundreds of thousands of years ago, even though their garments, undoubtedly made of animal skins, have not endured. It also seems certain that shelters were regularly constructed; as we have seen, the impressions of postholes and sapling tips at Terra Amata suggest that people knew how to make simple huts of branches (and probably animal hides).

A posthole here, a piece of wood there, a bit of sharpened bone, an occasional hearth—these are whispered hints of human achievement in remote times. Some clues to the past speak more firmly. Geological deposits reveal a good deal about climate, including the temperature and the amount of precipitation. Pollen can be identified under a microscope, indicating exactly what kinds of trees, grass, or other vegetation prevailed. But most important in the study of prehistory are, of course, stone tools.

Stone Industries

Stone tools reveal that, although the humans living 250,000 years ago were modern enough to deserve the title *Homo sapiens*, as toolmakers they still had a great deal in common with their less advanced *Homo erectus* forebears. They made their tools according to a style that had originally appeared hundreds of thousands of years earlier: the Acheulean tradition (Chapter 11), with its characteristic implement, the hand ax. As we have seen, the Acheulean hand ax would have been suitable for many purposes. It might have been wedged into a thick wooden club to form a compound implement like a modern hatchet or ax. More probably, it was hand-held; perhaps a piece of animal hide was wrapped around the butt to protect the user's hand.

The double-edged hand ax was supplemented by stone flakes, which were sometimes notched or given a saw-toothed edge for finer work on carcass or wood. Evidence shows that some people preferred flakes to the larger of the hand axes; others rounded out their tool kits with heavy cleavers. In general, though, at the time of archaic *Homo sapiens*, the basic outlines of the Acheulean tradition were still followed by people in all parts of the world except the Far East, where somewhat cruder single-edged implements were still being used, probably in combination with bamboo tools.

Prepared Tortoise Core: Levallois Technique

The lack of inventiveness indicated by the widespread uniformity of stonecrafting gave way very slowly. Gradually the hand ax was improved, if only in small ways: the cutting edges became sharper and more regular. Other stone tools in the deposits left by archaic *Homo sapiens* people point to greater willingness to experiment. Some particularly ingenious stone knappers initiated a major new technique for making flake tools. Instead of simply banging away at a large piece of flint to produce flakes, they developed a sophisticated and much less wasteful manufacturing process (see Figure 15–1). First, a flint nodule was chipped around the sides and on the top. Then this prepared core was rapped at a point on one

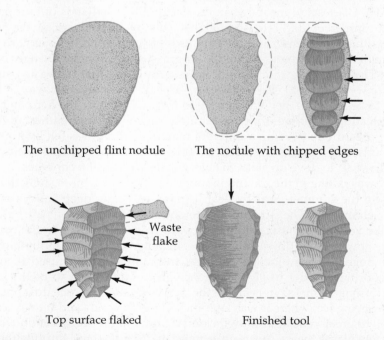

The unchipped flint nodule   The nodule with chipped edges

Waste flake

Top surface flaked   Finished tool

FIGURE 15–1 The Levallois flake has a distinctive predetermined shape. The toolmaker first prepares a nodule by trimming its sides (top right). This core is then further refined by the flaking of small chips from the front and back surfaces. This is known as a *tortoise core* because of its appearance. A final brisk blow at one end removes the finished flake (bottom right), already sharp and in need of no further retouching. These drawings are approximately one-fourth actual size.

Levallois technique: stone-knapping method in which a core is shaped to allow a flake of predetermined size and shape to be detached; originated about 200,000 years ago.

end. The blow resulted in a flake of predetermined size and shape, with long, sharp cutting edges. This *Levallois technique,* as it is called, represents a remarkable insight into the potential of stone, for no tool is visible until the very end of the process. In the making of a hand ax, the tool gradually and reassuringly takes shape; but a Levallois flake springs full-blown out of a core of flint that in no way resembles a tool. The Levallois method seems to have originated about 200,000 years ago in Africa, and to have spread outward from there, although it may have been discovered independently in several places.

When all the kinds of evidence of archaic *Homo sapiens* are put together— tools, a few fossils, and a bit of organic material, along with pollen and various geological clues to climate—the people of that remote time start to come alive. Pursuing their goal of subsistence security through hunting, scavenging, and gathering, these sturdy folk could cope with all but the harshest environments. Culturally they clung to the traditions of the past, but they were slowly inventing their way toward a tighter, more secure hold over nature.

In the tropics and subtropics, archaic *Homo sapiens* people inhabited a fairly hospitable world. At times in the higher latitudes, however, the environment became as inhospitable as hominids have ever known.

THE PENULTIMATE PLEISTOCENE GLACIAL CYCLE

Just after 200,000 years ago, the weather in the Northern Hemisphere began to grow colder. Glades and meadows in the deciduous woodlands of Europe broadened at an imperceptible rate; the tangled, lush woodlands along the Mediterranean gradually withered; and the expanses of spruce and fir in eastern Europe slowly yielded to the expanding steppe, or grassy plain. Similar changes occurred in China. The increasing cold did not necessarily mean that the basic patterns of human life were about to change. Because archaic *Homo sapiens*'s way of life was nomadic to begin with, they had simply to follow wherever the herd animals led or perhaps adopt a different mix of hunting, savenging, and gathering. But certainly the pressure to develop a different material culture was felt by groups that had formerly had no pressing need for fire, clothing, or artificial shelter. These groups now had to develop skills in cold-weather survival techniques.

Snow was falling in the mountain ranges of the world, more snow than could melt during the summer. Year by year it piled up, filling deep valleys and compacting itself into ice. The stupendous weight of the ice caused its lower layers to behave like very thick putty, sliding outward from the valleys as the ever-accumulating snow pressed down from above. Inching through the mountain ranges, the great fingers of ice plucked boulders from cliffsides and used them like a giant's scouring powder to grind the once-green land down to bedrock. In the summer, torrents of meltwater carried the debris of sand and rock dust out in front of the advancing ice, where it was later picked up by winds and blown across the continents in great yellowish-brown clouds. And still the snow continued to fall, until in some places the ice sheets grew more than a mile thick, burying the mountains and causing the very crust of the earth to sag under the load. At their fullest extent, the great sheets of ice called *glaciers* covered more than 30 percent of the world's land surface, compared to a mere 10 percent today. Europe was almost entirely icebound. The surrounding ocean and seas offered a limitless source of

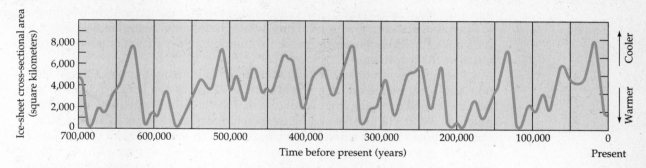

FIGURE 15–2   The Pleistocene ice ages were most probably caused by periodic variations in the geometry of the earth's orbit, and such variations as are believed to have occurred concur with evidence from other sources (oxygen isotope analysis of deep-sea cores). From these data it has proved possible to calculate the cross-sectional area of ice sheets at any time during the past 700,000 years. As we see in this chart, the main peaks of cold weather occurred approximately every 100,000 years, but many other cold oscillations came between these peaks.

moisture for snow, which fed separate glaciers that spread outward from the Alps and the Scandinavian ranges to cover vast stretches of the continent.

This glacial age, which lasted from about 186,000 to 128,000 years ago, was one of the worst climatic traumata in the 5-billion-year history of the earth. Although many similar glaciations are believed to have occurred during the past 1 million years of the Pleistocene (see Figure 15–2), humans had never before lived so far north and been so profoundly affected by such extreme changes in the earth's climate. The 186–128 kya (thousand years ago) glaciation was the first ice age to try the endurance of archaic *Homo sapiens*. They were to survive 60,000 years of bitter cold, interspersed with mild spells, before the northern part of the earth warmed up again—for a time.

Changes Around the World

The effect of the climatic changes was enormous. During these cold periods, the wind patterns of the world were disrupted. Rainfall increased in some places and diminished in others. Patterns of vegetation were greatly altered. Many animal species died out or evolved new, cold-adapted forms, such as the cave bear and the woolly rhinoceros.

During some particularly severe phases of the glaciation, what is now England and other parts of northern Europe, which had been so pleasant a few thousand years earlier, became so bitterly cold that midsummer temperatures were often below freezing. The temperate woodlands of central and western Europe were transformed into tundra or steppe. As far south as the shores of the Mediterranean, trees gradually died and were eventually replaced by grassland. No hominid fossils are known from Europe during the coldest phases of this glaciation, and it seems likely the climate was too cold for humans.

What happened in Africa is less clear. In some places, reduced temperatures were apparently accompanied by greater rainfall, allowing trees or grass to grow on formerly barren parts of the Sahara and the Kalahari. Woodland may have increased at the expense of savanna. At the same time, changing wind patterns had a drying effect on the dense Congo rain forest, causing it to give way in parts to open woodland or grassland. Thus, while Europe was becoming less habitable, Africa was probably becoming more so, favoring an expansion of people through much of that continent.

The land resources available to human groups during the 186–128 kya glaciation also were increased by a worldwide lowering of sea levels. So much water became locked up in the huge ice sheets that the level of the oceans dropped by as much as 330 ft (100 m), exposing to the elements large areas of the continental shelves, those shallow submarine plains that reach outward from the continental margins, in some places for hundreds of miles, before dropping off steeply to the ocean floor far below. The baring of formerly submerged land gave humans access to millions of square miles of new territory, and there is no doubt that they took advantage of this dividend of the ice age. Each year, bands of people and their game must have wandered farther into newly drained land.

Stimulus to Intelligence and Ingenuity

During the 60,000 years of glaciation, surviving inhabitants of the northern latitudes suffered hardships that were unknown during the balmy period of the earliest *Homo sapiens* peoples. These hardships may have had a stimulating influence on the evolution of human intelligence. It seems likely that archaic *Homo sapiens* people would have been under strong selection for cultural inventiveness and subsistence creativity.

Recently, at Lazaret in southern France, Henry and Marie-Antoinette de Lumley made a spectacular find that seems to reflect that inventiveness and creativity: remnants of shelters that had been constructed *inside* a cave. These simple shelters, dating to about 125,000 years ago, were tents, probably consisting of animal hides anchored by stones around the perimeter. Perhaps the hunters who occupied the cave from time to time set up the tents to give their families some privacy or to keep off water that dripped from the ceiling. But the weather must have been a consideration, too. The entrances of the tents faced away from the cave mouth, a fact suggesting that the winds blew cold and hard even at this spot close to the Mediterranean.

Finally, around 128,000 years ago, the long glacial agony began to taper off, and another period of relative warmth began. It was to last almost 60,000 years. Glaciers shrank back into their mountain fastnesses; the seas rose; and northern latitudes all across the world once again became an inviting place for humans. By 90,000 years ago, the "classic stage" of the western European Neandertals had begun.

Neandertal Cranial Capacity and Intelligence

The classic Neandertals had evolved gradually, we assume, from people like those from Arago, Atapuerca, and Swanscombe. As described in Chapter 14, the "classics" were characterized by a set of cold-adapted traits that served their ancestors well throughout the 186–128 kya glaciation and benefited the descendants during the final Pleistocene glacial period. The classic Neandertal body was stocky and had short limbs; the jaw was massive and chinless; the face was out-thrust; and the skull was still low, with a sloping brow. But the volume of the braincase was now at the present-day size.

Fossil Hominids

Some 5 to 7 million years ago, the human family (Hominidae) appeared in Africa as the result of an evolutionary divergence from the ancestors of chimpanzees and bonobos. The earliest hominids are classified into two genera—*Australopithecus* and *Paranthropus*—and placed in their own subfamily, the Australopithecinae. All are collectively referred to as *australopithecines.* Predictably, the australopithecines retained a number of apelike features while showing the diagnostic hominid traits of bipedalism and canine reduction. More advanced hominids—belonging to the subfamily Homininae and its sole genus, *Homo*—evolved from australopithecine stock around 2.4 million years B.P. Members of the genus *Homo* are collectively called hominines and they are distinguished from the australopithecines by larger brains, smaller faces, and a cultural way of life. Furthermore, while the australopithecines' geographic range was limited to Africa, hominines spread worldwide into virtually all inhabitable areas. The following photographs survey some of the more important hominid fossils.

◆　　◆　　◆

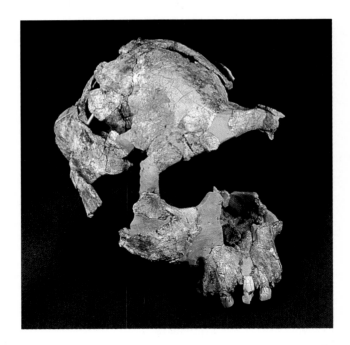

The reconstructed skull of one of the oldest australopithecine species, *Australopithecus afarensis,* is shown here. Combining a low-vaulted skull, an ape-sized brain, a prognathic face, and distinctive hominid bipedalism, *A. afarensis* inhabited East Africa from at least 4.0 to 2.5 million years ago. This skull of an adult male was announced in 1994.

This reconstruction of a running *A. afarensis* individual was done by paleoanthropologist Owen Lovejoy. Although *A. afarensis* retained apelike limb proportions—long arms and short legs—its pelvis showed the short, broad iliac blades of a biped.

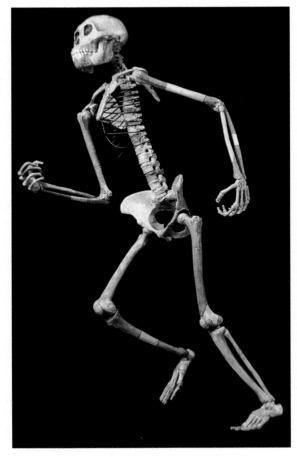

These figures from the American Museum of Natural History attempt to capture the appearance of *A. afarensis* in life. Limb proportions, degree of facial prognathism, and female-male size dimorphism are known from fossil material, but skin color, hair density, and the details of soft tissue anatomy are speculative.

Australopithecus africanus lived in South Africa between 3.0 and 2.5 million years B.P. Although its brain size was about the same as that of *A. afarensis* and the face was still markedly prognathic, the dentition of *A. africanus* was considerably more humanlike. This fossil is from the Sterkfontein site.

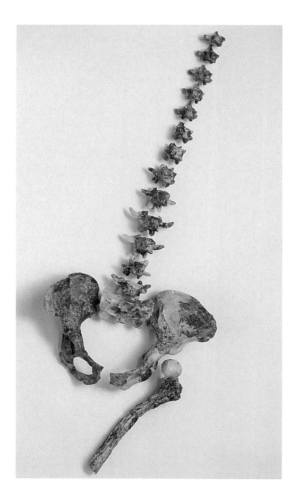

The pelvis of *Australopithecus africanus* was remarkably humanlike. Although still quite wide between the hip joints, it showed broad iliac blades and a nearly complete pelvic bowl.

Three species of "robust" australopithecines of the genus *Paranthropus* inhabited East and/or South Africa from about 2.6 to 1.0 million years ago. The genus is represented here by the massive skull of a male *P. boisei* from Olduvai Gorge, Tanzania. All of the *Paranthropus* species show remarkable enlargement of the grinding teeth, suggesting a diet of tough, chewy items.

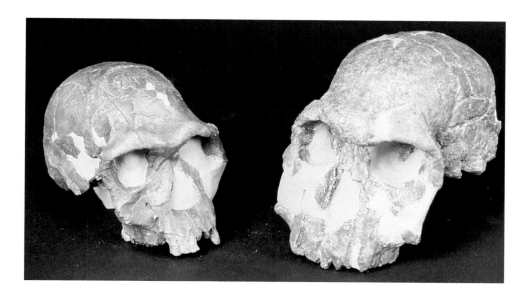

The first representatives of the genus *Homo* evolved in Africa over 2 million years ago. *Homo habilis* (at left, represented by KNM-ER 1813) inhabited both East and South Africa between 2.0 and 1.6 million years B.P., while *H. rudolfensis* (at right, represented by KNM-ER 1470) was strictly an East African species (2.4 to 1.6 million years B.P.). The two species are collectively called "early *Homo.*" *Homo habilis* had a somewhat smaller brain, a more prognathic face, and narrower grinding teeth than *H. rudolfensis.*

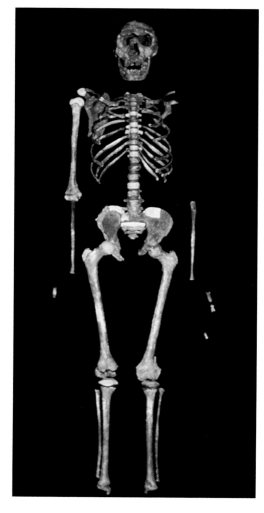

About 1.8 million years ago, *Homo erectus* evolved from some variety of early *Homo.* Represented here by the 1.5-million-year-old skeleton from Africa's Nariokotome site, *Homo erectus* people were tall and had modern limb proportions. Furthermore, they had brains that averaged almost 1000 cc in size. *Homo erectus* were found in Africa, Eurasia, and Asia, and their point of origin is currently a matter of some controversy.

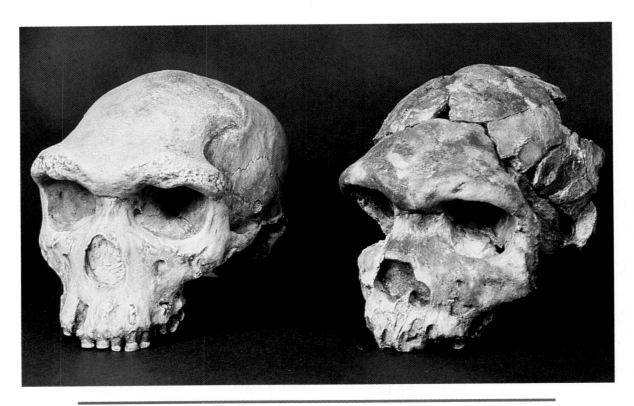

The species *Homo sapiens* dates back some 400,000 years into the past. Initially it was represented by "archaic" forms with larger brows, lower foreheads, and somewhat more prognathic faces than modern people. Shown here are archaic *H. sapiens* remains from two African sites. The Kabwe, or "Rhodesian Man," skull (left) may date to 250,000 years B.P., while the Bodo skull from Ethiopia (right) is over 300,000 years old.

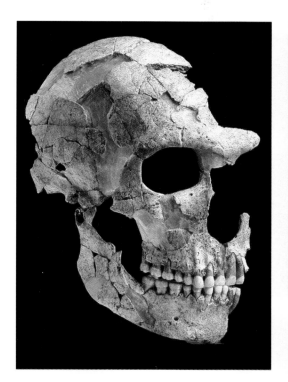

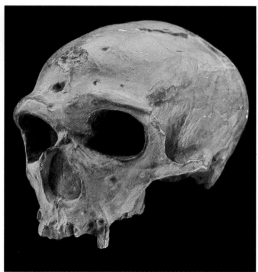

Late archaic *Homo sapiens* in Europe and the Middle East took the form of the Neandertals, here represented by skulls from Amud, Israel (top right); La Chapelle-aux-Saints, France (bottom right); and St. Césaire, France (top left). Robust and stocky, the Neandertals were characterized by large brows, midfacial prognathism, and very large brains.

Anatomically modern humans (*Homo sapiens sapiens*) first appear in the fossil record about 130,000 years ago, apparently having evolved in Africa or the Middle East. A skull from the Moroccan site of Jebel Irhoud (right; 90,000–190,000 years B.P.) is transitional between archaic and modern humans, while a skull from the Israeli site of Qafzeh (left; 80,000–120,000 years B.P.) is clearly modern.

In fact, from the limited sample available from this period, it seems that the mean size of the west European Neandertal brain (some 1,520 cc) was significantly larger than the modern human average (1,330 cc). This size has long presented paleoanthropologists with a puzzle, for the meaning of this figure is hard to determine. We know that brain size is related broadly to body size (Chapter 13), and it seems that the most likely explanation is that the large brain was a product of the powerful bodies of these people, whose physical adaptations can to some extent be compared with those of today's Eskimo. Whatever the reason, there is no justification in supposing that the Neandertal people lacked intelligence compared with ourselves, though that is not to say that their brains were necessarily entirely similar to our own.

The evidence of cranial capacity measurements of fossil skulls of the period shows, however, that the expansion of the brain, which had been so rapid during the *Homo erectus*-to-*Homo sapiens* transition, slowed down or possibly stopped altogether during the past 100,000 years. Because intelligence is of such obvious value to humanity, why would the brain stop growing larger and presumably better? Physical anthropologist C. Loring Brace has one interesting explanation. In his view, human culture reached a point at which almost all members of a band had a fairly adequate chance of survival as long as they could master the traditions of their band. If language were sufficiently developed and if intelligence were sufficiently high so that the least brainy members of a band could be taught the necessary survival techniques, then increased brain size would confer no further evolutionary advantage. Some individuals were especially innovative, of course, but their ideas would be communicated to everyone, and the whole band would benefit from any advance. Thus, according to Brace, the raw intelligence of humanity as a whole became stabilized, although people continued to increase their knowledge about the world.

This idea is certainly speculation, and most anthropologists prefer a more down-to-earth approach. They feel that the only fair way to assess the powers of the Neandertal brain is to find out how Neandertal peoples dealt with the world. These anthropologists turn to stone technologies and detect evidence of quickening intelligence everywhere. As we have seen, the old Acheulean tradition of hand axes persisted, but it was becoming ever more varied. The double-edged hand axes now came in many sizes and shapes, often so symmetrical and painstakingly trimmed that esthetic impulses seem to have guided their makers. When people made small hand axes for roughing out spears or notched flakes to strip the bark off spear shafts, they made them just right, taking care to shape the implements for maximum efficiency at their intended work (Figure 15–3). As described in a later section, this increased lithic complexity characterized not only the Neandertals but non-European "archaics" as well.

THE ICE SHEETS RETURN

After a respite of warmer weather between 128,000 and 71,000 years ago, the glaciers once again began to grow (Figures 15–2 and 15–4). This last major glacial cycle of the Pleistocene produced cold weather that lasted until about 13,000 years ago, but it was not overly severe at first. Initially it brought snowy winters and cool, rainy summers. Nevertheless, open grassland spread, and formerly wooded portions of Germany and northern France were transformed into tundra

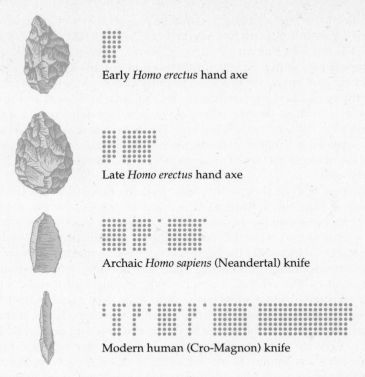

Early *Homo erectus* hand axe

Late *Homo erectus* hand axe

Archaic *Homo sapiens* (Neandertal) knife

Modern human (Cro-Magnon) knife

FIGURE 15–3   Steady progress in the manufacture of tools is traced in this diagram, which shows how increasing numbers of blows (dots) and of different steps (clusters of dots) in toolmaking led to finer tools and the more efficient use of the raw material. The most primitive tool required 25 blows and one step; the latest and most sophisticated took 251 blows and nine complex steps. The first and second tools shown represent the Acheulean toolmaking techniques of *Homo erectus;* they were rough-hewn from single pieces of flint. The third was made by the Mousterian technique, which involved chipping a flake from a core and then modifying the flake. The bottom tool, a knife so sharp that one edge had to be dulled to permit grasping, was shaped by the more intricate Aurignacian technique of the Cro-Magnons (see Chapter 16).

or a forest-tundra mixture where open areas of moss and lichens alternated with groups of trees.

During preceding ice ages, the archaic *Homo sapiens* bands had pulled back from such uncongenial lands. Now, in the summer at least, the northern populations stayed, subsisting on the herds of reindeer, woolly rhinoceros, and mammoth (see Figure 15–5). They had to be creative scavengers and hunters, for tundra country offered little vegetable food to tide them over on lean days. Evidence from Russia shows that settlements extended right up to the Arctic Ocean northwest of the Ural mountains. Here there are indications of huts or windbreaks built with mammoth tusks and skins, warmed by small fires, together with remains of polar bears, which evidently were hunted. No doubt the death toll was high on the northernmost frontier, and bands remained small and scattered. Away from the frigid border of the ice sheets, populations were denser.

To understand the extent to which these populations depended on cultural adaptations, we must remember that hominids are biologically adapted to a tropical climate. Hominids had evolved an efficient system of perspiration to prevent

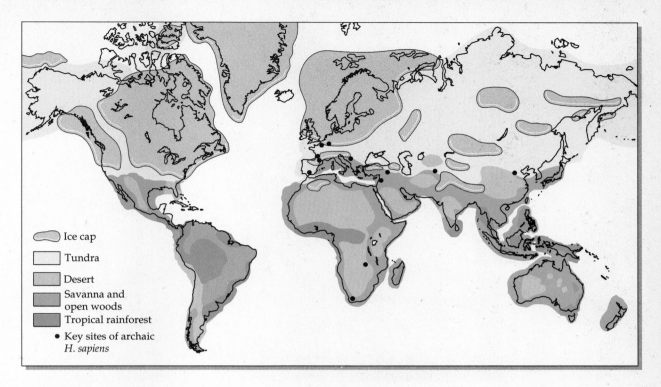

FIGURE 15–4 This map gives an idea of the climate and vegetation of the world at the first peak of the last glaciation, about 70,000 years ago.

overheating in the tropics but had not previously needed to develop a counter-balancing system equally effective against overcooling. Such changes require a long time to evolve. These people did not have to wait for such evolutionary changes to cope with the cold: they were intelligent enough to deal with the problem without depending on biological evolution. They generated extra heat with well-controlled fires, put on hide clothes, and either took shelter in caves or, where there were no caves, constructed their own shelters.

Sunlight and Skin Color

One noteworthy physical change that very likely coincided with *Homo sapiens*'s expansion into northern lands was associated less directly with cold than with the scarcity of sunlight during winter in the higher latitudes. Their skin probably got lighter. There is no certain evidence, but it seems likely that the australopithecines, and early, tropical *Homo* as well, had been quite dark-skinned. In equatorial regions, dark brown skin has an advantage. Overexposure to ultraviolet (UV) rays of the tropical sun is harmful to skin, and many experts feel that as the hominid skin became less hairy and more exposed, the melanocytes (the cells that produce the skin-darkening pigment melanin) compensated by producing extra pigment, which blocked the ultraviolet rays. This UV blockage could have prevented potentially lethal skin cancers.

FIGURE 15–5   The 8-ton woolly mammoth (12 ft, or 3.7 m tall) was ideally suited to the rigors of ice-age Europe. Shaggy hair and a layer of fat insulated it from the cold, and its ears were small to reduce heat loss. The woolly mammoth disappeared about 10,000 years ago, possibly being unable to adapt to the increasingly temperate climate of its last home, the grazing grounds in Siberia and North America. Complete animals, with muscles and skin intact, have been found in frozen ground in Siberia.

But the presence of a screen of pigment also inhibits the beneficial UV-induced synthesis of vitamin D in the skin. This decrease of vitamin production is not a serious problem in the tropics, where there is so much sunlight that enough of the essential vitamin is made anyway. When people settled permanently in regions with less sunlight, however, they did not produce enough vitamin D; pigment was no longer a protection but a drawback. This problem was exacerbated by the onset of the cold. Animal hides worn against the cold decreased the amount of sunlight that could fall on the skin. If the human of the north was to get enough vitamin D, any skin exposed would have to be able to absorb light and synthesize vitamin D extremely rapidly. In these conditions, a level of pigmentation that could further the contribution of vitamin D to the body's chemistry was better for survival, and lighter skin evolved. In this way we can account for the evolution of light-skinned humans in northern latitudes. Skin color is simply an evolutionary response to the intensity of UV light in different geographic regions and the extent of clothing required.

The significance of vitamin D in the lives of archaic *Homo sapiens* populations was probably considerable. Today we know that humans can obtain the vitamin only from milk and fish oils, and so eating fish can substitute for exposure to sunlight. Further, we have learned that deficiency in the vitamin causes the bone-bending disease rickets. It is no surprise, therefore, that we find many skeletons of early northern peoples, especially children, showing direct evidence of a deficiency in the vitamin. And it is equally unsurprising that, among the first modern people who followed them in these icy regions, and whom we know to have had fishing tackle, the incidence of the disease is greatly reduced. The importance of sunlight to the survival of archaic *Homo sapiens* in northern lands, and the limitations that it placed on their further expansion, cannot be exaggerated.

Disk-Core Technique: The Mousterian Industry

The tenacity of the archaic humans of the north and the thriving state of those in milder areas must have been due, at least in part, to further cultural advances. Early in the final glacial cycle, they invented a new stoneworking method that brought about the permanent ascendancy of the versatile tools made from flakes over those made by shaping a heavy core. Fine flake tools had now been made for a long time by the Levallois technique, but the new method was far more productive. Stone-tool remains indicate that at this period people began to trim a nodule of stone around the edges to make a disk-shaped core; then, aiming hammer blows toward the center of the disk, they repeatedly rapped at its edges, knocking off flake after flake until the core was almost entirely used up. Finally, the unfinished flakes were further trimmed so that they had edges for work on wood, carcasses, or hides (Figure 15–6).

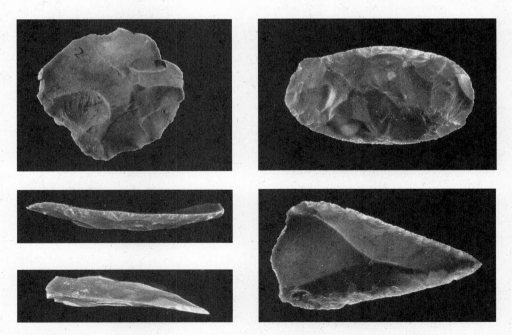

FIGURE 15–6 The disk (above left) is all that remains of what started as a much larger core. Refinements in the initial shaping of the core, and in the way it was struck, permitted the toolmaker to flake the core until it was almost all used up. Such technical mastery could then turn the flakes into tools like the double-edged scraper (upper right) and the thin-bladed point (lower right), both shown in full view and (lower left) in profile. The photographs are approximately 40 percent actual size.

Disk-core technique: Neandertal stone–knapping method in which a core is trimmed to disk shape and numerous flakes are then chipped off; the flakes are then generally retouched.

The great virtue of this new *disk-core technique* was twofold. It permitted the production of large numbers of usable flakes with little effort, and because flakes can be retouched easily so that they have a shape or an edge, the new technique ushered in an era of specialization in tools. Neandertal tool kits were far more versatile than those of earlier peoples. François Bordes, a French archaeologist who was at one time the world's foremost expert on Neandertal stonecrafting, listed more than 60 distinct types of cutting, scraping, piercing, and gouging tools. No one band of Neandertals used all these implements, but the kit of a given band nonetheless contained a great many special-purpose tools, such as saw-toothed implements and stone knives with one blunt edge that enabled the user to apply pressure more firmly. Different tool kits were probably prepared for different needs. New weapons may also have been made at this time. Spears may have been improved, when pointed flakes were attached to long pieces of wood by being wedged into the wood or tied with thongs. With such an arsenal of tools, archaic human beings could tap natural resources as never before.

Mousterian industry: a Middle Paleolithic tool industry from Europe and the Middle East; primarily associated with archaic *Homo sapiens*.

Everywhere north of the Sahara and eastward as far as Teshik-Tash, these retouched flakes became the preeminent tools (see Figure 15–7). The tools made within this broad area are collectively placed in the *Mousterian industry* (see Fig-

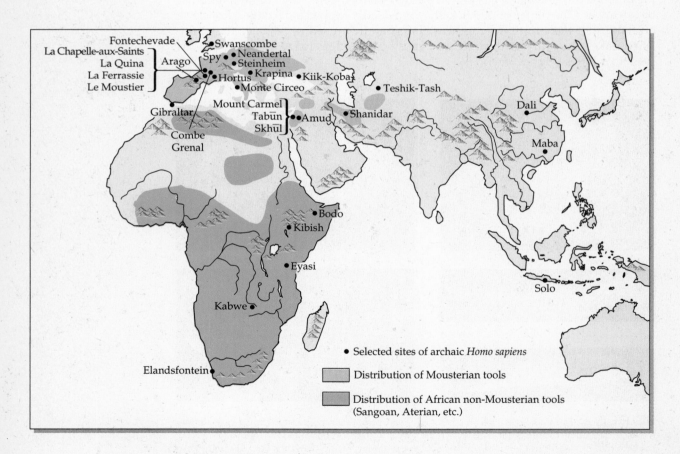

FIGURE 15–7 Archaic *Homo sapiens* people were widely dispersed throughout the Old World but were unable to expand their territory into northeastern Asia or Australia. They nevertheless adapted to a wide variety of ecological zones.

ure 15–8), after the French site of Le Moustier, where flake tools were first found in the 1860s. The makers of this wide-ranging culture were usually Neandertals, but in the Middle East, Mousterian tools have also been found in association with early anatomically modern people.

Non-Mousterian Industries

Outside Europe and the Middle East, archaic *Homo sapiens* people produced a variety of lithic industries that differed somewhat from the Mousterian. Nonetheless, these stone tool cultures are sufficiently similar to be classified along with the Mousterian as part of the *Middle Paleolithic,* a period of tool manufacture that lasted from 200,000 to about 35,000 years B.P. In Africa and western Asia extending to India, Middle Paleolithic assemblages included Levallois flake tools and such standard implements as scrapers, choppers, and *denticulates.* Interestingly, like the earlier Acheulean tradition, the Levallois stone-knapping technique is not found in eastern Asia, and most archaic *Homo sapiens* tools from that region are described as "nondescript flakes." A few examples will serve to indicate the nature of the non-Mousterian assemblages from Africa. First, in the north of the continent, archaic humans produced the *Aterian industry,* with tool assemblages characterized by points and scrapers that were stemmed for hafting onto a shaft or handle (Figure 15–9). Aterian implements probably date to the early part of the last glaciation, since northern Africa suffered from extreme aridity when the ice sheets were at their thickest. Second, in East and Central Africa, archaic *Homo sapiens* produced the *Sangoan industry.* Although the Sangoan included some hand axes and scrapers, its distinctive tool was a long, narrow, heavy implement called a *pick* (Figure 15–10) that may have been used for woodworking by archaic populations adapted to forested environments. And third, from Elandsfontein in South Africa and from some East African sites comes evidence that the Acheulean tradition persisted for a time after the emergence of archaic *Homo sapiens.*

But perhaps the most exciting tool assemblages from outside Europe are those that forecast the later development of the *blade tools* that characterized the *Upper Paleolithic* in much of the Old World. Blades are razor-sharp slivers of stone defined as being at least twice as long as they are wide. Amazingly versatile tools, whether used unmodified or given a distinctive shape by further flaking, blades appear in the cultural sequence of the Israeli site of Tabūn at over 90,000 years B.P. and at the South African site of Klasies River Mouth (see Figure 16–1) at perhaps 50,000 to 70,000 years B.P. At Tabūn the blade assemblages are overlaid by thick Mousterian deposits, and at Klasies River Mouth blade layers are sandwiched between older-style flake tools from the African Middle Stone Age. Unfortunately we cannot attribute these early flashes of Upper Paleolithic technology to a particular hominid type. At 50,000 to 90,000 years B.P., both archaic *Homo sapiens* and fully modern people were alive in the Old World, and the archaeological record is not clear on the identities of the first blade knappers.

Expansion and Adaptations

From 75,000 to about 35,000 years ago, archaic *Homo sapiens* people conquered a whole series of habitats that had repulsed their ancestors. The European Neandertals accepted the challenge of tundra country and won. Some of their African contemporaries, equipped with Sangoan tools, penetrated the fringes of the Congo forests and hacked paths through the dense vegetation that had replaced

Aterian industry: Middle Paleolithic tool industry from northern Africa; associated with archaic *Homo sapiens.*

Denticulates: stone implements made with toothed or notched edges.

Sangoan industry: Middle Paleolithic tool industry from south of the Sahara and dating about 45,000 to 35,000 years B.P.; associated with archaic *Homo sapiens.*

Middle Paleolithic: a period of stone tool manufacture in Europe, Africa, the Middle East, and western Asia that lasted from 200,000 to about 35,000 years B.P.

Blade tools: slender, razor-sharp flake tools that are at least twice as long as they are wide.

Upper Paleolithic: a period of stone tool manufacture in the Old World that lasted from about 40,000 to 10,000 years B.P; associated primarily with anatomically modern humans.

Convex side-scraper   Levallois point   Mousterian point   Mousterian point

Mousterian point   Canted scraper   Transversal scraper

Convergent scraper   Double scraper   Levallois flake

FIGURE 15–8   Flint tools of the typical Mousterian. The points are carefully worked and retouching is carefully done, usually on two sides. (Drawings are approximately one-half actual size.)

much of the grassland during rainy times. Others were spreading across the vast plains of central Russia, and still others ventured into the rugged mountain chains of southern Asia and out the other side. But this expansion was slow and was performed by the population as a whole, not just a few individuals. No band was suicidal enough to pack up its scanty possessions and walk a hundred miles into an area that its members knew nothing about. These conquests were achieved not by dramatic migrations, but by gradual budding and population spread.

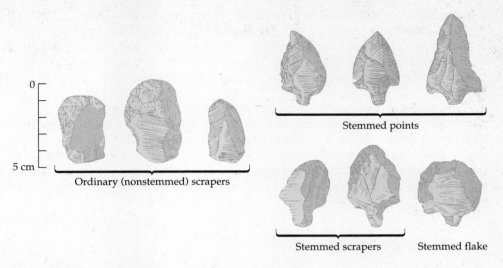

FIGURE 15–9   Aterian artifacts from North Africa. Note the predominance of stemmed pieces.

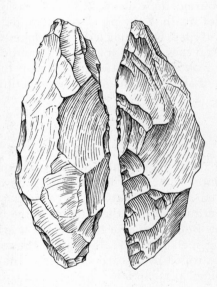

FIGURE 15–10   A Sangoan pick. The drawings are approximately one-third the actual size.

Specialization was the order of the day. The northern archaics surely must have been the supreme clothesmakers of the world, as indicated by their numerous scraping tools, which could be used in preparing hides. The Sangoans may have been the most skilled woodcrafters.

Where key resources were lacking, these people undoubtedly tried to overcome the difficulty. On the treeless plains of central Europe, they began to use bone in place of wood for various purposes. Water was another resource in short supply over large parts of the earth's surface, and humans had always been forced to stay within walking distance of streams, rivers, lakes, or springs. But some very dry lands may have been invaded by the use of water vessels. Recently, in the sun-baked Negev region of Israel, shells of ostrich eggs were unearthed along with Mousterian tools. These large eggshells would have held enough water to enable a band to survive a journey across the parched hills from one water hole to another.

The sheer abundance of archaic *Homo sapiens*'s tools is in itself enough to affirm that their makers outstripped their predecessors in their ability to gather a living from nature. There is no doubt that these people considerably enlarged the dominion of humankind. The colonizations of new territories that occurred during this period were the greatest expansion of humankind since *Homo erectus* had wandered out of the tropics and into cool latitudes hundreds of thousands of years earlier.

RITUALS AND ART

Discovery after discovery has suggested that the archaic humans probably started some of the activities and beliefs that are considered most characteristic of humankind. They buried their dead (at least occasionally) and may have conceived of a life after death. They possibly attempted to control their own destiny through magical rites. They may even have taken the first hesitant steps into the realm of art. And they cared for aged and handicapped individuals. In fact, it seems that they may have been the first humans to display the complete spectrum of behavior that can be regarded as constituting modern human nature.

Hunting Rites and Magic

It seems possible that these people, like modern hunters-and-gatherers, had rites related to that most vital activity, hunting. The outcome of the hunt affected every individual. It was a matter of great importance that the supply of animals remain plentiful and that the hunters of the band enjoy good luck and safety in the hunt. But nothing in their world was guaranteed. Hunters could be injured. A long spell of bad weather could cut down on the catch. Animal herds might be destroyed by disease, changes in the predator population, or a host of other ecological factors. Mysterious forces operating beyond the horizon could interfere with or prevent animal migrations, causing herds to disappear.

Before this era, these various liabilities had probably been regarded as largely beyond human control. But the Neandertals apparently attempted to manipulate the hidden forces of their universe that controlled success and failure in the hunt: they seem to have practiced hunting magic. One clue to their efforts comes from the Grotto della Basua (Cave of Witches) west of Genoa, Italy. In the depths of the cave, almost 1,500 ft (450 m) from the entrance, Neandertal hunters threw pellets of clay at a stalagmite that to this day has a vaguely animal shape. The inconvenient location of the stalagmite rules out the possibility that this was merely a game or a kind of target practice. The fact that the Neandertal hunters went so far back into the farthest reaches of the cave to throw the pellets suggests that this activity had a magical meaning of some kind.

In 1970 Ralph Solecki discovered apparent evidence of a deer ceremony at a cave in Lebanon. Here, about 50,000 years ago, a fallow deer was dismembered, and the meat was placed on a bed of stones and sprinkled with *red ocher*. The natural pigment was almost certainly intended as a symbol of blood—the blood of the earth, in a sense. The rite seems to represent a ritualistic or magical attempt to control life and death in the deer kingdom.

Red ocher: powdered mineral and earth mixture used as a pigment.

Bear Cult?

The most famous example of what has been claimed to be Neandertal hunting magic is the so-called bear cult. It came to light when a German archaeologist, Emil Bächler, excavated the cave of Drachenloch between 1917 and 1923. Located 8,000 ft (2,400 m) up in the Swiss Alps, this "liar of the dragons" tunnels deep into a mountainside. The front part of the cave, Bächler's work made clear, served as an occasional dwelling place for Neandertals. Farther back, Bächler found a cubical chest made of stones and measuring approximately 3.25 ft (1 m) on a side. The top of the chest was covered by a massive slab of stone. Inside were seven bear skulls, all apparently arranged with their muzzles facing the cave entrance. Still deeper in the cave were six bear skulls, seemingly set in niches along the walls. The Drachenloch find is not unique. At Regourdou in southern France, a rectangular pit, covered by a flat stone weighing nearly a ton, held the bones of more than 20 bears (Figure 15–11).

The original owner of these bones is not in dispute. It was the cave bear, *Ursus spelaeus*, now extinct. A barrel-chested brute that outweighed the grizzly, the cave bear measured 9 ft (2.7 m) from nose to tail. Swift, powerful, and unpredictable, cave bears competed with Neandertals for living quarters in caves. There is considerable dispute, however, over whether the Neandertals deliberately collected and stored cave bear bones (particularly skulls) for rituals of some sort. Supporters of the "bear cult" point to modern rites involving bears among several northerly hunting peoples. Certain Siberian tribes worship bears as the mythical first humans, and the Ainu people of northern Japan used to

FIGURE   15–11 Fact or fancy? For some researchers, the discovery of bear skulls apparently stacked in a pit supports the idea that the cave bear was the center of a Neandertal cult.

consider bears intermediaries between humans and the reigning spirits of the land. The Ainu sacrificed a bear annually in order to ensure good hunting for the coming year.

But skeptics, such as Stanford University's Richard Klein, maintain that purely natural processes may account for the observed occurrence and arrangement of cave bear bones. In Klein's view, bears moving about inside their dens would naturally displace skulls and other bones into depressions in the floor or against the cave walls. Furthermore, rock slabs falling from cave ceilings could give the appearance of covering deliberately cached bones. Finally, and most important, none of the bear bones are associated with Neandertal artifacts, nor do they show any cut marks from stone tools. Thus, for Klein, any association between the bear bones and Neandertals is based strictly on circumstantial evidence.

What conclusion can we draw from these various bits of evidence? A stalagmite pellet-target, an ocher-stained deer carcass, and cave bear bones that *may* have been given special handling and storage—even collectively they provide only shaky support for ritualistic practices by archaic *Homo sapiens* people. In sum, the evidence of a bear cult and other hunting rituals is tantalizing, but inconclusive. Additional discoveries are needed to settle the issue, and until they are forthcoming, the specialists will continue to disagree. The problem is complicated by the fact that the Neandertals and other archaics were so anatomically similar to modern people that we are sorely tempted to view them as like us behaviorally and psychologically as well. Good scientific practice, however, demands that we resist that temptation and not allow our speculations to outrun the available data. We must beware both of overmodernizing our archaic ancestors and of interpreting their behavior as less developed than it really was.

Beginnings of Art?

That the beginnings of art may also have occurred during archaic times seems logical, for the anatomically modern people who lived about 27,000 years B.P. were already accomplished artists who created engravings, statuary, and magnificent cave paintings. The only prehistoric arts of which there can be any surviving evidence are the visual kind. If music was played, it is lost forever. The archaics may have been excellent singers and perhaps even imaginative dancers; dancing is an important form of expression among all known hunting peoples. But what little is known about their visual art indicates a generally low level of artistic accomplishment.

The Neandertals occasionally made use of such natural pigments as red or yellow ocher and black manganese. These occur at Neandertal sites in powder form and sometimes in pencil-shaped pieces that show signs of being rubbed on a soft surface, such as human skin or animal hides.

There is no sign of a representational engraving or statue from this era, and only one or two perforated teeth that might have been used in a necklace, a very common personal ornament among hunters, including later Cro-Magnons. There are a few tantalizing indications, however, that the archaics were beginning to sense the visual possibilities of the materials around them. A cave at Tata in Hungary has yielded both a small engraved stone (Figure 15–12) and a piece of ivory that had been trimmed into an oval shape, polished, and then coated with ocher. At the cave of Pêch de l'Azé in southern France, a Neandertal bored a hole in an

FIGURE 15–12 This small stone from a Mousterian site at Tata in Hungary, dated 50,000 years B.P., carries an engraved cross. We do not know its significance, but the stone is one of the earliest possible examples of artistic or symbolic decoration. This photograph is approximately actual size.

animal bone; the bone may have been an amulet of sorts. From another French cave, at Arcy-sur-Cure, come a pair of oddities: two fossils of marine animals. These are very humble objects indeed, but as they have no obvious utilitarian function, they may be early examples of *objets d'art.* Overall, the evidence for art among archaic *Homo sapiens* is very scanty.

DEATH AND BURIAL

Of all the various indications of the humanlike behavior of the archaics, their practice of burying the dead is the best documented and easiest to interpret. Death is life's bitterest fact, the inescapable defeat at the end of the long struggle to survive and prosper, and humans are not the only creatures saddened by it. Many animals seem momentarily distraught when death claims one of their number; elephants, for instance, have been observed trying to revive a dying member of the herd, even attempting to get it back on its feet by lifting it with their tusks. But only people anticipate the event far in advance, acknowledging that it will inevitably occur, dreading it, refusing to accept it as conclusive, and taking some solace in belief in an afterlife. One mark pointing to this belief among the archaics is their occasional burial of the dead—not known from any earlier stage of human culture.

Evidence of Burial Customs

The Neandertals were not credited with deliberately meaningful burial of their dead until more than a half century after their discovery. The original Neandertal bones taken from the cave in the Neander Valley of Germany may have belonged to someone who was buried by members of the group, although no one suspected so when the bones were found in 1856. The two fossils discovered at Spy in Belgium in 1885 had indeed been buried; apparently fires had been lighted over the bodies, perhaps in an effort to counteract the chill of death. But no one had guessed in 1885 that Spy had been the scene of an ancient burial. Then, in 1908, the cave of La Chapelle-aux-Saints in France almost shouted its evidence of a

Neandertal funeral rite. The excavators found an ancient hunter who had been laid out carefully in a shallow trench. A bison leg may have been placed on his chest, and the trench was filled with broken animal bones and flint tools. These various articles may have been seen as provisions for the world beyond the grave, for it was well known at the time that many modern cultures bury their dead with food, weapons, and other goods. But most experts failed to make the connection.

La Ferrassie (1912–1934)

The evidence continued to turn up. In 1912 two more Neandertal graves were found at the site of La Ferrassie, not far from the cave at La Chapelle. The diggers who carried out the excavation wrote:

> We have been able to recognize, at the base of the Mousterian layer, the existence of two small trenches measuring 70 centimeters wide by 30 centimeters in depth, very precisely cut in half-sphere form in the underlying red-yellowish loamy gravel, filled with a mixture of nearly equal parts of the black earth of the Mousterian fireplace above and of the underlying gravel. The existence of artificially dug graves was absolutely obvious. . . . This is, then, in the clearest way, proof of a funeral rite.

The excavation of the Ferrassie site took many years, and the complete results were not published until 1934. This rock shelter appears to have served as a family cemetery. Six Neandertal skeletons were eventually exhumed: a man, a woman, three children 5 to 6 years old, and an infant (see Figure 15–13). The most perplexing grave was located in the rear of the shelter. Here, in a gently sloping trench, the skeleton and the skull of a child were interred, separated

FIGURE 15–13   The care that Neandertals sometimes lavished on their dead is made clear at La Ferrassie, in France. Here archaeologists have discovered what may be a 60,000-year-old family cemetery, containing the skeletons of two adults and four children. The drawing here shows a site about 85 ft, or 26 m, long. The presumed parents were buried head to head (at locations 1 and 2 in the drawing); two skeletons (3 and 4), possibly of their children, each about 5 years old, were neatly interred near their father's feet. The significance of the nine small mounds is not clear, but one contained the bones of a newborn infant and three beautiful flint tools (5). The triangular stone (6) covered the grave of a 6-year-old child.

by a distance of about 3 ft (0.9 m). The skull was covered by a triangular lime-stone slab whose underside displayed a number of cup-shaped impressions, possibly symbolic markings of some sort. Why were the head and the rest of the body separated? One authority, the Abbé Jean Bouyssonie, a French prehistorian, has suggested that the child was killed and beheaded by a wild animal, and that the head was intentionally buried upslope from the body so that, in the afterlife, it might somehow find its way down the slope and rejoin the trunk. This is a pure guess, but there must be some reason for the odd arrangement.

Middle Eastern and Asian Burials

Several non-European sites have yielded evidence that the Neandertal people buried their dead. Far to the east, on the Crimean peninsula that juts into the Black Sea, the graves of two individuals were found at a cave at Kiik-Koba in 1924. One trench held the remains of a 1-year-old child resting on his side with his legs bent. This skeleton was in poor condition because later inhabitants of the cave had dug a pit for their fire directly over the grave and inadvertently disturbed the bones. Three feet (0.9 m) away from the child was the grave of a man, also lying on his side with his legs tucked up. The body was oriented east to west—as were the Spy fossils and five out of six of the Ferrassie fossils. Possibly the orientation had something to do with the rising or setting sun.

Even farther to the east, at Teshik-Tash in Uzbekistan (Figure 15–7), the partial skeleton of a Neandertal boy was found in a shallow grave surrounded by several pairs of mountain goat horns. The horns may have served some ritual function, but this point is unclear, since goat horns are found throughout the Teshik-Tash deposit and not just in association with human remains.

Finally, perhaps the most amazing Neandertal burial of all was found in the Shanidar cave in Iraq (Figure 15–14). There Ralph Solecki dug down through compressed deposits to uncover a total of nine burials. At the back of the cave, in a layer estimated to be 60,000 years old, he found the grave of a hunter with a badly crushed skull. As a routine procedure, Solecki collected samples of the soil in and around the grave (shown in Figure 15–15) and sent them to a laboratory at the Musée de l'Homme in France. There his colleague Arlette Leroi-Gourhan checked the pollen count, hoping it would provide useful information on the prevailing climate and vegetation.

What she found was completely unexpected. Pollen was present in the grave in unprecedented abundance. Even more astonishing, some of it appeared in clusters, and a few clusters had been preserved along with the parts of the flowers that had supported them. Leroi-Gourhan concluded that no birds or animals or wind could possibly have deposited the material in such a way in the recess of the cave. Masses of flowers may have been placed in the grave by the companions of the dead man. Leroi-Gourhan believes that the hunter was laid to rest on a woven bedding of pine boughs and flowers; more blossoms may very well have been strewn over his body.

Microscopic examination of the pollen indicated that it came from numerous species of bright-colored flowers, related to grape hyacinth, bachelor's button, hollyhock, and groundsel. Some of these plants are used in poultices and herbal remedies by contemporary peoples in Iraq. Perhaps the mourners, too, felt that the blossoms possessed medicinal properties and added them to the grave in an

FIGURE 15–14   Kurdish shepherds, shown here helping with the excavations at Shanidar, still use the cave to shelter themselves and their animals during the cold winters, much as their predecessors did thousands of years ago.

effort to restore the fallen hunter to health in the afterlife. On the other hand, the flowers may have been put there in the same spirit that moves people today to place flowers on graves and gravestones.

These are powerful images, suggesting as they do the beginnings of modern reactions to death. But not all researchers agree with Leroi-Gourtian's interpretation. Some prefer instead a completely naturalistic explanation for the pollen distribution patterns. The case of the Shanidar flower burial remains somewhat problematic.

In sum, there is little doubt that archaic *Homo sapiens*, and perhaps the Neandertals in particular, performed deliberate burials. But does this prove that archaic humans were the first hominids to ritually dispose of deceased group mates? Probably, but the case rests on negative evidence to some extent and is therefore inconclusive. Burial is only one of several types of funeral rite, but it is the one most likely to preserve remains for discovery by later archaeologists. Other funeral patterns, such as ritual exposure of the body to the elements, could have been practiced before the advent of burial customs, leaving no traces. Precisely when hominids began to respond ritually to death remains unclear.

FIGURE 15–15 The skeleton known as Shanidar 4, which pollen tests suggest was buried with bunches of wild flowers related to hyacinths, daisies, and hollyhocks. The age is about 60,000 years.

Also still open to question are such issues as how frequently burials were performed by archaic *Homo sapiens*, how elaborate they were, and what they tell us about these peoples' belief systems. Some researchers feel that the burials reflect archaic humans' belief in a spirit or soul that continued to exist after an individual's death. If true, then we can date the beginnings of religion from archaic *Homo sapiens*. In contrast, skeptics such as Chris Stringer and Clive Gamble suggest that archaic burials were more akin to "corpse disposal" and may tell us little about spirituality. Once again, as with hunting ritual and art, there is abundant room for overmodernizing the archaics, and only additional, well-controlled excavations will clarify the meaning of their burial practices.

The Old and the Handicapped

For many researchers another indication of the archaics' similarity to modern humans was their treatment of old or handicapped individuals. The man of La Chapelle-aux-Saints, for instance, was long past his prime when he died. His skeleton reveals that he had been bent over by arthritis and could not possibly have taken part in a hunt. Even the act of eating must have been difficult for him because he had lost all but two teeth. Had he lived at some earlier time, he might well have been abandoned to starve after his economic usefulness to the group was over. But the Neandertals were evidently not ruled by such stern logic. This man's companions unselfishly provided food, and they probably even softened it for him by partially chewing it.

Concern for the handicapped is suggested also by remains at Shanidar. Some of the bones found there belonged to a 40-year-old man who was probably killed by a rockfall. Study of his skeleton revealed that before his accidental death he had had the use of only one arm; his right arm and shoulder were poorly developed, probably because of an accident in childhood or a birth defect. Despite the major disability, he lived to a ripe age. His front teeth are unusually worn, the wear suggesting that he spent much of his time chewing animal hides to soften them for use as clothes or perhaps that he used his teeth in lieu of his arm to hold objects.

Evidence of Violence

The fact that these people could find a place in their society for aged or handicapped individuals does not necessarily mean that they were always full of love for their fellow humans. It is impossible to know the reason for increased evidence of violence. Perhaps it was due to an increase in population coupled with dependence on inadequate technology to obtain resources. At many sites there is plentiful evidence of the darker side of human nature. A fossil of a man found at Skhūl bears the traces of a fatal spear wound. The point of a wooden spear, long since decayed, had passed through the top of the man's thighbone and the socket of the hipbone, ending up inside the pelvic cavity.

Another ancient act of violence is recorded in the Shanidar deposits. One of the ribs of the fossil of a hunter from the Iraq cave was deeply grooved by the point of a weapon, probably a wooden spear. The top had penetrated the man's chest and perhaps punctured a lung, but this hunter had somehow survived the wound, for the bone shows signs of healing. The original Neandertal man from Germany had also survived a grievous injury, although his recovery was incomplete: his left elbow bones were so misshapen that he could not have raised his hand to his mouth. Whether the damage was done by human or beast will never be known. There may be a hint, however; T. Dale Stewart points out that in the three specimens from Skhūl, Shanidar, and the Neander Valley, the injuries involved the left side of the body. This side would tend to be most easily injured in combat between right-handed opponents.

Evidence of Cannibalism?

That archaic *Homo sapiens* people sometimes killed one another should surprise no one. Perhaps more surprising is the suggestion that they also occasionally ate one another. Among the several reputed cases of archaic *H. sapiens* cannibalism three stand out: Krapina, Hortus, and Monte Circeo. Let us examine each case individually.

The Krapina site in Slovenia was excavated in 1899 and revealed the remains of about 20 Neandertal people—men, women, and children—who lived some 50,000 to 100,000 years ago. Their skulls were in fragments, and their long bones were split, a condition suggesting that both brains and marrow had been consumed. Early investigators interpreted Krapina as a cannibal feast. Recent reanalyses, however, have brought that interpretation into question. While cut marks from stone tools are found on the Krapina bones, it is impossible to tell whether they indicate cannibalism or some sort of preburial preparation of corpses. Furthermore, bone fragmentation at the cave site could have been the result of roof falls, crushing during fossilization, and the use of dynamite during excavation. Although cannibalism remains a possibility, it is not a foregone conclusion.

At Hortus, a French site excavated in 1965, broken and scattered Neandertal remains were once again discovered. The remains were mixed with other animal bones and food refuse, and some researchers drew the conclusion that the ancient inhabitants of the site had made no distinction between human meat and that of bisons or reindeer. Once again, however, careful reanalysis has not supported the original interpretation. At Hortus no stone cut marks are to be found on the Neandertal remains, nor can deliberate splitting of long bones be proved. In short, no evidence of cannibalism exists at this site.

Finally, at the 52,000-year-old site of Monte Circeo, Italy, the skull and jaw of a Neandertal man were discovered in 1939 (Figure 15–16). The find was determined to be evidence of ritual cannibalism because of the separation of the skull from its body, the fact that the foramen magnum had been greatly enlarged, and the apparent placement of the skull in a ring of stones (Figure 15–17). It was widely concluded that the original owner of the skull—a Neandertal man in his 40s—had been killed by a blow to the head and his brains extracted and eaten in some sort of ritual. As in the other cases, however, reanalysis of the Monte Circeo skull using modern techniques and information has told another story. It now appears clear that the Monte Circeo cave was a hyena den in Neandertal times and that the famous skull is all that's left of a hyena's meal. Indeed, close scrutiny reveals hyena gnaw marks at several

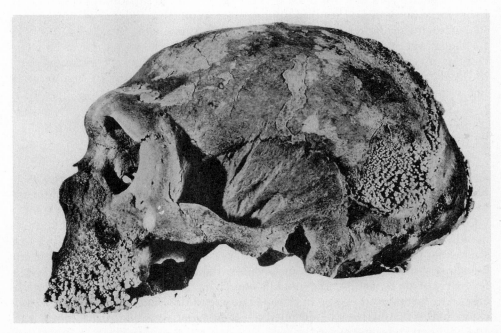

FIGURE 15–16 The skull from the cave at Monte Circeo was a classic Neandertal cranium and was mixed with other bones in a hyena den. Its base was broken open, but the opening showed the tooth marks of hyenas. In other respects the skull is very well preserved. Apart from the lower jaw, the rest of the skeleton has been destroyed. (This photograph is approximately one-half natural size.)

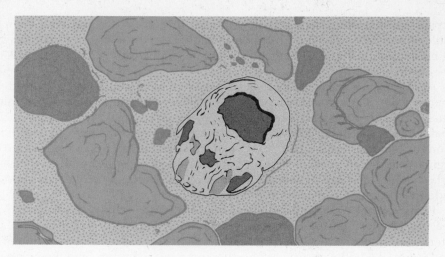

FIGURE 15–17 The Monte Circeo skull, with its enlarged foramen magnum, is shown inside the "ring of stones." Originally thought to reflect ritual cannibalism by Neandertals, the skull is now believed to have been gnawed open by hyenas and the stone ring to be the chance result of a landslide.

places on the skull, including the enlarged basal opening, and stone cut marks are absent. As for the "ring of stone," it appears to have been a natural occurrence caused by a landslide.

It thus appears that we must be very careful about attributing cannibalistic behavior to our archaic *Homo sapiens* ancestors. While the evidence of intraspecific violence—including the use of deadly force—is undeniable, conclusive proof of the consumption of human flesh is lacking. Should such evidence ever be forthcoming, investigators will be faced with determining whether it constitutes proof of ritual cannibalism or dietary cannibalism (the latter being motivated by nothing more than hunger). But for now, the argument is moot.

SUMMARY

Archaic *Homo sapiens* people clearly surpassed their *Homo erectus* ancestors in lithic technology and cultural complexity. Indeed, their cultural accomplishments, in combination with a few key biological adaptations, allowed them to exploit a wide range of climatic zones, including challenging periglacial regions. In the area of lithic technology, the archaic humans showed an increase in tool types and stone-knapping techniques. Of primary importance was the development of the Levallois stone-knapping method. Levallois flakes, disk-core flakes, and even a few early blade tools filled the tool kits of archaic *Homo sapiens* hunters-and-gatherers. The Neandertal people of Europe and the Middle East were generally associated with a distinctive tool kit called the Mousterian, while in Africa the Aterian and Sangoan styles developed.

Clear evidence exists that archaic *Homo sapiens* people occasionally buried their dead, but questions remain about the frequency of this practice and the elaborateness of the burial rituals. Few conclusions can be drawn at present about the state of spirituality, religious beliefs, and rituals among the archaics. Evidence once thought to support a Neandertal bear cult is currently in considerable doubt. The same may be said about evidence of cannibalism. There is no doubt, however, that the archaics occasionally used deadly violence on one another.

Overall, the archaics showed strong progress toward modernity compared to *Homo erectus*. And yet in many ways they were still hovering at the edges of what we today understand as human behavior and culture. One final transformation remained before fully modern people would walk the earth.

REVIEW QUESTIONS

1. Describe the culture (including the lithic technology) of archaic *Homo sapiens* people. How does their culture compare with that of *Homo erectus*, and what does the comparison tell us about the intelligence of the archaics?

2. Compare the nontechnological aspects of archaic *Homo sapiens*'s culture with that of modern people. Argue for or against the notion that the archaics were "human" in the modern sense.

3. Were the burial practices of the Neandertals simply "corpse disposal," or do they reveal a developing spirituality? Summarize the evidence for one or the other point of view.

4. In 1908 Marcellin Boule described the Neandertals as "bestial" creatures who represented "an inferior type [of hominid] closer to the Apes than to any other human group." Based on your knowledge of Neandertal anatomy and culture, how would you respond to Boule?

5. Why were early investigators so quick to read cannibalism into the evidence from Neandertal sites? Discuss the notion that this could be an example of "evolutionary xenophobia," that is, an (unconscious?) attempt to bestialize the Neandertals and thus exclude them from modern human ancestry.

POSTSCRIPT

Humans are simultaneously fascinated and horrified by the thought of cannibalism. It's one of those "Ugh, that's awful . . . but please tell me more!" kinds of topics. We wince and grimace, but we read every gory detail about survival cannibalism following a plane crash or the possibility of ritual cannibalism among the Aztecs. We can't imagine being cannibals ourselves, but for some reason we are fascinated that others might be.

This fascination is easily combined with other seemingly basic human tendencies: ethnocentricism and xenophobia. This nasty trio invariably leads to definitions of "us" as noncannibals and "them" (other ethnic groups, other nationalities, and other species) as at least *suspected* eaters of human flesh. Or to put the dichotomy more bluntly, as noncannibals "we" are *humans* while "they" are something less. And the logic can be conveniently reversed. If "we" already think that some "they" group falls somewhat below our own lofty standards of humanity—perhaps because "they" have a less complex technology—then cannibalism can almost be assumed. Even Charles Darwin succumbed to the lure of this inverted logic and (erroneously) labeled the Fuegian Indians as people who "when pressed in winter by hunger, [will] kill and devour their old women before they kill their dogs." For the civilized young Englishman, it was all too easy to believe that the "savages" of Tierra del Fuego had to be cannibals.

And the use of cannibalism as a yardstick for separating "humans" from "less than humans" has proved popular not only when applied to living people, but also when extended into prehistory. Thus it comes as no surprise that the Neandertals, described by Boule and others as "bestial" and "apelike," should come under suspicion. They didn't really *look* human, and so they probably didn't *act* human either. Discoveries of bodiless heads, opened braincases, and split long bones confirmed the worst suspicions: the Neandertals really weren't human like us because they ate each other!

Today the old knee-jerk tendency to label all "others" as cannibals is diminishing, but experts still disagree about the actual extent of the practice both historically and in prehistoric times. For example, in a little book called *The Man-Eating Myth*, American anthropologist W. Arens reexamined most of the primary claims of historic cannibalism and concluded that "the available evidence does not permit the facile assumption that [cannibalism] *was or has ever been* a prevalent cultural feature. It is more reasonable to conclude that the idea of the cannibalistic nature of others is a *myth*" (italics added). These sentiments were recently echoed by Paul Bahn of Hull University: "There are no reliable first-hand witnesses of [cannibalism], and almost all [historical and ethnographic] reports are based on hearsay."

Contrary to the position taken by Arens and Bahn, however, recent prehistory may provide a couple of reliable cases of cannibalism. At the site of Fontbrégoua Cave in southeastern France, butchery marks and bone breakage patterns strongly suggest that anatomically modern agricultural people practiced a bit of cannibalism there some 6,000 years ago (whether it was ritual or dietary—including starvation—cannibalism is impossible to tell). In a similar case, Tim White of the University of California at Berkeley recently published a convincing case for cannibalism among the twelfth-century A.D. Anasazi people of Mancos Canyon in southwestern Colorado. At Mancos, the evidence includes not only butchered and broken human bones, but also bones marked by the "pot polish" that results from being cooked in a ceramic vessel. As at Fontbrégoua, the explanation of cannibalism at Mancos remains unclear.

But despite these relatively well-documented cases (and even these are challenged by some other workers), older notions of widespread cannibalism in prehistory no longer seem tenable. With particular reference to the Neandertals, as noted earlier in this chapter, almost all reports of cannibalism are better explained in terms of skeletal damage during fossilization and excavation or damage by predators such as hyenas. So, were the Neandertals cannibals? Probably not. Are modern humans cannibals? Only rarely, despite our suspicions about people different from ourselves. It appears that the concept of cannibalism tells us more about how our own brains work than about the behavior of variously defined "they" groups now or in the past.

CHAPTER 15 TIMELINE

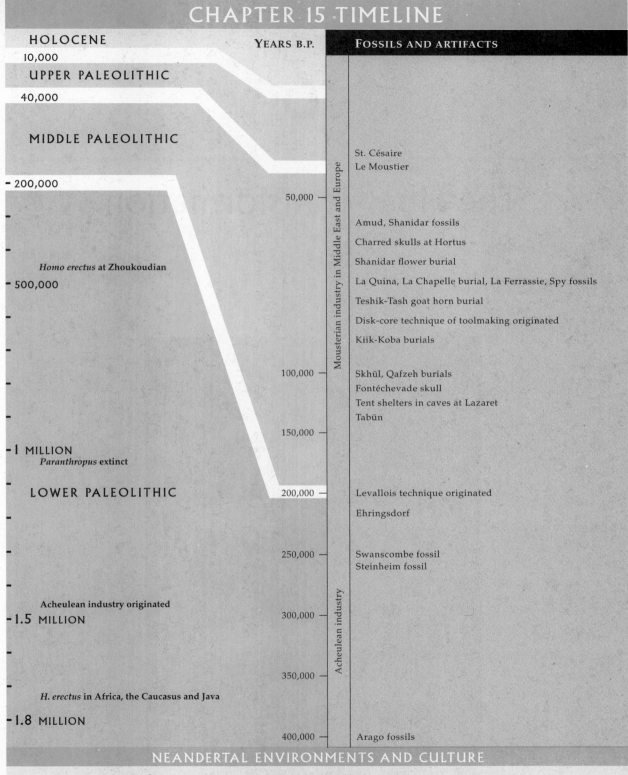

	YEARS B.P.	FOSSILS AND ARTIFACTS

HOLOCENE
10,000

UPPER PALEOLITHIC
40,000

MIDDLE PALEOLITHIC

− 200,000

Homo erectus at Zhoukoudian

− 500,000

− 1 MILLION
Paranthropus extinct

LOWER PALEOLITHIC

Acheulean industry originated
− 1.5 MILLION

H. erectus in Africa, the Caucasus and Java

− 1.8 MILLION

YEARS B.P.:
50,000
100,000
150,000
200,000
250,000
300,000
350,000
400,000

Mousterian industry in Middle East and Europe

Acheulean industry

FOSSILS AND ARTIFACTS:

St. Césaire
Le Moustier

Amud, Shanidar fossils
Charred skulls at Hortus
Shanidar flower burial
La Quina, La Chapelle burial, La Ferrassie, Spy fossils
Teshik-Tash goat horn burial
Disk-core technique of toolmaking originated
Kiik-Koba burials

Skhūl, Qafzeh burials
Fontéchevade skull
Tent shelters in caves at Lazaret
Tabūn

Levallois technique originated

Ehringsdorf

Swanscombe fossil
Steinheim fossil

Arago fossils

NEANDERTAL ENVIRONMENTS AND CULTURE

The age of many of these specimens is still in doubt but the order of antiquity shown here is probably correct.

CHAPTER
16

The Final Transformation

*T*he troubles of our proud and angry dust
  Are from eternity, and shall not fail.
Bear them, we can, and if we can we must.

A. E. HOUSMAN, 1859–1936.
Last Poems, IX.

OVERVIEW

Fully modern people (*Homo sapiens sapiens*) evolved from archaic stock around 130,000 years ago, but the details—biological, cultural, and geographic—of that transformation are matters of considerable controversy. Two major evolutionary scenarios are currently being debated. The "regional-continuity" model holds that modern humans evolved more-or-less independently in several geographic regions, the species' unity being maintained by gene flow. In contrast, the "rapid-replacement" model holds that anatomically modern people evolved only once, most likely in Africa or the Middle East, and then spread quickly across the Old World, replacing all nonmodern hominids. This chapter discusses the evidence—cultural, anatomical, molecular, and fossil—supporting these competing evolutionary models. In addition, the spread of modern humans to the Americas and to Australia is described. Important topics and concepts in this chapter include the anatomy of fully modern people; the emergence of the Upper Paleolithic; fossil evidence supporting the regional-continuity and rapid-replacement models; the fate of the Neandertals in the transformation to modernity; mtDNA evidence of the geographic origin of modern people; and the colonization of the Americas and Australia.

Homo sapiens sapiens: anatomically modern people; first evolved around 130,000 years B.P.

FIRST MODERN PEOPLE

In recent years prehistorians have begun to seek the origins of modern humankind in diverse parts of the globe: Africa, the Orient, and Australia. But the story of the discovery of the first modern people begins in the Dordogne region of France (Figures 16–1 and 16–2), where four generations of archaeologists from many countries have excavated and analyzed and argued since 1868, when the first site was laid bare. This important discovery takes us back again to the nineteenth century, 12 years after the first Neandertal find, but still long before anyone really understood its implications or the full meaning of human evolution.

Discovery in the Dordogne (1868)

The discovery was made prosaically enough by a gang of railway workers cutting into a hillside just outside the village of Les Eyzies. They dug out the earth from an overhanging rock shelter in one of the many limestone cliffs that loom over the village, and with the dirt came bones and what looked like stone tools. Scientists summoned to the site soon uncovered the remains of at least four human skeletons: a middle-aged man, one or two younger men, a young woman, and a child 2 or 3 weeks old. The skeletons were similar to those of modern humans and were

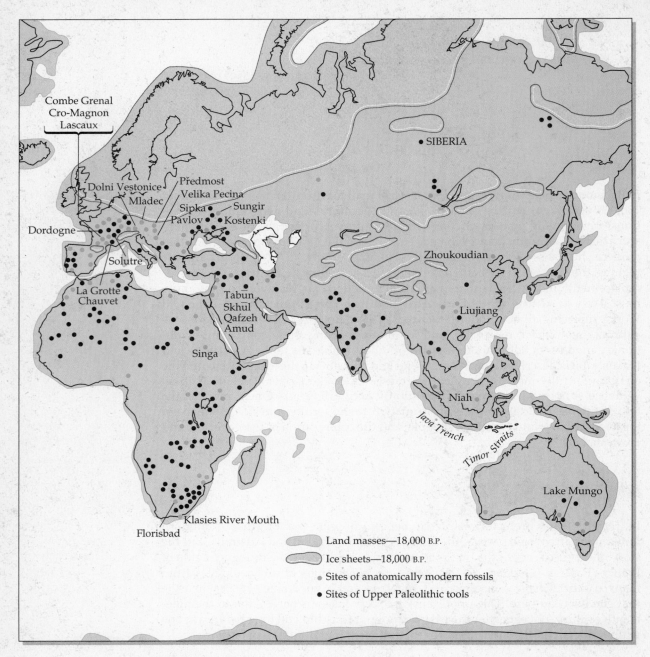

FIGURE 16–1 Anatomically modern fossils and related archaeological sites are today being discovered in many regions of the Old World. Humans of modern aspect lived in many places and varied environments and their population and technology rapidly developed.

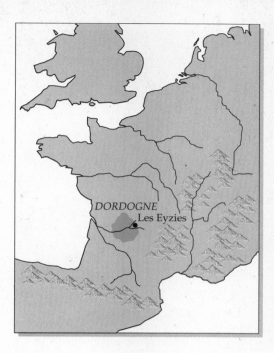

FIGURE 16-2 Many of the sites where humans are known to have lived about 30,000 years ago are in Europe, particularly in the Dordogne in southwestern France. The caves in which these people sheltered themselves from the ice age glaciers also protected and preserved their artifacts and bones for hundreds of centuries.

buried with flint tools and weapons, seashells pierced with holes, and animal teeth similarly perforated, probably to make ornaments.

The name of the rock shelter was Cro-Magnon, in garbled recognition of a local hermit called Magnon who had lived there. And so the name *Cro-Magnon* was affixed to these newfound humans. In the strict archaeological application, which we shall follow here, the name applies only to the people who lived in southwestern France from about 35,000 to 10,000 years ago, during a period in Europe technically known as the Upper Paleolithic.

The limestone cliffs in the Dordogne region seem peculiarly adapted to human habitation (see Figure 16–3). These masses of rocks were formed more than 100 million years ago by the accumulation of tiny lime-containing animals on the floor of the shallow ocean that once covered most of Europe. The skeletons of these minute animals formed, in time, a building material that was to be immensely useful to humankind. Strong but water-soluble, the exposed lime of the Dordogne cliffs is honeycombed with rivers, streams, and waterfalls, which have hollowed out ledges, shelters, and caves.

The entrance to one cave, Font-de-Gaume, halfway up a cliff that juts out into a little valley, effectively commanded the approach of animals, friends, or enemies. Surely, over tens of thousands of years, these cliffs positively affected the formation of human character in this region. In a sense, they provided a stage setting that enabled humans to see themselves as dominant creatures in their local environment. During the times when people lived there more-or-less permanently, the cliff dwellings must have enhanced their sense of identity and contributed to early stirrings of community pride. Here were their burial pits and the secret shrines where rituals of the hunt were performed. Here were the scenes of their mating and the birthplace of their children. The beauty of the area around Les Eyzies must have aroused strong attachments in the Cro-Magnon people, just as living humans have a special feeling for "home."

Cro-Magnon: anatomically modern humans living in southwestern France between 35,000 and 10,000 years ago.

FIGURE 16–3   Excavation of a rock shelter in the Dordogne called Abri Pataud. A steel grid has been constructed to enable the excavator to plot the depth and position of every fragment of archaeological evidence. The overhanging limestone cliffs extend upward and outward.

A more concrete advantage of the Dordogne region was the extraordinary natural riches it offered its prehistoric inhabitants. The Massif Central, a mountainous plateau that covers most of central France, begins about 50 mi (80 km) east of Les Eyzies. Its high plains would have been a fruitful summer hunting ground that provided reindeer, horses, and bison in abundance. West of Les Eyzies, the coastal plain stretching toward the Atlantic was also good grazing ground. The Vézère River ran then in much the same course as it does now, providing water and, to the successors of those who learned to take advantage of it, a ready supply of fish. Many of the caves and shelters face south, offering warmth and protection from the cold winds of winter. Although many peoples around the world 30,000 to 20,000 years ago were probably nomadic, following game through seasonal migrations, it seems likely that the hunters who lived in this fortunate region were able to stay there for the greater part of the year.

Characteristics of Anatomically Modern People

In the years since the discovery of the fossils in France, the ancient skeletal remains of anatomically modern people have been turning up all over the world:

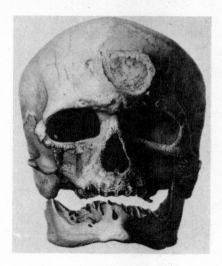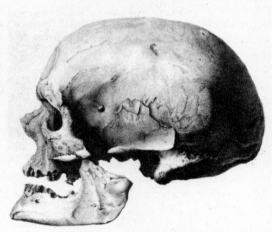

FIGURE 16–4   Nineteenth-century drawings of the fossilized skull from Cro-Magnon, France, the first of the very early specimens of modern *Homo sapiens* to be found. Notice the well-developed chin and the high forehead. The drawings are approximately one-third actual size.

in Hungary, in Russia, in the Middle East, in North and South Africa, in China and Southeast Asia, and even in Australia and North and South America (see Figure 16–1). Not all the fossils are complete, of course, and some are no more than fragments, but everywhere they are anatomically modern.

The bones of these fossils are frequently less massive than those of their predecessors. Further, their skulls are generally like the skulls of people living today, with a definite chin, a high forehead, and a cranial capacity equal to that of modern humans (see Figure 16–4). We also believe that these people had the necessary physical equipment to construct complex and elaborate patterns of speech such as we ourselves use. The existing human languages are closely related and probably originated about 40,000 years B.P. Possibly, the range of vocalizations available to them was also just as great as those we hear today. We have no evidence, beyond that discussed in Chapter 13, of the kind of language that may have preceded this period.

FATE OF ARCHAIC *HOMO SAPIENS*

But what became of the Neandertals and other archaics who struggled so hard against the world around them to sustain their developing humanity? Some paleoanthropologists believe that many, though not all, evolved into modern *Homo sapiens*. A few make no exceptions and feel that all, including the European Neandertals, evolved into modern humans. Many researchers, however, believe that most archaic populations became extinct and were replaced by modern people from elsewhere. Exactly where they may have originated is one of the main topics of this chapter.

Sequence of Tools

Only a few years ago textbooks cited the sequence of tool-bearing layers in caves and rock shelters in western Europe as proof that all Neandertals became extinct.

It was thought that the tools made by Neandertals declined in number and quality as the end of their period neared; then no tools were made at all, the result being sterile layers with no sign of human habitation; then brand-new styles of tools abruptly began. This was interpreted as a clear sign of one people's becoming extinct and another's arriving on the scene.

Although an off-and-on sequence of tool-bearing strata—Neandertal layers fading into sterile layers followed by Cro-Magnon layers—is indeed found at some Neandertal sites, archaeologists have now discovered many exceptions. At some sites, successive layers show that toolmaking proficiency rose, rather than declined. Also, sterile layers do not always appear between layers containing Neandertal and Cro-Magnon tools; more often, there is no break, a fact indicating that occupation of the site was virtually continuous. Finally, the differences between Neandertal and Cro-Magnon tools do not necessarily indicate that one culture disappeared to be replaced by an unrelated one.

Flakes and Blades

As explained in Chapter 15, with few exceptions, the tools associated with archaic *Homo sapiens* peoples all over the world are categorized as *Middle Paleolithic*, a word derived from the Greek *palai* ("long ago") and *lithos* ("stone"); the term is a broad one that covers Mousterian tools and related types like the Sangoan and Aterian from Africa, and also some Asian industries. (The *Lower Paleolithic* includes earlier stone industries such as the Oldowan and Acheulean.) The comparable term for tools associated *primarily* with anatomically modern people is *Upper Paleolithic*. Most Middle Paleolithic tools consist of flat flakes shaped and retouched to provide the desired working edge. Upper Paleolithic toolmakers produced flakes, too, but they specialized in a kind known as *blades,* which are essentially parallel-sided and at least twice as long as they are wide. This shift in the fundamental unit of the tool kit is marked enough so that many collections of Middle and Upper Paleolithic tools can be distinguished at a glance.

Blades are more economical to make than flakes because they yield more than five times as much cutting edge per pound of stone. Progress is also apparent in craftsmanship. Tools of the Upper Paleolithic are more finely made, requiring extremely precise chipping to produce the desired point, notch, or cutting edge. And there are many more kinds of special-purpose tools. Upper Paleolithic kits often include a high percentage of *burins*–chisellike tools useful, as we shall see, for cutting bone, antler, and ivory.

Burin: a chisellike tool used to shape other materials, such as bone, antler, and wood; a tool for making tools.

Indeed, the use of nonlithic materials that could be shaped, such as bone, antler and ivory, is an important marker distinguishing Upper Paleolithic assemblages from earlier cultures. In addition, as detailed in Chapter 17, the Upper Paleolithic saw the true beginnings of art, the full development of elaborate burial rituals, the refinement of shelter construction and use of fire, and the development of extensive trade networks.

The details of the technological shift from the Middle Paleolithic to the Upper Paleolithic are hazy despite many years of diligent archaeological work. In Southeast Asia, blade industries began to appear in some areas around 30,000 to 20,000 years B.P. In contrast, prehistoric Australians apparently never reached the level of Upper Paleolithic stone technology. And it has become clear recently that, in Europe, western Asia (including the Middle East), and Africa, the transition was not as clean as once thought. For example, the Mousterian industry included some blade tools although, compared to those of succeeding Upper Paleolithic industries, the frequencies were quite low. Furthermore, in both the Middle East (at Tabūn) and South Africa (at Klasies River Mouth), cultural sequences have been discovered that show Upper Paleolithic blade assemblages alternating with Mousterian or other Middle Paleolithic industries. Some archaeologists now speak of the early and tentative appearance of "pre–Upper Paleolithic" technology between 70,000 and 50,000 years ago, 10,000 years or more before the traditional date for the start of the Upper Paleolithic.

In fact, it is no longer even correct to attribute all Middle Paleolithic (especially Mousterian) artifacts to archaic *Homo sapiens* (especially Neandertals) and all Upper Paleolithic artifacts to fully modern people. At Skhūl and Qafzeh in the Middle East, early anatomically modern (or near-modern) fossils were accompanied by Mousterian implements, while at the French sites of Arcy-sur-Cure and St. Césaire, undoubted Neandertal fossils (dating to 36,000 years B.P. at St. Césaire) were found in association with an Upper Paleolithic industry called the *Chatelperronian*.

Chatelperronian: an Upper Paleolithic tool culture of western Europe, largely contemporaneous with the Aurignacian culture (40,000 to 27,000 years B.P.).

Aurignacian and Chatelperronian Industries

Known primarily from northern Spain and France, the *Aurignacian* and Chatelperronian industries marked the appearance of the Upper Paleolithic in Europe. Broadly contemporaneous, these cultural traditions shared an emphasis on blade technology, plus the appearance of well-made bone implements and objects of personal adornment such as beads and pendants. Despite their similarities, however, the Aurignacian and Chatelperronian industries appear to tell very different stories about the origins of the European Upper Paleolithic.

The Aurignacian industry (Figure 16–5), with its finely retouched blade tools, was so completely unlike any typical Middle Paleolithic style that it almost certainly was imported into western Europe, apparently from the east. Although the physical identity of the very earliest Aurignacians (ca. 40,000 years B.P.) remains

Aurignacian: an Upper Paleolithic, mainly European, tool culture that existed from about 40,000 to 27,000 years ago.

 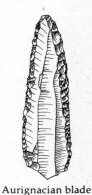 

Scraper   Aurignacian blade   Scraper

FIGURE 16–5 Typical Aurignacian tools of the Upper Paleolithic. The Aurignacian appears to have developed in the East, probably in western Asia. The most typical Aurignacian tool was the blade, much longer and narrower than any scraper. The Aurignacian retouching was very fine. The tools were made from a specially prepared core. The drawings are approximately one-half actual size.

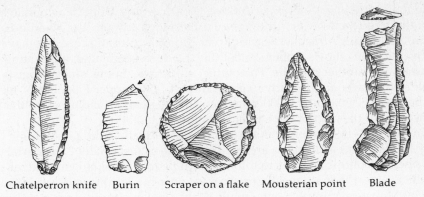

Chatelperron knife   Burin   Scraper on a flake   Mousterian point   Blade

FIGURE 16–6 Typical Chatelperronian tools of the Upper Paleolithic. This tradition began with strongly marked Mousterian features and included Mousterian points, flakes, and other tools (compare with Figure 15–8). Later tool kits contained a high proportion of burins and points. These drawings are approximately one-half actual size.

undetermined, by 30,000 years ago they were fully modern Cro-Magnons. At most European sites, the Aurignacian replaced the preceding Mousterian culture more-or-less abruptly, a fact suggesting to many anthropologists the rapid replacement of archaic *Homo sapiens* people by fully modern humans.

In contrast, the Chatelperronian industry (Figure 16–6) seems to have been an indigenous development that originated in Spain and France from a variant of the Mousterian (the Mousterian of Acheulean tradition). In addition to sidescrapers, denticulates, and Mousterian points, the Chatelperronian included blades, burins, endscrapers, and numerous bone artifacts. As noted above, the Chatelperronian is associated with Neandertal remains at St. Césaire and Arcy-sur-Cure. The question is: Do these sites really reflect Neandertal involvement in the development of the European Upper Paleolithic, and, more important, do they provide evidence that the Neandertals evolved physically into modern people? Although there are sharp differences of opinion on the subject, many paleoanthropologists agree with Richard Klein that the Chatelperronian is best explained as being the result of traits diffusing from the Aurignacian into an otherwise Mousterian cultural context. In other words, the Chatelperronian may simply represent cultural diffusion from modern humans to Neandertals and may not imply any ancestor-descendant relationship between the two.

At present, it appears safest to view the Upper Paleolithic as broadly starting in Europe, western Asia, and Africa about 40,000 years ago (thus overlapping briefly with the end of the Middle Paleolithic) and primarily as the result of cultural innovations by *Homo sapiens sapiens*. Klein and others think that the Upper Paleolithic transformation was the result of a "biologically based [advance] in human mental and cognitive capacity," that is, the achievement of full modernity of the human brain.

Fossil Record

Fossils would give us a more direct line of inquiry than tools into the fate of the archaic humans, provided enough could be found. With a complete series of fossils from all over the world dated from about 130,000 to 30,000 years ago, any amateur could study the remains and tell what happened to the archaics. Regrettably the trail of humanity through this period is not yet well enough marked by bones nor is it accurately dated.

No Neandertal fossil has been given a reliable date more recent than 36,000 years B.P. (St. Césaire). A date of about 34,000 years B.P. has been published for a frontal bone of modern form found at the European site of Velika Pečina. After that, the oldest securely dated modern skeletal material from Europe comes from a site near the town of Pavlov in the Czech Republic at about 26,000 years B.P. (Figure 16–1).

Sites bearing Upper Paleolithic cultures, most of which we can reasonably assume indicate the presence of humans of modern aspect, are much older. The earliest in Europe date from around 40,000 years B.P. and have been excavated in Poland, Hungary, and Spain. In contrast, the earliest such site known in France (which is very rich in archaeological remains of this period) is dated 34,000 years B.P., a date that suggests that the archaics survived longer in France than in the surrounding areas.

Elsewhere in the world we have few well-dated sites, but the overall picture is that modern *Homo sapiens* appeared earlier there than in Europe. A cave in south China, at Liujiang, has yielded anatomically modern remains dated at 67,000 years B.P., and from similar fossils found at a place called Salawuzu, we have a date of 37,000 to 50,000 years B.P. A skull from Niah in Sarawak on the island of Borneo carries an early (but questionable) date of 40,000 years B.P. but is supported by Australian evidence from two skeletons with a date of 25,000 years B.P. There is also impressive archaeological evidence from Australia going back beyond 40,000 years B.P.

Africa (south of the Sahara) has yielded some very early sites containing remains which are modern in form. Some may be over 130,000 years old. While the dating of many of these sites can be questioned, the evidence as a whole (which is reviewed in a later section) is impressive. Our conclusions at present must be that western Europe was, at this period, a backwater, almost isolated from the mainstream of human evolution, and this state of affairs may well be attributable to the barriers of ice of the last glaciation (Figure 16–1).

The main landmasses of the Old World were probably fully, if sparsely, populated at 130,000 years B.P. by archaic humans. But from 40,000 years B.P. onward we find increasing evidence of anatomically modern people more-or-less indistinguishable from the present populations of these lands. They were modern from head to toe, talented as artists, and skilled in a wide range of technology. We must now ask ourselves how the transition was made, and where, when, and why.

Anatomical Comparison: Archaic and Modern People

The first step in attempting to trace human evolution through this fascinating 90,000-year period is to assess the physical difference between archaic and modern humans, a procedure that is not as easy as it sounds. When two extreme fossil types—for example, the old man from La Chapelle-aux-Saints and the middle-aged man from the original Cro-Magnon site—are viewed side by side, the difference seems tremendous (Figure 16–7). The classic Neandertal skull has a long, low cranium, bulging at the sides, with a protruding bun at the rear, a slanting forehead, and a heavy brow ridge. The modern skull has a high cranium, rounded at the rear and vertical at the sides, with a vertical forehead and no brow ridge to speak of. The faces are quite dissimilar, too. The Neandertal has

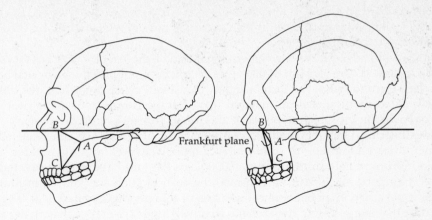

FIGURE 16–7   The (somewhat reconstructed) Neandertal skull of La Chapelle, left, is here compared with an anatomically modern skull. The horizontal line, called the *Frankfurt plane*, which passes through the lower margin of the orbit and the auditory meatus, or ear hole, enables the skulls to be drawn in the correct orientation. The differing triangles, A-B-C, indicate the altered position of the jaws in relation to the braincase and the face. Other striking differences include the size of the brow ridges, the development of the chin, and the shape of the braincase.

an out-thrust face, a broad nose, and a large, chinless jaw. By contrast, the modern face is flat and carries a smaller nose and a distinct chin. But these are the extremes. Some other archaics, such as Swanscombe and Steinheim (Figure 14–10), had smaller jaws, higher-vaulted craniums, little sign of a torus at the back of the skull, fairly steep foreheads, and only a moderate brow ridge. And some Upper Paleolithic peoples had a rather pronounced brow ridge, sloping foreheads, and large jaws.

Visual comparison of fossils is such a fallible approach that paleoanthropologists have been resorting more and more to statistical comparisons of tooth size, cranial height, brow formation, and so on. These efforts have gone a long way toward dispelling old impressions. Many scientists once believed that Neandertals had strayed far from the mainstream of human evolution. But as we saw in Chapter 14, they had not: the range of variability of many archaic features overlapped with the modern range of variability. Similarly, most early authorities believed that the western European Neandertals were remarkably homogeneous. Their alleged lack of variety was interpreted to mean that they had somehow lost evolutionary flexibility, had become specialized, and had come to a dead end. Now, however, statistical analyses have indicated that the range of variability within archaic populations was as great as the variability among *Homo sapiens* populations today.

The Regional-Continuity Model

It helps to know that archaic humans came in many shapes and sizes, and that these were sometimes matched by the various conformations of the first modern humans. There is no doubt that somewhere the evolutionary gap was crossed by a steady progression of changes, each so small as to be imperceptible, yet all adding up to the differences between archaic and modern. What follows is a brief, region-by-region summary of the skeletal material supporting the belief that,

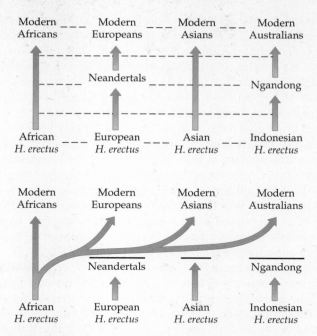

FIGURE 16–8 The hypothesis of regional continuity is illustrated above: *Homo erectus* people on each continent evolved through archaic *H. sapiens* into modern humans. Below is the hypothesis of rapid replacement, in which modern *H. sapiens* from Africa migrated throughout the world and replaced archaic populations living in Eurasia and Africa. (After C. B. Stringer and C. Gamble, 1993.)

through a long series of small changes, the features of most archaic populations in the world become those of modern peoples. This is the hypothesis of regional continuity (Figure 16–8).

In the Middle East, an ancestral relationship between the archaic and modern people seems possible. This is the only locality where a series of candidates for an intermediate type of human has appeared. The fossils from Skhūl and Qafzeh in Israel seem to bridge the gap somewhat. Although generally regarded as modern, the skulls display several distinctly archaic traits.

In eastern Europe, although intermediates are missing, an ancestral relationship seems possible, for the most recent of the archaic specimens appear rather advanced, and the oldest of the modern forms appear rather robust. In particular, the skulls from Mladec, Pavlov, and Předmost and a jaw from Sipka in the Czech Republic (Figure 16–1), which are among the oldest Upper Paleolithic skulls (some probably more than 30,000 years old), have some archaic features.

In Southeast Asia, an ancestral relationship seems remotely possible, because fossils from Australia (dated to only about 10,000 years B.P.) are claimed to suggest an anatomical link between the skulls from the Solo River in Java and the most ancient fossils of Australian Aborigines, which date back to 25,000 years B.P. and were full-fledged modern *Homo sapiens*. Regional-continuity supporters also point out several distinctive features of the forehead and brows that seem to link modern Aborigines to Javanese *Homo erectus*.

In Africa there are a number of skulls known from the period between 130,000 and 90,000 years B.P., some of which can be interpreted as intermediate in form, though they hardly constitute a series. Very robust archaic skulls include the famous skull found in 1921 at Kabwe, Zambia, and the Elandsfontein skull fragments from South Africa. Then there are more lightly built intermediate remains from Omo and Ngaloba, Tanzania. These are all dated between 130,000 and 100,000 years B.P. A partial skeleton from Omo Kibish appears particularly modern.

The most significant finds from Africa, however, come from cave deposits at the Klasies River Mouth on the Tsitsikama coast of Cape Province, in the Republic of South Africa (RSA). Here lower jaw fragments (including a well-developed chin) and cranial fragments have been excavated which are believed to be as much as 130,000 years old. The date has been checked and rechecked and appears to be sound. What is extraordinary is that the remains almost certainly belong to an anatomically modern population of *Homo sapiens.* This site has therefore delivered some of the earliest known anatomically modern people in the world and supports the view that Africa was the center of this important evolutionary development. This claim is supported further by finds from another cave site, Border Cave, far to the north, on the Swaziland border, and from other sites (Table 16–1) which are somewhat younger (60,000 to 75,000 years B.P.).

Thus, although the evidence is still sparse and many dates need further confirmation, a minority of researchers believe that the fossils reveal a broad-scale transformation of *Homo erectus* into modern humans via an archaic *Homo sapiens* stage. In this view, archaics all over the Old World—including the Neandertals—very likely contributed to the modern human gene pool. How this transformation may have taken place is shown in Figure 16–8. Basically, the regional-continuity model depends on the occurrence of extensive gene flow between the various populations of *Homo erectus* and, later, archaic *Homo sapiens* people. Africa is viewed as having exchanged genes with Eurasia, which in turn shared with East and Southeast Asia

Table 16–1 REMAINS OF SOME ANATOMICALLY MODERN AND ARCHAIC *HOMO SAPIENS* FOSSILS FROM AFRICA, DATED BETWEEN 50,000 AND 400,000 YEARS B.P.

Site	Anatomical Type	Approximate Age	Date of Discovery
Ndutu, Tanzania	Archaic	200,000–400,000	1973
Elandsfontein, RSA	Archaic	130,000–300,000	1953
Kabwe, Zambia	Archaic	130,000–250,000	1921
Omo Kibish 2, Ethiopia	Archaic	ca. 130,000	1967
Florisbad, RSA	Intermediate	100,000–200,000	1932
Ngaloba, Laetoli, Tanzania	Intermediate	ca. 130,000	1978
Omo Kibish 1, Ethiopia	Modern	ca. 130,000	1967
Singa, Sudan	Intermediate	100,000–200,000	1924
Klasies River Mouth, RSA	Modern	120,000–130,000	1972
Border Cave, RSA	Modern	50,000–85,000	1941
Die Kelders Cave, RSA	Modern	60,000–75,000	1976
Equus Cave, RSA	Modern	60,000–75,000	1985
Dar-es-Soltan, Cave 2, Morocco	Modern	50,000–70,000	1975

Note: Several of the times given are approximate, but they do give some idea of the antiquity of the evidence.

and Australia. In Figure 16–8, these genetic connections are shown as horizontal dashed lines between the various regions. Because of gene flow, regional-continuity supporters argue, new traits evolving in one region would have been carried inevitably to all other regions, and thus all of humanity would have evolved more-or-less simultaneously from the level of *Homo erectus* to full modernity.

If the theory of regional continuity is correct, the emergence of modern people from *Homo erectus* stock occurred by means of phyletic transformation, the gradual conversion of an entire species (see Fig. 3–17). This is very different from the branching model of allopatric speciation described in Chapter 3. Under allopatric speciation, a peripheral population first becomes geographically isolated from its parent species. Then evolutionary processes such as natural selection and genetic drift modify the population so that it ultimately becomes *reproductively isolated* from the parent unit and must be recognized as a new species and given its own name. In the allopatric model the naming situation is clear: new names are given when new branches, each believed to be reproductively isolated from every other branch, appear on the evolutionary bush. In contrast, in the model of phyletic transformation, the identification and naming of new species is less clear-cut, primarily because of the temporal and geographic breadth of the process. This problem of identifying and naming species can be illustrated by the two transformationist interpretations that can be applied to the hominid case. In most instances of phyletic transformation, a new name is introduced after the achievement of some *arbitrary* amount of specieswide change. Thus, on the human continuum, one might establish two *chronospecies: Homo erectus*, including all hominines alive between 1.6 and 0.4 million years B.P., and their successors, *Homo sapiens*. Alternately, if you believe that only *intraspecific* transformation has occurred, no new name is justified. If this second argument is applied to humans, for reasons of historical priority all hominines of the last 1.6 million years would be labeled *Homo sapiens*.

Naming confusion aside, at present most anthropologists reject the regional-continuity model for several reasons. First, it seems likely that in most organisms speciation occurs much less often through phyletic transformation than by allopatric isolation and branching, and there is little reason to think that humans should be an exception to the rule. Second, as detailed below, the hominid fossil record actually lends itself better to a branching model than to one of broad-scale transformation. And third, molecular studies generally point to an allopatric, branching origin for modern people. The branching model favored by most anthropologists is variously called the *rapid-replacement*, or *"out-of-Africa," hypothesis*, and it is to that model that we now turn our attention.

Chronospecies: the sort of "species" that are created when an unbroken evolutionary continuum is arbitrarily divided into time-defined units.

The Rapid-Replacement Model

Without doubt, the strongest evidence for the rapid-replacement model is the clear occurrence of anatomically modern humans in the adjacent regions of Africa and the Middle East long before they showed up in Europe, Asia, and Australia—a pattern that strongly implies a single, branching origin. As shown in Table 16–1, modern humans were apparently living in South and East Africa as early as 130,000 years ago. Relevant fossils come from Omo Kibish and the Klasies River Mouth. The archaic and archaic-modern transitional populations that were likely to have given rise to these early moderns have been discovered at Elandsfontein,

Kabwe, Ngaloba, and Singa. In addition, very early (90,000 to 190,000 years B.P.) archaic-modern transitional fossils have been found in North Africa at the Moroccan site of Jebel Irhoud. By 80,000 to 120,000 years ago, essentially modern people were inhabiting such Middle Eastern sites as Skhūl and Qafzeh.

In comparison, the appearance of anatomically modern humans outside Africa and the Middle East was everywhere much later. Cro-Magnon people first appeared in Europe sometime after 40,000 years ago, and as shown by the skull from Liujiang, anatomically modern humans were present in China by 67,000 years B.P. In addition, Niah Cave in Sarawak has produced modern fossils dating to 40,000 years B.P., just slightly older than the modern material from the Upper Cave at Zhoukoudian (ca. 25,000 years B.P.). And finally, there is evidence of the occupation of northern Australia—presumably by modern people—by 55,000 years B.P. A brief survey of the fossil record, therefore, provides rather stark evidence in favor of an African–Middle Eastern birthplace for anatomically modern people.

Detailed comparative analyses of the known fossils also seem primarily to support the rapid-replacement model. For example, University of Cambridge anthropologist Marta Mirazon Lahr recently took a close look at the cranial traits claimed to reflect morphological continuity from *Homo erectus* to modern people in East Asia and Australia. She concluded that the features in question "are not exclusive to these regions, either spatially or temporally, and some occur at a higher incidence in other populations." Based on her studies, Lahr favors the hypothesis of a single African origin for modern humans. In a similar vein, American paleoanthropologist Diane Waddle recently conducted a matrix correlation test of the regional-continuity and rapid-replacement models in which she compared the fossils from 12 geographical and chronological regions of the Old World. In this study several different matrix correlation values were calculated based on varying assumptions about the place of initial appearance of modern people and the degrees and patterns of gene flow. Waddle concluded that her work "support[s] a single African and/or [Middle Eastern] origin for modern humans."

Finally, there are now several genetic studies that bear on the regional-continuity versus rapid-replacement question. Without doubt, the best known of these studies is the controversial mitochondrial DNA (*mtDNA*) work of the late Allan Wilson and his colleagues. Before going into detail about mtDNA analyses, however, let's take a quick look at new research into variation in satellite DNA in modern humans. A team of researchers led by A. M. Bowcock of the University of Texas recently analyzed diversity in humans' polymorphic microsatellite alleles, reasoning that the oldest populations should show the greatest amount of genetic variation. (As a reminder, satellites are usually noncoding DNA sequences that accumulate at certain points on chromosomes; see Chapter 3). Using genetic information from 148 people representing 14 indigenous populations and five continents, Bowcock et al. found that the "diversity of microsatellites is highest in Africa, which . . . supports the hypothesis of an African origin for [modern] humans."

And so a considerable amount of anatomical and genetic data is starting to come together to support the rapid-replacement model. This discussion would not be complete, however, without a description of the mtDNA work that has attracted so much media attention to the possibility of an "African Eve." As described below, the study of humans' mtDNA has been something of a "two steps forward, one step backward" affair, the results of which have generated heated disagreement among anthropologists. Indeed, some workers think that the mtDNA studies are so seriously flawed that they should be junked entirely, while

mtDNA: genetic material found in the mitochondria of cells.

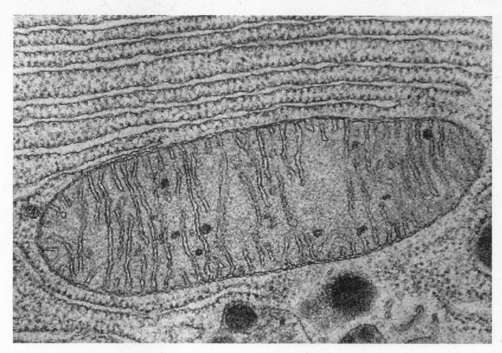

FIGURE 16–9 Mitochondria, like the oblong body in the center of this photograph, are the only structures in the cells of vertebrates, apart from the nucleus, which carry DNA and synthesize proteins. Their special properties suggest strongly that they were originally free-living organisms that invaded the cells of other animals and adapted to a symbiotic existence within them.

others feel that the studies provide important information regarding the origin of modern humans. Let's take a look at this controversial research.

Analyses of mtDNA (Figure 16–9) were pioneered by the late Allan Wilson of the University of California, Berkeley, working with numerous colleagues. In the late 1980s, Wilson's research team set out to measure the variations in mtDNA in people from several living populations. Because mtDNA is found only in the cytoplasm of the cell and because sperm provides almost no cytoplasm to the fertilized egg, no mtDNA is inherited from the father (that is, fertilization involves the combination of only the *nuclear* DNA of egg and sperm). Thus the genetic codes carried by a cell's mtDNA come from the mother alone, and each of us carries the mtDNA that we inherited from our mother, her mother, our maternal great-grandmother, and so on along a single genealogical line. This is quite a different mode of inheritance from that of nuclear DNA, which comes from an expanding network of grandparents of both sexes. Our ancestral mtDNA lineage converges with that of others with whom we share female grandparents, to produce an expanding inverted tree of relationships (Figure 16–10). Using identifiable differences in the mtDNA of their subjects—differences which presumably accumulate through mutations at the rate of 2 to 4 percent per million years—the Wilson team attempted to construct a branching dendrogram similar to those generated in albumin research (Figure 1–17). The resulting dendrogram is shown in Figure 16–11, and it led Wilson and his co-workers to the following set of conclusions:

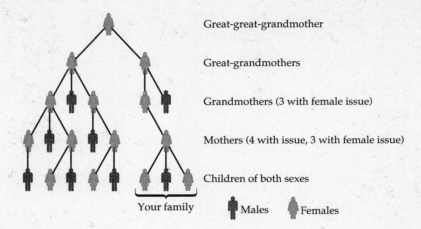

Great-great-grandmother

Great-grandmothers

Grandmothers (3 with female issue)

Mothers (4 with issue, 3 with female issue)

Children of both sexes

Your family   Males   Females

FIGURE 16–10   Mitochondrial DNA (mtDNA) is passed from one generation to another only through females in the cytoplasm of their egg cells. None is carried in the spermatozoa. If you trace your ancestry through your mother and your maternal female grandparents you will eventually find that you share a single great-great-grandmother with the entire human race. The hypothesis of Wilson and his colleagues suggests that this ancestor was an African who lived about 200,000 years ago. In this chart such an ancestry is set out for five generations.

1. The mtDNA structure of the female common ancestor of all modern humanity was closer to that of most living Africans than to any other geographic group. Therefore the common female ancestor of modern humanity was most probably a woman living in Africa. The media predictably named her Eve!

2. The amount of genetic change (0.6 percent) recorded between the most different individuals tested (calibrated on the basis of 5 million years B.P. for the chimpanzee-hominid split) suggests a period since that common ancestor lived of between 150,000 and 200,000 years or to take a rough mean, say, 175,000 years. This was roughly the time of late archaic *Homo sapiens* and just prior to the appearance of anatomically modern humans.

3. It follows that the population to which Eve belonged gave rise to all living humans through a process of successful diversification, adaptation, and expansion out of Africa and throughout the world. It does not mean that Eve was the only woman alive at that time, but that her female progeny alone gave rise to the existing human race. She was undoubtedly a member of a large interbreeding population, but the female progeny of other individuals living at that time must have eventually died out.

4. It also follows that other populations of *Homo* that lived before about 250,000 years B.P. in places other than Africa (that is, European and Asian *Homo erectus* and archaic *Homo sapiens*) did not contribute to the mtDNA of modern humankind unless there were very rapid migrations back into Africa before the critical date of origin. This reasoning suggests that living humans have no common female ancestors from among these early Eurasian groups, though we could in theory have male ancestors.

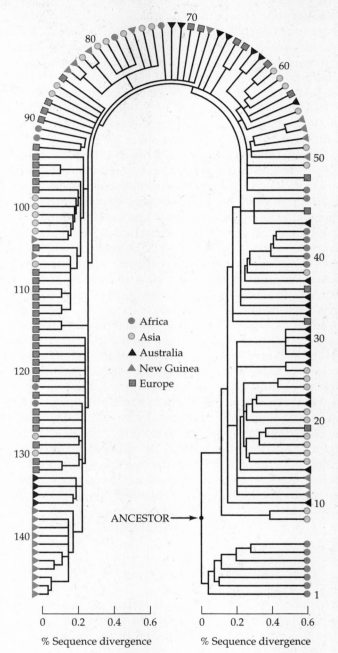

FIGURE 16-11 This diagram was prepared by Allan Wilson and co-workers to present their results of his analysis. It would normally have been drawn unfolded, but in order to save space the "tree" has been folded round a point toward the top of the page. The hypothetical ancestor Eve is to the bottom right, and the distances between the branching points and the tips of the branches leading to 147 modern individuals reflect the percentage of the molecular sequence which has mutated. The geographic origin of the individual tested is shown in the key. It is of interest that the members of each geographic region fall into more than one group. The branching pattern within the African group suggests that the population there has been more-or-less constant since the time of Eve. Elsewhere the branching pattern suggests an expanding population— exactly as might be predicted. The African populations are more diverse mitochondrially, and this diversity suggested to the Wilson team that the population is older.

These are broad and sweeping conclusions, and wrapped in the scientific sophistication of molecular studies, the mtDNA research initially seemed to provide proof positive of a common African ancestor for all living humans. But to survive in science, research results must withstand the challenges of skeptics, and this the mtDNA studies have not done. Indeed, it now appears that the critics may have uncovered fatal flaws in the mtDNA research. For one thing, the validity of these studies depends on the ability of modern computer programs to produce accurate ancestor-descendant trees, and skeptics have pointed out that the geographic identity of "Eve" is affected by such apparently simple things as the order in which individual subjects' mtDNA types are entered into the computer for analysis. Enter the data in one sequence, and the computer says "Eve" was African. Enter the same data in another sequence, and the computer may well put "Eve" in an entirely different location. Additionally some critics have strongly challenged the selection of subjects for the original mtDNA studies, claiming that the researchers did not control adequately for recent (historic, as opposed to prehistoric) interbreeding between representatives of different geographic populations.

Problems such as these have led some anthropologists to dismiss the validity of mtDNA studies altogether. Nonetheless, in a recent review article on the subject, mtDNA researcher Mark Stoneking urged against throwing the baby out with the bathwater. While admitting that there were serious problems with the first mtDNA analyses, Stoneking maintained that "an African origin still appears to be the best explanation for the [original and other] mtDNA datasets." Stoneking also noted that a second measure of mtDNA variation—information on sequence changes by nucleotide bases (presumably a reliable indicator of accumulated mutations)—also points to African populations as the oldest on earth.

In summary, the mtDNA controversy notwithstanding, the evidence currently available seems strongly in favor of the rapid-replacement hypothesis rather than the regional-continuity model. It appears likely that modern humans first evolved in Africa around 130,000 years ago and then spread into the remainder of the Old World (and later the New World), replacing all of their archaic predecessors. But does this mean that the Neandertals and other archaic *Homo sapiens* people contributed *no* genes to the modern gene pool? That probably is going a bit overboard. The archaics were, after all, members of our species—at most, subspecifically different from us—and thus could theoretically have interbred with early moderns. Given the eclectic sexual appetites of modern people, it seems likely—and perhaps inevitable—that some degree of subspecific mixture occurred. But while we should not completely debar the Neandertals and other non-African archaics from the ancestry of modern humans, it seems probable that their contribution was small. The biological core of every living person is overwhelmingly African.

THE BIOLOGICAL AND CULTURAL TRANSITION

A fundamental question remains. If archaic humans evolved into anatomically modern populations, and some most certainly did, why did such a change take place? What evolutionary forces could explain remodeling of the human skull from the form that had characterized humans since *Homo erectus* times, a quarter of a million years or so before?

The most striking change in the skull is a reduction in the masticatory apparatus. This seems to have begun toward the end of *Homo erectus* times—say, 0.8 million years ago—and reached its end point about 70,000 years ago, with our present head shape. The masticatory apparatus includes both the jaws, the teeth, the associated musculature, and the supporting structures on the cranium to which the muscles are attached. Thus the skull responds in its shape to the stresses placed on it by the jaws, and these stresses are caused not just by the action of the jaw muscles, but also by the weight of the entire apparatus. Thus the heavy jaws of *Homo erectus* and the Neandertal people were balanced by a relatively large occipital bone, which in many Neandertals projected backward as a bun-like torus. Well-developed nuchal (neck) muscles held the head up and balanced the weight of the jaws.

A number of reasons for the reduction of the jaws and teeth among anatomically modern people have been proposed. The first and most obvious would seem to be that some changes had occurred in diet and food preparation that reduced the requirement for very powerful jaws, and it is significant that this change was accompanied by a marked development in technology—certainly toward the end of the period in question. Earlier developments may have occurred that are not recorded in the archaeological record. We can only guess that by grinding grain, chopping vegetation and meat, and eventually cooking food, early moderns reduced their need of heavy jaws.

Second, according to Loring Brace, the size of the front teeth in particular was a sort of "technological" adaptation. Brace thinks that archaics such as Neandertals regularly used their front teeth as a built-in tool, serving as pliers to hold one end of some material such as wood or hide so that one hand would be free to cut, scrape, or pierce the material with a stone implement. This application is also inferred from examination of the wear on the incisor teeth and of their form, which is called *shovel-shaped*. This term implies that the incisors were strengthened on their inner borders in a way that gave them a curved and shovellike shape. Patterns of wear on the incisors of some fossils suggest that the Neandertals softened animal hides by chewing them; people may also have twisted plant fibers or straightened wooden shafts with the aid of their teeth.

Improvements in stone implements may have caused the immediate ancestors to modern humans to rely less and less on their front teeth as a built-in tool. This decreased reliance then possibly led to a gradual reduction in tooth and jaw size, which in turn permitted reduction in the face and other features of the skull, giving rise to people with heads like ours.

Pilbeam's Hypothesis

Many scientists feel that this hypothesis cannot account adequately for the transformation of the archaic humans into people of modern appearance, and they offer alternatives. David Pilbeam proposed another sort of evolutionary mechanism that may have contributed to the changes in the human skull. He suggested that, with the possible exception of western European Neandertals, the archaic head gradually became more modern in form because of the evolution of the upper part of the throat into a pharynx capable of producing the full range of modern vocalizations. As we saw in Chapter 13, when, in modern human development, this essential part of the vocal tract starts to take on its final shape, the larynx moves down in the throat, and the base of the skull, which is rather flat at birth, takes on a concave arch. The pharyngeal space is thus formed in front of the topmost vertebra, and the arch in the base of the skull serves as a roof.

Pilbeam believes that the evolution of the pharynx's arched roof may have affected the overall structure of the human skull. As the arch formed, the base of the skull shortened (just as the ends of a piece of cloth that is lifted slightly in the middle pull together). If the starting point of this process were a long, low skull, the shortening of the skull base might have caused the facial region to pull inward from its formerly out-thrust position. With the face thus pulled in, the whole braincase would have had to become higher to contain the same amount of brain tissue. And as this shaping happened, the brow and the sides of the skull would have become more vertical. Thus the archaic skull could have been transformed into a modern *Homo sapiens* skull. Archaic and modern skulls are, in effect, just different ways of packing the same quantity of brain tissue. The overall shape of the package is dictated by only one of its dimensions—the length of the base of the skull—which is in turn related to the presence of a modern pharynx.

Pilbeam's logical chain of events explains the evolutionary changes that perhaps turned archaic into modern humans. The development of a modern pharynx may have occurred rapidly, for speech was now becoming an extremely valuable adaptation. This is not to say that archaic humans or possibly even *Homo erectus* were completely incapable of speech. What we see in the evolution of the Upper Paleolithic people is the final, very significant, step. Natural selection may have worked at maximum speed to weed out the slow talkers and to foster better speaking ability. It is almost impossible today, tens of thousands of years later, to sense the powerful evolutionary pressures that may have been launched when this new element was introduced into the vocal tract. The development of a modern pharynx, with its enormous potential for communication, may very well explain a leap in physical and cultural evolution.

The Appearance of the Chin

Shortening the skull base, as described above, tucked the face and jaws of newly modern humans downward and backward into close proximity to the neck. This shift in position, although affecting a set of dwindling structures (teeth, jaws, and supporting facial bones), led to the evolution of that distinctive modern trait, the chin. Analyses of the mechanics of chewing have revealed how and why the chin was produced. During chewing, the mandible is subjected to bending and twisting stresses as the jaw muscles pull it backward and forward and from side to side. Furthermore, lateral grinding on the molars concentrates stress specifically at the *mandibular symphysis* (the midline of the lower jaw). Symphyseal stresses continue to be an issue for living people because, although we have small jaws and teeth, we can still generate powerful grinding by the molars. Typically, skeletal stresses like those on the mandible are counterbalanced by thickening the bone in question and in premodern hominids (as in nonhuman primates) lower jaw reinforcement usually involved internal thickening (Figure 16–12). This option

Mandibular symphysis: the midline connecting the right and left halves of the lower jaw.

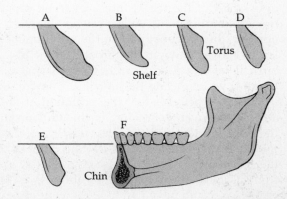

FIGURE 16–12 This figure shows crosssections of the symphyseal region of several nonhuman primates and hominids: (A) gorilla, (B) chimpanzee, (C) *A. africanus*, (D and E) archaic *Homo sapiens*, and (F) modern human. For all drawings, the front of the jaw is to the left and the internal surface to the right. Note that internal buttressing can occur as a shelf of bone at the lower margin of the jaw and/or a mandibular torus higher on the symphysis.

was not open to modern humans, however, because tucking an internally but-tressed mandible up against the neck could have threatened to constrict vital soft structures such as blood vessels, the windpipe, and the larynx. Given these anatomical constraints, natural selection found a compromise—the lower margin of our lightly buttressed symphysis was everted slightly (turned outwards). This simple modification produced an externally reinforced jaw that was adequately spaced from the neck and in the process gave us a chin.

Transition Completed

The most probable answer to our question of why modern head and jaw forms evolved is that all the factors that have been mentioned were at work: the phar-ynx certainly increased in length, and the jaws, teeth, and associated bony struc-tures were indeed reduced in size. The changes at the back of the skull were most probably no more than a product of the important new developments taking place at the front.

Much has been learned of the period of transition, but much remains to be learned. Hardly any relevant fossil evidence is available from some crucial areas of the world: Arabia, at the crossroads of two continents; the endless reaches of Central Asia; and the subcontinent of India, rich in game and characterized by the sort of warm climate that early humans favored for millions of years.

Whenever and wherever it began, the evolutionary transition transformed humankind. By about 30,000 years ago the changes were largely complete, and the world was populated with people who looked like ourselves. People were living in larger bands than they ever had before. Cultures were branching and rebranch-ing along countless idiosyncratic paths, like a plant that has lived long in the shade and is suddenly offered the full strength of the sun. Successful initiatives in technology or art or symbol making brought on more initiatives, and cultural change steadily accelerated.

A NEW BREED

Variability

Like people living today, these first modern people developed characteristic phys-ical types from region to region, and even from site to site within a region (Figure 16–13). Their environment, its climate, and its food supply account for some of these variations. Such physical characteristics as tallness and shortness, dark skin and light skin, straight hair and curly hair had formed and would continue to evolve during the millennia when the human body had to accommodate itself to both heat and cold and to the variations of sunlight in different latitudes. The rel-atively short, thick body of the Eskimo, for instance, conserves heat better than the tall, thin bodies of some sub-Saharan Africans, which present a much greater area of skin to be cooled by the air. Similarly, thick, straight hair, in the opinion of some scholars, may help to maintain the temperature of the brain in cold climates, whereas tightly curled hair seems to be an adaptation guarding against hot tropi-cal sunshine.

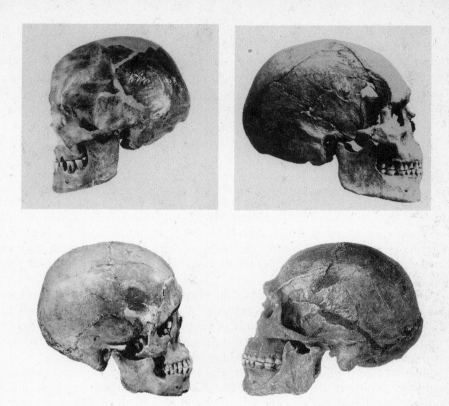

FIGURE 16–13   Four anatomically modern European skulls show some of the variation we would expect to find in a population the size of the one that occupied Europe. These are from Chancelade and Combe Capelle in France (top, left and right); from Grimaldi in Italy, near the border with France on the Mediterranean coast (bottom left); and from Předmost in Czechoslovakia (bottom right). All are dated at about 20,000 to 25,000 years B.P. These photographs are approximately one-fifth actual size.

Advantages of the Large Gene Pool

It is likely that by 20,000 years B.P. many of the physical changes wrought by the environment had largely reached their present state. That peoples varied in physical type from one location to another may be related as much to demography as to geography, for there was a great increase in numbers of people and a continued division of human populations into many fairly isolated groups. The gene pool grew with the expanding total population, but it remained divided into small breeding populations that still partially inhibited gene flow.

When the population of a species is relatively small, the genetic material available to it is relatively limited in scope, and trait variation may be similarly limited. But as the population increases, it also begins to vary more, simply because greater numbers provide more opportunities for variations to appear. When gene flow within a large population is limited, as it may have been at this period, the variations may become specialized, adapting to local environments according to the dictates of natural selection and perhaps the chance consequences of the founder effect (Chapter 3).

NEW LANDS

These first anatomically modern people lived through the last ice age. Warm and cold periods followed one another in close succession—close at least in geologic time—and with each cold interlude the glaciers advanced and withdrew. Islands rose and fell, and natural causeways and corridors appeared, making new traffic routes for the coming and going of humans. Along one of these ancient routes these people may have moved northward from what is now China into the chilly reaches of Siberia. Along another one they apparently migrated from Siberia, across the wide land bridge of Beringia, now covered by the Bering Sea, into the continent of North America (Figure 16–14).

FIGURE 16–14 Much is still to be learned about the arrival of humankind in the New World. This map gives an idea of the migrants' most probable route, and of the extent of the landmass during the last glaciation. Carbon 14 and other dates from many sites suggest that humankind entered North America before 20,000 years B.P. and possibly as early as 40,000 years B.P.

The Americas

Exactly when early humans first entered the Americas is still quite uncertain. It has been believed for many years that the oldest evidence for the first Americans did not predate 10,000 years B.P., and there was no sure evidence of tool traditions of very much greater antiquity. Today we have good evidence of stone arrowheads and spear points from North America, called *Clovis points*, back to 11,500 years B.P. These points were produced by big-game hunters who were most accomplished, as their butchery sites make clear. But radiocarbon dates are beginning to accumulate from much earlier times.

One important—but controversial—early date from the New World comes from Brazil, at Pedra Furada in the state of Piaui. Here the French archaeologists Niede Guidon and Georgette Delibrias excavated a cave site with remarkable results. They obtained a series of radiocarbon dates from well-stratified deposits, with hearths and a stone industry, which apparently take human occupation at the site back to over 32,000 years B.P. There is even evidence of rock painting estimated at 17,000 years B.P. as spalls of paint that have fallen from the painted cave walls are present in the deposits. The Pedra Furada dates are still considered tentative by many archaeologists, but if confirmed, they will support other claims of early dates from South and Central America, such as Pikimachay (Peru) at 19,000 years B.P. and the Alice Boer site (Brazil) at 14,200 years B.P. Additionally, in Mexico the site of El Cedral may be older than 30,000 years B.P., and deposits at Hapacoya may date to 24,000 years ago. And finally, in Chile there is a site, Monte Verde, that has yielded a very reliable date of 12,300 years B.P. and questionable dates back to 33,000 years ago.

The various extremely early dates from the New World are exciting, but many archaeologists prefer to remain skeptical pending confirmation. A conservative view, based on the solid date of 12,300 years B.P. from southern Chile, suggests entry into the New World via the Bering Strait by *at least* 20,000 years B.P. Greater precision in dating is needed, and the final answer may not be long in coming. The land bridge from Asia was open only intermittently (although immigration by boat may have been possible at other times), as was the passage through the Rocky Mountains in northern Canada. Genetic evidence from yet another set of mtDNA studies supports an entry date of 21,000 to 42,000 years B.P. The whole story has yet to be told. Meanwhile, one thing is clear: All the known skeletal remains are anatomically modern; there is no evidence of archaic humans or of their tool industries.

Australia

Although the vast ice caps of the last glaciation locked up enough of the world's water to drop sea levels over 330 ft (100 m), adding great expanses of dry land to the continents, such extensions never joined Australia to the mainland of Southeast Asia. The subsidence of waters from the comparatively shallow Sunda Shelf united Borneo, Java, and Sumatra to the mainland of Southeast Asia and probably exposed enough small islands to make island-hopping feasible. But between Australia and the shelf at the edge of the Asian mainland still remained the waters of the Timor Trough, 10,000 ft (3,050 m) deep and 60 mi (97 km) wide. How did humankind manage to get across it?

It was long assumed that humans did not reach this major island continent until the ancestors of the modern Aborigines migrated there by boat, probably from Southeast Asia, some 8,000 to 10,000 years ago. Then in the 1930s finds indicated an earlier human arrival, and in 1968 archaeologists digging near Lake Mungo in New South Wales discovered a 25,000-year-old skeleton of a woman, unmistakably modern in her anatomy, and artifacts dating back as far as 32,000 years B.P. (Figure 16–15).

A site from Arnhem Land in Australia's Northern Territory, called Malakunanja, has recently yielded artifacts and dates which stretch the evidence for human occupation (and our imagination) back to 55,000 years B.P. The dating has been obtained by both C^{14} and thermoluminescence and for this reason is reasonably secure. Such an early date is supported by dates from northeast Papua New Guinea of 40,000 years B.P. and from southern Australia of 38,000 years B.P. Although there are no human remains from any of these sites, the evidence from artifacts makes it clear that humans were present in Australia at this early time. If the earliest Australians settled there as early as 55,000 years B.P., they would have had considerably greater problems than if they had arrived as late as 30,000 years B.P. during the last glaciation, as the sea level at 55,000 B.P. was only about 98 ft (30 m) below its present levels, which means that far wider straits and far more ocean would have had to be crossed by watercraft than if sea levels had been lower. There was, however, a cold spell between 60,000 and 70,000 years ago, and during this time the sea level dropped 195–225 ft (60–70 m). On the present evidence, this might have been the opportunity that made it possible for this historic

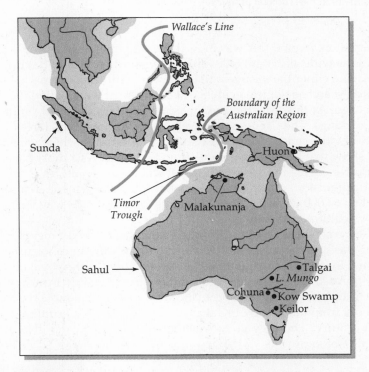

FIGURE 16–15 Map of Southeast Asia and part of Australasia showing the two ancient landmasses Sunda and Sahul, which were separated by the Timor Trough. The shaded area indicates the coastline that would be exposed by a drop in the sea level of 490 ft (150 m). Wallace's Line represents the edge of the Sunda region. Important archaeological sites are marked with a dot, and those mentioned in the text are labeled. (Adapted from J. P. White and J. F. O'Connell in *Science*, 203; 1979, 21–28, Fig. 1.)

Home base   Food-gathering region

FIGURE 16–16   The term *unearned resources* refers to migratory herds that live for part of the year outside the home range of the hunting bands. Herds that feed in the mountains during the summer may, during the winter, come down to the valleys, where they are hunted. Thus the valley hunters are drawing on food resources of the entire region without actually traveling through it. The figure shows the relationship of the zones of food production to the home base.

human migration. Even if this was indeed the case, these early people must have crossed seas as wide as 250 mi (400 km), an extraordinary undertaking. It is very hard to imagine either the means or the motivation for such a remarkable journey.

The earliest archaeological evidence of any form of watercraft dates from only 5,500 years ago. At this time the predynastic Egyptians depicted sailing boats in their rock carvings. The Chinese may well have developed the junk at an earlier date, but the evidence is lacking. Excavations in Australia, which we have briefly reviewed, show that these early people from Southeast Asia must have mastered to a remarkable degree the arts of sea travel and navigation at an extremely early point in our prehistory. Their almost unbelievable achievement, at a time probably more than 60,000 years B.P., should lead us to reassess the way we think about their society, culture, and technology.

Was their craft simply a raft of bundled bamboo and reeds, meant for offshore fishing? Or was it perhaps a primitive version of the dugout canoe used today by Melanesians? Even more intriguing is the question of how the voyagers happened to journey to Australia. Were they carried there inadvertently by a wayward current or, according to one far-out speculation, by a massive tidal wave like the one that rolled out from the island of Krakatoa during a volcanic eruption there in the nineteenth century? Did they go to Australia purposefully, and if so, what drew them? We do not know.

Diet and Hunting

Like the migrations of all the peoples who had gone before them, the movements of these people were probably activated by a search for food. In the means they

Winter grazing and hunting grounds

Summer feeding grounds

used to achieve this end—in their implements, their techniques, their social organization, and their choice of habitation—they went far beyond what anyone had done before. Their diet included almost every sort of food the earth provided, and they became enormously adept at acquiring those foods. Indeed, in living off the land, and living well, they must have been far more successful than anyone before their time or since.

When early hominids developed their skills as hunters, they tapped a source of food energy unavailable to their mainly vegetarian predecessors. When they began to hunt migratory grazing animals and an occasional predatory animal whose territory extended beyond their own, their intake of food energy began to draw on a still wider range of resources. Thus, when territorial expansion took humans into the temperate zone, where grazing herd animals sometimes migrate between winter and summer feeding grounds, their food intake tapped nutritional energy from distant sources that were sometimes extremely different from the resources supplied by their own immediate environment. Cro-Magnons, harvesting the reindeer of the Dordogne region, were benefiting from the nutrients of the northern pastures and coastal plains where the reindeer herds did some of their grazing, but where people seldom, if ever, ventured. Anthropologists call this kind of long-distance food collection living on *unearned resources* (see Figure 16–16). Of all the ways in which organisms had adapted to and drawn sustenance from their environment (short of actually controlling it), this was the most sophisticated. Not until pastoralism and agriculture were developed did humans' exploitation of nature become more effective.

Modern archaeological techniques give us a glimpse of the variety and complexity of the ecological adaptations accomplished by the Upper Paleolithic people. In the next chapter we will look at the technology of these people in more detail, at their arts, and at what we know of their beliefs about the world in which they lived.

Unearned resources: resources that are outside a predator's range, but to which it nonetheless gains secondary access by consuming prey animals with larger ranges.

BOX 16–1
CHARACTERISTICS OF ANATOMICALLY MODERN PEOPLE
(HOMO SAPIENS SAPIENS)

Trait	Homo sapiens sapiens
Height (sexes combined)	<5 to >6 ft (140–185 cm)—extremely variable (F is 90%–95% of M)
Weight (sexes combined)	<100 to >200 lb (40–70 kg)—extremely variable (F is 90%–95% of M)
Brain size (sexes combined)	1,330 cc mean (1,000–2,000 cc range)
Cranium	High-vaulted, globular skull with widest point high on the sides; small brows; high forehead; little facial prognathism; flexed cranial base
Dentition	On average, smaller front and rear teeth, and more lightly built jaws than Homo erectus; definite chin
Limbs	Relatively long legs and short arms overall; body build that varies strongly with climatic conditions
Distribution	Africa, Asia, Europe, Australia, Americas
Known dates (thousands of years)	ca. 130,000 years B.P. to present

SUMMARY

The oldest fossils of anatomically modern people (Homo sapiens sapiens) date from about 130,000 years ago and come from Africa. Modern fossils that are only slightly younger have been found in the Middle East. The complete replacement of archaic Homo sapiens by modern people took quite some time, however, and was not completed until perhaps 30,000 years B.P. Precisely how the archaic-to-modern transition occurred is currently a matter of much debate among paleoanthropologists, but there seem to be two primary possibilities. The rapid-replacement hypothesis holds that modern people evolved once, by allopatric branching, in Africa and/or the Middle East. After that single origin, modern people then spread all across the Old World, replacing archaic humans everywhere. This rapid-replacement (or out-of-Africa) hypothesis seems to be well supported by the fossil record and also by comparative anatomical and DNA studies. The second, and considerably less likely, hypothesis holds that modern people evolved more-or-less simultaneously in several different regions of the Old World. This model, dubbed the regional-continuity hypothesis, envisions broad-scale phyletic transformation of Homo erectus into archaic Homo sapiens and then into anatomically modern humans. As noted, the weight of the evidence strongly favors rapid replacement. This means that most archaic humans are debarred from the direct ancestry of modern people. However, some non-African or Middle Eastern archaics, including some Neanderthals, *may* have contributed to the modern gene pool since interbreeding between resident archaics and invading moderns was theoretically possible (at most, they belonged to different subspecies).

The physical changes from archaic *Homo sapiens* to anatomically modern humans were subtle and involved mainly a remodeling of the cranium and the face. Skulls became more rounded and higher-vaulted; foreheads became more vertical; faces and teeth were reduced in average size; the chin was added; and, perhaps of particular importance, the cranial base became sharply flexed (Box 16–1). The last change may well have allowed the full development of modern speech and may have facilitated rapid cultural progress.

Once anatomical modernity had been achieved, humans did not waste much time spreading to Australia and the Americas. Modern people were living in Australia some 55,000 years ago, and they may have entered the New World via the Bering Strait between 21,000 and 42,000 years B.P.

REVIEW QUESTIONS

1. Summarize the evidence supporting the rapid-replacement hypothesis of the appearance of anatomically modern people. What weaknesses do you see in the model?

2. Summarize the evidence supporting the regional-continuity hypothesis of the appearance of anatomically modern people. What weaknesses do you see in the model? How would wide-scale phyletic transformation take place?

3. Compare the anatomy of archaic *Homo sapiens* with that of anatomically modern people. Do you think there are sufficient differences to justify subspecific distinctions? On what basis would a physical anthropologist make such a judgment?

4. One of the new traits of anatomically modern humans was a fully developed vocal tract. Speculate on how the achievement of modern speech may have contributed to the replacement of archaics by *Homo sapiens sapiens*.

5. Describe the peopling of Australia and the Americas. When and how were these regions first entered and by whom?

POSTSCRIPT

In this chapter we have argued that over roughly a 100,000-year period archaic humans were generally replaced worldwide by fully modern people. We believe that, genetically speaking, the replacement was rather clean, although it must be admitted that some interbreeding between resident archaics and invading moderns probably occurred. But precisely what form the replacement process took remains unclear. Were archaic humans violently exterminated by moderns or simply outcompeted ecologically and thus driven to extinction? As it is usually framed with reference to the Neandertals, did they go out with a bang or a whimper?

Several early writers envisioned a violent replacement. Thus Henry Fairfield Osborn in his 1915 classic *Men of the Old Stone Age* wrote as follows:

We may infer that the new race [anatomically modern humans] competed for a time with the Neanderthals before they dispossessed them of their principal stations and drove them out of the country or killed them in battle. The Neanderthals, no doubt, fought with wooden weapons and with the stone-headed dart and spear, but there is no evidence that they possessed the bow and arrow. There is, on the contrary, some possibility that the newly arriving Cro-Magnon race may have been familiar with the bow and arrow [and thus the Cro-Magnons may have been] armed with weapons which, with their superior intelligence and physique, would have given them a very great advantage in contests with the Neanderthals.

In a similar vein, in his 1921 short story "The Grisly Folk," H. G. Wells describes how modern "true men" hunted down and exterminated the hairy, beetle-browed, low-vaulted Neandertals.

Such scenes of combat and carnage, however, now appear to have been the products of overactive imaginations. There is simply no archaeological evidence of violent replacement of archaics by moderns. Although present-day humans often seem all too ready to engage in warfare and genocide, there is no reason to believe that our subspecies got its start through such violent practices. Most anthropologists now attribute the demise of the Neandertals (and archaic *Homo sapiens* in general) to behavioral differences that allowed them to be outcompeted by early modern humans. William Howells's recent statement in his book *Getting Here* (1993) is a good example of current views:

> We do not have to imagine bloody battles or in fact any serious conflict: a small erosion of Neanderthals in each generation would have quickly led to extinction. Also, the Upper Paleolithic people were manifestly more numerous than their predecessors. Another simple explanation is one of vastly different life styles and hunting capacities, with available game going mostly to the new people.

Outcompeted by more skillful anatomically modern hunters, the Neandertals may have withdrawn into marginal habitats and experienced increased mortality rates. Archaeologist Ezra Zubrow has calculated that, if the Neandertals suffered from only 2 percent greater mortality than the invading moderns, Neandertal extinction was likely to have followed within about 1,000 years. Similar fates may have awaited archaic populations all across the Old World. In sum, faced with a choice between a whimper and a bang as an explanation for the replacement of archaic *Homo sapiens*, most of today's researchers would opt for the whimper.

NEOLITHIC AND MESOLITHIC	YEARS B.P.	EMERGENCE OF MODERN HUMANS	TYPES OF *HOMO SAPIENS*
10,000		Iron Age	
UPPER PALEOLITHIC		Bronze Age: pottery	
40,000		Copper Age	
		New Stone Age (Neolithic)	
MIDDLE PALEOLITHIC	10,000	Mesolithic	
Archaics in Europe, Asia, and Africa		First agriculture: domestication of plants and animals	
		Monte Verde, Chile	
200,000	20,000		
			MODERN HUMANS
Swanscombe and Steinheim; Levallois technique		Lake Mungo, Australia: skeletons	
		Předmost: robust modern skulls	
	30,000	Cro-Magnon, Dordogne	
400,000 Arago		Lake Mungo, Australia artifacts	
		Velika Pecina	
500,000		Most recent Mousterian tools; St. Césaire	
	40,000	Le Moustier	
		Possible entry into Americas	
		Sipka jaw fragment: blend of archaic and modern features.	
	50,000	Monte Circeo, Amud, Shanidar: Archaic skulls; very few modern features	
		Malakunanja, Australia	
	60,000		
		La Quina, La Chapelle, La Ferrassie, and Spy	
1 MILLION *Paranthropus* extinct		Border Cave	
	70,000		
			ARCHAICS AND MODERNS
LOWER PALEOLITHIC	80,000		
	90,000		
1.5 MILLION Acheulean industry		Skhūl and Qafzeh: modern features	
	100,000		
		Florisbad: modern and archaic features	
Homo habilis at Olduvai	110,000		
1.8 MILLION *Homo erectus* in Africa, the Caucasus, and Java			
	120,000		
2 MILLION Oldowan industry			**FIRST MODERN HUMANS IN AFRICA AND WESTERN ASIA**
	130,000	Omo Kibish and Klasies River Mouth	

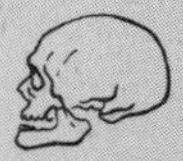

THE FINAL TRANSFORMATION

This chart shows the approximate chronology of the Middle to Upper Paleolithic sequence. Many dates are approximate.

CHAPTER
17

Technology, Magic, and Art

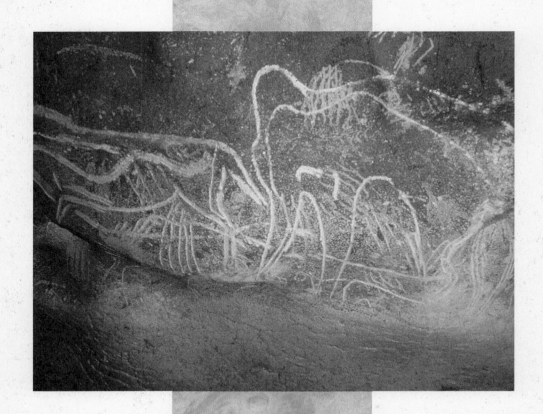

Human life is everywhere a state in which much is to be endured and little to be enjoyed.
                    SAMUEL JOHNSON, 1709–1784. *Rasselas*, CH. 7.

OVERVIEW

The evolution of anatomically modern humans—*Homo sapiens sapiens*—was followed by a significant upswing in cultural complexity, and this chapter is concerned with describing that cultural surge. Increased control was gained over the production and use of fire; improved gathering, fishing, and hunting techniques ensured a dependable food supply and allowed a degree of sedentary living; and technology was broadened by the invention of new tool types and the increased use of bone, antler, and ivory as raw materials. Additionally, there was a strong improvement in artistic skills and endeavors—resulting in beautiful rock-shelter and cave art, carved ivory and bone implements, and clay sculptures—and also the elaboration of funeral rites, very likely reflecting the development of religion. Humankind was now modern not only anatomically, but intellectually as well. Important topics and concepts in this chapter include new fire-making techniques; technological innovations and the use of new raw materials; improvements in subsistence activities; and the development of art and ritual.

AN END TO WANDERING

In the fertile valleys of Egypt, on the frigid plains of Siberia, and along the seacoast of Africa, Upper Paleolithic people were demonstrating that they not only could stay alive but could actually prosper under conditions of extraordinary diversity. Cold was no barrier to their existence; when meat was scarce, their food became fish; and in at least one area we have evidence that with foresight and planning they harvested natural grains. After centuries of nomadism, of moving from place to place in pursuit of game or fresh supplies of plant food, humans were finally able to stay in one place and systematically exploit the seasonal resources of one locality. They were, in short, gaining ever-increasing control over their relations with the natural world.

A New Lifestyle

A sedentary way of life, and the changes in subsistence that it accompanied, amounted to a minor revolution in human society and lifestyle. More efficient exploitation of resources and the permanence of living quarters brought an increase in the human population. The skeletal evidence also suggests that the life span was extended (perhaps exceeding the Neandertals' life expectancy by 20 percent), which enabled people to accumulate more knowledge and pass on more of this knowledge to their children and grandchildren.

Along with an increasing population, their efficiency as food producers gave them other advantages. Because they were often able to lead a more sedentary life, they could acquire more material goods, objects which would have been impractical to own as long as they were on the move, but which made providing for food and shelter easier. The inhabitants of several Upper Paleolithic sites in central Europe, for instance, were shaping objects from clay and, as we shall see, even firing them in dome-shaped kilns. Even more important than material wealth was the evolution of social behavior—a base for the full development of language, art, and religion and for the complex forms of social and political organization that are the hallmark of all developed human cultures.

During the past 20,000 or so years of their tenure, these people made more technological progress and, in doing so, gained more control over their environment, than had been made or gained in all the million years of human experience that had preceded them. They were the master stoneworkers of all time, improving old techniques to produce stone tools of greater effectiveness and variety. They also exploited other materials—bone, antler, and ivory—that had been little used earlier, selecting and working each to its best advantage in fashioning not only new weapons and new tools but domestic inventions and decorative objects as well. They learned to build better fires more easily and to use them for new purposes. Some shelters were only a step away from real houses; they were more durable than earlier shelters and afforded more protection against the elements. And when the climate changed, these people invented ways to deal with it. Technological innovation and cultural adaptation increasingly reduced the need for physical evolution, and humans' links to their animal past were now beginning to lie more and more behind them. People still depended on nature, but nature's control was being lessened.

Mastery of Fire

These people added new dimensions to the use of fire. For one thing, they were the first to leave proof of their ability to strike a fire quickly whenever they needed one. A cave site in Belgium yielded a beautifully rounded piece of *iron pyrite* (Figure 17–1). This substance is one of the few natural materials from which flint will

Iron pyrite: a mineral substance (iron disulfide) that, when struck with flint, makes sparks that will start a fire.

FIGURE 17–1 The oldest known firestone, this iron pyrite is from a Belgian cave, Trou-du-Chaleux. The Upper Paleolithic Magdalenian people were apparently the first to discover that flint and iron pyrite used in combination yielded sparks hot enough to ignite tinder. The stone is here enlarged about two times.

strike sparks that will set dry tinder on fire; sparks struck from two flints or two ordinary rocks are not hot enough to do so. What is more, the Belgian pyrite has a groove showing where it had been struck again and again with pieces of flint. Because iron pyrite is not easy to find lying about on the ground, each such firestone was undoubtedly a cherished item that would have been carried wherever a band roamed.

A more dramatic example of the growing mastery of fire, evidence of which has turned up at sites in Russia and France, seems prosaic at first glance: shallow grooves dug into the bottom of a hearth, and a channel curving away from the hearth like a tail. So simple an innovation may well have been overlooked many times in earlier archaeological excavations, but in fact it was the first small step toward the blast furnaces of modern steel mills. The grooves and channels in those prehistoric fireplaces allowed more air to reach the fuel, and fires in them would thus burn hotter.

The people who built these special hearths needed them because of the type of fuel they used. In an area where wood was scarce, they had to turn for fuel to a material that normally does not burn well: bone. Although bone is hard to ignite and burns inefficiently, being only about 25 percent combustible material, it gives off adequate heat. That these people did burn it is proved by the lack of charred wood and the considerable quantities of bone ash found in their specially vented hearths.

The hearth was home, and the Upper Paleolithic people, who changed so much else also changed the concept of home. Though some lived in the same caves and rock shelters that had protected their predecessors, they seem, in some places at least, to have kept cleaner house than those earlier tenants; litter was thrown outside instead of being allowed to pile up inside.

It was in regions that offered no ready-made habitations that the home improvements were most noticeable. Particularly in central and eastern Europe and Siberia, remnants of many sturdily built shelters have been found in open country (see Figure 17–2).

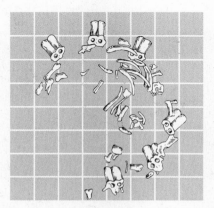 

FIGURE 17–2   Careful mapping of an Upper Paleolithic site in Ukraine shows mammoth bones lying in a semicircle, a configuration suggesting that they were part of a round structure. The original dwelling was probably dome-shaped, covered with hides, and weighted down with other bones, as depicted in the reconstruction.

Solutrean Laurel-Leaves

Improvement in stone tools was crucial to the developing Paleolithic technical mastery. It is ironic that, despite all efforts to decipher them, no one really knows what purpose was served by the most beautiful examples of this new skill. Anyone who has ever held and examined a tool such as the magnificent "laurel-leaf" blade (Figure 17–3) must eventually wonder how this implement could have been used. Too delicate for a knife, too big and fragile for a spearhead, so beautifully crafted a piece of flint seems to be a showpiece. Clearly, to produce an object of such daring proportions required craftsmanship bordering on art, and many archaeologists think this masterpiece and others like it may have been just that: works of art that served an aesthetic or ritual function rather than a utilitarian one, and that may even have been passed from one person or group to another as highly prized items.

If the large laurel-leaf blades were made for no useful purpose, they were clearly an instance of technology transcending itself. The smaller, everyday implements on which such showpieces were modeled had strictly practical functions. They are known in the thousands and come in various styles from sites all over the world. Stone points in various sizes have been found in western and central European excavations at cultural levels called *Solutrean*—a style typified by finds from Solutré in France. There is no doubt that many of these points could have served most effectively as spear points or knives with razor-sharp edges. They were significant items in the armory of a people who depended for their existence less and less on the simple strength of their biceps and more and more on their brainpower and the efficacy of their tools.

The small stone blades were unquestionably sharp and efficient. Modern experiments have shown that well-made flint projectile points are sharper than iron points of a similar type and penetrate more deeply into an animal's body. Flint knives are equal, if not superior, to steel knives in their cutting power. The only drawback of flint is that, because of its brittleness, it breaks more easily than metal and has to be replaced more often.

Solutrean: an Upper Paleolithic culture existing in western Europe between 21,000 and 16,500 years B.P. Best known for its "laurel-leaf" blades.

FIGURE 17–3　A laurel-leaf blade is so delicate that it could have served no practical purpose. This blade—11 in. (28 cm) long but only 4/10 in. (1 cm) thick—may have been a ceremonial object or even the proud emblem of a master toolmaker. These finely chipped blades are part of the Solutrean tool industry.

The importance of such blades in the lives of hunters lends authority to the theory that the large, nonutilitarian examples, of which at least several dozen have been found, may have been ritualistic objects representing the quintessential spear point. They may, too, have been used as a primitive currency for trade. On the other hand, it has also been suggested that a magnificent laurel-leaf may have simply been a tour de force tossed off by a virtuoso toolmaker as a demonstration of talent. If so, any admiration or praise the work received was well deserved. The laurel-leaf is without doubt a splendid creation, and fewer than a handful of people in the world today are skilled enough in the ancient craft to produce one.

Tool Specialization

However different the various tool industries of this period may have been in style, in character they had much in common. Human groups everywhere produced tools more specialized than any used before. Archaeologists identify 60 to 70 types of tools in the kits of some Neandertals: scrapers meant to be held horizontally, knives with blunted backs, others with double edges, and so on. But they count more than 100 types in the tool kits of Upper Paleolithic humans: knives for cutting meat, knives for whittling wood, scrapers for bone, scrapers for skin, perforators, stone saws, chisels, pounding slabs, and countless others. Among the innovations are two-part composite tools. These people are believed to have begun putting bone and antler handles on many of their stone tools, such as axes and knives. By providing them with a firmer grasp and enabling them to use much more of the muscle power in their arms and shoulders, the handles, through leverage, increased the power the users could put into a blow with a tool by as much as two to three times.

One of the most important tools developed was the cutter called a *burin* (see Figure 17–4). It is tempting to say that Upper Paleolithic people invented the burin, but it had existed in a few Neandertal tool kits, and a few burinlike tools are sometimes found in the tool assemblages of *Homo erectus*. In the hands of these modern people, however, the burin was gradually improved and became more important and much more prevalent. A burin was a kind of chisel. Today the name is given to a fine steel cutting tool used by engravers in preparing copper plates. In the Stone Age it was a tool with a strong, sharply beveled edge or point used to

FIGURE 17–4 This Upper Paleolithic burin is the first chisel, a new and important technological development. Its main use was perhaps to make other tools of wood or bone. This photograph is approximately one-half actual size.

cut, incise, and shape other materials, such as bone, antler, wood, and sometimes stone. It differed from most other stone tools of prehistory in that it was not used by itself to kill animals, cut meat, clean hides, or chop down saplings for tent poles. Rather, like the machine tools of the modern age, its chief function was the manufacture of other tools and implements. With a tool that made other tools, technology could expand many times faster than ever before.

The burin probably helped produce many wooden implements, but only fragments of these have survived. The best record of the object's effectiveness, then, is found in the surviving tools it shaped. These superb tools, like the burin itself, stand out as a mark of sophistication. Besides wood, three organic raw materials—bone, antler, and ivory—helped supply the needs of an ever-expanding economy, and the burin made possible their widespread exploitation. *Homo erectus* and archaic *Homo sapiens* had used bone to some extent for scraping, piercing, or digging, but not nearly so much as the Upper Paleolithic people did. At a typical Neandertal site, perhaps 25 out of 1,000 tools turn out to be made of bone; the rest are stone. In some Upper Paleolithic encampments, the mix may be as much as half and half, or an even greater proportion of bone.

Bone, antler, and ivory were the wonder materials of these times, much as plastics are today. Less brittle and therefore more workable than flint, much stronger and more durable than wood, they could be cut, grooved, chiseled, scraped, sharpened, and shaped. They could be finely worked into tiny implements like needles, or they could be used for heavy work. A deer antler makes an excellent pick. A mammoth's leg bone cracked lengthwise needs only minor modifications and a handle to become an efficient shovel. Ivory could be steamed and bent, processes adding yet another dimension to toolmaking.

Best of all, the very animals hunted and depended on for food provided these materials in abundance. All animals have bone, of course, and many large animals—red deer, reindeer, mammoth—had antlers or tusks as well. Antlers seemed almost to be nature's gift to humans, because they did not even have to kill an animal to obtain them: every year deer shed their old ones, which lie on the ground for the picking up. Because reindeer and red deer were at one time or another perhaps the most abundant game animals in western Europe, antler was used there more than bone or ivory. In parts of eastern Europe and Siberia, where wood was relatively scarce, the skeletons of giant mammoths that had died a natural death or had been trapped by hunters were a source of tools. A mammoth tusk might measure more than 9 ft (2.7 m) and weigh more than 100 lb (45 kg); a lot of implements could be made from that much ivory.

With its strong chisel point, the burin could easily scratch or dig into ivory or bone without breaking. To cut up a bone, the toolmaker could incise a deep groove around the bone and then, with a sharp blow, break it cleanly at the cut, just as a glazier today cuts a groove in a glass pane before breaking it. To get slivers for needles, points, and awls, it was necessary only to draw a burin repeatedly lengthwise down a bone to score two parallel grooves deep enough to hit the soft center. Then the piece of hard material between the grooves was pried out and ground to shape (Figure 17–5). Other pieces of bone could be turned into spatulas, scrapers, beads, bracelets, digging tools, and more.

In addition to domestic utensils, bone and antler provided spear points, lances, and barbed harpoon tips, with which the hunters took advantage of bountiful supplies of game. Probably at no time since have there been so many grazing animals roaming the earth: Europe and Asia had mammoth, horses, red deer, pigs,

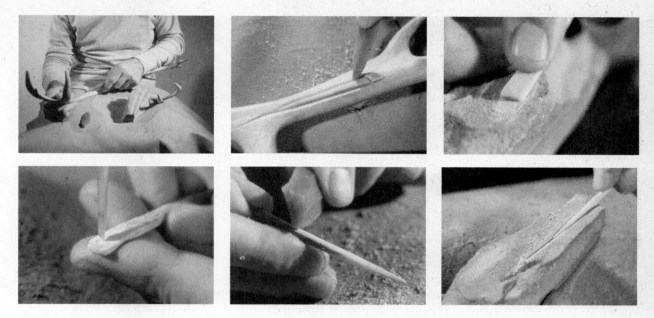

FIGURE 17–5 The slow process of making a needle out of an antler can be broken down into six steps.

reindeer, and bison. Africa had all the animals known there today, as well as a great many others that are now extinct: enormous relatives of buffalo, hartebeest, and zebra.

The scene was set for hunting-and-gathering humans to reach the peak of successful adaptation. Full exploitation of these rich resources gave an extraordinary amount of control over their environment and formed the stable basis for still further cultural developments.

Hunter Par Excellence

Two dazzling examples of Upper Paleolithic hunting success have been unearthed by archaeologists in Europe. Near the town of Pavlov, in the Czech Republic, excavations have revealed the remains of more than 100 mammoths in one giant bone heap; near Solutré, in France, an even more staggering bone pile contains the fossils of an estimated 10,000 wild horses lying in a tangled heap at the bottom of a high cliff. The mammoth bones are apparently the remains of the giant beasts trapped in pitfalls; the horses had perhaps been stampeded off the cliff over many years, even generations, by intelligent hunters who were familiar down to the last detail with the terrain of the region and the behavior of their victims.

It is likely that the people of this period all across the world understood as much about hunting large herd animals as any humans in history. They undoubtedly knew just what plants the animals preferred to eat; when seasonal migrations began and how fast the animals traveled; what panicked them and what soothed them. They knew how to drive the animals into pit traps; how to snare them with baited thong nooses; and how to guide them into natural or human-made corrals, either by stampeding them or herding them quietly from a discreet distance. Once trapped, the animals could be dispatched with spears or knives and butchered on the spot. The meat was then taken back to camp, perhaps in processed form, possibly cut up in strips and smoked or sun-dried.

There can also be little doubt that these hunters knew a great deal about the anatomy of their victims and the virtue of eating certain of their organs. Today the inland Alaskan Eskimos save the adrenal glands of slaughtered caribou to give to young children and pregnant women. Chemical analysis of the gland reveals an astonishingly high content of vitamin C, an essential element but one hard to come by in the standard diet of the Eskimo. Without overestimating the earlier hunters' knowledge in these matters, it can be assumed that they, too, knew exactly which parts of the animals they hunted were good, and also which parts were good for them.

Spear Throwers and Points

Atlatl: Aztec name for the spear thrower, a rodlike device used as an extension of the arm that greatly increases both distance and impact of throw.

These people's profound understanding of their prey, combined with significant technical advances in their hunting equipment, paid off in increased food supplies. Hunters had long had wooden spears with fire-hardened tips or sharp stone heads to thrust or throw at their prey, but the effectiveness of a thrown spear against even a young deer, to say nothing of a thick-skinned giant auroch (a kind of extinct wild ox), must have been limited, especially if the animal was in full retreat. These hunters made the spear an effective weapon for killing their prey at a greater distance by inventing the spear thrower (commonly referred to today by its Aztec name, the *atlatl*).

The oldest tangible evidence of this rodlike device dates from about 14,000 years B.P., and it comes from the cave of La Placard in France. Here several fragments of spear throwers were discovered, including a length of bone with a hooked end that looks like nothing so much as an oversized crochet needle. All told, more than 70 reindeer-antler spear throwers have turned up in southwestern France and near Lake Constance along the northeastern border of Switzerland. There is a curious dearth of them elsewhere in the Old World, perhaps because they may have been made of perishable wood and rotted away. By about 10,000 years ago, the wooden spear thrower was being used by the Indians of North and South America. The Eskimos used it until recently, and some Australian Aborigines still use it today, calling it a *womera* (Figure 17–6).

The spear thrower is, in the simplest explanation, an extension of the arm. It is 1–2 ft (30–60 cm) long, with a handle at one end and a point or hook at the other that engaged the butt end of the spear. Hunters hold the thrower behind their shoulder, hook up, and lay the spear along it so that the spear points forward and slightly upward. During the throw they keep hold of the thrower, which may have a thong tied to its end to go around their wrist. When throwing, they swing their arms forward and snap their wrist, launching the spear with great velocity from the end of the thrower at the top of its arc, in this way taking advantage of the centrifugal force generated. The spear travels faster than if hand-thrown because the extension of the throwing arm provides more leverage; the spear thrower's end moves faster than the hand holding it.

Modern experiments have demonstrated the great advantage a spear thrower gives. A 7-ft (2 m) spear can be thrown no more than 180–210 ft (55–65 m) when launched directly from a hunter's hand, but it can be projected up to 450 ft (135 m) with a spear thrower, and it can kill a deer at 90 ft (25 m). This increase in range

FIGURE 17–6 The method of throwing a spear has not changed since spear throwers were introduced in Magdalenian times, about 14,000 years ago. Here an Australian is shown poised to throw his stone-tipped spear. The womera, or spear thrower, can be clearly seen.

gave hunters a tremendous advantage. No longer having to get within a short distance of their prey, they could more often get a throw at the animals before the game ran away. Now they could, when the occasion arose, hunt alone instead of in a group, because it was no longer necessary to surround an animal in order to spear it. And of course, the spear thrower made hunting safer, for hunters did not have to get as close to dangerous teeth, antlers, and hooves. The benefits are obvious: hunters who killed more often and got hurt less lived better and longer lives.

The first spear throwers were undoubtedly of wood, as the Australian womeras are today, but soon they were also being made from antler. People of the late Upper Paleolithic *Magdalenian* culture embellished many of their throwers with carved figures and designs and may even have painted them. One ancient Magdalenian thrower bears traces of red ocher in its hollows, and some have black painted into the eyes. Other throwers display exquisite renderings of animals, including horses, deer, ibex, bison, birds, and fish. At least three show an ibex defecating, held still by the art of the engraver in a vulnerable moment, when a kill may be made. These carvings on weaponry represent a combination of aesthetics and utility that is echoed in many aspects of Magdalenian life.

Other functional advances were in the spear itself. By this time hunters had realized that a barbed point does more damage than a smooth one. Harpoon-style points, fashioned from bone or antler, often had several barbs on one or both sides (Figure 17–7). Another development stemmed from the difficulty of killing an animal outright by one spear wound alone; hunters would have to follow their wounded prey for a while until loss of blood made it weak enough for them to kill. To speed this process, some hunters carved bone spearheads with grooves along each side—runnels apparently designed to increase the flow of blood from the wound.

Magdalenian: Upper Paleolithic culture existing in western Europe from about 16,500 to 11,000 years B.P. Produced many blade tools and prototype harpoons.

FIGURE 17–7 This Magdalenian harpoon was beautifully made and was part of a highly developed collection of fishing tackle. This photograph is one and one-half times actual size.

Bow and Arrow

An interesting puzzle is the use of the bow and arrow. There is no clear-cut archaeological evidence that people used such a weapon until the very end of the Upper Paleolithic. But because bows are normally made of wood and sinew or gut, it would be a lucky accident indeed if any had survived the last ice age, and so the lack of evidence cannot be taken as conclusive. A couple of bows have been uncovered in Denmark that date back approximately 8,000 years, and a larger number of stone-tipped wooden arrow shafts, perhaps 10,000 years old, have been found at the campsites of ancient reindeer hunters in northern Germany. In a cave in La Colombière, in France, there have been found small stones, possibly more than 20,000 years old, with pictures scratched on them that may represent feathered projectiles; whether these were arrows or dartlike spears, however, is uncertain. Among the best early evidence of the bow and arrow are approximately 20,000-year-old microliths and bone foreshafts from Africa. These artifacts closely resemble historic arrow points and foreshafts from the region.

Certainly the bow would have given hunters an enormous advantage. The spear thrower, no matter how valuable an aid, required them to break cover and stand out in the open where they could be spotted by their prey; an unsuccessful launch would scare off the target. But with the bow, hunters could remain hidden. If they missed with the first arrow, they could shoot again. Moreover, the arrow was swifter than the spear and its striking power was greater over a longer distance. It could be shot at a variety of animals—big and small, standing, running, or on the wing—with a better chance of hitting them.

Fishing Gear

Perhaps even more significant than the invention of the spear thrower or the bow in helping Upper Paleolithic people expand their food supply and make a living in varied environments was their development of fishing gear. Human groups had earlier availed themselves of the bounty offered by streams, rivers, and the sea, but for some, fishing now became almost a way of life.

The oldest known bone fishhooks come from European sites about 14,000 years old. A slightly younger development (about 12,000 years B.P.) was a device called the *leister* (Figure 17–8): a tridentlike spear with a point and two curving prongs of bone that held the fish securely after it had been lanced. Another was the fish gorge, a small silver of bone or wood, perhaps 2 in. (5 cm) long, with a leather or sinew line tied around its middle. When the baited gorge was swallowed by a fish, it cocked sideways in its throat in such a way as not to come out easily, and the catch was made.

Leister: a three-pronged spear used for fishing.

FIGURE 17–8   The leister is a three-pronged fishing spear. The middle prong (not visible here) is shorter than the other two. Here an Australian employs the implement, which has been in use for perhaps 12,000 years.

From a slightly later date, we have evidence suggesting that, in South Africa and perhaps in Europe, people began catching fish in much greater numbers than ever before. Small, grooved cylindrical stones found in South Africa may have been weights on nets made of thongs or plant fibers. With a net, two or three people could catch a whole shoal of fish on one sweep.

The *weir*, a stone corral for trapping fish still used by some modern peoples, was probably also used at this time. This technique would have been especially effective on rivers such as the Dordogne and the Vézère in France, where spawning salmon swarm upstream in great numbers. It seems likely that, at the spawning season, parties went to the fishing grounds to lay in a supply of salmon for the whole band, which may have had its home base miles away. The fish may have been cleaned and perhaps sun-dried or smoked where they were caught, and then carried to camp. At Solvieux, in France, a large rectangular area carefully paved with small stones has been excavated; its placement and design strongly hint that it was a fish-drying platform.

Weir: barrier or dam made of stones or sticks set out in a stream or river and used as a fish trap.

Sedentary Life and Sewn Clothing

As modern human groups learned to tap the potential of rivers and seas, climatic changes complemented their improving technologies. The rising sea level that was associated with the retreat of the ice submerged the Atlantic continental shelf and increased the area of warm, shallow sea in which many species of fish could breed. The systematic exploitation of the waters' abundant protein resources—which included great quantities of shellfish as well as fish—was highly significant, not only because it broadened the base of the human diet, but because it helped lead humans toward the next great step in cultural evolution: settled living. With fish and shellfish as a dependable supplement to their regular meat and plant food, people did not have to move around so much in quest of sustenance. With nets they could gather more food with less effort than they could as nomadic hunters-and-gatherers, and thus one place could support a greater number of people. The beginning of a sedentary way of life—*sedentism*—was a crucial development, closely related to what became a rapidly expanding population.

Sedentism: a way of life marked by the lack of migratory movements and by the establishment of permanent habitations.

As the last ice-age peoples learned to help themselves more efficiently to nature's bounty, they also found ways to protect themselves more effectively from nature's rigors. Carefully sewn, fitted clothing was part of the equipment that enabled them to conquer the far north and eventually to penetrate North America.

The hide clothing of these people was probably much like that of today's Eskimos. A tunic or pullover with tightly sewn seams to keep heat from escaping, pants easily tucked into boots, and some sort of sock, perhaps of fur, would have been warm enough in all but the coldest weather. For frigid days, outer clothing consisting of a hooded parka, mittens, and high boots would have kept a person from freezing. What is our evidence that the people had clothing of this sort? Female figurines from Stone Age Russia look as if they are clothed in fur. Furthermore, even in more moderate climates, well-sewn clothing seems to have been an advantage; the earliest eyed needles that have yet been discovered were fashioned by the same expert Solutrean workers of Europe who produced the laurel-leaf blades.

ART AND RITUAL

Cave Art

Until now, our discussion of Upper Paleolithic peoples has centered on their improvements in working stone and particularly bone, and on the cultural developments furthered by these technological improvements. Notable as these changes are, it is the intellectual and spiritual achievements of these people that make them so impressive to us today. Particularly striking is their astounding artistic ability, a talent that seems to have sprung full-blown out of nowhere. There are dozens of examples of cave art in France alone. These date from over 30,000 to 10,000 years B.P. and are attributed primarily to the Solutrean and Magdalenian peoples. Equally ancient rock art sites have been found in Tanzania and in Namibia's Apollo Cave. By the latest Pleistocene, rock art had appeared in India, Australia, and the Americas. All of these sites show that Upper Paleolithic peoples were close observers of the animals they hunted as well as magnificent artists. More than that, the record they left behind shows that they had a sufficiently sophisticated way of life to be able to appreciate and encourage their own talents and to work them into their rituals.

Traditionally, the paintings and carvings of these people have been interpreted as closely associated with their spiritual life. One strong indication is seen in the places they chose to put wall paintings. The caves in the Dordogne are basically of two kinds. The rock overhangs, more-or-less open and facing out over the valleys, could be made livable by adding barriers of brushwood or animal skins to keep out the wind and snow (Figure 17–9). They are full of the signs of many generations of occupancy; tools lie in all strata in their floors, together with buried skeletons. Hearths abound, tending to become bigger as they become more recent.

Some fragments of wall decoration have been found in these open shelters; perhaps originally there were more that have since been destroyed by exposure to the elements. But the most spectacular wall art is confined to true caves: deep underground fissures with long galleries and passages. These caves have their own subterranean pools, rivers, and festoons of stalactites and stalagmites. They

FIGURE 17–9 Near the village of Les Eyzies, the Vézère Valley presents a peaceful panorama little changed since Paleolithic people surveyed the scene. In this area, numerous rock shelters and other prehistoric sites are still unexcavated.

are dark, mysterious, and very cold; they could be entered only by people holding stone lamps or torches. Certainly these caverns were inappropriate as dwelling places, and they contain little or no evidence of having been lived in. By nature removed from day-to-day life, these caves may well have been used as shrines and for the performance of certain rites (Figure 17–10).

Painting and Hunting Magic

Important observations about the location of cave art were made by the late Abbé Henri Breuil, the French priest who devoted his life to the study of prehistory, and by Johannes Maringer, who has also studied this art intensively. The paintings or engravings were often made in the least convenient places for viewing: in narrow niches, behind protrusions of rock, sometimes in areas that must have been not only difficult but actually dangerous for the artist to work in. "It is simply impossible," says Maringer, "that this art should have been invented, in these locations, to give pleasure to the eye of the beholder; the intention must always have been to veil it in mysterious secrecy."

What was its purpose, then? The traditional explanation, accepted by Maringer and numerous other experts, is that cave art was a vehicle for magic— more specifically, a vehicle for a form known as *sympathetic hunting magic*. Upper Paleolithic people were strong and intelligent, and they were well equipped with all kinds of weapons, from spears and knives to slings. They knew how to make traps for small animals and pitfalls for large ones. They could ambush animals and stampede them. And, as we have seen, they left behind them impressive

Sympathetic hunting magic: the use of rituals (and associated artifacts) to ensure success and safety in the hunt.

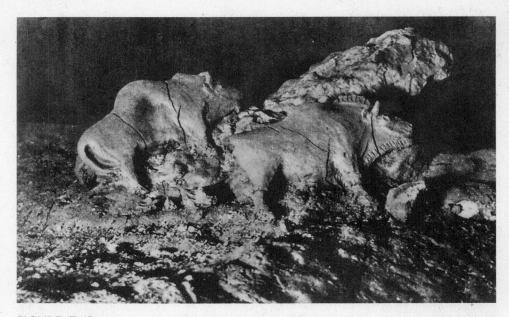

FIGURE 17–10　The clay bison, 24 in. (61 cm) long, lean against a limestone block in a remote chamber of Le Tuc d'Audoubert Cave near Ariège, France. These may have been ritual objects.

records of their prowess. Nevertheless, despite their formidable powers, they walked always in the shadow of unpredictable and incomprehensible events, which they may have seen as malign forces. Doubtless they felt it necessary to try to forestall misfortune and injury—and perhaps death, for some of the animals they came up against were extremely dangerous. Doubtless, too, they believed, like so many people living today, that magic could help them not only dodge misfortune but also gain control over the animals they wished to kill. By painting the animals' pictures, they became, in effect, the animals' masters and strengthened their chances of dealing the prey a mortal wound during the hunt. Even today people of many societies believe that creating the likeness of a person or thing gives the person who created it some supernatural power over the subject.

This interpretation of the paintings as hunting magic has a variety of evidence to support it. First, and most direct, is the large number of animals painted with spears lodged in them or marked with the blows of clubs, as though the artists intended to illustrate what they hoped would be the outcome of a chase (Figure 17–11). Less obvious are the drawings of rectangular enclosures with animals seemingly trapped in them. The most frequently seen example of these is in a cave at Font-de-Gaume near Les Eyzies, where a magnificent painted mammoth seems to be caught in a pitfall even though its enormous tusks thrust beyond the snare.

There is also a hint of hunting magic in the practice of superimposing one picture over another. This phenomenon has been observed over and over again in the caves. In one spot at Lascaux in France, the paintings are four layers deep, even though there is plenty of empty wall space nearby. If the painters had meant simply to express themselves or give pleasure to others, they would probably have started with a clean wall surface for each animal depicted. The concentration of paintings in one spot, one atop another, suggests that the placement of the painting was somehow important and that the overpainting was done for a purpose.

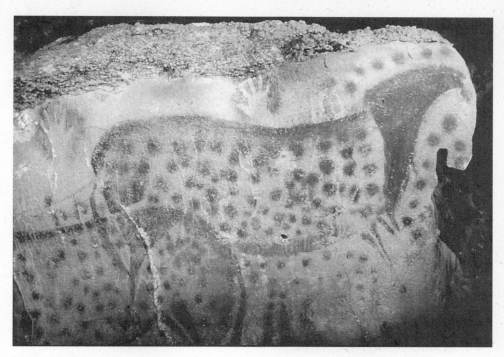

FIGURE 17–11 Pelted with dots, a painting of two horses in the Pech-Merle cave (Dordogne) combines two kinds of symbols for what could be simple decoration, or signs of hunting magic. The dots, in black and red ocher, could represent projectiles; the handprints surrounding the horses, a person's power over the prey. Taken together, the dots and the handprints would then be an invocation to the supernatural, intended to assure the hunters of a successful kill.

Certain areas of the cave were favored for some reason, and it would be logical to suppose that paintings that had previously brought hunters good luck came, in themselves, to be regarded as good hunting magic. Because all ritual depends on duplicating as closely as possible a procedure that has proved successful in the past, certain spots in the cave would come to be regarded as lucky.

In some instances entire caves seem to have been imbued with an aura of good fortune. In Les Combarelles in southwestern France nearly 300 animals crowd onto the cave walls. Perhaps it was this crowding that produced still another phenomenon of wall art: the tendency to overpaint one animal's head on another's body. Where space was at a premium, it would have been more provident to use the magic already available than to start afresh. Or perhaps artists simply looked for a less arduous way of working magic, for many of the cave paintings obviously took time and effort to execute. It is not difficult to imagine wishful hunters contemplating a beautifully painted bison and deciding to take a magical shortcut by substituting a deer's head for the bison's.

Hunting magic may also explain the occasional human-beast figures found in caves, strange-looking creatures with human bodies and animal or bird heads called *therianthropes*. According to South African archaeologist David Lewis-Williams, these creatures represented shamans or sorcerers, who must have played an important part in the lives of the artists. Lewis-Williams believes that many of the paintings were created by shamans in deep trance, and he has made a good case for this supposition. Such a hypothesis would account for many of the curious features of cave art that have no other obvious explanation. His ideas certainly reinforce the belief that the paintings carried powerful magical connotations.

But despite the logic and the long-term popularity of the hunting-magic hypothesis, some researchers feel that it is not the only—and perhaps not even the best—interpretation of cave imagery. For example, Margaret Conkey, of the University of California at Berkeley, and others have pointed out that the cave paintings and sculptures are generally of animal species *other* than those that figured heavily in Upper Paleolithic diets. While roughly 65 percent of the European cave images depict either horses or bison, two other species—red deer and reindeer—actually dominate the food refuse. Thus, if the images were intended to ensure success in the hunt, they didn't work very well—at least as reflected by the remains of ancient meals. Furthermore, the idea that many of the cave sites were shrines whose images accumulated over long periods and repeated visits has been called into question. Recent analyses of pollen in cave sediments and of paint composition ("pigment recipes") suggest that in some cases complex images, including depictions of groups and/or superimposed animals, were painted quickly and on one occasion. Results such as these tend to weaken (though not completely refute) the traditional notion that the caves were used over thousands of years by many generations of hopeful hunters.

Art and Fertility

Thus, although hunting magic may explain a great deal of cave art, that interpretation is not airtight. For some authorities these animals and cryptic geometrical signs are sexual in nature, and the paintings were fertility magic. Pairs of animals were often shown together, sometimes in the act of mating. Horses, does, and cows were painted with swollen bellies (as in Figure 17–12), which have been interpreted as a sign of advanced pregnancy. In other paintings, udders were enlarged, as if to emphasize the rich supply of milk that the mother would be capable of giving to any offspring that might be born.

The fertility of prey animals was a natural concern of the hunters. Scarcity of food must have been a periodic problem in many regions. During the colder episodes of the last glacial period, Magdalenian hunters killed mammoths, woolly rhinoceros, ibex, steppe horses, and particularly reindeer, which flourished in large numbers in the tundra environment. When the climate warmed from time to time, they undoubtedly hunted the deer, bison, and wild cattle that replaced the cold-adapted species, but the need to feed increasing numbers may well have led these people to encourage the natural productiveness of their game with fertility magic.

Other authorities think that cave art, though sexual in content, was far less utilitarian in its purpose. Instead of fertility magic, they see it as an attempt to express in visual symbols the dual forces in human nature: male and female. The most notable spokesperson for this post-Freudian point of view is French anthropologist André Leroi-Gourhan, who has made an extensive study of cave art. Leroi-Gourhan has charted the frequency of occurrence of the various kinds of animals and signs, along with their locations in the caves and their positions in relation to each other. He thinks that most of the paintings and drawings have specific sexual connotations—that deer and bear are masculine, as are such signs as

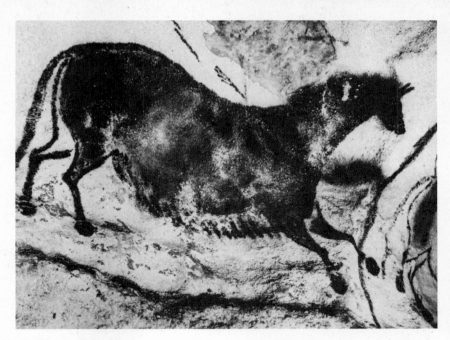

FIGURE 17–12   A pregnant horse gallops across the limestone ceiling of Lascaux. The slash marks above its shoulders may indicate spears. Lascaux, among the finest of all the painted caves of southwestern France, is a Magdalenian masterpiece, dated about 17,000 years B.P. The newly discovered cave of La Grotte Chauvet may surpass even Lascaux in its works of art.

spears and clubs, whereas cattle and bison, as well as the enclosed figures that other authorities identify as traps in support of the theory of hunting magic, are feminine.

Taking an entirely new approach, Alexander Marshack has been examining the smaller portable items of Upper Palaeolithic art under a low-powered microscope. He has made many surprising observations and has drawn some startling if controversial conclusions. A beautiful horse 2.5 in. (6 cm) long, carved in mammoth ivory and from the site of Vogelherd in Germany, is the earliest known example of animal sculpture, dating from about 30,000 years B.P. The carefully carved ear, nose, mouth, and mane have been worn down by persistent handling. At some time during this use, a fresh angle or dart was engraved in its flank, apparently symbolizing an act of actual or ritualized killing. The object was touched and used often and seems to have served some important purpose.

A second example described by Marshack is the image of a horse engraved on a horse's pelvis from the site of Paglicci in Italy. Microscopic examination of the image indicated that the horse had been symbolically killed 27 times. Twenty-seven feathered darts or spears were engraved on and around the horse, each made by a different engraving point and in a different style, possibly over a considerable period of time. This horse was clearly a symbol that could be used in an appropriate way when required.

The large painted horse from the cave of Pech-Merle (Figure 17–11) proves to have somewhat similar characteristics: The black and red dots on its body are made of many pigments and ochers, suggesting that they were applied over a period and that the horse was used continually as an important symbol.

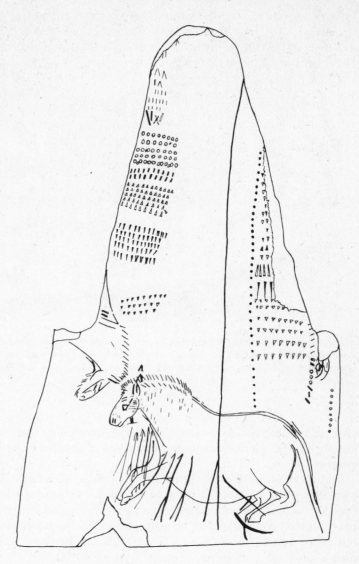

FIGURE 17–13   Fragment of antler tool from La Marche, France. This is the earliest known artifact containing two types of notations: cumulative markings and naturalistic sketches. The markings may be related to the gestation period of a horse. The line drawing shows the entire surface of the antler fragment.

But Marshack has noticed other details. On some portable items he has found small marks, often in series, made at different times by different tools, which seem to indicate some sort of notation or numerical record. One particularly interesting antler fragment, from La Marche in the Dordogne, shows both a pregnant horse (which has been "used" a number of times) and a lengthy notation consisting of small notches in rows made from the tip downward, in lines of 11 (Figure 17–13). Marshack points out that 11 is the number of months in the gestation of a horse. Other notations on other fragments suggest that the phases of the moon were being logged.

Marshack's work has opened our eyes to the fact that these people were very much more sophisticated than anyone had supposed, and that they were not only great artists but also possibly on the brink of developing arithmetic, and even perhaps the beginning of very primitive writing. We do not yet understand the meaning of all the material that they have left us, but we do know that they are ancestors for whom we should have the greatest respect.

When the work of Leroi-Gourhan, Marshack, and others is combined with traditional interpretations, it becomes clear that Upper Paleolithic art may have had multiple functions—as hunting magic or fertility magic, as part of initiation rites, perhaps for communication between groups (see the Postscript to this chapter), and possibly even as a part of complex religious ceremonies (as described below). But how can we tease apart these various functions for a more complete understanding? The first and most important step, according to Margaret Conkey, is to stop viewing Upper Paleolithic imagery as a functionally monolithic phenomenon and to begin disentangling it into its component "sign systems," which can be linked to specific social and historical contexts. Future analyses using this approach promise to produce fascinating results.

But whatever the images' meaning, the skill of the artists and the beauty of their work are astonishing. Every animal is an individual portrait, drawn from life, by painters in complete control of their medium. Their outlines are sure and bold. They painted in various tones of black, red, yellow, and brown obtained from natural clays and mineral oxides. Sometimes they mixed their colors with charcoal and animal fat to make a thick pigment, which they used like a crayon or daubed on with moss, frayed twigs, or even a primitive paintbrush made of hair. At other times, they seem to have blown dry colors directly onto the wall in powder form, possibly through a hollow bird bone. Some researchers even think that Upper Paleolithic artists occasionally masticated their pigments and then spat the paint onto cave walls. Once applied to a wall, the colors were slowly absorbed by the limestone. This absorption begins to explain their phenomenal durability. Thanks to the constant humidity and temperature of the caves, much of Paleolithic art in western Europe has retained its original brilliance for 10,000 to 20,000 years, some of it for even longer.

Spectacular New Painted Cave Found in Southern France (1994)

As if to remind us that even well-explored areas may still hold archaeological secrets, the discovery of a new and spectacular painted cave in the Ardèche region of southern France was announced to the world on December 18, 1994. The new cave is called La Grotte Chauvet and it is located near the town of Vallon-Pont-d'Arc, some 40 mi (64 km) northwest of Avignon. Dating from about 33,000–30,000 years B.P., the site is particularly valuable to archaeologists because of its undisturbed nature and very early date. Prior to its discovery, the cave apparently had been completely sealed by fallen debris for thousands of years.

Initial reports suggest that the art of La Grotte Chauvet may surpass even that of the famous caves of Lascaux and Altamira. It is estimated that the new cave, which consists of at least 4 huge halls, contains over 300 paintings by Upper Paleolithic artists. Included in the vivid images are human hands, bears, mammoths, woolly rhinos, lions, and hyenas, as well as the first known images of owls and a panther. In addition to its art works, the cave is said to contain stone tools, hearths, and numerous bones, including the skull of a cave bear that may have been deliberately displayed amidst a group of bear paintings.

The potential importance of La Grotte Chauvet is shown by the fact that it has been placed under French government protection and at present only archaeologists are allowed to enter the cave. As this book goes to press, scientific studies of the site are just beginning, but it seems certain that this new painted cave will yield important new insights into Upper Paleolithic life.

Sculpture and Ceramics

In addition to painting, Upper Paleolithic people showed considerable proficiency as sculptors and engravers (see Figure 17–10). In early examples of their skill, they incised the outlines of animals on cave walls. Later artists went on to develop the more advanced technique of carving subjects in high relief, often using the contours of the walls. Le Cap Blanc, near Les Eyzies, has a marvelous set of horses done in this way. The entire frieze is about 40 ft (12 m) long; the largest horse is 7 ft (2 m) long. As the bulging sides of the horses' bodies reveal, the artists incorporated the natural curves of the rock into their work with great skill. Apparently more than one artist was guided by the formation and the structure of the rock in carving this frieze, for the animal figures appear to have been worked on at various times.

These artists also made complete statues in the round. In doing so, they left us a means of gaining further insights into Stone Age life and thought. The statues are usually of stone, bone, or ivory, although some were carved out of a mixture of clay and ground bone that had been hardened by firing. The first evidence of firing comes from the site of Dolni Vestonice in the Czech Republic. At a settlement dated about 27,000 years B.P. is a kiln where the bone and clay mixture was fired into a new, rock-hard material. This is the first example in technological history of a process that was to become ubiquitous and would eventually be used in producing glass, bronze, steel, nylon, and most of the other materials of everyday life, that is, the combination and treatment of two or more dissimilar substances to make a useful product unlike either starting substance. It would be another 15,000 years or so before other people, living in Japan, learned to turn clay into pots; yet, as the evidence from Dolni Vestonice attests, ceramics had already been invented.

When the kiln hut was first investigated in 1951, its sooty floor was littered with fragments of ceramic figurines. There were animal heads: bears, foxes, lions. In one particularly beautiful lion head was a hole simulating a wound, perhaps intended to help some hunter inflict a similar wound on a real lion. The floor was also cluttered with hundreds of scrap pellets that were probably pinched off the lump of unbaked clay when sculpting began and that still bore the artisan's fingerprints. And there were limbs broken from little animal and human figures. They may have cracked off in the baking, or when the ancient ceramist tossed aside a failed work.

Female Figurines

More intriguing than any waste fragments of clay animal figures on the hut floor are the human statuettes found there, particularly the female figures. Unlike the animals, these are not naturalistic but almost surreal. Such figurines have a very wide distribution at Upper Paleolithic sites over much of Europe and eastward as

FIGURE 17–14 This Czech clay figure from Dolni Vestonice shows the Venus's typical traits: huge breasts and belly and shapeless arms. This figure's legs are now broken, but they probably had no feet. This photograph is approximately 80 percent actual size.

far as western Siberia and Ukraine. Although they vary a good deal in appearance, they have some significant things in common, the most obvious being that the sculptors' interest was focused on the torso. The arms and legs are extremely small in proportion to the trunk, and in some cases they are merely suggested (see Figures 17–14 and 17–15). The heads are also small and typically show little attempt to portray facial features, although the famous Venus of Willendorf, a 4-in. (10 cm) figurine made of limestone, does have a wavy hairdo executed with considerable care (Figure 17–16). All the emphasis is on the bodies, with their female characteristics—breasts, belly, and buttocks—greatly exaggerated in size. They look like tiny earth goddesses or fertility figures, and a good deal of informed speculation suggests that this is what they were. Many of them show the polish of long use and some the remains of red ocher, which indicates that they were symbolically painted.

Some evidence supporting the idea that they were fertility figures is based on where these statuettes are found and when they are believed to have been made. The majority of them come from the period of the Upper *Perigordian* (or Gravettian), a Paleolithic culture of western Europe that existed between 27,000 and 21,000 years ago. During this period, the weather ranged from cool to very cold. In the cold periods it was bitter in the extreme, especially on the eastern European plains; nevertheless, many people continued to live there. Some made their homes in shallow pits that they dug in the ground and then roofed over with hides or other material. The vague outlines of the walls of many of these sunken huts may still be seen. The interesting thing is that these sites contain abundant

Perigordian: Upper Paleolithic culture of western Europe dating 27,000 to 21,000 years B.P.

FIGURE 17–15 The Venus of Abri Pataud, the armless body of a woman incised in a small piece of rock, is one of the few art objects found at the excavation. It was made some 20,000 years ago.

examples of these female figurines, and they are often found lying right next to the walls or buried near hearths. The figurines themselves often taper to a point at the bottom, as if they had been designed to be stuck into the earth or into a base of some sort.

On this evidence it is fairly clear that the figurines were closely associated with the daily life of the peoples who made them and have a significance utterly unlike that of the wall art that was created in secret, deep in underground caves. Speculating on their purpose, several authorities have proposed various theories. To Johannes Maringer the figurines seem to point to an enhancement in the status of women. Maringer thinks that a combination of harsh climatic conditions and a relatively sedentary way of life account for that change. When people settle down in one place for considerable periods, the home becomes important, and home-making is usually regarded as the woman's prerogative. In the cold of the windswept eastern steppe, it was perhaps the women who had the critical jobs of planning, rationing, storing, and using supplies so that the group could get through the winter. Storage pits were found at many sites, some with animal remains. Probably women were also responsible for making the fur clothing that the people are thought to have dressed in. Sewing carefully with eyed needles of

FIGURE 17–16 Small figurines like the 4.3-inches-high (11 cm) Venus of Willendorf in Austria were widespread in Europe 20,000 years ago. Note the intricate hairdo.

bone, they could have made warm clothing that fitted the body well, particularly around the arms and legs.

But the role of women would also have been important because of their procreative function. The mysteries of fertility and birth made women the guardians not only of hearth and home but of life itself. In the minds of some modern experts, the female figurines are cult objects. They represented the tribal ancestresses from whom the group was descended, assuring them of continuity as a group and increasing their population and the population of the animals they hunted. Whether the little figures were worshipped as goddesses or simply venerated as good-luck charms is not known.

Burial Customs and Rites

Upper Paleolithic people were concerned about death as well as life, and their treatment of the dead was careful and thoughtful. The bodies were often placed in graves dug in the ashes of previously occupied living sites, and in many places it was a common practice to sprinkle the deceased with red ocher, perhaps in an effort to bring back the flush of life to pallid skin (Figure 17–17). The practice of including grave offerings, begun by the Neandertals, was expanded by their successors in Eurasia to extraordinary heights of funerary luxury. An example is the grave of two boys (shown in Figure 17–18) that was excavated during the 1960s in a Paleolithic settlement about 130 mi (210 km) northeast of Moscow, at Sungir. The

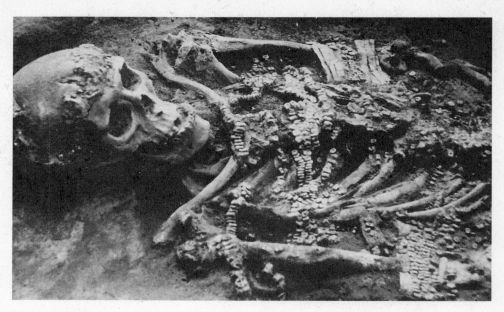

FIGURE 17–17   The skeleton of a man lies just as the body was buried 23,000 years ago in an ocher-sprinkled grave at Sungir, northeast of Moscow. The man was ceremoniously laid to rest, laden with beads, a headband of carved mammoth ivory, and the teeth of arctic foxes, in what appears to have been a burial ground—suggesting the hunter-gatherers of Sungir lived part of the year in a settled community where they developed complex customs.

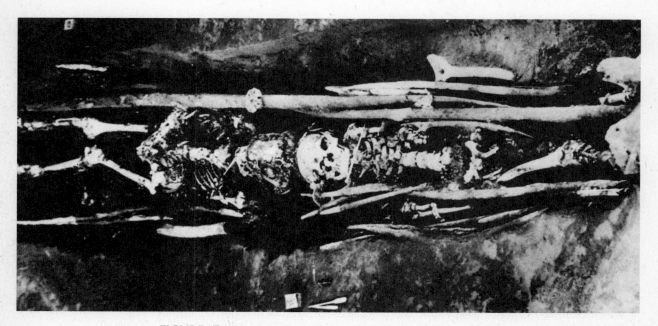

FIGURE 17–18   The skeletons of two boys who died 23,000 years ago lie head to head in a grave at Sungir in Russia. The elaborateness of their grave suggests that the boys were laid to rest amid solemn ritual, perhaps with a view to an afterlife.

grave suggests either that the boys were very important or that the settlers who lived at Sungir 23,000 years ago had some fairly elaborate ideas about an afterlife. The boys—one 7 to 9 years old, the other 12 or 13—were laid out in a line, skull to skull. Both had been dressed from head to toe in clothing decorated with ivory beads carved from mammoth tusks, and they wore bracelets and rings of the same material. On the older boy's chest lay a disk of mammoth tusk carved into the shape of a horse, and both boys were equipped with an assortment of ivory weapons, such as lances, spears, and daggers. The lances had been formed from a split mammoth bone that had been warmed over a fire in order to be straightened, a technique that requires considerable sophistication.

Synthesizing Art, Ritual, and Religion in the Upper Paleolithic

American archaeologist D. Bruce Dickson has recently synthesized all of the available evidence on European Upper Paleolithic burial practices and art, and he has reached a set of interesting—and heuristically valuable—conclusions. Dickson believes that the elaborate burials of the Upper Paleolithic indicate a more complex and socially differentiated society than that of the Middle Paleolithic. Furthermore, since complex societies are supported by complex institutions, religious institutions in the Upper Paleolithic probably exceeded the simple shamanistic cult with its part-time religious specialist. Dickson believes that religious rituals, conducted fundamentally in "an attempt to control nature and society by supernatural means," involved shamanistic direction of a community of participants. Community rituals, according to Dickson, were likely to be performed seasonally when, following the rhythms of their subsistence activities, Upper Paleolithic groups aggregated at the painted caves that served as their ceremonial centers. Annual visits to such ceremonial centers may account for the evidence that they were used, and their art added to, repeatedly. Seasonal aggregations and society-wide rituals would have fostered group integrity and continuity, and shared religious beliefs may even have promoted friendly interactions and information sharing among widely separated cultures. Finally, Dickson believes that woven into the ritual practices of the Upper Paleolithic people were concepts about the passage of time and about human sexuality, "especially the periodicity and fecundity of women." Thus the Venus figurines and also artifacts suggesting notation systems are seen as facets of a larger, and quite elaborate, belief system.

The more we learn about these earliest of modern people from the evidence of their living sites, the narrower the gap becomes between them and us. But it will never be entirely closed. The intimate details of social life, the games children played, the gestures and courtesies that give a society flavor—all these have necessarily vanished. We have no knowledge of how one addressed another or what words they used. And we will never know.

Some details have enlightened us, however, and some generalizations can be made. As these first modern people stretched their powers, they came to separate themselves from nature's control in ways that their ancestors could not have dreamed of. Spread as they now were throughout the Old and New Worlds, they were adapting to a vast range of environments and developing a host of different cultures and languages. What we have described is based mainly on archaeological research in Europe—a very small part indeed of the whole world. Everywhere culture moved ahead and blossomed in an endless variety of forms, and society developed in a thousand complex ways. The ability to exploit such a variety of environments led to great growth in the numbers of people, and populations increased as much as tenfold in some parts of the world. By the end of this period, some 10,000 years ago, these people had set the stage for the last steps in the emergence of modern culture: agriculture, domestication of animals, metalworking, complex forms of social and political life, writing, and perhaps even war.

SUMMARY

The sedentary lifestyle (sedentism), as distinct from nomadism, was very unusual in human prehistory, but by 30,000 years B.P. it became more common with increased control of the environment. People had learned to make fire and had developed a wide range of specialized stone tools. With these they created objects made of wood, bone, antler, and ivory—all invaluable materials available in reasonable quantities. They made beads and bracelets and a whole range of hunting weapons, including spears, spear throwers, spear points, fishing gear of different kinds, tailored clothing, and eventually the bow and arrow.

Ritual life became very important and, with it, art and magic. Cave paintings may have served to influence hunting success and the fertility of game. Sculpture (female figures) and the first ceramics may have been involved in fertility rites. At Magdalenian sites we find the first evidence of numeracy, and an artistic eye can be seen in the design of the artifacts. Considered collectively, the evidence of Upper Paleolithic burials and art suggests an extremely elaborate belief system and complex religious institutions. Clearly, Upper Paleolithic peoples were modern not only anatomically, but intellectually.

REVIEW QUESTIONS

1. Many researchers argue that Upper Paleolithic people were more sedentary than their Middle Paleolithic predecessors. What sorts of technological innovations and/or environmental changes would have allowed the development of sedentism? What sorts of cultural change may have resulted from a less mobile lifestyle?

2. Some of the world's most beautiful flaked stone artifacts were made by Upper Paleolithic artisans. As exemplified by several of the Solutrean blades, however, the artifacts often seem to be too delicate or the wrong size for practical use. Speculate on the possible functions of such "showpiece" artifacts.

3. Describe the evidence of increased hunting efficiency in the Upper Paleolithic.

4. Describe the cave art of the Upper Paleolithic. Speculate on how cave paintings and sculptures may have been incorporated into rituals of various sorts. Compare your speculations with the use of icons in modern religions.

5. Speculate about the relative status of women and men within Upper Paleolithic societies. Which sex do you think made the greater contribution to subsistence activities? To toolmaking? To art? To religion? In each case, explain the basis of your speculations. In particular, do you think the female figurines

indicate that European Upper Paleolithic people traced their descent matri- lineally or that they worshiped female deities?

POSTSCRIPT

Many students of Upper Paleolithic art believe that the cave paintings and sculp- tures preserve a kind of "text," and that, if we can once break the "code" of the various symbols, we will be able to reconstruct a good deal of what Upper Pale- olithic people thought and how they interacted. Shared symbolism may have facilitated trading or cooperative hunting between widely scattered human groups. Additionally, some artistic symbols may have conveyed complex mes- sages either within or between groups. Consider the case of the handprints.

In several, but by no means all, of the painted caves, images of animals and other objects are accompanied by impressions of human hands (see Figure 17–11). Sites known for their handprints include Gargas, Abri Labatut, Tibiran, and Les Combarelles in France, and El Castillo and El Pindal in Spain. These handprints have several binary features: they are either traced (negative representation) or painted (positive representation); left- or right-handed; red or black in color; whole or "mutilated" (apparently missing digits). As discussed by D. Bruce Dick- son, the various attributes combine to produce 16 distinct types of handprints (e.g., traced-left-red-whole versus painted-right-black-mutilated). Furthermore, as Dickson points out, if one counts fingers, the number of possible combinations rises to 40. Since humans around the world more-or-less consistently associate the left hand with evil and the right hand with good, and also the color red with life and black with death, the handprint code—if that's what it is—seems to be charged with potential meaning. One can imagine handprints being used simply as signatures after the completion of particularly elaborate pieces of cave art ("So- and-so painted this") or as complex, coded messages between groups that rou- tinely visited the same cave sites ("So-and-so was here recently and wishes the reader of this message ill").

Alternately, of course, the handprints may carry no meaning whatsoever, in which case they would fall into the same category as modern doodles. Messages or doodles? Only time and further research will tell. One thing is clear, however: The full meaning of Upper Paleolithic art remains to be revealed, and many sur- prises lie ahead.

CHAPTER 17 TIMELINE

NEOLITHIC AND MESOLITHIC	YEARS B.P.	FOSSILS AND ARCHAEOLOGICAL RECORD	MAJOR TOOL INDUSTRIES OF WESTERN EUROPE

NEOLITHIC AND MESOLITHIC
10,000

UPPER PALEOLITHIC
40,000

MIDDLE PALEOLITHIC

- 200,000

Swanscombe
and Steinheim;
Levallois technique
Beijing finds
- 400,000   Arago

- 500,000

LOWER PALEOLITHIC

- 1 MILLION   *Paranthropus* extinct

- 1.5 MILLION   Acheulean industry

Homo habilis at Olduvai

- 1.8 MILLION   *Homo erectus* in Africa,
the Caucasus, and Java

- 2 MILLION   Oldowan industry

YEARS B.P.

10,000 —

—

—

50,000 —

—

—

—

—

—

100,000 —

—

—

130,000 —

FOSSILS AND ARCHAEOLOGICAL RECORD

Arrows used in N. Germany

First farmers
Clay pots, Japan
Iron pyrite in Belgium, spear thrower
  at La Placard, France
Sungir burials, bow and arrow in Africa
Cave art and figurines
Oldest dated European moderns: Pavlov
Lake Mungo, Australia, fossils
Cro-Magnon
Chauvet cave art
St. Césaire
Modern skull at Niah

Possible entry into Americas

Monte Circeo skull

Amud and Shanidar fossils
  and flower burial

La Quina, La Chapelle,
  La Ferrassie fossils

Disk-core technique used

Skhūl and Qafzeh fossils
Solo skulls

Kabwe, Elandsfontein, Jabel Irhoud,
  Klasies River, and Jingniushan fossils

MAJOR TOOL INDUSTRIES OF WESTERN EUROPE

NEOLITHIC

MESOLITHIC CULTURES

MAGDALENIAN

SOLUTREAN

PERIGORDIAN
(=GRAVETTIAN)

AURIGNACIAN/
CHATELPERRONIAN

MOUSTERIAN

ACHEULEAN

TECHNOLOGY, MAGIC, AND ART

Many of the dates given to finds are based on indirect evidence and are estimates; the dates given to cultural phases are approximations.

CHAPTER
18

The Human Condition

515

*B*ut man, proud man,
Drest in a little brief authority,
Most ignorant of what he's most assured,
His glassy essence, like an angry ape,
Plays such fantastic tricks before high heaven
As make the angels weep.
      WILLIAM SHAKESPEARE, 1564–1616. *Measure for Measure*, II, ii.

OVERVIEW

Hominid evolution has been under way for an estimated 5 to 7 million years. The earliest phase involved the australopithecines, whose lifeways (although noncultural) and anatomies served them in good stead for millions of years. About 2.4 million years ago, however, a new and significantly brainier type of hominid evolved: the first representatives of the genus *Homo*. The hominines changed rather dramatically after their first appearance. They became bigger and smarter and better communicators; radically broadened their subsistence systems by domesticating plants and animals; and evolved a tremendously complex cultural lifestyle. Although several extinct hominine species are known, today the subfamily (and indeed the entire family Hominidae) is represented by only one species: modern humans, *Homo sapiens sapiens*. This final chapter deals primarily with the extreme physical variability of living humans and with our traditional way of understanding that variability—through the construction of racial classifications. It shows how most anatomical variations can be understood as adaptations to different environments, mere surface features rather than deep lines of division across humanity. It argues that, among humans, race has no validity as a biological concept (although it is quite important sociologically) and that therefore biology cannot be used as a justification for racist attitudes and behavior. The chapter concludes with a discussion of some of the challenges that await humans in the future, including limiting global population size and wisely using our growing control over our own evolution. Important concepts and topics in the chapter include human altruism; plant and animal domestication; the beginnings and effects of settled living; physical variation among living humans; human traits as evolutionary adaptations; biological races; sociological races; racism; human population growth; and humans' control over their evolutionary future.

THE STORY OF HUMANKIND

It is hard to realize that the story we have recounted in these chapters took tens of millions of years in its enactment. The development of technology alone has taken well over 2 million years. During this incredibly long period of emergence, the animal that became *Homo sapiens* has been shaped by environment and social experience—both body and culture changing in adaptation.

Evolutionary biology, of which paleoanthropology is a division, makes this much clear to us: Each species is a product of its genes and its environment. That is, with few exceptions each characteristic of every species is a product of mutation and natural selection and in a very immediate way *fits* its environment. Fishes have fins, horses have hooves, primates have hands. Each characteristic of the human body is also a direct product of the interaction between genes and environment. This is not to say that natural selection is directed or moved toward any goal, nor does it mean that the characteristics that *have* been selected by the environment are the only ones that could have been. Nature shows us that there is more than one solution to any problem. If in the long run we do not understand the genesis of every human characteristic, we know at least that we can never understand either the genesis or the function of a characteristic without considering the environment in which it evolved.

Environmental History and Adaptation

The story of the human environment is relatively clear and forms the first strand of the story of human evolution. The tropical rain forest was the womb from which our human ancestors emerged into the world. As our ancestors evolved, they moved out of the shelter of the forest to occupy more open woodland and the tropical savannas throughout the Old World. As they expanded north into the temperate zones, they came to occupy an increasing number of different biomes, or ecological zones. To temperate grassland and woodland alike they adapted, and eventually to the cool *taiga* (subarctic coniferous forests) and icy tundra. They moved in and out of the northern taiga and followed game to alpine pastures. They began to exploit the regions bordering deserts and re-entered the tropical rain forests. They evolved the flexibility to live in all these different biomes—and were the first organism to do so.

Taiga: northern coniferous forest bordering the tundra.

This flexibility humankind owed, of course, to the second strand of our story: the evolution of a remarkable and extraordinarily adaptable body and of an astounding brain. We have seen how the australopithecines have come to be recognized as the first hominids and that these creatures—at least after *Australopithecus ramidus*—were certainly bipeds with very human teeth. By the time of *A. afarensis*, the genus was adapted well to the new lifestyle of the savanna dweller: flexible in behavior, very likely omnivorous, and highly social. *Australopithecus* seems to have been a constant part of the savanna fauna for at least 1.5 million years. From this genus sprang bigger-brained forms: early *Homo*, including *H. rudolfensis* and *H. habilis*. Next in line came *H. erectus*, the first hominids enough like us to be called *humans*, who invaded the temperate zones. Expansion continued northward until archaic *H. sapiens* entered the arctic regions, equipped with highly developed technology (Figure 18–1). Following them, we find modern people, arising most probably in Africa, who were indistinguishable physically from ourselves, spreading throughout the Old World and entering the New World and Australia. This expansion was probably complete before the end of the Paleolithic and brings us almost to the later stone ages, the Mesolithic and Neolithic.

The human organism, miraculous though it may seem in its complexity, was still a product of natural selection: the human brain was no more than what was needed for survival and successful reproduction in a variety of different physical and social environments. From an average of perhaps 400 cc some 4 million years ago, human cranial capacity has risen to vary between 1,000 and 2,000 cc. This increase in size has been exceedingly rapid by evolutionary measure and has produced a brain of unprecedented complexity.

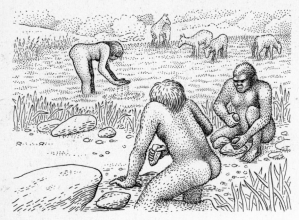

Early *Homo*

Homo erectus

FIGURE 18–1   From bipedal *Australopithecus* on the African savanna to *Homo sapiens* worldwide, from Oldowan choppers to complex technology, human development has been the result of the interaction of environment, body, and culture.

Altruism and Bioaltruism

The question inevitably arises of whether we are more than a superior kind of animal, and if so, in what way? Have we in some sense escaped from the constraints of our animal ancestry? Are we really different in kind from the animals that share our world? For centuries, philosophers have been trying to define the unique qualities that would set us apart from the animal kingdom. We have language, technology, complex society, even civilization. Some writers have proposed ethics as the most profound characteristic that clearly divides human from beast. Do humans alone show the virtue of unselfishness, or altruism? If they do, does this not finally separate them at a profound level from the selfish and competitive law of natural selection? Altruism—the act of helping others at some cost to oneself— has been claimed to be a unique characteristic of humans, and for many years biologists were unable to see how such a characteristic could possibly emerge as a result of natural selection. The question was discussed by J. B. S. Haldane as long ago as 1932, and he suggested that altruism of a kind would be selected if it prompted the survival of dependents or near relations. This sort of altruism obviously applies to the situation when parents risk their lives for their offspring. Since the essence of natural selection is competition, however, it was not clear how behavior that went against that overriding fact could be selected.

One hypothesis, put forward originally by Charles Darwin and later developed by the British biologist V. C. Wynne-Edwards, was based on the concept of *group selection.* If natural selection operated on social groups rather than individuals, then any behavior that benefited the social group, even at the expense of the individual, would presumably be selected. This point of view was discussed at length during the 1960s. It was not, however, generally accepted, and it was soon pointed out that other explanations were available that did not depend on the idea of a totally integrated group. Indeed we know that, however well integrated the social group may be, a certain amount of competition continues within it.

Group selection: theoretical model in which natural selection is presumed to operate not on the individual animal but on a social group as a unit.

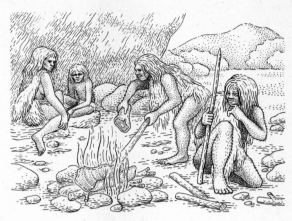

Archaic *Homo sapiens*

Anatomically modern *Homo sapiens*

Recent work by sociobiologists has, however, thrown light on this difficult question, and their ideas are of immense interest to anthropologists. When W. D. Hamilton introduced the concept of inclusive fitness in 1964, he gave us the key to understanding altruism in many social species (see Chapter 3). The examples of altruism seen among insects and, for example, among birds which give warning calls are not of course what we think of as altruism among humans. This animal type of altruism has been conveniently called *bioaltruism*. Human altruism is expected to be voluntarily performed and disinterested.

When we come to examine social primates, we can identify a new kind of altruism. When baboons or chimpanzees form alliances, they will often take risks on behalf of one another that look very like human altruism. While in some cases the altruist and the recipient are related, this is not always so. The American biologist Robert Trivers has examined situations of this kind and has introduced the term *reciprocal altruism*. Evidently there is an unspoken understanding between such individuals that "one good turn deserves another." It is in many ways a very human behavior pattern when members of a group of individuals exchange favors. All that is required is that altruism should be reciprocated and that the advantages of such behavior outweigh the disadvantages. It is also necessary that individuals not cheat. Reciprocity is an important basis of much of human social life, and there are strong sanctions against cheating.

Do humans show any kind of altruism that is not based in some biological advantage and is not seen in other species? Edward O. Wilson, who discussed this question at some length in his book *Human Nature*, has concluded that since we, too (with our brains), are a product of natural selection, it is not likely that we should have developed behavior that operates against natural selection. If biological fitness demands altruism, then it will appear in human societies, but if altruism operated to lower individuals' inclusive fitness, then it surely would never become established as a common behavior pattern. Wilson writes:

> Genes hold culture on a leash. The leash is very long, but inevitably values will be constrained in accordance with their effect on the human gene pool. . . . Human behavior—like the deepest capacities for emotional response which drive and

guide it—is the circuitous technique by which human genetic material has been and will be kept intact. Morality has no other demonstrable ultimate function.

A review of instances of human altruism produces few examples in which there is not a well-recognized reward for the risks taken, even if the reward is promised in the next life. Human society has developed reciprocal altruism to the point where it is all-pervasive, and society has developed sanctions against failure to act altruistically, that is, against selfishness. Experienced swimmers are expected to save a drowning person even if that person is completely unknown to them, and they frequently do so. So strong is the pressure to act in this way that a police officer recently drowned in England trying to rescue a dog from the waves.

Much human behavior appears nonadaptive or maladaptive: we can choose not to bear children; we can commit suicide. As Wilson says, the genetic leash is long. Reason has given us freedom from the lower brain centers, the limbic system, which makes animals do what they have to do. We can determine our actions without reference to our limbic needs, and we can if we wish go against our nature—as individuals. But for the species, such behavior would spell suicide. In this sense we are still held by our genes on that unbreakable leash.

The ultimate human mystery lies perhaps in locating the origin of the dreams that seem so far removed from our biological needs: dreams of dazzling creativity; dreams of a better world founded in equality; dreams of achievements and experience in poetry, music, art, and science. The mystery lies in understanding these new goals that our dreams have set us, goals that arise far from our biological heritage and yet give meaning to the lives of so many people. Human adaptability and reason give us, as individuals, freedom to follow these goals at whatever cost. It is in this sense that we have left the kingdom of animals and gained considerable freedom from our genes.

Cultural History

Adaptability and reason have also led to the third strand in our story, the uniquely human characteristic that was also a response to the environment: culture. Culture consists in the first place of those behaviors and ideas which are the property of the society and which are maintained by mutual learning and teaching by its members. In human evolution, language became a new means of transmitting and recording cultural data. Language was a unique and revolutionary organic adaptation, certainly one of the most important developments in human evolution. It opened up new possibilities of existence and allowed a surge in human technology.

The first developments of technology came at an unimaginably slow rate. Any idea of progress would have been entirely foreign to early people; only the very simplest ideas were entering their heads. But progress did occur, however slowly. From using stone flakes they found on the ground as knives, hominids progressed to prepare their own sharp flakes and their own simple choppers. Slowly, over millions of years, they improved the cutting edge and varied the form of their tools for different purposes. The large hand ax and the knifelike blade appeared; manual skill became essential to the development of technology. Fire began to be kept alive in the hearth. The rate of change quickened, and cultural developments came more rapidly (Figure 18–2). In the cold northern winters a relatively complex technology was particularly crucial for human survival. Although we have little direct evidence, we can safely assume that not only containers but also clothing,

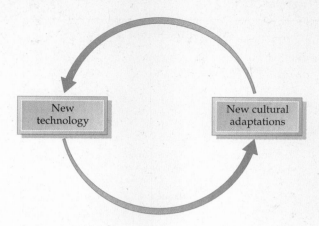

FIGURE 18–2 Positive feedback loops can be either constructive and creative or destructive. In either case, they tend to accelerate change in their components. This loop brings about accelerating cultural and technological changes.

wood and bone tools, and shelters of different kinds became an essential part of our ancestors' survival kit. People learned from each other, and from time to time an invention was made, but what today we see as a progressive journey was for these early people simply the way things were; their lifestyle was the only one they could imagine.

Domestication of Plants and Animals

Eventually, humans learned to change their environment in a more fundamental way. They became increasingly skilled and effective hunters-and-gatherers. They learned to select and breed animals; they domesticated sheep and cattle. They planted seeds and harvested cereals, becoming farmers.

Identification of the first evidence of the domestication of animals presents problems: the process of turning wild animals into tame ones will generate no identifiable archaeological remains, though after a considerable period of selective breeding, new breeds can be recognized by changes in skeletal structure. Dogs, sheep, goats, and cattle were probably the first animals to be bred selectively, at an approximate date of 10,000 years B.P. in the Middle East (Figure 18–3). By 9,000 years B.P. the domestic goat and sheep had become the principal source of meat and raw materials for the early farmers of this region, and cattle and pigs were almost certainly undergoing domestication at this time. There is some uncertain evidence from cave art in western Europe that horses may have carried bridles at a somewhat earlier time. But the hard evidence comes from a much later period. One of the most significant sites is that of Lukenya Hill, near Nairobi, Kenya, where cattle bones dated 4,000 years B.P. are present on human occupation floors. Earlier sites (ca. 6,500 years B.P.) are known from Algeria. Since cattle are not indigenous to Africa, these animals must have been driven in from Eurasia, which proves that they had reached a certain level of domestication by this time. Indeed, from that date on, domesticated cattle, sheep, goats, and horses are found widely throughout the Old World.

The beginning of agriculture is still a mystery, and its details may always remain so. The first evidence of agriculture—of sowing, harvesting, and selecting wild barleys and wheats—dates from about 10,000 years B.P. and again comes from the Middle East (Figure 18–3). It also appeared about this time, or soon after, in at least three other parts of the world: north China, Mexico, and Peru. The cultivation of rice—a crop that supports an enormous percentage of modern

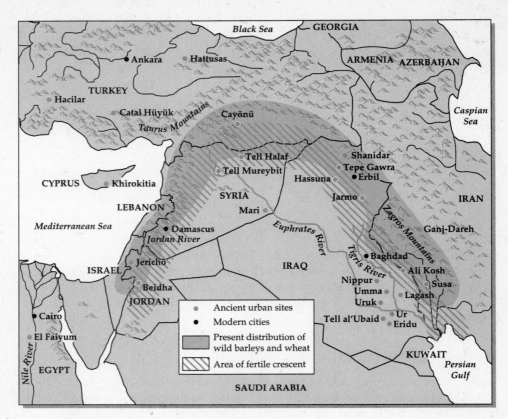

FIGURE 18–3   This map of the Middle East shows the Fertile Crescent, where the domestication of certain plants began about 10,000 years ago. During the past 5,000 years the rainfall of this region has diminished. Now much of the area is no longer suitable for agriculture. The reduction of rainfall was accompanied by the development of the earliest known system of irrigation in the valleys of the Tigris and Euphrates rivers. The earliest villages and towns also developed in this region of agricultural wealth.

humans—was an early occurrence in eastern Asia. The independent development of agriculture in these different regions is one of the most remarkable events in human prehistory. The plants and animals domesticated in each area were different (Table 18–1), but the techniques were the same: the farmers collected and sowed seeds and then selected the high-yielding varieties for continued planting.

Hunting persisted in many areas, and in some, where humans herded animals, agriculture did not follow until much later, even though the land and the climate were suitable. Clearly the development of agriculture must have been slow, involving a number of steps. Some researchers believe that the development of agricultural techniques brought with it a rapid increase in population; others contend that the increase in population came first (following sedentism) and that the pressures for food which resulted stimulated the development of agriculture and animal husbandry ("Necessity is the mother of invention"). Whichever the order of events, it seems clear that the two factors would soon have come to interact in the manner of positive feedback, which would have resulted in a period of relatively rapid change in both population and culture. Certainly the increase in population that we believe accompanied sedentism would have triggered the need for an even greater and more reliable food supply. And resource domestication

Table 18–1 SOME WILD VEGETABLES AND ANIMALS DOMESTICATED
IN THE THREE PRIMARY ZONES OF AGRICULTURAL DEVELOPMENT

Zone	Plants	Animals
Middle East	Almonds Apricots Barley Dates Figs Grapes Lentils Olives Peas Rye Wheat	Cattle Dogs Goats Horses Pigs Sheep
China and Southeast Asia	Bananas Coconuts Millet Rice Soybeans Sugarcane	Banteng Cattle Pigs Yak
South and Central America	Avocados Beans Chili Cocoa Corn Gourds Peanuts Potatoes Squashes	Alpaca Guinea pig Llama

occurred only where the appropriate plants and animals existed and the climate was right. One such environment was the Fertile Crescent in the Middle East. Robert Braidwood of the University of Chicago, who worked during the 1960s in northeastern Iraq, describes how some 10,000 years ago the climate and plant and animal life were ideal for the innovation of agriculture. Within the zone, he wrote, "occur in nature a remarkable constellation of the very plants and animals which became the basis for the food producing pattern of the Western cultural tradition. Nowhere else in the world were the wild wheats and barley, the wild sheep, goats, pigs, cattle and horses to be found together in a single environment." The rainfall was right for agriculture without irrigation, but not sufficient to encourage the dense growth of forest, which would have been a stumbling block to primitive farmers.

Civilization

Although the agricultural revolution has not to this day reached all the earth's peoples, just about all the land suitable for agriculture is being farmed. Agriculture has made possible a vast increase in the world's population (see Figure 18–19)

FIGURE 18–4   An aerial view of Jericho encompasses the modern city and the dirt mound 50 ft (15 m) high under which lie buried the many cities and walls of ancient Jericho. One of the most recent excavations can be seen: the trench cutting from left at the bottom of the photograph.

and it set the stage for a further cultural development of equal significance; the development of cities and metal technology, the coming of civilization.

The most ancient city known to us is Jericho, which lies on the west bank of the Jordan River (Figures 18–3 and 18–4). This city was first built about 10,000 years B.P. and was no doubt a smaller settlement before then. The surplus food that agriculture made available in the region evidently enabled people to live in dense communities where they depended on farmers to supply them with their food— as we do today. This entirely novel situation allowed the city-dwellers to special-ize in arts and crafts of an ever-widening variety, and this kind of specialization was to form, in due time, the basis of modern civilization. Trade flourished: At Jericho, hematite, greenstone, obsidian, seashells, and salt all passed through the city, together with much else of which we have no trace. The north-south trade route on which the city lay was an important stimulus to its development. But civ-ilization probably would not have grown from these early roots without improve-ments in agriculture. The greatest cities grew in areas of rich agricultural land, where the productivity was greatest; they reflected the agricultural foundation on which they necessarily were based.

The earliest achievements of civilization, including organized religion and government, weaving, writing, and metal technology, are too numerous to list, let alone discuss, but they bring us by an accelerating process of development from prehistory into history. Above all, it was developing technology that brought about the astonishing growth and complexity of human culture.

Environment, human biology, culture: these three are the threads of the human story we have told. During humankind's emergence each acted on the others in mutual feedback (see Figure 18–5); any change in one necessitated adjustment in the others. This relationship was something new in evolution, for learning to change the environment was something no animal had ever done before, beyond building a nest or preparing a small arena for courtship.

The changes in environment brought about by these early farmers were often fatal to the people who initiated them. Gary Rollefson and Ilse Köhler of San Diego State University have uncovered strong evidence that deforestation caused a collapse of early civilization in the Levant (present-day Israel, Jordan, and southern Syria, see Figure 18–3) around 6,000 years B.P. The area was rapidly depopulated at this time, and evidence suggests clearly that this depopulation was due not so much to a change in rainfall as to the extensive felling of woodland. Trees were used as fuel for, among other things, the production of lime plaster. As time passed, houses were built with smaller and smaller timbers, and the final destruction of the woodland habitat was completed by the herds of goats that ranged over the onetime forest lands and consumed the tender saplings. Then the steep hills eroded rapidly, the soils were lost, and the flourishing communities, which had developed throughout the area, disappeared.

This is just one very significant example of how humans have changed and, in doing so, destroyed their own productive environments. Such changes have occurred in many parts of the world since the coming of animal husbandry and agriculture brought our ancestors to the doors of civilization. The pattern has been repeated the world over but was especially devastating around the Mediterranean basin and in the Middle East, where the goat had been so widely domesticated. Humans may change their environment drastically—and as we can now see, such changes can turn out to be to their ultimate disadvantage. But this was

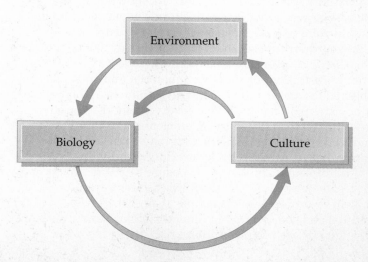

FIGURE   18–5 This feedback loop shows the increasing influence of culture on our biology: our heredity. The biological rate of change always lags behind the cultural rate of change.

humankind's unique achievement, and it constitutes a central theme in the last phases of human prehistory. Human work and human nature are indeed one. All are directly and systematically related to each other.

HUMAN VARIABILITY

Within this dynamic system unique to humankind, in which the human body and its environment are related through culture, all three components show considerable variability. In our physical variability, humankind is not alone in the animal or plant worlds. Variability in behavior and appearance is characteristic of all living organisms as their environment varies, and it is probably no greater in humans than in many other species. Every individual (except identical twins) carries different genetic material; differences due to age and sex also exist. Beyond this, we find variability that has evolved in response to local (and equally variable) environmental conditions. Humans' physical variations may be found both within and between populations, and in the past such physical differences were often used by anthropologists to construct racial classifications that subdivided humanity. We will argue in a later section that all such classifications are invalid, and that race is not a useful biological concept when applied to humans. Nonetheless, there are many good reasons for studying human variation apart from race construction, including learning how trait variations correlate with differing environments and susceptibility to certain diseases. Therefore, before addressing the race issue, let's review some of the major physical variations of humankind. We will be concerned with traits of three main kinds: (1) anatomical features, such as skin color, hair form, and body shape; (2) physiological traits, such as metabolic rate and hormone activity, growth rate, color blindness, and genetic diseases; and (3) characteristics of the blood (biochemical traits).

Anatomical Traits

Perhaps the most easily noticed physical characteristic of humans is skin color. Depending on the amount of melanin in the epidermis, human skin varies from very light ("white") to very dark (dark brown or black). As shown in Figure 18–6, skin color is found to be very closely correlated with latitude when analyzed globally. People with dark skin colors are found nearest to the equator, and lighter populations inhabit higher northern and southern latitudes. As explained to some extent in Chapter 15, this distribution of skin tones seems to reflect a complex pattern of adaptation by our ancestral populations. In equatorial and subequatorial regions, people are subjected to intense ultraviolet (UV) radiation, and bombardment by UV rays can be extremely harmful. One relatively short-term effect is sunburn, which may result in an inability to sweat efficiently and thus to reduce body heat. Sunburn-induced impairment of sweating may even lead to hyperthermia and death during heavy exercise by light-skinned individuals with a heavy solar heat load. And of course, prolonged exposure to UV radiation may lead to skin cancer and its sometimes deadly consequences. Heavy epidermal concentrations of melanin help to protect tropical people against the ravages of UV radiation. Among equatorial and subequatorial populations, skin cancer rates are relatively low, and sweat glands are protected from UV-induced blockage. Thus

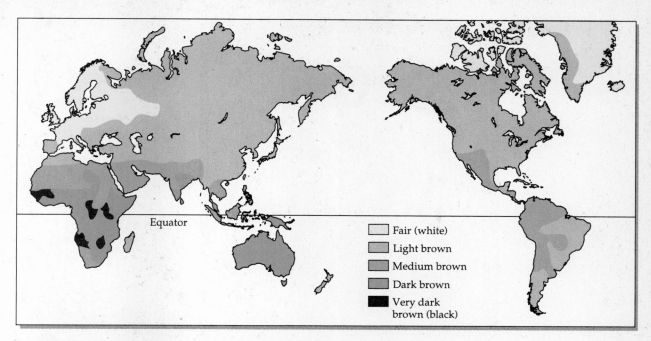

FIGURE 18–6 This global map shows the distribution of skin colors in indigenous populations. Note the clear correlation between skin color and latitude.

there has been strong selection for dark skin colors in regions of intense and prolonged sunlight.

The sun-and-skin problem took on a different dimension in those human populations that migrated north and south away from the sunny regions. In the higher latitudes, sunburn damage and skin cancer became less significant threats, while an inability to produce enough vitamin D gained in importance. Research has shown that human skin synthesizes vitamin D following the transmission of UV rays into the lower layers of the epidermis. However, because melanin filters out UV radiation, little may reach the lower epidermis in dark-skinned persons. For evolving human populations in the tropics, this was not a problem. Despite heavy pigmentation, enough skin was exposed to sufficiently strong UV radiation so that adequate vitamin D was usually produced. Populations at higher latitudes, however, probably exposed less skin (it was colder) and lived in regions of less intense UV radiation. Therefore, in these populations, selection favored lighter-skinned individuals who, even with only limited skin exposed to a weak sun, could produce enough vitamin D. Skin color thus turns out to be a very clear example of evolutionary adaptation among modern people. It is a very striking trait, but very superficial, both literally and figuratively.

Another trait with clear adaptive consequences is body build. In 1847 Carl Bergmann, a German physiologist interested in the relationships among body mass, surface area, and heat production in warm-blooded animals, observed that populations occupying the coldest parts of a species' range tended to be bulkier, that is, more compact, than those living in the warmer parts ("Bergmann's rule"). In 1877, the American J. A. Allen added that animals with the largest bodies are

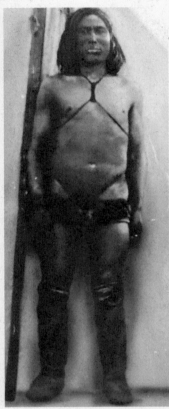

FIGURE 18–7 These individuals represent populations that demonstrate Bergmann's and Allen's rules. The African on the left, tall and slim, has long extremities and a high ratio of surface area to weight. The Eskimo on the right has short extremities and a low ratio of surface area to weight, which reduces heat loss. The photographs are of the same scale.

found not in the coldest part of the range but somewhere in the center. He further stated that the protruding parts of the body, such as limbs, fingers, ears, and tails, tend to be relatively shorter in the cooler parts of the range than in its warmer regions ("Allen's rule"). In cool regions, these adaptations in body build decrease surface area in relation to weight, reducing heat loss. In warm regions, they increase surface area in relation to weight, thus increasing heat loss (Figure 18–7). Human populations follow these rules derived from animal studies, and it seems clear that populations known only from their fossilized remains did the same (see the description of the Nariokotome *Homo erectus* skeleton in Chapter 10).

Living humans also show variations in hair form, from tight curls to waves to straight hair. Although the adaptive significance, if any, of the various hair pat-

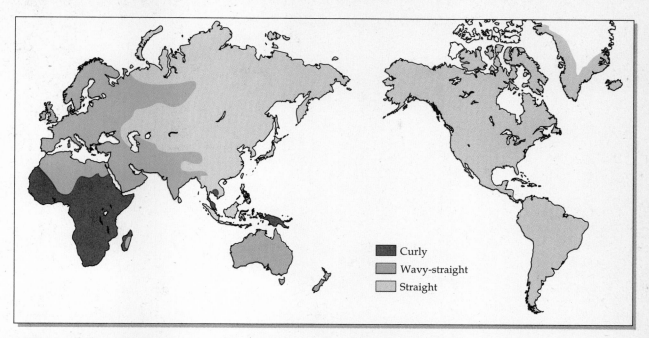

FIGURE 18–8   Hair form varies both within and between human populations. This map shows the distribution of "typical" hair form around the globe.

terns has yet to be discovered, living populations around the world clearly differ in their typical hair form while also showing much intrapopulational variation (Figure 18–8). Similarly, no clear adaptive function has yet been proved for the fold of skin that occurs in the upper eyelid of some living people, the *epicanthic fold* (Figure 18–9). Epicanthic folds are common among Asian people, some Native Americans, and the Khoisan (Bushmen and Hottentot) people of South Africa (see also Figure 18–16). Research is continuing on the significance of these and other variable human traits. No doubt, in some cases, differences in selection and adaptation will be the correct explanation; for other traits, variation may be the result of more random processes, such as genetic drift.

Epicanthic fold: a fold of skin above the inner border of the eye; characteristic of Asiatic, Native American, and Khoisan people.

One of the neatest demonstrations of environmental adaptation is that relating nose shape (expressed as the nasal index: breadth/height × 100) to the humidity of the air (expressed as vapor pressure). Moistening the air is a prime function of the nasal epithelium; the moisture content of the air must be brought up to 95 percent relative humidity at body temperature before the air enters the lungs; otherwise they will be damaged. It seems clear that people adapted to areas of dry air (deserts and high mountains) will tend to have narrow noses, while those adapted to moist air will usually have broad noses. The correlation can be demonstrated statistically, and the explanation appears valid (see Figure 18–10).

The important thing to remember is that differences are slight. Anatomical traits vary continuously: noses vary from narrow to broad, hair varies by infinitesimal gradations from straight to tightly curled, and skin color varies from very light to black. Anthropologists have recognized as many as 36 gradations in this color spectrum. These features are determined by numerous genes and are not discretely segregated into just a few phenotypes.

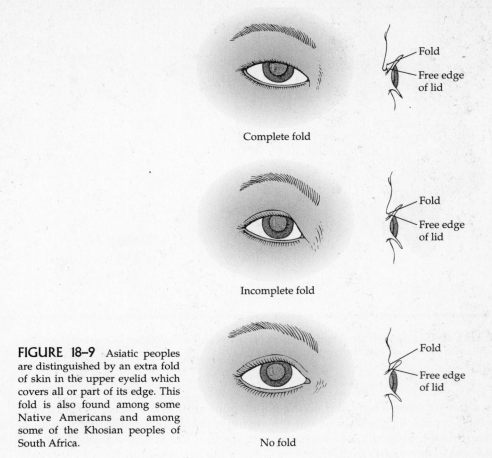

Complete fold

Incomplete fold

No fold

FIGURE 18–9 Asiatic peoples are distinguished by an extra fold of skin in the upper eyelid which covers all or part of its edge. This fold is also found among some Native Americans and among some of the Khosian peoples of South Africa.

Physiological Traits

Physiological traits that vary within and between human populations are probably less well known than the more obvious anatomical differences, but they are also significant and reflect adaptation. The basal metabolic rate, which is related to the level of body heat production, varies, as might be predicted, according to the mean annual temperature. Bone growth rate and maturation age also seem to vary, though both are also greatly influenced by nutrition. The age at which teeth appear and their order of eruption vary significantly. Third molars (wisdom teeth), which appear in Europeans between 17 and 20 years of age, appear in East Africans at age 13. Protein structure, keenness of taste, drug sensitivity, balance of urinary substances, color blindness, and sex hormone activity also show measurable differences. And, as we have seen, DNA carries recognizable differences. The better we become able to measure these sometimes trivial differences, the more of them we are likely to find.

Probably the most important physiological differences are those subtle genetic variations that give rise to disease. Because they are based on only one or two genes, these traits are discrete; that is, they are either present or absent. We discussed one of them—sickle-cell anemia—in Chapter 3. Some other genetic diseases are just as dangerous but are limited to small populations. In the Mediterranean region, there is favism, which is a genetically determined allergy to the

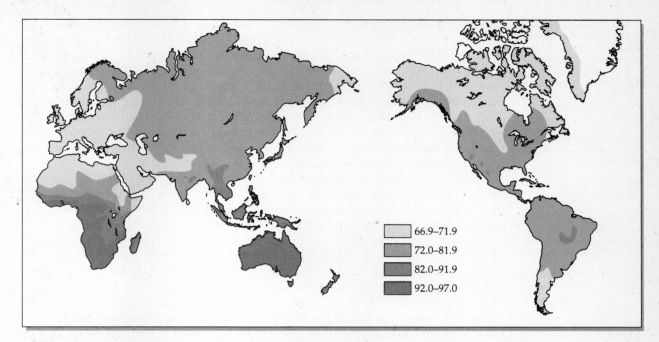

FIGURE 18–10 Nose form varies both within and between human populations. This map shows the distribution of "typical" nasal index (breadth/height × 100) values around the globe.

Legend:
- 66.9–71.9
- 72.0–81.9
- 82.0–91.9
- 92.0–97.0

broad bean and results in severe anemia; the same area also has familial Mediterranean fever, an obscure condition causing acute fever and much pain. Other hereditary disorders are much more widespread and occur more commonly in one population than another. One such disorder is phenylketonuria (PKU), an inability to develop an essential enzyme, which usually results in brain damage and mental retardation. PKU is most common in some areas of Europe. It is rare among persons of African or Asian descent.

A disease like sickle-cell anemia, but appearing mostly in the Mediterranean region and in parts of Asia rather than in Africa, is thalassemia. In the homozygous state (two Th_2 alleles), the resulting anemia is so serious that afflicted individuals rarely reach reproductive age. But homozygous individuals who completely lack the Th_2 allele may die early of serious malaria. It is in the heterozygous state that the trait is present but not serious and provides some protection from malaria. Thus the advantages and disadvantages of the gene in the population have remained in balance while malaria itself continues to thrive. Although most genetic diseases may simply be part of humans' genetic load, it is likely that some, like sickle-cell anemia and thalassemia, are part of such an adaptive equilibrium, termed *balanced polymorphism*.

Blood Groups

The third group of variable traits, the blood groups, have great medical significance. When the possibility of blood transfusions was first investigated during the nineteenth century, it quickly became clear that introducing one individual's blood into

Serum (plasma): a clear liquid component of blood that carries the red blood cells, white blood cells, and platelets.

Red blood cells (corpuscles): vertebrate blood cells lacking nuclei and containing hemoglobin.

White blood cells (leukocytes): vertebrate blood cells lacking hemoglobin.

Platelets: minute blood cells associated with clotting.

Antigens: any organic substances, recognized by the body as foreign, that stimulate the production of an antibody.

Antibody: a protein produced as a defense mechanism to attack a foreign substance invading the body.

Blood groups: groups of individuals whose blood can be mixed without agglutination (e.g., Groups A, B, O, or AB).

Agglutination: the clumping of red blood cells as a result of the reaction of antibodies to an antigen.

another's bloodstream could be fatal. Blood consists of a liquid component, the *serum*, or *plasma*, and three main types of cells: the *red blood cells*, which contain the red pigment hemoglobin and carry oxygen to all the parts of the body; the much larger *white blood cells*, or *leukocytes*, which defend against infection; and the smallest cells, the *platelets*, which maintain the circulatory system as a whole. The red cells have a protein coat whose molecules function as *antigens;* when introduced into another individual, antigens trigger the production of specific *antibodies,* other proteins that help protect the body against foreign substances. Microscopic examination of the blood of two people mixed together has shown that difficulties with transfusions come from the reactions between antigens and antibodies.

Safe transfusions now rest on biologist Karl Landsteiner's brilliant discovery in 1901 of the existence of different *blood groups.* Transfusions of the wrong kind of blood can cause the recipient's red blood cells to agglutinate, or clump together, and sometimes to burst. The *agglutination* can result in clots that block the blood's flow. Landsteiner discovered that the blood (actually the antigens) of one individual may trigger the production and agglutination of another's individual's antibodies, causing clots. Landsteiner labeled with the letter O the blood of individuals which was never agglutinated by the serum of other persons, but which would in turn agglutinate the blood cells of others. Blood of individuals that was agglutinated he labeled A. The blood that agglutinated A blood (and was not group O) and could itself be agglutinated by A blood, he labeled type B. Thus he had three types: A, B, and O. Blood group A carries antigen A and develops anti-B antibodies. Blood group B contains antigen B and develops anti-A antibodies. Group O contains no antigens but develops both antibodies. Group AB (discovered later) carries antigens A and B but produces neither antibody. Thus type AB people can receive A, B, or O blood, but types A and B can receive only their own groups and type O, and type O people can receive only type O blood. Type O people, then, are universal donors, while type AB people are universal recipients. (The distribution of types A and O throughout the world is shown in Figure 18–11.)

Discovery of the ABO blood groups was followed by the discovery of many others (some of which are listed in Figure 18–12), the most important of which is the rhesus (Rh) system (1940). The rhesus system is responsible for an important disease that can kill newborn babies by destroying their blood cells. The cause of the disease is incompatibility between mother and child for the rhesus antigen D. If the mother is Rh-negative (lacks the D antigen) and the child is Rh-positive (possesses the D antigen), then the mother may form anti-D antibodies at the time of the child's birth, when some of the child's blood may enter the mother's bloodstream. In a second pregnancy, this antibody may pass through the placental barrier, coating and destroying the red blood cells of the child if it has Rh-positive blood. This second child will have acute anemia at birth (there is no problem if the second child has Rh-negative blood). The anemia can be treated only with extensive blood transfusions, but the disease can now be prevented by giving the mother an injection of powerful anti-D antibody after the birth of the first Rh-positive child. The injection destroys any Rh-positive red cells from the infant remaining in the mother's bloodstream and so inhibits future anti-D antibody production.

The alleles that determine blood types vary widely both within and between populations. Some data on the occurrence of these alleles are given in Figure 18–12. Note how many of the alleles show extensive intrapopulational variation and also overlap between populations.

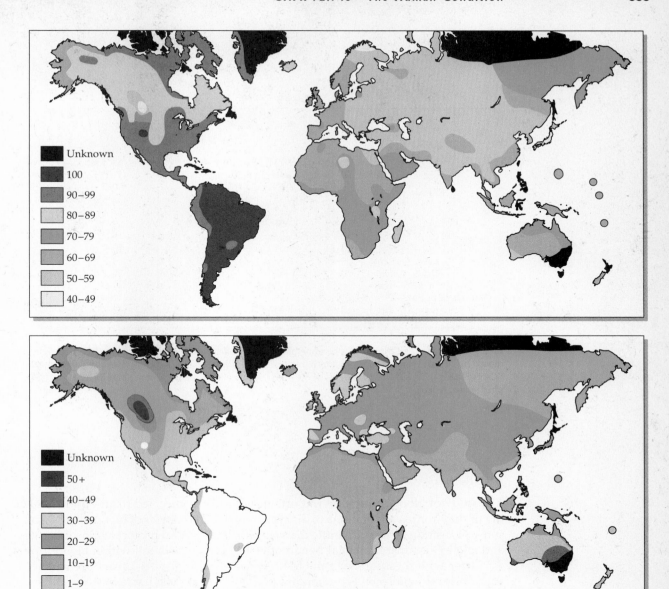

FIGURE 18-11   These maps give some idea of the distribution and frequency of the two commonest ABO blood group alleles, *O* and *A*. This is an example of the kind of genetic data now available for human populations. The upper map charts the distribution of the predominant group O allele, which is common in the New World and especially in South America. The lower map plots the group A allele, which is reasonably common in the Old World, but rare in many parts of the New World and virtually absent from South America. Remarkable concentrations of the group A allele are found among the Scandinavian Lapps and the Blackfoot Indians of Western Canada. The latter is possibly the result of a local smallpox epidemic, introduced perhaps by Europeans, in which the allele was favored.

Blood group system	Allele	World range	Europeans	Africans Non-Khoisan	Africans Khoisan	Asians	Native Americans	Australians and Oceanics
ABO	A_1	0–45	5–40	8–30	0–15	0–45	0–20	8–38
	A_2	0–37	1–37	1–8	0–5	0–5	0	0
	B	0–33	4–18	10–20	2	16–25	0–4	0–13
	O	39–100	46–75	52–70	75–78	39–68	68–100	51–79
Rhesus	cde–	0–46	25–46	4–29	0	0–5	0	0
	cDe+	0–95	1–5	34–82	84–89	0–4	0–7	1–9
	CDe+	0–95	39–55	0–21	9–14	60–76	32–68	68–95
	cDE+	0–61	6–17	0–19	2	19–31	23–61	2–20
MNS	N	8–78	33–51	39–53	41	37–45	9–35	73–97
	NS	5–74	25–65	22–59	41	38	5–22	69–74
P	P	4–84	41–64	50–84	?	17	15–79	12–67
Lewis	Lewis	0–67	34–50	41	?	39	0–34	0–67
Duffy	Duffy	0–100	37–82	0–6	8	90–100	22–99	100
Diego	Diego	0–34	0	0	0	0–5	0–34	0
Gamma globulin	Gm	23–100	23–37	100	100	100	100	100
Haptoglobin	Hp^1	9–87	9–44	40–87	29	23–28	32–73	46–63

FIGURE 18–12 The frequencies of some blood group alleles present in different populations show the extent of variation in these genetic characters. Three different alleles for the rhesus-positive condition are listed (cDe, CDe, cDE). Alleles of the blood serum components gamma globulin and haptoglobin are also listed.

Blood Groups and Disease

The study of blood groups, an important medical advance, led to an understanding of their role as adaptations to disease antigens. The carrier of blood allele B has some protection against infantile diarrhea, alleles A_1 and B protect against plague, and allele O against bronchial pneumonia. (A_1 and A_2 both fall within blood type A.) Those with rhesus gene D and MNS gene N (see Figure 18–12) are particularly susceptible to smallpox. Type A individuals also seem most liable to stomach cancer and pernicious anemia, while gastric and duodenal ulcers tend to affect persons who are homozygous for allele O. Thus the frequency of genetic diseases and blood group genes may result from selection by the infectious diseases to which different populations have been exposed.

Research into the relationship of disease and human genetics is still in an early stage but is progressing rapidly. A particular medical and genetic problem is presented by people who carry a genetic condition like sickle-cell anemia in places where malaria is no longer present. Without the malaria to maintain the balance of the polymorphism, the sickle-cell gene should be reduced in the gene pool as a result of natural selection against both homozygotes and heterozygotes. But as long as the sickle-cell allele exists, physicians have little help for those who carry the gene and suffer anemia.

THE QUESTION OF RACE

Biological Races

The preceding sections have documented what we already know: humans, both within their local populations and around the world, are extremely variable both anatomically and physiologically. Traditionally patterns of physical variation have been used by anthropologists (and also by nonspecialists, in the form of "folk concepts") to divide humanity into *races*. Over the past few decades, however, as information on human variation has accumulated and analytical procedures have improved, more and more anthropologists have grown dissatisfied with racial classifications. As explained below, racial classifications are arbitrary in their construction, and they fail to reflect the realities of humans' biological variation. Thus, according to a 1982 survey of physical anthropology textbooks used in American colleges and universities, by the late 1970s twice as many authors argued that human races do not exist as maintained that races are real. The authors of the present text align themselves with the majority on this issue. We do not believe that race is either a valid or a useful *biological concept* as applied to humans, and our reasons for taking this view are as follows.

First, there is no clear agreement among anthropologists about how human races should be defined and measured. Some definitions stress genetic or physical differences, while others maintain that the most important measure is reproductive isolation. Furthermore, those typologists who use genetic or physical markers to subdivide humans disagree on which traits are most important in reflecting racial distinctions. These disagreements have led to a bewildering array of major and minor races being identified by various workers. Harvard's Earnest Hooton, writing in 1946, recognized 3 "primary" races and 21 "primary subraces," or "composite" races; Carlton Coon and his colleagues listed 6 "major racial stocks" in 1950; and in 1965 Stanley Garn identified 9 large "geographical" races and 32 "local" races!

It is now recognized that there are no key "racial marker" traits just waiting to be identified that will yield a "true" or "natural" subdivision of humankind. Furthermore, because there is little concordance of occurrence of humans' genetic and physical traits, one cannot even use *clusters* of traits with any confidence when constructing racial classifications. For example, as shown in Box 18–1, if one chooses a particular trait, say cephalic index (CI; one of anthropologists' favorite cranial measurements, calculated as skull breadth/length × 100), and groups human populations into lowest, intermediate, and highest CI values, one ends up lumping Australian Aborigines with Bantus, Bushmen with Eskimos, and Chinese with Norwegians. A similar sorting based on the particular trait of body size yields a different grouping pattern. Now several Asian populations are lumped with Bushmen as "intermediate" in height, while Finns, Batutsis, and northern Chinese are combined in the "tall" category. Finally, if one categorizes human populations based on the ability to taste the substance PTC (phenylthiocarbamide), one groups Navajos with West Africans and Finnish Lapps, Malaysians with Spaniards, and English with Bombay Indians.

Races: among humans, an essentially arbitrary concept based on perceived physical or behavioral differences. As a biological concept, race is no longer used by most physical anthropologists.

BOX 18-1
SUBDIVIDING HUMANITY

There are innumerable ways to subdivide modern humans. Here are a few and the various subgroupings that result. Note that the subgroupings differ strongly from one measure to another.

CEPHALIC INDEX

Long-headed (CI < 75)	Intermediate (CI 75–80)	Round-headed (CI >80)
Native Australians	!Kung Bushmen	Iranians, Armenians
Bantus	Veddas	Japanese
	Ituri Pygmies	Norwegians
	Melanesians	Chinese
	Eskimos	Germans
	Native American Sioux	Hawaiians
	New Guineans	Lapps

BODY SIZE (AVERAGE HEIGHT)

Short (56–60 in., or 142–153 cm)	Intermediate (60–65 in., or 153–164 cm)	Tall (65–69 in., or 164–176 cm)
Pygmies	!Kung Bushmen	Kikuyu (African)
Efe (African)	Burmese	Hong Kong Chinese
	Vietnamese	Berbers
	Ecuadorans	Finns
	Kazakh (Turkistan)	English
	Central Chinese	Batutsi (African)
	Japanese	Scots
	Koreans	Northern Chinese
	Sundanese	Sicilians

ABILITY TO TASTE PTC (PHENYLTHIOCARBAMIDE)

Rare (0%–15% of Pop.)	Occasional (16%–30%)	Common (> 30%)
Native Formosans	Malaysians	Norwegians
Native American Navajo	Northeastern Brazilians	Danes
Native American Cree	Belgians	English
Chinese	Spaniards	Native Venezuelans
West Africans	Finns	Labrador Eskimos
Japanese	U.S. "whites"	Bombay Indians
Lapps (Finland)	Negritos (Malaya)	Swedes

(All data taken from S. Molnar, 1992, *Human Variation*, 3rd ed., Prentice Hall.)

As noted, even multivariate analyses using information from many different traits fail to sort humans into biologically meaningful and consistent groups. As shown in Figure 18–13, summed data from 58 different blood group genes seem to link Europeans with Africans, and native Australians with Asians. In contrast, an analysis of 57 skull measurements (from the 5,000 that researchers have devised) pairs Australians with Africans and widely separates both from Europeans (Figure 18–14). Interestingly, in the skull analysis shown, all measurements were taken

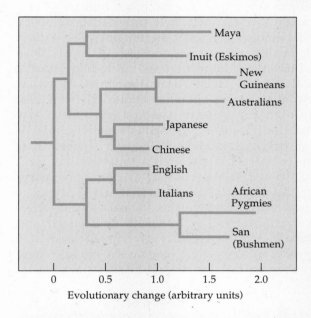

FIGURE 18–13 This figure shows the linkages calculated between living human populations based on an analysis of 58 different blood group genes. Note the association of Europeans with Africans and Australians with Asians.

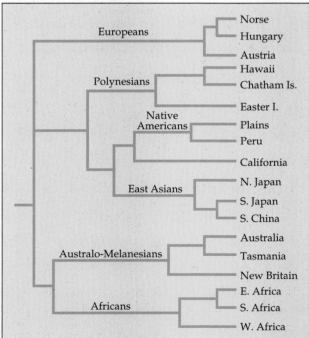

FIGURE 18–14 Here linkages are shown between living human populations based on an analysis of 57 measurements of male skulls. Note the separation of Europeans from Africans and the link between the latter and Australians.

from males. When the study was redone using measurements from female skulls, the population clusters changed significantly, so that Australo-Melanesians were separated from Africans and linked primarily with Polynesians! The fact that different grouping patterns can result if the sex of the subjects is changed does not generate much confidence in multivariate racial classifications.

The subject of multivariate analyses brings us to the second main reason to reject race as a biological concept applicable to humans. Ironically, while these studies have failed to identify human races, they have succeeded brilliantly in the other direction; that is, multivariate investigations have provided unequivocal proof that human races don't exist in any biologically meaningful sense. In 1974 Harvard biologist R. C. Lewontin published the results of a study of genetic diversity within and between several traditional human "races" (including Africans, Native Americans, Mongoloids, Caucasians, South Asian Aborigines, Australian Aborigines, and Oceanians). Lewontin's results, shown in Figure 18–15, revealed that just over 85 percent of human genetic diversity, based on genes for physiological character traits, lies between individuals belonging to the same population (i.e., generally, the same nation or tribe). An additional 8.3 percent of genetic variation is accounted for by differences between populations within the same "race" (e.g., between West Africans and Bantus). This leaves only 6.3 percent of genetic diversity accounted for by interracial differences! Thus, even if one is inclined to believe in the existence of biological races among humans, these data make it clear that such entities make only a trivial contribution to genetic (and phenotypic) variation among humans. As one non-African geneticist is reported to have said, "There could possibly be more genetic differences between myself and my wife [a member of the same "race"] than there are between me and a Kalahari Bushman."

Gene	Total $H_{species}$	PROPORTION		
		Within populations	Within races between populations	Between races
Hp	.994	.893	.051	.056
Ag	.994	.834	—	—
Lp	.639	.939	—	—
Xm	.869	.997	—	—
Ap	.989	.927	.062	.011
6PGD	.327	.875	.058	.067
PGM	.758	.942	.033	.025
Ak	.184	.848	.021	.131
Kidd	.977	.741	.211	.048
Duffy	.938	.636	.105	.259
Lewis	.994	.966	.032	.002
Kell	.189	.901	.073	.026
Lutheran	.153	.694	.214	.092
P	1.000	.949	.029	.022
MNS	1.746	.911	.041	.048
Rh	1.900	.674	.073	.253
ABO	1.241	.907	.063	.030
Mean		.854	.083	.063

FIGURE 18–15 Analyses such as this one indicate that the vast majority of genetic diversity in humans exists *within* so-called races and not *between* them.

The existence of "intraracial" variation can be shown rather simplistically by a brief review of photographs from a few of the traditional categories. Figure 18–16 shows three adult Africans. These people differ in skin color, facial prognathism, lip form, and cephalic index values. Furthermore, the individual from South Africa possesses epicanthic eye folds whereas the others do not. In Figure 18–17, the same sorts of comparisons may be made in three "white" individuals. Notice that they differ in skin color, hair color, facial prognathism, nose form, lip form, and cephalic index. Finally, Figure 18–18 compares two full-blooded Australian Aborigines. These individuals differ slightly in eye color and strongly in facial prognathism and nose form.

What sense, then, can we make of humans' biological races? Clearly we are a species of wonderful genetic and physical diversity, but that diversity is in fact swamped by our overwhelming global similarities. In strong contrast to traditional folk wisdom, by far the greatest amount of human diversity occurs *within* the units we usually call races, not *between* them. Simply put, the genetic and physical traits of humans are not concordant. Each trait has its own distinctive distribution pattern (often related to its adaptive function), and traits do not co-occur as consistent and reliable clusters that may be used to define racial units. Therefore, *race is not a valid biological concept as applied to humans.* In the words of Yale University's Jonathan Marks, "You may group humans into a small number of races if you want to, but you are denied biology as a support for it." In order to understand human variation, we must study traits, not "races."

FIGURE 18–16 Variation in people traditionally classified as "black." CI = cephalic index (skull breadth/skull length × 100). The CI values are for populations; the other traits are for the individual shown.

West Africa	Central Africa	South Africa
Skin: Dark brown/black	Skin: Medium brown	Skin: Yellowish brown
Hair: Black, curly	Hair: Black, curly	Hair: Black, tight curly
Eyes: Dark brown/black (no eye fold)	Eyes: Dark brown/black (no eye fold)	Eyes: Dark black brown/black (epicanthic fold present)
Prognathism: Moderate	Prognathism: Little	Prognathism: Little
Nose: Short, wide	Nose: Short, wide	Nose: Short, wide
Lips: Thick	Lips: Thin	Lips: Thin
Head: CI ≤ 75	Head: CI ≥ 80	Head: CI < 78

FIGURE 18–17 Variation in people traditionally classified as "white." CI = cephalic index (skull breadth/skull length × 100). The CI values are for populations; the other traits are for the individual shown.

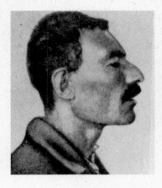  

Middle East	Northern Japan (Ainu)	Europe
Skin: Medium light	Skin: Medium light	Skin: Light
Hair: Dark brown/black, wavy/straight	Hair: Dark brown/black, wavy/straight	Hair: Brown/red, wavy/straight
Eyes: Brown (no fold)	Eyes: Brown (fold present)	Eyes: Brown (no fold)
Prognathism: Moderate	Prognathism: Little	Prognathism: Little
Nose: Long, narrow	Nose: Short, wide	Nose: Short, narrow
Lips: Thin/moderately thick	Lips: Moderately thick	Lips: Thin
Head: CI > 80	Head: Mean CI = 77	Head: Mean CI = 76

FIGURE 18–18 Variations in native Australians. CI = cephalic index (skull breadth/skull length × 100). The CI values are for regional populations; the other traits are for the individual shown.

 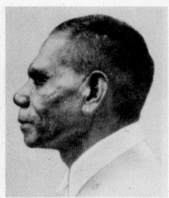

Southeastern	Northeastern
Skin: Medium brown	Skin: Dark brown
Hair: Dark brown with red tints, wavy	Hair: Dark brown with red tints, wavy
Eyes: Medium brown (no fold)	Eyes: Dark brown (no fold)
Prognathism: Little	Prognathism: Moderate
Nose: Short, narrow	Nose: Short, wide
Lips: Thin	Lips: Thin
Head: CI < 80	Head: CI < 80

Ethnic and Other Social Groups

Although we do not believe that human biological races have any objective scientific basis, it is abundantly clear that humans have a strong tendency to divide the world into "we-they" dichotomies. Such classifications are often based on perceived physical characteristics such as skin color (as in the children's Sunday School song "Red and yellow, black and white, they are precious in His [Jesus's] sight"); eye form (round-eye, slant-eye); or hair form ("woolly," "straight"). They may also be based on perceived behavioral or cultural differences, such as sexual orientation (homosexual, heterosexual, bisexual); religion (Muslim, Christian, Buddist, Jew, etc.); politics (liberal, conservative, Communist); or social status (royalty, commoner, upper class, lower class). And finally, perhaps most commonly of all, humans categorize others based on their *ethnic group* (Asian-Americans, African-Americans, Euro-Americans, Native Americans, Hispanics, Hutu, Tutsi, etc.).

> **Ethnic group:** a group of people perceived as sharing a common and distinctive culture.

Now, of course, these groups are not mutually exclusive; quite the contrary, the various categories overlap extensively: a homosexual, Asian-American, Christian, liberal person will serve as one example. Nonetheless, it should be clear from the multitude of possible categories (and we have barely scratched the surface of naming them) that people are experts at identifying or imagining differences and using them to create pigeonholes for categorizing their fellow humans. Indeed, the multiplicity of categories in use in any modern culture strongly suggests that—like biological race—the categories or dichotomies exist to some extent in our minds and are limited only by our imagination.

None of this is to deny that sociological groups sometimes serve good and valid purposes. They may foster unity and pride within minority communities, may serve as the focal point for political solidarity, or may facilitate the preservation of a population's cultural heritage. On the other hand, when the concept of race or ethnic group is combined with another seemingly universal feature of human nature—namely, *xenophobia*—all too often the result is either discrimination or *racism*, defined here as the belief that human groups can be ranked as superior or inferior to one another and their members treated accordingly. As we are all keenly aware, racism is responsible for a multitude of evils ranging from job discrimination to genocide (or to use a recently created term, *ethnic cleansing*).

> **Xenophobia:** hatred of foreigners.
>
> **Racism:** the assumption of inherent superiority of certain "races," and the consequent discrimination against others.

Perhaps the most strongly held folk belief—and certainly the most divisive—is the notion that all other races and groups are less intelligent than one's own. In fact, *there is simply no good evidence to support this belief.* Intelligence is such a broad concept that it is impossible to define and measure precisely. So-called *IQ tests* actually tell us little about intellectual differences between individuals even within the same culture because a multitude of factors can influence test scores (e.g., genotype, educational history and family background—particularly parents' socioeconomic status). Furthermore, since none of the IQ tests is culture-free (all operate through linguistic and other cultural modes not shared by all people), none can be used cross-culturally. Unfortunately anthropology has played a historical role in perpetuating the myth of biological races; and psychology in perpetuating the myth of interracial differences in intelligence. Hopefully, by demonstrating that human races are basically the products of our imagination, modern anthropologists can begin to dismantle both myths. In the meantime, although it should go without saying, anthropological studies provide absolutely no justification for any sort of racist attitude or behavior.

> **IQ tests:** tests that supposedly measure an individual's "intelligence quotient." Many consider such tests flawed and of little value, particularly for cross-cultural comparisons.

CHALLENGES FOR THE FUTURE

Population and Evolutionary Success

The hominid story began some 5 to 7 million years ago in Africa. From rather humble beginnings, our species has evolved to become the dominant force on the planet. Physically and culturally diverse, humans are spread throughout all regions of the globe. Yes, we are a grand evolutionary success, and yet, ironically, our very success may contribute to our undoing. Consider the issue of human population size. Edward S. Deevey estimates that the hominid population of the earth 2 million years ago was little more than 100,000 individuals. By 300,000 years ago, at the end of *Homo erectus*'s known tenancy, the human population had climbed to 1 million, and by 25,000 years ago, during the Upper Paleolithic, it had jumped to perhaps more than 3 million. It has risen at an increasingly steep pace since then (Figure 18–19). Deevey brings home the extraordinarily rapid mushrooming of today's human population when he shows that about 3 percent of all humans who have ever lived are alive today.

The population, according to Deevey, has not risen in a steady curve. Rather, the increase in the world's population has had a series of surges, reflecting the great cultural innovations associated with hominid evolution. The first cultural innovation, of course, was the development of stone tools. This advance allowed a population increase in two ways: stone tools enabled hominids to venture out into a vast number of environments that people without such tools could not have survived in; it also made populations more efficient, enabling them to exploit

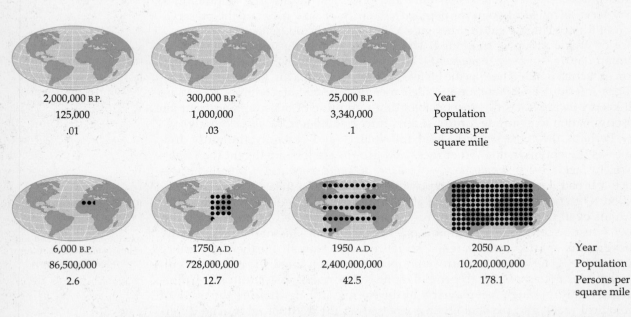

2,000,000 B.P.	300,000 B.P.	25,000 B.P.	Year
125,000	1,000,000	3,340,000	Population
.01	.03	.1	Persons per square mile

6,000 B.P.	1750 A.D.	1950 A.D.	2050 A.D.	Year
86,500,000	728,000,000	2,400,000,000	10,200,000,000	Population
2.6	12.7	42.5	178.1	Persons per square mile

FIGURE 18–19 Until about 25,000 years B.P. humankind was a stable part of the equilibrium existing among animals and plants. With better hunting technology, animal domestication, and agriculture, humans began to increase dramatically and to destroy the wilderness of which they had been a part. The figures given for the populations of the past are, of course, estimates. That for 2050 A.D. is a projection that might be reduced by an effective, worldwide population-control policy or by extensive famines.

those various environments more intensively. The population density of Africa 2 million years ago, in the days of the crude Oldowan industry, has been estimated at only one individual per 100 square miles (260 km²). By the end of the Paleolithic, humans had spread throughout Europe and Asia as well as Africa, and their density had probably risen tenfold.

The second innovation was the double discovery of how to grow crops and how to domesticate animals. This event came about 10,000 years ago. This second innovation enabled people to settle permanently for the first time, and for the first time to live together in large numbers. Even nomads herding animals could exist in far greater concentrations on a given area of land than could hunters. The effect on world population was extraordinary. In 4,000 years it jumped from an estimated 5 million to 86 million.

The third innovation was the industrial age. It had its beginnings about 300 years ago, when the human population of the world was in the neighborhood of 550 million. World population has been ballooning ever since and today is over 5.6 billion. If it continues at its present rate of increase, it will double within 50 years.

Although these figures are impressive, even more impressive is the *acceleration* in population growth. It took 1 million years to get through the first phase; the second took only 10,000 years; and the third has been going on for only a few hundred. How long it will continue or what the human population of the earth will ultimately be is anybody's guess. But we can be sure that, because the surface of the earth is finite, as are its resources, present rates of increase will bring us to the limit very soon.

Limits to Growth

It seems clear that the increase in our population is due primarily to making greater and greater use of the available resources. When a forest is cleared and crops are grown in its place, all the sunlight in that area is contributing to synthesis of food for humans. When wild animals grazing in meadows and savanna grasslands are killed and replaced by cattle, sheep, and goats, conversion of plant energy into animal protein is turned fully to human benefit. In these cases we can see that the ultimate limitation is the amount of energy that can be delivered by the sun to the earth's surface and turned into carbohydrates by photosynthesis in green plants. Every green plant needs a place in the sun. Other limiting factors are the other requirements of plants: water, minerals, and appropriate soil. Lack of water in particular has long been a problem for farmers, though they have occasionally overcome it with irrigation. But even with advanced technology, we cannot obtain food from all the earth; the ultimate limits are firm both on land and in the oceans. Eventually, as Thomas Malthus predicted in 1798, these limits will indeed halt human population growth, if we do not bring about stabilization voluntarily.

But the continuing expansion of agriculture and animal husbandry cannot be taken to the ultimate limits set by the area of the earth's landmasses without destroying all our natural wilderness and the miraculous array of wild plants and animals that occupy it. As discussed in Chapter 4, the continued destruction of the tropical forests poses a serious and immediate threat of extinction for many non-human primate species and the indigenous humans. The further expansion of agribusiness, or even peasant agriculture, will be destructive to the quality of life we value, and ecologists have made it clear that the continuing loss of forest in particular has very dangerous and irreversible results. We now know that much of the earth's land surface is, in fact, not well suited to agriculture but is best left in its natural state.

In some parts of the world, famine is already becoming a normal condition, and malnutrition is found on many continents. People are dying of hunger by the tens of thousands, partly because the increase in population is due not merely to increased resources but also to advances in medicine. These have brought about an increased *life expectancy*. *Australopithecus* may have had an average life expectancy of 15 to 20 years; *Homo erectus* lived for 20 to 30 years; today, a citizen of the United States can expect to live over 70 years (females 79 and males 72.3 years) (Figure 18–20). A doubling of life expectancy has brought a doubling of population without a corresponding increase in our efficiency in using resources. Thus in many countries people live longer, but not enough food is grown to feed them all.

Large segments of human society have certainly come a long way: in life span, in efficiency in extracting resources, in population density, in technological complexity, and in increased physical comfort. Whether we are really better off as a species, and whether our progress will continue, remains to be seen. For a species like ours, whose survival depends on culture (which is based on knowledge), it is essential to use all available knowledge and understanding to achieve better adaptation to a changing environment. This is perhaps our most difficult problem: Each new cultural adaptation we make alters the environment to which we are adapting. New adaptations increase population; greater population densities require further adaptations; new adaptations deplete world resources; resource depletion requires further adaptation. And so it goes on. We find ourselves in a vicious circle of ever-increasing instability (Figure 18–21). Essential now is an all-out attempt to break that accelerating positive feedback loop and bring about new

Life expectancy: the average age at death of individuals born into a particular population.

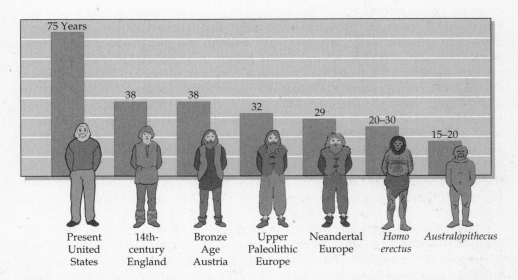

FIGURE 18–20   Since the Upper Paleolithic, life expectancies have doubled in countries with modern medicine and technology. We probably live three to four times as long as *Australopithecus* did. The increased life span has made possible a rapid increase in cultural complexity, skill, and knowledge.

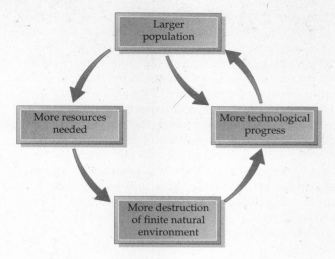

FIGURE 18–21 This positive feedback loop is the most dangerous to us, since it is accelerating very rapidly and involves environmental destruction. With the resource base of our livelihood seriously depleted, the survival of even our present number is threatened.

stability in global population size, in technological investment and in resource consumption.

Population size is certainly a measure of evolutionary success, but another measure that may be more significant is evolutionary longevity. *Homo sapiens*'s 400,000 years is nothing in universal and geologic time, and millions of species have evolved and become extinct in earth history. Compared with most mammals, we are infants of evolution. From this point of view our apparent present success can continue only if we can achieve some sort of stability in our relationship with the earth's resources. Otherwise we shall surely perish as a species.

Gaining Control over Our Evolution

The scale of global overpopulation is so great and the solutions so seemingly elusive that most of us have a hard time even imagining, much less dealing with, the problem. Other challenges of the twenty-first century will be much more immediate and personal. For example, with each passing year humans gain more and more control over their health, reproduction, and evolutionary future. With more control, however, will come increasingly difficult choices.

The evolutionary processes described by Charles Darwin and later biologists will, of course, continue to operate in the future. Mutations and new gene combinations will continue to provide the raw material for natural selection. According to British geneticist Steve Jones, the mutation rate due to external agents will probably remain stable in the near future. Mutations due to delayed reproduction, however, may be expected to rise. This rise will be related to the fact that modern people are having children later than has been true during most of human evolution. Jones estimates that today's mean age at first reproduction is about five years later than it was 10,000 years ago (before the agricultural revolution). Because cells (including those that produce sperm and eggs) become increasingly mutation-prone as they age, we can expect an increased number of newborns carrying mutant alleles.

This predicted rise in the mutation rate will coincide with the medical and scientific communities' increased ability to deal with genetic problems. As discussed at the end of Chapter 3, by using procedures such as amniocentesis, we can already learn not only the sex but also a great deal about the genotype of a developing fetus—information that parents may use to terminate a pregnancy for one reason or another. In the future, prospective parents will be able to learn even more about their unborn children, including genetic predispositions for numerous diseases, and the presence or absence of genes for desired phenotypic traits. How will this information be used? Will we limit ourselves to curing (through such procedures as gene therapy) or preventing diseases? Or will our desire for "perfect" children result in increased abortions and genetic engineering for cosmetic effects? And looking beyond parents and offspring, how will society use additional genetic information? In their recent book *The Secret of Life*, science writer Joseph Levine and geneticist David Suzuki give several examples of how such information might be abused. Here are two actual cases:

> In the early 1970s . . . compulsory screening for sickle-cell trait [i.e., for persons carrying a copy of the gene for sickle-cell anemia] was instituted in at least twelve states. Screening was usually restricted to African-Americans (although 7 percent of subjects with sickle-cell trait were not black), and it was often conducted without informed consent. Inadequate regard for confidentiality, coupled with a preexisting history of racial prejudice, led to denial of insurance coverage and loss of employment for black people, including those who were simply carriers of the sickle-cell trait and showed no symptoms of the disease.

> One couple who knew that they were CF [cystic fibrosis] carriers asked their HMO [health maintenance organization] to pay for a genetic test on their unborn child during pregnancy. They were told that if the child tested positive, the HMO would cancel their health plan unless they agreed to an abortion. Only threatened legal action induced the HMO to withdraw that demand.

With our already sophisticated medical knowledge, humans have taken several steps down the path of *artificial selection* within our own species. Increased knowledge of human genetics and improved ability to manipulate the genotype will take us even farther down that path. Many people are very concerned about these developments, and the issue will become even more pressing in the twenty-first century. Natural selection, genetic drift, mutation, and other natural processes got us where we are today. Are we wise enough to meddle with the selection systems of the future? Jeremy Rifkin of the Foundation for Economic Trends and other opponents of genetic engineering believe that the answer is "no." According to Rifkin, "Perhaps none of us are wise enough, have the clairvoyance, the wisdom, to dictate basic changes in millions of years of genetic evolution. I don't think any of us should have that power. I think it's an unwarranted power and should not be exercised."

We are in the midst of a revolution in biological information and medical sophistication that has far-reaching implications for the future of humans. That future will also be affected by our burgeoning global population and by our stressed and deteriorating global environment. Our intelligence and cultural ingenuity—both products of our evolutionary history—brought us this far. We have no choice but to trust them to give us the vision and the tools to cope with our own "success."

SUMMARY

Cultural developments have proceeded at an ever-accelerating pace since the evolutionary appearance of anatomically modern humans. Plant and animal domestication was under way by 10,000 years B.P., and the establishment of modern civilization soon followed. These developments facilitated or accompanied a strong surge in human population growth around the world. Human evolution did not stop with the attainment of modernity, however, and differential adaptation (very likely combined with a bit of genetic drift) led to physical diversity within and between human populations. In contrast to our folk traditions, modern analyses indicate that biological races among humans cannot be demonstrated. It is now known that most human variation occurs *within* traditionally defined races, and that only a small percentage occurs *between* them. Nonetheless, in line with humans' strong tendency to dichotomize the world into "we-they" groups, distinct social groups most definitely exist and may serve good and valid purposes within society. The existence of such groups, however, may also lead to racist and discriminatory attitudes and behaviors, and we must be constantly on guard against these evils.

The primary challenges for humankind in the twenty-first century include gaining control over global population growth, restricting our runaway use of the earth's finite resources, and dealing with the technological, genetic, and medical advances that allow us an ever-increasing measure of control over our evolutionary future.

REVIEW QUESTIONS

1. Discuss the connection between genes and culture. Specifically, discuss how humans' moral systems may have evolved.

2. Humans' global population is currently burgeoning. Describe the various developments over the course of human evolution that have allowed massive population growth.

3. Argue for or against the proposition that humans can be subdivided into biological races. Be sure to provide supporting evidence for your argument.

4. What is the difference between race and racism? Can races exist without racist attitudes and behavior?

5. Argue for or against the proposition that future human evolution will be controlled mainly by *self-directed artificial selection*, not by natural selection.

6. What, if anything, can we learn from the study of human evolution that will help guide our individual and societal decisions in the future?

POSTSCRIPT

This short section brings to an end our history of human evolution. We hope you have enjoyed it and that this is only one of many anthropology books you will read during your college years and beyond. The story of humankind, whether read from the viewpoint of physical or cultural anthropology, is endlessly fascinating, and new discoveries are constantly being made. It is fascinating partly because it tells of a mammalian family that began with only one outstanding attribute—bipedalism—and that evolved the intelligence and the behavioral complexity to hold the fate of the world in its prehensile hands. But primarily, of course, it is fascinating because it's *our* story and ends with modern humans representing the sole surviving twig of the hominid evolutionary bush.

But the hominid story goes beyond being merely fascinating. It is also *important* because it gives us a clear picture of modern human equality and thus allows us to look to the future with a degree of optimism. Optimism is sometimes a rare commodity. As we prepare the seventh edition of this textbook, the world is commemorating the final events of World War II, a conflict that included one of history's most horrendous examples of genocide; in the African nation of Rwanda people are massacring each other in staggering numbers; and in the former Yugoslavia "ethnic cleansing" continues unabated. How, one might ask, in the light of these events, can we speak of optimism?

We are optimistic because of our deep belief in the unity of humankind. The fossil record shows that all modern people are the descendants of African or Middle Eastern ancestors who lived a short 100,000 to 150,000 years ago. Although in the intervening years people have spread all over the globe, adapted to a variety of environments, and have developed substantial genetic and physical diversity, that diversity is swamped by our overwhelming similarities. As noted in this chapter, only 6.3 percent of genetic diversity occurs between traditionally defined human "races." Recent common ancestry and overwhelming genetic similarities—from these two facts flows the inescapable inference of *human unity*.

We are certainly not the first to make this inference, nor will we be the last. Human unity is a principle worth discovering and describing over and over, in the hope that humanity will finally get the message and move from genocide and international confrontation to peaceful coexistence and cooperation. The challenges facing humankind in the next century will put a premium on human unity and cooperation as never before. In order to make any significant headway against population growth, resource depletion, and human misery, we must act as a global community. But the development of such a community clearly hinges on our acceptance of one another as absolute equals. It will take a massive team effort, and we implore every reader of this book to contribute to that effort.

Glossary

Note: Words in *italics*, excepting some Latin names and self-explanatory terms, are defined elsewhere in the glossary.

Absolute dating: determining the actual age of geologic deposits (and the fossils in them) by examining the chemical composition of rock fragments and organic remains containing radioactive substances such as uranium 238, potassium 40, and *carbon 14*, which decay at a known rate. Also known as *chronometric dating*. (Compare with *relative dating*.)

Acheulean industry: stone tool tradition that appeared 1.4 to 1.7 million years B.P. in Africa and originated with *Homo erectus*.

Adapidae: one of the two families of Eocene prosimians, now extinct.

Adaptation: an evolutionary change, generally resulting from *natural selection*, which better suits a *population* to its environment, thus improving its chances of survival; a characteristic resulting from such a change.

Aegyptopithecus: a basal catarrhine from the Fayum in Africa; dated to the *Oligocene* epoch.

Agglutination: the clumping of *red blood cells* as a result of the reaction of *antibodies* to an *antigen*.

Algeripithecus: tentatively, the oldest known anthropoid primate, from the early-middle Eocene epoch of North Africa.

Alleles: *genes* occupying equivalent positions in paired *chromosomes*, yet producing different effects in the *phenotype* when they are *homozygous*. They are alternative states of a gene, originally produced by *mutation*.

Allomothering: typically, care or attention directed toward an infant by a female other than its mother (also called *aunting behavior*).

Allopatric speciation: the production of new species through the branching or splitting of existing ones. The process begins with the geographic isolation of one or more populations from the bulk of the parent species.

Altiatlasius: the oldest known primate fossil; a prosimian from the late Paleocene of North Africa.

Altricial: the state of being born helpless and requiring parental care.

Amino acids: a group of organic compounds that act as building blocks for proteins.

Amphipithecus: a possible anthropoid from the late Eocene of Burma.

Angular gyrus: part of the human *cerebral cortex* that allows information received from different senses to be associated.

Anterior inferior iliac spine: a projection from the ilium that serves as an attachment point for certain thigh muscles and for the *iliofemoral ligament*.

Anthropoid: relating to humans, apes, and monkeys.

Anthropology: the science of humankind; the systematic study of human evolution, human variability, and human behavior, past and present.

Antibody: a protein produced as a defense mechanism to attack a foreign substance invading the body.

Antigens: any organic substances, recognized by the body as foreign, that stimulate the production of an *antibody*.

Ape: among living animals, a large, tailless, semi-erect mammal of the order *Primates*. Living types are the *chimpanzee, bonobo, gorilla, gibbon, siamang,* and *orangutan*.

Aphasia: the loss or distortion of speech.

Apidium: primate of the *Oligocene* epoch, found in Egypt; possibly a basal *anthropoid*.

Arboreal: adapted for living in or around trees, as are most monkeys and apes.

Archaeology: the systematic study of prehistoric human cultures; finding and interpreting the cultural products of prehistoric people.

Archaic humans: early members of the species *Homo sapiens* who preceded anatomically modern humans.

Arcuate fasciculus: a bundle of nerve fibers in the human brain transmitting signals from *Wernicke's area* to *Broca's area,* making possible vocal repetition of words heard and memorized.

Articulation: in anatomy, the joint between two bones; in linguistics, the action of the tongue and lips to form the consonants of speech.

Artifact: a purposefully formed object.

Aterian: Middle Paleolithic tool industry from northern Africa; associated with archaic *Homo sapiens*.

Atlatl: Aztec name for the spear thrower, a rodlike device used as an extension of the arm that greatly increases both distance and impact of throw.

Attractiveness: in primate studies, the aspect of female sexuality reflected by attention from males.

Auditory bulla: a bulbous bony development that houses the middle ear region.

Aurignacian: an *Upper Paleolithic,* mainly European, tool culture that existed from about 40,000 to 27,000 years ago.

Australopithecus: a genus of the family Hominidae, subfamily Australopithecinae; contains three species: *A. afarensis, A. africanus,* and (provisionally) *A. ramidus.*

Australopithecus afarensis: a gracile australopithecine species that inhabited East Africa 4.0–2.5 mya; if the Lothagam jaw is included in the species, it goes back to 5.6 mya.

Australopithecus africanus: a gracile australopithecine species that inhabited South Africa 3.0–2.5 mya.

Australopithecus aethiopicus: the original name for the robust australopithecine species now called *Paranthropus aethiopicus.*

Australopithecus ramidus: species provisionally classified as a hominid; lived in East Africa 4.4 mya.

Autosome: a chromosome other than the sex chromsomes.

Baboon: a large monkey with a long, doglike muzzle; most baboons have short tails and live on the ground in troops. They live close to the trees in East and Central Africa and in rocky desert in Ethiopia (see also *gelada* and *hamadryas*).

Balanced polymorphism: maintenance in a *population* of different *alleles* of a particular *gene* in proportion to the advantages offered by each (e.g., *sickle-cell* and normal *hemoglobin*).

Band: a small, economically independent group of primates, smaller than a troop.

Beijing man: see *Sinanthropus pekinensis.*

Biface: a tool made by chipping flakes off both sides of a core, producing an edge straighter and sharper than those made in earlier cultures, which were chipped on one edge only. A common tool of the *Acheulean industry.*

Bilophodonty: the lower molar cusp pattern of Old World monkeys, featuring four cusps arranged in front and rear pairs.

Bioaltruism: behavior that appears to be altruistic, but that in fact is believed to benefit the animal indirectly, by increasing its *inclusive fitness.*

Bioethicist: a person who specializes in exploring the ethical dimensions of biological decisions.

Biomass: the total weight of living material of a species or population.

Biome: an area characterized by a broadly uniform climate and consisting of a distinctive combination of plants and animals.

Bipedal: moving erect on the hind limbs only.

Biretia: a late Eocene anthropoid from Algeria.

Birth canal: the passage through the mother's pelvis by means of which infants are born.

Blade tools: slender, razor-sharp *flake tools* at least twice as long as they are wide.

Blending inheritance: an outmoded theory stating that offspring receive a combination of all characteristics of each parent through the mixture of their bloods; superseded by Mendelian genetics.

Blood groups: groups of individuals whose blood can be mixed without *agglutination* (e.g., Groups A, B, O, or AB).

Bola: two or more stones connected by thongs or a cord and used as a weapon.

Bonobo: Central African apes very similar to the common chimpanzee and sometimes called *pygmy chimpanzees;* display some behavioral similarities to humans.

Brachiation: an arboreal locomotor pattern featuring manual swinging from branch to branch.

Branching: the splitting of a family tree into separate evolutionary lines: The monkeys, apes, and living prosimians diverged from a common prosimianlike ancestor; the hominid line diverged from the apes.

Branisella: Oligocene platyrrhine monkeys from Bolivia.

Broca's area: part of the human *cerebral cortex* involved with the hierarchial organization of grammar and the manual combination of objects.

Brow ridge: a continuous ridge of bone in the skull, curving over each eye and connected across the bridge of the nose. An extremely prominent brow ridge is characteristic of the Neandertal people.

Budding: the gradual expansion of a species into new areas, accomplished by a group splitting off from a prospering *population* to set up in an unexploited area near the original territory.

Burin: a chisellike tool used to shape other materials such as bone, antler, and wood; a tool for making other tools.

Canines: pointed teeth in the front of the mouth between the incisors and the premolars. In monkeys and apes, canines are usually large, projecting beyond the other teeth, and are used for tearing up vegetation and for threats and fights. Hominid canines are much smaller.

Carbon 14 (C^{14}): a radioactive form of carbon present in the atmosphere as CO_2 that disintegrates at a predictable rate. The amount of carbon 14 remaining in fossils indicates their age.

Catarrhines: an infraorder of the anthropoids that includes Old World monkeys, apes, and hominids.

Catastrophism: Georges Cuvier's theory that vast floods and other disasters wiped out ancient life forms again and again throughout the earth's history.

Catopithecus: a particularly well-known *oligopithecine* from the Fayum in Africa.

Cenozoic: geologic era that began about 65 mya.

Centrioles: minute granules present in many cells outside the nuclear membrane. The centriole divides in cell division (*mitosis*), and the parts separate to form the poles of the spindle.

Cephalic index: a skull measurement sometimes used by anthropologists; defined as skull breadth/length × 100.

Cerebral cortex: gray, wrinkled, outer layer of the brain; largely responsible for memory and, in humans, reasoned behavior and abstract thought. (Also referred to as the *neocortex*.)

Chain of Being: pre-Darwinian theory of a hierarchy ranking living things from lowest to highest, with humankind at the top; the chain was thought to have been fixed forever at Creation, which meant that no species could change into other forms.

Chatelperronian: an *Upper Paleolithic* tool culture of western Europe, largely contemporaneous with the *Aurignacian* culture (40,000 to 27,000 years B.P.).

Chemical signature: unique chemical nature of a geologic deposit; for volcanic rocks, it is usually determined by an analysis of the ash and lava content.

Chiasmata: points where the chromatids of a tetrad overlap and segment exchange may occur; crossover points.

Chimpanzee: African great ape thought to be somewhat like the ancestor from which apes and humans are descended. In the trees it climbs; on the ground it usually moves by *knuckle walking.*

Choppers: small, generally ovoid stones with a few flakes removed to produce a partial cutting edge.

Chordata: the *phylum* of animals characterized by the possession of a notochord (a gelatinous dorsal stiffening rod) at some stage of life.

Chromatid: one of the two elements in a duplicated chromosome.

Chromosomes: coiled, threadlike structures of *DNA,* bearing the *genes* and found in the nucleus of all plant and animal cells. (See also *meiosis* and *mitosis.*)

Chronospecies: the sort of "species" that are created when an unbroken evolutionary continuum is arbitrarily divided into time-defined units.

Clade: members of an evolutionary cluster (e.g., sister species) plus their common ancestor.

Cladistic analysis: the grouping of *species* by their shared derived traits, with the aim of identifying groups of organisms descended from a common ancestor.

Cladistic classification: evolution-based *taxonomy* that gives equal weight to traits and requires sister groups to be similarly ranked.

Class: a *taxonomic* rank in biology. Humans belong to the class *Mammalia.*

Cleaver: an *Acheulean* stone implement with a straight cutting edge at one end; probably used for butchering animal carcasses.

Cline: the gradual change in frequency of a trait or gene across a geographic range.

Close-knee stance: standing with the feet and knees closer together than the hip joints.

Cobble: stone worn smooth by sand and water in running streams or on a rocky seashore. Often used as a core for making a stone tool.

Coccyx: the bones at the end of the human and ape spine, the remnants of an ancestral tail.

Co-dominant: the term for alleles which, in heterozygous combination, produce a phenotype distinct from either type of homozygote.

Codon: a *nucleotide* triplet that codes for the production of a particular *amino acid* during protein production.

Collective phenotype: the set of phenotypic averages and norms that characterize a *population* or *species.*

Colugos: nonprimate mammals from Asia known for arboreal gliding; misnamed "flying lemurs."

Condyle: the part of a bone that fits into another bone, forming a movable, hingelike joint, like the part of the lower jaw that bears on the skull.

Consortship: generally, a period of exclusive sexual association and mating between a female and a male.

Conspecifics: members of the same species.

Continental drift: a theory that describes the movements of continental landmasses throughout the earth's history.

Core area: a portion of the home range that is used frequently.

Core tool: implement made from the core of a rock nodule. (Compare with *flakes.*)

Cranium: the skull without the jaw.

Creationism: the belief that humans and all life forms were specially created by God or some other divine force.

Cro-Magnon: anatomically modern humans living in southwestern France between 35,000 and 10,000 years ago.

Crossing-over: the exchange of sections between homologous chromosomes.

Cultural evolution: changes in human *culture* resulting from the accumulated experience of humankind. Cultural evolution can produce *adaptations* to the environment faster than organic evolution can.

Cultural swamping: overwhelming of one *culture* by a technologically more powerful one, often leaving the culture with the weaker technology extinct or nearly so.

Culture: humans' systems of learned behavior, symbols, customs, beliefs, institutions, artifacts, and technology, characteristic of a group and transmitted by its members to their offspring.

Cusps: conical projections on the biting surfaces of teeth (see also *molars*).

Cytoplasm: the contents of a cell excluding the nucleus.

Darwinian fitness: see *fitness.*

Débitage: debris produced during stone tool manufacture.

Deep time: the theory that the earth is billions of years old and thus has a long history of development and change.

Demography: study of the size, density, distribution, and other vital statistics of *populations.*

Dental formula: the numbers of incisors, canines, premolars, and molars in half of the upper and lower toothrows.

Denticulates: stone implements made with toothed or notched edges.

Deoxyribonucleic acid: see *DNA.*

Derived traits: recently evolved characteristics shared by a small number of closely related species.

Diastema (pl. diastemata): space in the toothrow that accommodates one or more teeth in the opposite jaw when the mouth is closed.

Differential reproduction: the effect of *natural selection* that individuals with certain traits are less *fit* than those with other traits.

Diploid number: the full *chromosome* count in somatic cells (all cells other than *gametes*). (Compare with twice the *haploid* number.)

Directional natural selection: *natural selection* that operates in response to environmental change and produces shifts in the composition of a *population*'s *gene pool* and *collective phenotype.*

Disk-core technique: Neandertal stone-knapping method in which a core is trimmed to disk shape and numerous flakes are chipped off; the flakes are then generally retouched.

Diurnal: active during the day, as apes, monkeys, and humans are.

DNA (deoxyribonucleic acid): chemical substance found in *chromosomes* and *mitochondria* which reproduces itself, and carries the *genetic code.*

Dominance hierarchy: rank structuring of a primate group, usually based on winning and losing fights. For some purposes, the ranks within a subset of animals, such as the adult males, may be analyzed separately.

Dominant: describes a trait that is expressed in the *phenotype* even when the organism is carrying only one copy of the underlying hereditary material (one copy of the responsible gene).

Dorsal: pertaining to the back of an animal or one of its parts; opposite of *ventral.*

Dragon bones: the ancient Chinese term for fossils of various sorts that were collected and ground into medicines.

Drift: see *genetic drift.*

Dryopithecus: extinct primitive ape of the *Miocene* epoch.

Early Homo: general term referring collectively to *Homo habilis* and *Homo rudolfensis.*

Ecosystem: ecological system; the interacting community of all the organisms in an area and their physical environment, together with the flow of energy among its components.

Emissary veins: veins that pass through the bones of the skull by means of small openings called *foramina.*

Encephalization quotient (EQ): in mammals, a number expressing observed brain size in a particular species relative to expected brain size calculated from body weight.

Endocast: a fossilized cast of the interior of a skull; may reveal much about brain size and shape.

Endogamy: selecting a mate from inside one's own group.

Eoanthropus dawsoni: see *Piltdown man.*

Eocene: the geologic epoch extending from 58 to 35 million years B.P.

Eosimias: probable basal anthropoid from the mid-Eocene of China.

Epicanthic fold: a fold of skin above the inner border of the eye; characteristic of Asiatic, Native American, and Khoisan people.

Estrus: the period, usually around ovulation, of sexual attractiveness and activity by primate and other mammalian females.

Estrus cycle: the interval between periods of sexual attractiveness and activity by primate females; correlated with ovulation and the menstrual cycle, but with great flexibility among catarrhines.

Ethnic group: a group of people perceived as sharing a common and distinctive culture.

Ethnographic analogy: an analogy between the ethnography of a society and the supposed ethnography of a prehistoric one.

Ethology: study of the social behavior of animal species in their natural environment.

Evolution: cumulative changes in the average characteristics of a *population* that occur over many generations (see also *natural selection*).

Exogamy: among modern humans, the pattern of marrying (and mating) between individuals of different social groups; incipient exogamy like that envisioned for *Homo erectus*, need not have included formal marriages.

Exons: segments of a gene's *DNA* that code for protein production.

Extinction: the loss of a species due to the death of all its members.

Family: in human society, generally a unit marked by subsistence interdependence, sexual relationships among adults, and parent-offspring relationships.

Fauna: animal component of the ecosystem at a given place and time.

Faunal correlation: dating a site by the similarity of its animal fossils to those of another site that may carry a reliable absolute date.

Feedback: process by which a change in one component in a system affects other components, which in turn bring about changes in the first component.

Femur (pl. femora): the thighbone.

Fish gorge: device for catching fish on a line using a moving part that opens at right angles and sticks in the fish's mouth.

Fission-track dating: method of determining the age of rocks from tracks left by the spontaneous fission (that is, the splitting of the nucleus) of uranium 238. Because the rate of fission is known, the rock's age can be calculated by an assessment of the original quantity of uranium and the density of the tracks.

Fitness: individuals' relative degrees of success in surviving and reproducing, and thus in gaining genetic representation in succeeding generations.

Flakes: sharp-edged fragments struck from a stone; the flake may then be used as a tool. (Compare with *core tool.*)

Flake tool: implement made from a flake struck from a stone.

Folivore: a leaf-eating animal.

Foramen magnum: large opening in the cranial base, through which the spinal cord passes to the brain.

Fossil: the remains of an organism, or direct evidence of its presence, preserved in rock. Generally only the hard parts of animals—teeth and bones—are preserved.

Fossil magnetism: naturally occurring property of rocks indicating the polarity of the earth's magnetic field when they were laid down. By a comparison of the polarity of one layer with that of others, the age of a rock can, under certain conditions, be approximated.

Founder effect: genetic difference between a newly founded, separated *population* and its parent group. The founding population is usually different because its *gene pool* is only a segment of the parent group's.

Founder principle: the fact that founders of a new colony, if few in number, will contain only a fraction of the total genetic variation of the parental *population* or *species*. The founder colony will therefore most likely differ genetically from the parent population.

Fovea: an area of the anthropoid retina that allows extremely detailed vision.

Frenulum: the flap of skin that tethers the upper lip to the jaw in prosimians. It is reduced or absent in anthropoids and tarsiers.

Frontal bone: bone of the primate skull that constitutes the forehead and comes down around the eye sockets (orbits).

Frugivore: a fruit-eating animal.

Fusion-fission community: a society that includes several individuals of both sexes and all ages and is characterized by the formation and dissolution of temporary subgroups.

Gametes: reproductive *haploid* sex cells generated by *meiosis*, which fuse with gametes of the opposite sex in fertilization. In animals, the female gamete is the ovum; the male gamete, the sperm.

Gelada: species of terrestrial monkey related to baboons, found in the mountains of Ethiopia.

Gene: primarily, a functional unit of the *chromosomes* in cell nuclei, which controls the coding and inheritance of phenotypic traits; some genes also occur in a closed loop in the *mitochondria*.

Gene flow: transmission of genes between *populations* through *exogamy*, which increases the variety of genes available to each and creates or maintains similarities in the genetic makeup of the populations.

Gene frequency: the number of times a gene occurs in proportion to the size of a *population*.

Gene pool: all the genes of a *population* at a given time (summing genes within a *species* yields the species' gene pool).

Genetic code: the chemical code based on four *nucleotides*, carried by *DNA* and *RNA*, which specifies amino acids in sequence for protein synthesis.

Genetic drift: genetic changes in *populations* caused by random phenomena rather than by *natural selection*.

Genetic load: *recessive* genes in a population that are harmful when expressed in the rare *homozygous* condition.

Genetic swamping: the overrunning and absorption of a small *population* by a larger one; the *genes* of the minority are preserved but contribute little to the successors' physical characteristics.

Genome: the totality of the DNA unique to a particular organism or species.

Genotype: the genetic makeup of a plant or animal; all information contained in each *gene* of the organism. (Compare with *phenotype*.)

Genus: *taxonomic* category composed of a group of *species* that are similar because of common ancestry.

Geology: study of the earth's physical formation, its nature, and its continuing development.

Gibbon: small, long-armed, tree-dwelling, brachiating ape of Southeast Asia.

Gigantopithecus: extinct giant ape dating from *Pliocene* and *Pleistocene epochs*. Found in Asia.

Gluteus medius: one of the muscles of the hip; a lateral stabilizer of the pelvis in modern humans.

Gluteus minimus: one of the muscles of the hip; a lateral stabilizer of the pelvis in modern humans.

Gorilla: the largest ape; a social, terrestrial, knuckle-walking vegetarian living in the rain forests and mountain forests of equatorial Africa.

Grades: arbitrarily defined levels of evolutionary development (e.g., prosimians vs. anthropoids).

Gradualism: the hypothesis that *evolution* has consisted for the most part of gradual, steady change. (Compare with *punctuated equilibrium*.)

Gravettian: see *Perigordian*.

Group selection: theoretical model in which natural selection is presumed to operate not on the individual animal but on a social group as a unit.

Half-life: the time taken for half of any quantity of a radioactive element to decay to its fission products.

Hamadryas: a species of baboon adapted to the desert regions of Ethiopia.

Hamstrings: muscles of the hips and the back of the thigh; thigh extensors.

Hand ax: a bifacially flaked stone implement that characterized the *Acheulean industry*.

Haploid number: the number of *chromosomes* carried by *gametes*; equal to one-half the full chromosome count of somatic cells. (Compare with *diploid number*.)

Harem polygyny: in zoology, a group including one breeding male and multiple females; among humans, one husband and multiple wives and concubines.

Hemispherical asymmetry: the condition in which the two cerebral hemispheres differ in one or more dimensions. In most modern humans, the left hemisphere is somewhat larger than the right.

Hemoglobin: a red protein found in *red blood cells* that carries oxygen through the circulatory system of vertebrates and some other animals.

Heritability: a property of phenotypic traits; the proportion of a trait's interindividual variance that is due to genetic variance.

Heterodont: having several different types of teeth (incisors, canines, etc.), each with a different function.

Heterozygous: having different versions of a *gene* (*alleles*) for a particular trait. (Compare with *homozygous*; see also *dominant*.)

Heuristic devices: devices that facilitate or stimulate further investigation and thought.

Home base: camps where hominid groups gathered at evening for socializing, food sharing, and sleeping.

Home range: the area a primate group uses for foraging, sleeping, and so on in a year. (Compare with *territory*.)

Hominids: living or fossil members of the primate family Hominidae, which includes *Homo sapiens*, earlier species of the genus *Homo*, *Australopithecus*, and *Paranthropus*.

Hominoid: a primate of the superfamily Hominoidea, including the apes and humans.

Homo: a genus of the family Hominidae, subfamily Homininae; contains at least 4 species: *H. habilis*, *H. rudolfensis*, *H. erectus*, and *H. sapiens*.

Homo erectus: hominid species that inhabited much of the Old World 1.8 to 0.3 million years ago; successor to "early *Homo*."

Homo ergaster: this name is given by some specialists to certain African fossils regarded by most workers as being *Homo erectus*. The authors of this text side with the majority.

Homo habilis: one of the two species of "early *Homo*"; inhabited South and East Africa 2.0–1.6 million years ago.

Homo neanderthalensis: species designation suggested in 1864 for the Neandertal fossils. This name is not used in this text, as all Neandertal remains are included in "archaic *H. sapiens*."

Homo rudolfensis: one of the two varieties of "early *Homo*"; inhabited East Africa 2.4–1.6 mya.

Homo sapiens: among living primates, the scientific name for modern humans; archaic members of the species first appeared about 400,000 years ago.

Homo sapiens sapiens: anatomically modern people; first evolved around 130,000 years B.P.

Homozygous: having identical version of a *gene* (*alleles*) for a particular trait. (Compare with *heterozygous*.)

Hyoid: a bone of the throat positioned just above the larynx and just below the mandible. The hyoid provides attachment for one of the muscles of the tongue and for certain muscles at the front of the neck.

Ignacius: a genus of the plesiadapiforms.

Iliac blade: the broad portion of the *ilium*, one of the bones of the pelvis.

Iliofemoral ligament: ligament that prevents backward movement of the trunk at the human hip.

Ilium: the hipbone, part of the *pelvis.*

Inbreeding: mating among related individuals.

Incest: legally prohibited sexual relations between kin. How closely related individuals must be for mating to be considered incestuous differs from culture to culture.

Inclusive fitness: the sum total of an individual's personal reproductive success (number of offspring) plus portions of the reproductive success of genetic kin.

Infanticide: the killing of infants.

Interglacial: a period in which glaciers retreat and the climate warms.

Introns: segments of a gene's *DNA* that do not code for protein production (so-called noncoding *DNA*).

IQ tests: tests that supposedly measure an individual's "intelligence quotient." Many consider such tests flawed and of little value, particularly for cross-cultural comparisons.

Iron pyrite: a mineral substance (iron disulfide) that, when struck with flint, makes sparks that will start a fire.

Ischium: one of the bones of the *pelvis.*

Java man: see *Pithecanthropus.*

Kin selection: the selection of characteristics (and their genes) that increase the probability of the survival and reproduction of close relatives.

Knuckle walking: *quadrupedal* walking on the knuckles of the hands and the soles of the feet, used by bonobos, chimpanzees, and gorillas on the ground.

Language: the cognitive aspect of human communication, involving symbolic thinking structured by grammar.

Langur: slender, long-tailed Asian monkey.

Larynx: the voice box; the organ in the throat containing vocal cords, important in human speech production.

Laurel-leaf blade: *Upper Paleolithic* stone artifact so finely worked that it may have had an aesthetic or ritual function. Associated with *Solutrean* tool kits.

Leister: a three-pronged spear used for fishing.

Levallois technique: stone-knapping method in which a core is shaped to allow a flake of predetermined size and shape to be detached; originated about 200,000 years ago.

Life expectancy: the average age at death of individuals born into a particular population.

Limbic system: the emotional brain; a group of structures in the brain important in regulating such behavior as eating, drinking, aggression, sexual activity, and expressions of emotion. Proportionately smaller in humans than in other primates, it operates below the level of consciousness.

Lithic technology: stone-tool technology.

Locus: position of a nuclear *gene* on a *chromosome;* each locus can carry only one *allele* of a gene.

Loris: a prosimian of India, Southeast Asia, and Africa that is small, solitary, *quadrupedal,* and slow moving.

Lower Paleolithic: the earliest part of the Old Stone Age, lasting from more than 2 million to about 200,000 years ago.

Lumbar curve: forward curvature of the vertebral column in the lower back that helps bring the hominid trunk over the hip joints.

Magdalenian: *Upper Paleolithic* culture existing in western Europe from about 16,500 to 11,000 years B.P. Produced many *blade* tools and prototype harpoons.

Mammalia: the class of four-legged vertebrates— including humans—having hair or fur, milk glands for suckling their young, and warm blood.

Mandible: the lower jaw.

Mandibular symphysis: the midline connecting the right and left halves of the lower jaw.

Manuports: Unmodified stones that could not have occurred naturally at an archaeological site and must have been carried there; how manuports were used is unknown.

Matrilineal kinship: kinship traced through the maternal line.

Meiosis: cell division resulting in the formation of sex cells, each of which will have half the number of *chromosomes* present in the original cell (the haploid number).

Melanocyte: a kind of cell in the skin that produces pigment, giving the skin color.

Menstrual cycle: the interval (generally, monthly) between periods of menstrual bleeding; especially characteristic of catarrhine females.

Microwear: the microscopic pattern of scratches, pits, and polish produced during the use of a stone tool.

Midden: a refuse heap or dunghill at an archaeological site in which artifacts and food remains may be preserved.

Middle Paleolithic: a period of stone tool manufacture in Europe, Africa, the Middle East, and western Asia that lasted from 200,000 to about 35,000 years B.P.

Midfacial prognathism: forward protrusion of the upper jaw, the midface and the nasal regions; characteristic of Neandertals.

Miocene: the geologic epoch extending from 25 to 5 million years B.P.

Mitochondria: granular or rod-shaped bodies in the cytoplasm of cells that function in the metabolism of fat and proteins. Probably of bacterial origin.

Mitosis: cell division in somatic cells; two identical *diploid* cells result.

Molars: grinding teeth, which bear many *cusps.* Primate molars have three to five cusps, depending on the animal; premolars normally have two.

Molecular clocks: a variety of molecular measures for estimating the time of divergence of living species from their common ancestor.

Monkey: usually a small or medium-sized, long-tailed arboreal, *quadrupedal,* vegetarian primate. The two groups are *New World monkeys* and *Old World monkeys.*

Monogamy: among humans, having only one spouse. (Compare with *polygamy.*)

Monogyny: in zoology, generally having only one mate. (Compare with *polygyny.*)

Monomorphic: both sexes showing the same trait (e.g., similar body size).

Monophyletic clade: a group of species sharing a common ancestor that would be included in the group.

Morphological pattern: the distinctive form of a *species;* those anatomical features common to members of a species, which as a group distinguish them from other animals.

Mosaic evolution: *evolution* of different parts of the body at different rates over long periods.

Mousterian industry: a *Middle Paleolithic* tool industry from Europe and the Middle East; primarily associated with archaic *Homo sapiens.*

Mousterian of Acheulean tradition (MAT): a variety of the *Mousterian industry* that included very diverse tools, including numerous *hand axes;* associated with *Neandertals* in western Europe during the *Middle Paleolithic* period.

Movius Line: the geographic dividing line between the Acheulean tradition in the west and non-Acheulean lithic traditions in eastern and southeastern Asia.

mtDNA: genetic material found in the mitochondria of cells.

Mutation: generally, spontaneous change in the chemistry of a gene that can alter its phenotypic effect. The accumulation of such changes may contribute to *evolution* of a new *species* of animal or plant. See also *point mutation.*

Natural selection: the principal mechanism of Darwinian *evolutionary* change, by which the individuals best adapted to the environment contribute more offspring to succeeding generations than others do. As more of such individuals' characteristics are incorporated into the *gene pool*, the characteristics of the *population* evolve.

Neandertals: often spelled *Neanderthal*, these people were a variety of archaic *Homo sapiens* that lived in Europe and the Middle East between 300,000 and 35,000 years ago. In this text, they are classified as *Homo sapiens neanderthalensis*.

Neurons: nerve cells; the basic units of the nervous system.

New World monkeys: members of the *Primate* order belonging to the superfamily Ceboidea, including marmosets and howler, spider, and squirrel monkeys, among other species. (Compare with *Old World monkeys*.)

Niche: precise environment and resource base of a *species* or population.

Nocturnal: active during the hours of darkness.

Nuclear family: a *family* group of two parents and their children.

Nucleic acid: a long, chainlike compound formed by a large number of *nucleotides*; present in all organisms in one or both of two forms: *DNA* and *RNA*.

Nucleotides: organic compounds, consisting of bases, sugars, and phosphates; found in cells either free or as part of polynucleotide chains.

Occipital condyles: pads of bone on the base of the skull that articulate with the uppermost vertebra.

Occipital torus: a ridge running side-to-side across the occipital bone.

Occlusal plane: the plane lying parallel to the biting surfaces of the teeth.

Occupation level: land surface occupied by prehistoric hominids.

Oldowan tool industry; earliest known stone-tool culture, dating 2.4 million years into the past and first made by early *Homo*. The products were very crude stone choppers and flakes. (See also *chopper*.)

Old World monkeys: members of the *Primate* order belonging to the superfamily Cercopithecoidea, including langurs, baboons, and macaques, among other species. (Compare with *New World monkeys*.)

Oligocene: the geologic epoch extending from 35 to 25 million years B.P.

Oligopithecines: late Eocene anthropoids; many have been collected from Egypt's Fayum Depression.

Omnivore: an animal that eats both meat and vegetation.

Omomyidae: one of the two families of Eocene prosimians, now extinct.

Open words: words that can be used alone by children to convey meaning; that is, nouns and some verbs. (Compare with *pivot words*.)

Opportunistic mating: mating done whenever and wherever the opportunity presents itself, and with whatever partner is available.

Opposable thumb: ability to hold thumb and index finger together in opposition, giving a *precision grip*.

Orangutan: a tree-dwelling ape of Borneo and Sumatra. Has *prehensile* hands and feet for seizing and grasping; limbs articulated for reaching in any direction; and very long arms. Orangutans move on the ground rarely but are then *quadrupedal*.

Order: a *taxonomic* rank. Humans belong to the order *Primates*.

Oreopithecus: enigmatic late *Miocene* hominoid from Europe that showed adaptations for suspensory locomotion.

Osteodontokeratic culture: the culture of bone, tooth, and horn tools hypothesized by Raymond Dart for *A. africanus;* now largely dismissed.

Otavipithecus: a recently discovered fossil ape from the mid-*Miocene* of southern Africa.

Outbreeding: mating among unrelated individuals. (Compare with *inbreeding*.)

Pair bond: a psychological relationship between mates; thought to be marked by sexual faithfulness.

Palate: the bony plate separating the mouth from the nasal cavity. It is arched in humans and flat in apes.

Paleoanthropology: the study of the fossil and cultural remains and other evidence of humans' extinct ancestors.

Paleocene: the geologic epoch extending from 65 to 58 million years B.P.

Paleolithic: see *Stone Age*.

Paleomagnetism: magnetism preserved in rock originally generated by the earth's magnetic field. Past fluctuations in the intensity and direction of this field allow correlation between strata (rock layers).

Paleontology: the study of the fossil remains and biology of organisms that lived in the past.

Parallel evolution: the evolution of similar but not identical adaptations in two or more lineages.

Paranthropus: a genus of the family Hominidae, subfamily Australopithecinae; contains three species: *P. robustus, P. boisei,* and *P. aethiopicus.*

Paranthropus aethiopicus: newly recognized robust australopithecine species that inhabited East Africa 2.6–2.3 mya.

Paranthropus boisei: robust australopithecine species from East Africa that lived 2.4–1.3 million years ago; formerly *Australopithecus boisei.*

Paranthropus robustus: robust australopithecine species that lived in South Africa 2.0–1.0 mya; formerly *Australopithecus robustus.*

Parapithecus: a primate of the *Oligocene* epoch, from Egypt; probably a basal *anthropoid.*

Parental investment: any behavior toward offspring that improves the chance of the offspring's survival.

Particulate inheritance: the transmission of hereditary characteristics by discrete units of genetic material; first proposed by Gregor Mendel (see also *genes*).

Pelvis: a bony structure forming a basinlike ring at the base of the vertebral column with which the legs articulate.

Perigordian: an Upper Paleolithic culture of Western Europe, dating 27,000 to 21,000 years B.P.

Persistence hunting: hunting by chasing the prey until it stops, exhausted, when it can be killed.

Pharynx: the throat, above the *larynx.*

Phenetic classification: *taxonomy* based on physical similarities or differences between *species* or other taxa.

Phenotype: the observable characteristics of a plant or an animal; the expression of the *genotype.*

Phonation: the production of vowel sounds by the passage of air through the *larynx* and the *pharynx.*

Phonemes: the smallest sound components of language.

Phyletic transformation: the conversion (through gradual *natural selection* and *gene flow*) of an entire *species* into a new species.

Phylogenetic classification: a *taxonomy* that reflects evolutionary descent and is based on the pattern of primitive and derived traits; in traditional evolutionary classifications, traits may be given different weights.

Phylogeny: the evolutionary lineage of organisms; their evolutionary history.

Phylum: a major *taxonomic* rank. Humans are in the phylum *Chordata.*

Piltdown man: a "doctored" modern human skull and ape jaw "discovered" in 1911 that was supposed to represent a very primitive human, *Eoanthropus dawsoni,* but was exposed as a hoax in 1953.

Pithecanthropus: the original genus name given by Eugene Dubois to fossil material from Java now classified as *Homo erectus.*

Pivot words: words—like prepositions, adjectives, and some verbs—used by children to modify *open words* to make two-word sentences.

Platelets: minute blood cells associated with clotting.

Platycephalic: a term describing a skull that is long, low-vaulted, and wide.

Platyrrhines: an infraorder of the anthropoids that includes the New World monkeys.

Pleistocene: the geologic epoch that lasted from about 1.6 million to 10,000 years ago.

Plesiadapiformes: fossil mammals of the Paleocene and Eocene that were once thought to be primitive primates but are now classified as relatives of *colugos*.

Pliocene: the geologic epoch extending from 5 to 1.6 million years B.P.

Plio-Pleistocene: a combination of the last two epochs of the Cenozoic era; the Pliocene lasted from 5 to 1.6 million years B.P. and the Pleistocene from 1.6 million to 10,000 years B.P.

Point mutation: usually the substitution of one *nucleotide* in a single *codon* of a *gene* that affects *protein* synthesis and *genotype*; gene *mutation*.

Polyandry: a female having multiple male sexual partners (among humans, multiple husbands).

Polygamy: having many spouses. (Compare with *monogamy*.)

Polygenic traits: traits determined by more than one *gene*.

Polygyny: in zoology, the tendency for a male to have regular sexual access to two or more females.

Polymorphism: the appearance of a gene in more than one form among individuals of a *population*.

Pondaungia: late Eocene fossil from Burma; possibly an anthropoid.

Population: usually a local or breeding group; a group in which any two individuals have the potential of mating with each other.

Positive feedback: a process in which a positive change in one component of a system brings about changes in other components, which in turn bring about further positive changes in the first component.

Postcranial: referring to any anatomical feature that is behind the head (in quadrupeds) or below the head (in bipeds).

Postorbital bar: a bar of bone running around the outside margin of the orbits of prosimians.

Potassium-argon dating: *chronometric dating* in which age is determined by measurement of the decay of radioactive potassium 40.

Power grip: a grip involving all fingers of the hand equally, as in grasping a baseball. (Compare with *precision grip*.)

Precision grip: a grip that involves opposing the tip of the thumb to the tips of the other fingers, allowing fine control of small objects. (Compare with *power grip*.)

Prehensile: adapted for grasping.

Primates: an *order* of placental mammals, mostly arboreal, with two suborders: the *anthropoids* and the *prosimians*.

Proceptivity: the aspect of female sexuality reflected by inviting copulation.

Proconsul: an ape from East Africa that lived during the *Miocene* epoch.

Prognathic: having the lower face and jaws projecting in front of the upper parts of the face.

Promiscuous: both females and males having access to multiple sexual partners.

Propliopithecus: an *Oligocene* fossil from Egypt believed to be a basal *catarrhine*.

Prosimians: the "premonkeys"; Old World arboreal mammals, including the small lemurs, lorises, and tarsiers. Less closely related to humans than other primates, some have survived with little change for nearly 50 million years.

Protein clock: a method for determining evolutionary relationships by using variations in the proteins of different living animal species to indicate the length of time since they diverged in their *evolution*. The method assumes a fairly constant rate of protein evolution, an assumption still open to some doubt.

Proteins: molecules composed of chains of *amino acids*.

Proteopithecus: a genus of late Eocene *anthropoids* from Africa.

Punctuated equilibrium: the hypothesis that most species have long periods of stasis, interrupted by episodes of rapid evolutionary change and speciation by branching. (Compare with *gradualism*.)

Quadrupedal: moving on four limbs.

Races: among humans, an essentially arbitrary concept based on perceived physical or behavioral differences. As a biological concept, race is no longer used by most physical anthropologists.

Racism: the assumption of inherent superiority of certain "races," and the consequent discrimination against others.

Ramapithecus: a fossil ape now subsumed within the genus *Sivapithecus;* thought to be an ancestor of the orangutan.

Rapid-replacement hypothesis: a theoretical model for the evolution of anatomically modern humans which proposes that the existing populations all evolved from a single ancestral population that probably appeared in Africa or the Middle East perhaps 150,000 to 100,000 years ago. (Compare with *regional-continuity hypothesis.*)

Receptivity: the aspect of female sexuality reflected by cooperating in copulation.

Recessive: describes a trait that is expressed only when the organism is carrying two copies of the underlying hereditary material (two copies of the responsible gene).

Reciprocal altruism: trading of apparently altruistic acts by different individuals at different times; a variety of *bioaltruism.*

Reconciliation: the act of restoring friendly relations.

Rectus femoris: one of the muscles that flexes the hominid thigh.

Red blood cells (corpuscles): vertebrate blood cells without nuclei and containing *hemoglobin.*

Red ocher: powdered mineral and earth mixture used as a pigment.

Regional-continuity hypothesis: a theoretical model of the evolution of anatomically modern humans which proposes that the existing *populations* evolved from ancestral populations of *Homo erectus* age that already existed in the various geographic areas of their range. (Compare with *rapid-replacement hypothesis.*)

Relative dating: estimating the age of geologic deposits (and the fossils in them) by determining their stratigraphic level in relation to that of other deposits whose relative or absolute age is known. (Compare with *absolute dating.*)

Replication: the capacity of *DNA* to generate copies of itself in the nucleus of a cell.

Reproductive success: the production of viable offspring that reproduce in turn; levels of reproductive success may differ between individuals.

Retromolar gap: a space posterior to the lower M3s; characteristic of *Neandertals.*

Rhinarium: the moist, hairless nose characteristic of all prosimians except tarsiers, and of most non-primate mammals.

Ribonucleic acid: see *RNA.*

Ribosomes: cellular organelles that contribute to protein synthesis.

Rickets: a pathological condition involving curvature of the bones; caused by insufficient vitamin D.

RNA (ribonucleic acid): a compound found with *DNA* in cell nuclei and chemically close to DNA; transmits *genetic code* from DNA to direct the formation of proteins. May take two forms: messenger RNA (mRNA) or transfer RNA (tRNA).

Sacrum: the part of the vertebral column that articulates with the pelvis and forms the dorsal portion of the pelvic girdle.

Sagittal crest: a ridge of bone running front to rear along the midline of the skull; serves to attach certain jaw muscles. (Compare *sagittal keel.*)

Sagittal keel: a slightly raised ridge running down the midline of a skull; smaller than a *sagittal crest.*

Sagittal suture: the line of union joining the two main side bones of the braincase.

Sangoan: Middle Paleolithic tool industry from south of the Sahara and dating about 45,000 to 35,000 years B.P.; associated with archaic *Homo sapiens.*

Satellite DNA: tandem repetitions of DNA sequences that accumulate at certain locations on chromosomes and are usually noncoding.

Savanna: tropical or subtropical grassland, often with scattered trees (woodland savanna).

Sciatic notch: a deep indentation of the *dorsal* edge of the hominid *ilium.*

Scraper: a stone or bone tool for preparing hides and leather, used to scrape the fat and other tissues from the inner surface of the skin.

Secondary altriciality: the phenomenon of an infant's motor skills requiring a lengthy period of postnatal development, as opposed to its sensory systems, which are functional at birth or soon after; characteristic of *H. erectus* and *H. sapiens*. See *altricial*.

Secondary sites: archaeological sites in which the artifacts have been disturbed by natural forces and then redeposited.

Sectorial: literally, "cutting"; refers to the first lower premolar of apes and some monkeys, which acts as a cutting edge in moving against the upper canine.

Sedentism: a way of life marked by the lack of migratory movements and by the establishment of permanent habitations.

Selection: see *natural selection*.

Selective pressure: the influence exerted by the environment that promotes the maintenance of traits that facilitate survival in that environment and eliminates other, nonadaptive traits (see also *natural selection*).

Semicircular canals: fluid-filled canals of the inner ear that control balance and coordination.

Serum (plasma): a clear liquid component of blood that carries the *red blood cells, white blood cells,* and *platelets*.

Sex chromosomes: those chromosomes that carry genes that control gender (maleness or femaleness).

Sex-linked trait: an inherited trait coded on the sex *chromosomes*, and thus having a special distribution related to sex.

Sex swellings: hormone-induced swellings on the hindquarters of certain primate females; generally correlated with ovulation.

Sexual dimorphism: characteristic anatomical (and behavioral) differences between the males and females of a *species*.

Sexual selection: a category including intrasexual competition for mates (usually aggressive and among males) and intersexual mate selection (usually of males by females).

Siamang: a large-bodied gibbon of Asia; formerly placed in its own genus, *Symphalangus*, it is now classified as a species of *Hylobates*.

Sickle-cell anemia: a genetically caused disease that can be fatal, in which the *red blood corpuscles* carry insufficient oxygen.

Sinanthropus pekinensis: the original name given by Davidson Black to ancient fossils from Zhoukoudian, near Beijing. These fossils are now classified as *Homo erectus*.

Sister groups: in *cladistics*, the groups resulting from a dichotomous evolutionary branching event; initially ranked as sister species, these groups may change rank because of subsequent branching, but must always maintain the same taxonomic level.

Sivapithecus: a genus of Miocene apes that includes *Ramapithecus* and was probably ancestral to orangutans.

Sociobiology: science of the biological (especially, genetic) basis of social behavior.

Socioecology: the connection between species' ecological relations and their social behavior; also the study of this connection.

Solutrean: an *Upper Paleolithic* culture existing in western Europe between 21,000 and 16,500 years B.P. Best known for its laurel-leaf blades.

Speciation: the gradual separation of interbreeding *populations* into two or more groups that do not interbreed.

Species: a group of *populations* of organisms that are enough alike in structure and behavior so that individuals can interbreed and produce fertile offspring if they have access to one another. Individuals from one species are reproductively isolated from other species.

Speech: the oral expression of language, or "spoken language" (other expressions include gestural or written language).

Spheroids: spherical stone tools probably used as hammers or missiles or to pound food.

Splicing: the action of messenger *RNA* that removes *intron* information, leaving only information from *exons*.

Stabilizing natural selection: *natural selection* that operates during periods when the environment is stable and maintains the genetic and phenotypic status quo within a *population*.

Stasis: a period of evolutionary equilibrium or inactivity.

Stereoscopic vision: vision produced by two eyes with overlapping fields, giving a sense of depth and distance; most highly evolved in hunting animals and primates.

Stone Age: the earliest period in cultural evolution, from more than 2 million to 5,000 years ago. Recognizable periods are the Paleolithic, or Old Stone Age; the Mesolithic, or Middle Stone Age; and the Neolithic, or New Stone Age (see also *Lower Paleolithic, Middle Paleolithic,* and *Upper Paleolithic*).

Stone knapping: stone flaking; generally, the production of flake and core tools by striking a stone module with a hammer stone or other object.

Strategy: in the special zoological sense, a complex of *adaptations* that brings about an effective and efficient means of reproduction or resource use (e.g., a species' reproductive strategy or feeding strategy). No conscious choice is implied.

Stratigraphy: the sequence of geologic strata, or rock layers, formed by materials deposited by water or wind; also, the study of this sequence.

Suprainiac fossa: a characteristic depression in the occipital bone of Neandertals.

Sympathetic hunting magic: the use of rituals (and associated artifacts) to ensure success and safety in the hunt.

Syntax: the rules of structure in language.

Szalatavus: *Oligocene platyrrhine* monkey from Bolivia.

Taiga: northern coniferous forest bordering the *tundra.*

Taphonomy: the scientific study of the conditions under which objects are preserved as fossils.

Tarsier: a small Asian *prosimian* with large eyes and a long tail.

Taxonomy: classification of plants or animals into groups according to their relationships, and the ordering of these groups into hierarchies.

Taxonomic levels are ranks within these classifications, e.g., *species* or *genus.*

Terrestrial: adapted to living on the ground.

Territoriality: an animal's distinctive behavior toward and tendency to defend a recognizable area of land.

Territory: the area occupied and defended by individuals or groups of animals against conspecifies. (Compare with *home range.*)

Thermoluminescence: light produced by heating a substance (such as pottery) to release trapped electrons. The density of electrons trapped since the substance was last heated (proportional to the light emitted) can be used to date the substance.

Theropithecus oswaldi: an extinct species of gelada baboon.

Thorax: the region of the rib cage.

Tool kit: all the tools or implements used by a primitive culture; its technology. *Neandertals* had 60 or 70 kinds of known tools; *Cro-Magnons* had more than 100.

Toothcomb: a dental specialization of *prosimians* in which the lower front teeth are closely spaced and forwardly inclined.

Triangulation: in the context of anthropology, the process of interpreting the behavior of extinct hominids by using both apes and modern humans as analogue models.

True breeding (breeding true): situation in which the members of a genetic strain resemble each other in all important characters and show little variability.

Tufa: tuff; a rocklike substance formed from volcanic ash.

Tundra: treeless, low-vegetation arctic or subarctic plain, swampy in summer, with permanently frozen soil just beneath the surface.

Turnover pulse: the hypothesis that organisms periodically experience spurts of speciation, extinction, and dispersion in response to relatively rapid changes in the physical environment.

Type specimen: the fossil specimen that serves as the basis for identifying all other individuals in a species, usually the original specimen to be found.

Unearned resources: resources that are outside a predator's range, but to which it nonetheless gains secondary access by consuming prey animals with larger ranges.

Uniformitarianism: Charles Lyell's theory that the forces now affecting the earth—water and wind erosion, frost, volcanism—acted in a similar way in the past, and that change is always gradual and nondirectional.

Upper Paleolithic: a period of stone tool manufacture in the Old World that lasted from about 40,000 to 10,000 years B.P.; associated primarily with anatomically modern humans.

Veld (or veldt): South Africa's open savanna grassland, which has few bushes or trees.

Ventral: pertaining to the belly side of an animal or one of its parts; the opposite of *dorsal*.

Vertebrata: a subphylum of the chordates containing all animals with backbones; comprising fishes, amphibians, reptiles, birds, and mammals.

Victoriapithecinae: extinct subfamily of the earliest catarrhine monkeys.

Weir: barrier or dam made of stones or sticks set out in a stream or river and used as a fish trap.

Wernicke's area: part of the human *cerebral cortex* essential in comprehending and producing meaningful speech.

White blood cells (leukocytes): blood cells of vertebrates containing no hemoglobin.

Wide-knee stance: standing with the feet and knees about as far apart as the hip joints.

Xenophobia: hatred of foreigners.

Y-5 pattern: an arrangement of the cusps and grooves of the lower molars that is characteristic of living hominoids.

Zinjanthropus boisei: original name of the australopithecine species now called *Paranthropus boisei*.

Selected Bibliography

PART I EVOLUTION

General References for Further Reading

Campbell, Bernard. *Human Evolution*, 3rd ed. Aldine, 1985.

Ciochon, R. L., and J. Fleagle, eds. *The Human Evolution Source Book*. Prentice Hall, 1993.

Dobzhansky, Theodosius. *Mankind Evolving*. Yale University Press, 1962.

——. *Genetics and the Origin of Species*. Columbia University Press, 1969.

——, Francisco J. Ayala, G. Ledyard Stebbins, and James W. Valentine. *Evolution*. W. H. Freeman, 1977.

Ebert, James D., et al. *Science and Creationism: A View from the National Academy of Sciences*. National Academy Press, 1984.

Gould, Stephen J. *Times's Arrow, Time's Cycle*. Harvard University Press, 1987.

Grant, Verne. *The Evolutionary Process*. Columbia University Press, 1985.

Jones, S., R. Martin, and D. Pilbeam, eds. *The Cambridge Encyclopedia of Human Evolution*. Cambridge University Press, 1992.

Le Gros Clark, Wilfrid E. *The Antecedents of Man*, 3rd ed. Quadrangle Books, 1971.

Mayr, Ernst. *Population: Species and Evolution*. Harvard University Press, 1970.

Sources

Aitken, M. J. *Science-based Dating in Archaeology*. Longmans, 1990.

Ayala, Francisco J. "The Mechanisms of Evolution." *Scientific American*, 234, no. 3, 1978.

Brothwell Don, and Eric Higgs, eds. *Science in Archeology*, 2nd ed. Praeger, 1970.

Burckhardt F., and S. Smith. *The Correspondence of Charles Darwin*. Cambridge University Press, 1988.

Darwin, Charles. *The Descent of Man and Selection in Relation to Sex*. John Murray, 1871.

——. *On the Origin of Species* (facsimile of 1st ed.). Harvard University Press, 1966.

——, and Alfred R. Wallace. *Evolution by Natural Selection*. Cambridge University Press, 1958.

Darwin, Francis, ed. *The Life and Letters of Charles Darwin*, 2 vols. Basic Books, 1959.

——, and A. C. Seward, eds. *More Letters of Charles Darwin*, 2 vols. John Murray, 1903.

De Vries, Hugo. *Species and Varieties*. Open Court, 1905.

——. *The Mutation Theory*, 2 vols. Open Court, 1909–1910.

Eiseley, Loren. *Darwin's Century: Evolution and the Men Who Discovered It*. Doubleday, 1958.

Fisher, Sir Ronald Aylmer. *The Genetical Theory of Natural Selection*. Clarendon Press, 1930.

Grant, V. *The Evolutionary Process*, 2nd ed. Columbia University Press, 1991.

Grayson, D. K. "Differential Mortality and the Donner Party Disaster." *Evolutionary Anthropology*, 2, 1993.

Haldane, J. B. S. *The Causes of Evolution*. Longmans, Green, 1932.

Huxley, Julian. *Evolution—The Modern Synthesis*. Allen & Unwin, 1942.

Huxley, Thomas Henry. *Man's Place in Nature*. University of Michigan Press, 1959.

Maynard Smith, J. "Bacteria Break the Antibiotic Bank." *Natural History*, 103, 1994.

Mayr, E. *The Growth of Biological Thought: Diversity, Evolution, and Inheritance*. Harvard University Press, 1982.

——. *One Long Argument*. Harvard University Press, 1991.

Morgan, Thomas Hunt. *Evolution and Adaptation*. Macmillan, 1903.

——. *The Physical Basis of Heredity*. Lippincott, 1919.

——. *The Mechanism of Mendelian Heredity*. Constable, 1915.

Muller, Hermann J. *Genetics, Medicine and Men*. Cornell University Press, Oxford University Press, 1947.

Numbers, R. L. *The Creationists*. Knopf, 1992.

Prescott, D. M. *Cells*. Jones & Bartlett, 1988.

Raup, D. M. *Extinction: Bad Genes or Bad Luck?* W. W. Norton, 1991.

Simpson, George Gaylord. *The Meaning of Evolution.* Oxford University Press, 1950.

———. *The Major Features of Evolution.* Simon & Schuster, 1953.

Singer, M., and P. Berg. *Genes and Genomes.* University Science Books, 1991.

Wallace, Alfred Russel. *My Life: A Record of Events and Opinions,* 2 vols. Chapman & Hall, 1905.

Woodward, V. *Human Heredity and Society.* West, 1992.

PART II THE ORIGIN OF HUMANKIND

General References for Further Reading

Ciochon, R., and J. Fleagle. *Primate Evolution and Human Origins.* Benjamin/Cummings, 1986.

——— (eds.). *The Human Evolution Source Book.* Prentice Hall, 1993.

Conroy, G. C. *Primate Evolution.* W. W. Norton, 1990.

Day, Michael H. *Guide to Fossil Man,* 4th ed. Cassell, 1986.

Delson, Eric, ed. *Ancestors: The Hard Evidence.* Alan R. Liss, 1985.

Fleagle, J. *Primate Adaptation and Evolution.* Academic Press, 1988.

Fobes, James, and James King, eds. *Primate Behavior.* Academic Press, 1982.

Fossey, Dian. *Gorillas in the Mist.* Houghton Mifflin, 1983.

Goodall, Jane. *The Chimpanzees of Gombe.* Harvard University Press, 1986.

Hamburg, David A., and Elizabeth R. McCown. *The Great Apes.* Benjamin/Cummings, 1979.

Jones, S., R. Martin, and D. Pilbeam, eds. *The Cambridge Encyclopedia of Human Evolution.* Cambridge University Press, 1992.

Kinzey, W. G., ed. *The Evolution of Human Behavior: Primate Models.* State University of New York Press, 1987.

Le Gros Clark, W. E. *The Antecedents of Man.* Edinburgh University Press, 1959.

———. *Man-Apes or Ape-Man?* Holt, Rinehart & Winston, 1967.

———, and Bernard G. Campbell, *The Fossil Evidence for Human Evolution.* University of Chicago Press, 1978.

Napier, J. R., and P. H. Napier. *The Natural History of the Primates.* British Museum (Natural History) and Cambridge University Press, 1985.

Szalay, Frederic S., and Eric Delson. *Evolutionary History of the Primates.* Academic Press, 1979.

Waal, Frans de. *Chimpanzee Politics: Power and Sex Among Apes.* Harper & Row, 1982.

Wraugham, R. W., W. C. McGrew, F. B. M. deWaal, and P. G. Heltme, eds. *Chimpanzee Cultures.* Harvard University Press, 1994.

Sources

Aiello, L., and C. Dean *An Introduction to Human Evolutionary Anatomy.* Academic Press, 1990.

Bailey, W. J. "Hominoid Trichotomy: A Molecular Overview." *Evolutionary Anthropology,* 2, 1993.

Bartlett, T., R. Sussman, and J. Cheverud. "Infant Killing in Primates: A Review of Observed Cases with Specific Reference to the Sexual Selection Hypothesis." *American Anthropologist,* 95, 1993.

Beard, K. C., Tao Qi, M. R. Dawson, Banyue Wang, and Chuankuei Li. "A Diverse New Primate Fauna from Middle Eocene Fissure-Fillings in Southeastern China." *Nature,* 368, 1994.

Begley, S. "Out of Africa, A Missing Link." *Newsweek,* October 3, 1994.

Boesch-Achermann, H., and C. Boesch. "Hominization in the Rainforest: The Chimpanzee's Piece of the Puzzle." *Evolutionary Anthropology,* 3, 1994.

Broom, Robert. *Finding the Missing Link.* Watts, 1950.

Brown, B., A. Walker, C. V. Ward, and R. E. Leakey. "New *Australopithecus boisei* Calvaria from East Lake Turkana, Kenya." *American Journal of Physical Anthropology,* 91, 1993.

Butzer, Karl W. *Environment and Archeology: An Ecological Approach to Prehistory.* Aldine-Atherton, 1971.

Cartmill, M. "Rethinking Primate Origins." *Science,* 184, 1974.

Cheney, D. L. "Interactions and Relationships Between Groups," in B. Smuts et al., eds., *Primate Societies.* University of Chicago Press, 1987.

Cheney, D. L., and R. M. Seyfarth. *How Monkeys See the World.* University of Chicago Press, 1990.

Chivers, David L., Bernard A. Wood, and Alan Bilsborough, eds. *Food Acquisition and Processing in Primates.* Plenum Press, 1984.

Ciochon, Russell L., and Robert S. Corrucini. *New Interpretations of Ape and Human Ancestry.* Plenum Press, 1983.

Clark, J. Desmond. *The Prehistory of Africa.* Praeger, 1970.

Coffing, K., C. Feibel, M. Leakey, and A. Walker. "Four-Million-Year-Old Hominids from East Lake Turkana, Kenya." *American Journal of Physical Anthropology,* 93, 1994.

Conroy, G. C., M. Pickford, B. Senut, and P. Mein. "Diamonds in the Desert: The Discovery of *Otavipithecus namibiensis.*" *Evolutionary Anthropology,* 2, 1993.

Coppens, Y., F. Clark Howell, G. L. Isaac, and Richard E. F. Leakey, eds. *Earliest Man and Environments in the Lake Rudolf Basin.* University of Chicago Press, 1976.

Coppens, Y. "East Side Story: The Origin of Humankind." *Scientific American,* 270, 1994.

Dart, Raymond. *Adventures with the Missing Link.* Viking Press, 1959.

Dalh, J. F. "Cyclic Perineal Swelling During the Intermenstrual Intervals of Captive Female Pygmy Chimpanzees (*Pan paniscus*)." *Journal of Human Evolution*, 15, 1986.

Dunbar, R. I. M. "The Price of Being at the Top." *Nature*, 373, 1995.

Falk, D. *Braindance*. Henry Holt, 1992.

Fischman, J. "Putting a New Spin on the Birth of Human Birth." *Science*, 264, 1994.

Fleagle, J. G., D. T. Rasmussen, S. Yirga, T. M. Bown, and F. E. Grine "New Hominid Fossils from Fejej, Southern Ethiopia." *Journal of Human Evolution*, 21, 1991.

Furuichi, T. "The Prolonged Estrus of Females and Factors Influencing Mating in a Wild Group of Bonobos (*Pan paniscus*) in Wamba, Zaire," in N. Itoigawa et al., eds., *Topics in Primatology, vol. 2: Behavior, Ecology, and Conservation*. University of Tokyo Press, 1992.

Gabunia, L., and A. Vekua. "A Plio-Pleistocene Hominid from Dmanisi, East Georgia, Caucasus." *Nature*, 373, 1995.

Giacobini, G. *Hominidae: Proceedings of the Second International Congress of Human Paleontology, Turin, September–October 1987*. Jaca Book, 1989.

Greenfield, L. O. "Origin of the Human Canine: A New Solution to an Old Enigma." *Yearbook of Physical Anthropology*, 35, 1992.

Grine, F. E. "Australopithecine Taxonomy and Phylogeny: Historical Background and Recent Interpretation," in R. L. Ciochon and J. G. Fleagle, eds., *The Human Evolution Source Book*. Prentice Hall, 1993.

———, B. Demes, W. L. Jungers, and T. M. Cole, III. "Taxonomic Affinity of the Early *Homo* Cranium from Swartkrans, South Africa." *American Journal of Physical Anthropology*, 92, 1993.

Harris, Jack W. K. "Cultural Beginnings; Plio-Pleistocene Archaeological Occurrences from the Afar, Ethiopia." *African Archaeological Review*, 1, 1983.

Hartwig-Scherer, S. "Body Weight Prediction in Early Fossil Hominids: Towards a Taxon-Independent Approach." *American Journal of Physical Anthropology*, 92, 1993.

Hausfater, G. *Dominance and Reproduction in Baboons (Papio cynocephalus)*. S. Karger, 1975.

———, and Sarah Blaffer-Hrdy, eds. *Infanticide: Comparative and Evolutionary Perspectives*. Aldine, 1984.

Hawkes, N. "'Missing Link' Ate Fruit and Leaves." *The Times (London)*, September 22, 1994.

Heltne P. G., and L. A. Marquandt. *Understanding Chimpanzees*. Harvard University Press, 1989.

———, and B. Brown. "Anatomy and Age of the Lothagam Mandible." *Journal of Human Evolution*, 22, 1992.

Hill, Andrew, and S. Ward. "Origin of the Hominidae: The Record of African Large Hominoid Evolution Between 14 My and 4 My." *Yearbook of Physical Anthropology*, 31, 1988.

Hohmann, G., and B. Fruth. "Field Observations on Meat Sharing Among Bonobos (*Pan paniscus*)." *Folia Primatologica*, 60, 1993.

Howells, W. *Getting Here*. Compass Press, 1993.

Hrdy, Sarah B. *The Langurs of Abu: Female and Male Strategies of Reproduction*. Harvard University Press, 1977.

Huffman, M. A., and R. Wrangham. "Diversity of Medicinal Plant Use by Chimpanzees in the Wild," in R. Wrangham et al., eds., *Chimpanzee Cultures*. Harvard University Press 1994.

Isaac, G. L., and Elizabeth R. McCrown, eds. *Human Origins*. Staples Press, 1976.

Jablonski, N. G., and G. Chaplin. "The Origin of Hominid Bipedalism Re-examined." *Perspectives in Human Biology, 2/Archaeology in Oceania*, 27, 1992.

Johanson, Donald C., and Maitland A. Edey. *Lucy: The Beginnings of Humankind*. Simon & Schuster, 1981.

———, and Tim D. White. "A Systematic Assessment of Early African Hominids." *Science*, 203, 1979.

Jolly, Clifford. "The Seed-Eaters." *Man*, 5, no. 1, March 1970.

Kay, R. F., J. G. M. Thewissen, and A. D. Yoder "Cranial Anatomy of *Ignacius graybullianus* and the Affinities of the Plesiadapiformes." *American Journal of Physical Anthropology*, 89, 1992.

———. "Evolution of Human Walking." *Scientific American*, 259, 1988.

Kummer, Hans. *Social Organization of Hamadryas Baboons*. University of Chicago Press, 1968.

Lancaster, Jane B., and C. S. Lancaster. "Parental Investment: The Hominid Adaptation," in D. J. Ortner, ed., *How Humans Adapt: A Biocultural Odyssey*. Smithsonian Institute Press, 1983.

Leakey, Mary D. *Olduvai Gorge*, vol. 3. Cambridge University Press, 1971.

Leakey, M. G., C. S. Feibel, I. McDougall, and A. Walker. "New Four-Million-Year-Old Hominid Species from Kanapoi and Allia Bay, Kenya." *Nature*, 376, 1995.

Lovejoy, C. Owen. "Evolution of Human Walking." *Scientific American*, 259, 1988.

———. "Modeling Human Origins: Are We Sexy Because We're Smart, or Smart Because We're Sexy?" in D. T. Rasmussen, ed., *The Origin and Evolution of Humans and Humanness*. Jones & Bartlett, 1993.

———. "The Origin of Man." *Science*, 211, no. 4480, 1981.

Martin, R. D. *Primate Origins and Evolution: A Phylogenetic Reconstruction*. Chapman & Hall, 1990.

———. "Primate Origins: Plugging the Gaps." *Nature*, 363, 1993.

McGrew, W. C. *Chimpanzee Material Culture*. Cambridge University Press, 1992.

McHenry, H. M. "How Big Were Early Hominids?" *Evolutionary Anthropology*, 1, 1992.

———. "Behavioral Ecological Implications of Early Hominid Body Size." *Journal of Human Evolution*, 27, 1994.

McKee, J. K. "Faunal Dating of the Taung Hominid Fossil Deposit." *Journal of Human Evolution*, 25, 1993.

Melnick, D. J., and M. C. Pearl. "Cercopithecines in Multimale Groups: Genetic Diversity and Population Structure," in B. Smuts et al., eds., *Primate Societies*. University of Chicago Press, 1987.

Napier, John, and P. H. Napier. *Handbook of Living Primates*. Academic Press, 1967.

Nishida, T. *Chimpanzees of the Mahale Mountains*. University of Tokyo Press, 1990.

Nishida, T., and M. Hiraiwa-Hasegawa. "Chimpanzees and Bonobos: Cooperative Relationships Among Males," in B. Smuts et al., eds., *Primate Societies*. University of Chicago Press, 1987.

Oakley, Kenneth, Bernard G. Campbell, and Theya I. Mollison, eds. *Catalogue of Fossil Hominids—Part I*, 2nd ed. Trustees of the British Museum (Natural History), 1977.

Packer, C., D. A. Collins, A. Sindimwo, and J. Goodall. "Reproductive Constraints on Aggressive Competition in Female Baboons." *Nature*, 373, 1995.

Parish, A. R. "Sex and Food Control in the 'Uncommon Chimpanzee': How Bonobo Females Overcame a Phylogenetic Legacy of Male Dominance." *Etiology and Sociobiology*, 15, 1994.

Potts, R. "Archeological Interpretations of Early Hominid Behavior and Ecology," in D. T. Rasmussen, ed., *The Origin and Evolution of Humans and Humanness*. Jones & Bartlett, 1993.

———. *Early Hominid Activities at Olduvai*. Aldine de Gruyter, 1988.

Rasmussen, D. T., and E. L. Simons. "Paleobiology of the Oligopithecines, the Earliest Known Anthropoid Primates." *International Journal of Primatology*, 13, 1992.

Rightmire, G. P. "Variation Among Early *Homo* Crania from Olduvai Gorge and the Koobi Fora Region." *American Journal of Physical Anthropology*, 90, 1993.

Roberts, N. "Climatic Change in the Past," in S. Jones et al., eds., *The Cambridge Encyclopedia of Human Evolution*. Cambridge University Press, 1992.

Rodman, P. S., and J. C. Mitani. "Orangutans: Sexual Dimorphism in a Solitary Species," in B. Smuts et al., eds., *Primate Societies*. University of Chicago Press, 1987.

Schaller, George B. *Year of the Gorilla*. University of Chicago Press, 1964.

———, and Gordon Lowther. "The Relevance of Carnivore Behavior to the Study of Early Hominids." *Southwestern Journal of Anthropology*, 25, no. 4 (University of New Mexico Press).

Schick, K. D., and N. Toth. *Making Silent Stones Speak*. Simon & Schuster, 1993.

Schrenk, F., T. G. Bromage, C. G. Betzler, U. Ring, and Y. M. Juwayeyi. "Oldest *Homo* and Pliocene Biogeography of the Malawi Rift." *Nature*, 365, 1993.

Senut, B. "New Ideas on the Origins of Hominid Locomotion," in T. Nishida, W. McGrew, P. Marler, M. Pickford, and F. de Waal, eds., *Topics in Primatology: Vol. 1. Human Origins*. University of Tokyo Press, 1992.

Simons, E. "Egypt's Simian Spring." *Natural History*, 102, 1993.

Shipman, Pat. "Scavenging or Hunting in Early Hominids: Theoretical Framework and Tests." *American Anthropologist*, 88, 1986.

Skelton, R. R., and H. M. McHenry. "Evolutionary Relationships Among Early Hominids." *Journal of Human Evolution*, 23, 1992.

Small, M. F. *Female Choices*. Cornell University Press, 1993.

Smuts, B. et al., eds. *Primate Societies*. University of Chicago Press, 1987.

Spoor, F., B. Wood, and F. Zonneveld. "Implications of Early Hominid Labyrinthine Morphology for Evolution of Human Bipedal Locomotion." *Nature*, 369, 1994.

Stewart, I. "Real Australopithecines Do Eat Meat." *New Scientist*, 134, 1992.

Stewart, K. I., and A. H. Harcourt. "Gorillas: Variation in Female Relationships," in B. Smuts et al., eds., *Primate Societies*. University of Chicago Press, 1987.

Strum, Shirley C. *Almost Human: A Journey into the World of Baboons*. Elm Tree Books, 1987.

Susman, R. L., ed. *The Pygmy Chimpanzee: Evolutionary Biology and Behavior*. Plenum Press, 1984.

———. "Fossil Evidence for Early Hominid Tool Use." *Science*, 265, 1994.

Sussman, R. W. "Primate Origins and the Evolution of Angiosperms." *American Journal of Primatology*, 23, 1991.

Szalay, Frederic S., and Eric Delson. *Evolutionary History of the Primates*. Academic Press, 1979.

Tanner, Nancy M. *On Becoming Human*. Cambridge University Press, 1981.

Tobias, P. V. *Hominid Evolution*. Alan R. Liss, 1985.

———. *The Brain in Hominid Evolution*. Columbia University Press, 1971.

———. "The Brain of *Homo habilis*: A New Level of Organization in Cerebral Evolution." *Journal of Human Evolution*, 16, 1987.

Trevathan, W. *Human Birth: An Evolutionary Perspective*. Aldine de Gruyter, 1987.

————. "Fetal Emergence Patterns in Evolutionary Perspective." *American Anthropologist,* 90, 1988

Turner, A., and B. Wood. "Comparative Palaeontological Context for the Evolution of the Early Hominid Masticatory System." *Journal of Human Evolution,* 24, 1993.

Tuttle, Russell, ed. *The Functional and Evolutionary Biology of Primates.* Aldine-Atherton, 1972.

Vrba, E. S. "Ecological and Adaptive Changes Associated with Early Hominid Evolution" in R. L. Ciochon and J. G. Fleagle, eds., *The Human Evolution Source Book.* Prentice Hall, 1993.

————. "The Pulse That Produced Us." *Natural History,* 102, 1993.

Waal, F. de. *Peacemaking Among Primates.* Harvard University Press, 1989.

Walker, Alan, Richard E. Leakey, John M. Harris, and Frank H. Brown. "2.5 myr *Australopithecus boisei* from West of Lake Turkana, Kenya." *Nature,* 322, 1986.

Ward, C. V., A. Walker, M. F. Teaford, and I. Odhiambo. "Partial Skeleton of *Proconsul nyanzae* from Mfangano Island, Kenya." *American Journal of Physical Anthropology,* 90, 1993.

Wheeler, P. "The Influence of Bipedalism on the Energy and Water Budgets of Early Hominids." *Journal of Human Evolution,* 21, 1991.

————. "The Thermoregulatory Advantages of Hominid Bipedalism in Open Equatorial Environments: The Contribution of Increased Convective Heat Loss and Cutaneous Evaporative Cooling." *Journal of Human Evolution,* 21, 1991.

————. "Human Ancestors Walked Tall, Stayed Cool." *Natural History,* 102, 1993.

White, F. J. "Activity Budgets, Feeding Behavior, and Habitat Use of Pygmy Chimpanzees at Lomako, Zaire." *American Journal of Primatology,* 26, 1992.

White, T. D., G. Suwa, and B. Asfaw. "*Australopithecus ramidus,* A New Species of Early Hominid from Aramis, Ethiopia." *Nature,* 371, 1994 (also 375, 1995).

————, G. Suwa, W. K. Hart, R. C. Walter, G. WoldeGabriel, J. de Heinzelin, J. D. Clark, B. Asfaw, and E. Vrba. "New Discoveries of *Australopithecus* at Maka in Ethiopia." *Nature,* 366, 1993.

————, Donald C. Johanson, and William H. Kimbel. "*Australopithecus africanus:* Its Phyletic Position Reconsidered." *South African Journal of Science,* 77, 1981.

Wilford, J. N. "New Fossils Take Science Close to Dawn of Humans." *The New York Times,* September 22, 1994.

WoldeGabriel, G., T. D. White, G. Suwa, P. Renne, J. de Heinzelin, W. K. Hart, and G. Helken. "Ecological and Temporal Placement of Early Pliocene Hominids at Aramis, Ethiopia." *Nature,* 371, 1994.

Wood, B. "Origin and Evolution of the Genus *Homo.*" *Nature,* 355, 1992.

————. "The Oldest Hominid Yet." *Nature,* 371, 1994.

PART III THE EVOLUTION OF HUMANKIND

General References for Further Reading

Flint, Richard Foster. *Glacial and Quaternary Geology.* Wiley, 1971.

Howells, William E. "*Homo erectus*—Who, When and Where: A Survey." *Yearbook of Physical Anthropology,* 23, 1980.

Le Gros Clark, Wilfrid E., and Bernard G. Campbell. *The Fossil Evidence for Human Evolution.* University of Chicago Press, 1978.

Savage-Rumbaugh, S., and R. Lewin. *Kanzi: The Ape at the Brink of the Human Mind.* Wiley, 1994.

Sources

Aiello, L., and C. Dean. *An Introduction to Human Evolutionary Anatomy.* Academic Press, 1990.

Begun, D., and A. Walker. "The Endocast," in A. Walker and R. Leakey, eds., *The Nariokotome Homo erectus Skeleton.* Harvard University Press, 1993.

Bellomo, R. V. "Methods of Determining Early Hominid Behavioral Activities Associated with the Controlled Use of Fire at FxJj 20 Main, Koobi Fora, Kenya." *Journal of Human Evolution,* 27, 1994.

Binford, Lewis K. *Bones: Ancient men and Modern Myths.* Academic Press, 1981.

————. *Faunal Remains from Klasies River Mouth.* Academic Press, 1984.

————, and C. K. Ho. "Taphonomy at a Distance. Zhoukoudian, 'The Cave of Beijing Man'?" *Current Anthropology,* 26, 1985.

Binford, L. R., and N. M. Stone. "Zhoukoudian: A Closer Look." *Current Anthropology,* 27, 1986.

Brown, Frank, John Harris, Richard E. Leakey, and Alan Walker. "Early *Homo erectus* Skeleton from West Lake Turkana, Kenya." *Nature,* 316, 1985.

Butzer, Karl W. "Acheulian Occupation Sites at Torralba and Ambrona, Spain: Their Geology." *Science,* 150, no. 3704, 1965.

————, and G. L. Isaac, eds. *After the Australopithecines: Stratigraphy, Ecology, and Culture Change in the Middle Pleistocene.* Mouton, 1975.

Campbell, Bernard G., ed. *Sexual Selection and the Descent of Man, 1871–1971.* Aldine, 1972.

Cartmill, M. *A View to a Death in the Morning.* Harvard University Press, 1993.

Chang, Kwang-chih. *The Archaeology of Ancient China.* Yale University Press, 1968.

Cheney, D. L., and R. Seyfarth. *How Monkeys See the World.* University of Chicago Press, 1990.

Convey, Curt. "Earth's Orbit and the Ice Ages." *Scientific American,* 250, 1984.

de Lumley, Henry. "A Paleolithic Camp at Nice." *Scientific American,* 220, no. 5, 1969.

Duchin, Linda E. "The Evolution of Articulate Speech," *Journal of Human Evolution,* 19, 1990.

Falk, D. *Braindance*. Henry Holt, 1992.

Gardner, R. Allen, and Beatrice T. Gardner. "Teaching Sign Language to a Chimpanzee." *Science*, 165, no. 3894, 1969.

Geschwind, Norman. "The Neural Basis of Language," in K. Salzinger and S. Salzinger, eds., *Research in Verbal Behavior and Some Neurophysiological Implications*, Academic Press, 1967.

Gibson, K. R. "Continuity Theories of Human Language Origins Versus the Lieberman Model." *Language and Communication*, 14, 1994.

Gould, Stephen J. *The Mismeasure of Man*. Norton, 1981.

———. *Hen's Teeth and Horse's Toes: Further Reflections on Natural History*. Norton, 1983.

Gouzoules, H., S. Gouzoules, and P. Marler. "Vocal Communication: A Vehicle for the Study of Social Relationships," in R. Rawlins and M. Kessler, eds., *The Cayo Santiago Macaques*. State University of New York Press, 1986.

Greenfield, P. M. "Language, Tools and Brain: The Ontogeny and Phylogeny of Hierarchically Organized Sequential Behavior." *Behavioral and Brain Sciences*, 14, 1991.

Hockett, Charles F. "The Origin of Speech." *Scientific American*, 203, no. 3, 1960.

Holloway, Ralph L. "The Evolution of the Primate Brain: Some Aspects of Quantitative Relations." *Brain Research*, 7, 1968.

Hood, Dora. *Davidson Black: A Biography*. University of Toronto Press, 1971.

Howell, F. Clark. "Observations on the Earliest Phases of the European Lower Paleolithic." *American Anthropologist*, 68, no. 2, 1966.

Howells, W. *Getting Here*. Compass Press, 1993.

Isaac, Glynn L. "Studies of Early Culture in East Africa." *World Archaeology*, 1, no. 1, 1969.

———. "The Diet of Early Man: Aspects of Archaeological Evidence from Lower and Middle Pleistocene Sites in Africa." *World Archaeology*, 2, no. 3, 1971.

Jelinek, A. J. "The Lower Paleolithic: Current Evidence and Interpretations." *Annual Review of Anthropology*, 6, 1977.

Jerison, Harry J. *Evolution of the Brain and Intelligence*. Academic Press, 1973.

Jia, Lanpo, and Huang Weiwen. *The Story of Peking Man*. Oxford University Press, 1990.

Jones, S., R. Martin, and D. Pilbeam, eds. *The Cambridge Encyclopedia of Human Evolution*. Cambridge University Press, 1992.

Ju-kang, Woo. "The Skull of Lantian Man." *Current Anthropology*, 7, no. 1, 1966.

Klein, R. G. *The Human Career*. University of Chicago Press, 1989.

Kramer, A. "A Critical Analysis of Claims for the Existence of Southeast Asian Australopithecines." *Journal of Human Evolution*, 26, 1994.

Krantz, Grover S. "Brain Size and Hunting Ability in Earliest Man." *Current Anthropology*, 9, no. 5, 1966.

Kurtén, Björn. *Pleistocene Mammals of Europe*. Aldine, 1968.

Laitman, Jeffrey T., and Raymond C. Heimbuch. "The Basicranium of Plio-Pleistocene Hominids as an Indicator of Their Upper Respiratory Systems." *American Journal of Physical Anthropology*, 59, 1982.

Lancaster, Jane B. "Primate Communication Systems and the Emergence of Human Language," in Phyllis C. Jay, ed. *Primates: Studies in Adaptation and Variability*, Holt, Rinehart & Winston, 1968.

Lieberman, Philip. *On the Origins of Language*. Macmillan; 1975.

———, Edmund S. Crelin, and Dennis H. Klatt. "Phonetic Ability and Related Anatomy of the Newborn and Adult Human, Neanderthal Man, and the Chimpanzee." *American Anthropologist*, 74, no. 3, 1972.

MacLarnon, A. "The Vertebral Canal," in A. Walker and R. Leakey, eds., *The Nariokotome Homo erectus Skeleton*. Harvard University Press, 1993.

McHenry, H. "How Big Were Early Hominids?" *Evolutionary Anthropology*, 1, 1992.

Murrill, R. I. *Petralona Man*. Charles C. Thomas, 1981.

Myers, Ronald E. "Comparative Neurology of Vocalization and Speech," in S. L. Washburn and E. R. McCown, eds., *Human Evolution: Biosocial Perspectives*. Benjamin/Cummings, 1978.

Napier, John. "The Evolution of the Hand." *Scientific American*, 207, no. 6, 1962.

Oakley, Kenneth P. *Man the Tool-Maker*, 6th ed. Trustees of the British Museum (Natural History), 1972.

Passingham, Richard L. *The Human Primate*. Freeman, 1982.

Petersen, S. E., P. T. Fox, M. I. Posner, M. Mintun, and M. E. Raichle. "Positron Emission Tomographic Studies of the Cortical Anatomy of Single-word Processing." *Nature*, 331, 1988.

Pope, G. G. "Bamboo and Human Evolution." *Natural History*, 98, 1989.

———. "Ancient Asia's Cutting Edge." *Natural History*, 102, 1993.

Povinelli, D. J. "What Chimpanzees (Might) Know About the Mind," in R. Wraugham et al., eds., *Chimpanzee Cultures*. Harvard University Press, 1994.

Rightmire, G. P. *The Evolution of Homo erectus*. Cambridge University Press, 1990.

———. "*Homo erectus*: Ancestor of Evolutionary Side Branch." *Evolutionary Anthropology*, 1, 1992.

Savage-Rumbaugh, S. "Language Training of Apes," in S. Jones et al., eds., *The Cambridge Encyclopedia of Human*

Evolution. Cambridge University Press, 1992.

———, and R. Lewin. "Ape at the Brink." *Discover,* 15, 1994.

Schick, K., and N. Toth. *Making Silent Stones Speak.* Simon & Schuster, 1993.

Semenov, S. A. *Prehistoric Technology.* Cory, Adams & Mackay, 1964.

Seyfarth, Robert M., Dorothy L. Cheney, and Peter Marler. "Monkey Responses to Three Different Alarm Calls: Evidence of Predator Classification and Semantic Communication." *Science,* 210, 1980.

———. "Vervet Monkey Alarm Calls: Semantic Communication in a Free-Ranging Primate." *Animal Behavior,* 28, 1980.

Shapiro, Harry, L. *Peking Man.* Simon & Schuster, 1974.

Spencer, Frank. *Piltdown: A Scientific Forgery.* Natural History Museum, London and Oxford University Press, 1990.

Stringer, C., and C. Gamble. *In Search of the Neanderthals.* Thames & Hudson, 1993.

Swisher, C. C., G. H. Curtis, T. Jacob, A. G. Getty, A. Suprijo, Widiasmoro. "Age of the Earliest Known Hominids in Java, Indonesia." *Science,* 263, 1994.

Theunissen, B. *Eugene Dubois and the Ape-man from Java.* Kluwer, 1989.

Tobias, Phillip V. *The Brain in Hominid Evolution.* Columbia University Press, 1971.

———. "The Brain of *Homo habilis:* a New Level of Organization in Cerebral Evolution." *Journal of Human Evolution,* 16, 1987.

von Koenigswald, G. H. R. *Meeting Prehistoric Man.* Harper, 1956.

Vygotskii, L. S. *Mind in Society: The Development of Higher Psychological Processes.* Harvard University Press, 1978.

Walker, A. "The Origin of the Genus *Homo,*" in D. T. Rasmussen, ed., *The Origin and Evolution of Humans and Humanness.* Jones & Bartlett, 1993.

———, and C. Ruff. "The Reconstruction of the Pelvis," in A. Walker and R. Leakey, eds., *The Nariokotome Homo erectus Skeleton.* Harvard University Press, 1993.

Walker, A., and R. Leakey. *The Nariokotome Home erectus Skeleton.* Harvard University Press, 1993.

Wallace, Alfred Russel. *Darwinism: An Exposition of the Theory of Natural Selection.* Macmillan, 1889.

Washburn, Sherwood L. *Social Life of Early Man.* Aldine, 1961.

———, and Phyllis Dolhinow, eds. *Perspectives on Human Evolution,* 4 vols. Holt, Rinehart & Winston, 1968–1976.

Weidenreich, Franz. *Apes, Giants, and Man.* University of Chicago Press, 1946.

Wood, Bernard A., Lawrence Martin, and Peter Andrews, eds. *Major Topics in Human and Primate Evolution.* Cambridge University Press, 1986.

Wu, Rukand, and Lin Shenglong. "Peking Man." *Scientific American,* 248, 1983.

PART IV MODERN HUMANITY

General References for Further Reading

Bordes, Francois. *The Old Stone Age.* McGraw-Hill, 1968.

Campbell, Bernard G. *Human Ecology: The Story of Our Place in Nature from Prehistory to the Present.* Aldine, Second edition, 1995.

Cavalli-Sforza, L. L., P. Menozzi, and A. Piazza. *The History and Geography of Human Genes.* Princeton University Press, 1994.

Clutton-Brock, Juliet. *A Natural History of Domesticated Animals.* British Museum (Natural History) and Cambridge University Press, 1987.

Corruccini, R. S., and R. L. Ciochon, eds. *Integrative Paths to the Past: Paleoanthropological Advances in Honor of F. Clark Howell.* Prentice Hall, 1994.

Jones, S., R. Martin, and D. Pilbeam, eds. *The Cambridge Encyclopedia of Human Evolution.* Cambridge University Press, 1992.

Leakey, L. S. B., and Vanne Morris Goodall. *Unveiling Man's Origins.* Schenkman, 1969.

Marks, J. *Human Biodiversity: Genes, Race, and History.* Aldine de Gruyter, 1995.

Nitecki, M. H., and D. V. Nitecki, eds. *Origins of Anatomically Modern Humans.* Plenum, 1994.

Service, Elman R. *The Hunters.* Prentice-Hall, 1966.

Smith, Fred H., and Frank Spencer, eds. *The Origins of Modern Humans: A World Survey of the Evidence.* Alan R. Liss, 1984.

Wilson, Edward O. *On Human Nature.* Harvard University Press, 1978.

Sources

Aiello, L., and C. Dean. *An Introduction to Human Evolutionary Anatomy.* Academic Press, 1990.

Arens, W. *The Man-Eating Myth.* Oxford University Press, 1979.

Arsuaga, J.-L., I. Martinez, A. Garcia, J.-M. Carretero, and E. Carbonell. "Three New Human Skulls from the Simi de los Huesos Middle Pleistocene Site in Sierra de Atapuerca, Spain." *Nature,* 362, 1993.

Bada, Jeffrey L. "Aspartic Acid Racemization Ages of Californian Paleoindians." *American Antiquity,* 50, 1979.

Bahn, P. G. "Cannibalism or Ritual Dismemberment?" in S. Jones, R. Martin, and D. Pilbeam, eds., *The Cambridge Encyclopedia of Human Evolution.* Cambridge University Press, 1992.

Bordes, François. *A Tale of Two Caves.* Harper & Row, 1972.

Bowcock, A. M., A. Ruiz-Linares, J. Tomfohrde, E. Minch, J. R. Kidd, and L. L. Cavalli-Sforza. "High Resolution of Human Evolutionary Trees with Polymorphic Microsatellites." *Nature*, 368, 1994.

Brace, C. L. "A Nonracial Approach Towards the Understanding of Human Diversity," in A. Montagu, ed., *The Concept of Race*. Free Press, 1964.

Breuil, Abbé H. *Four Hundred Centuries of Cave Art.* Centre d'Études et de Documentation Préhistoriques, 1952.

Brose, David S., and Milford H. Wolpoff. "Early Upper Paleolithic Man and Late Middle Paleolithic Tools." *American Anthropologist*, 73, 1971.

Cann, Rebecca L., Mark Stoneking, and Allan C. Wilson. "Mitochondrial DNA and Human Evolution." *Nature*, 325, 1987.

Chapman, Frank M. *Handbook of Birds of Eastern North America*. Dover, 1966.

Clark, J. Desmond. *The Prehistory of Africa*. Praeger, 1970.

Clark, J. Grahame D. *Prehistoric Europe: The Economic Basis*. Philosophical Library, 1952.

Conkey, M. "Humans as Materialists and Symbolists: Image Making in the Upper Paleolithic," in D. T. Rasmussen, ed., *The Origin and Evolution of Humans and Humanness*. Jones & Bartlett, 1993.

Daniel, Glyn A. *A Hundred and Fifty Years of Archaeology*. Duckworth, 1975.

Dickson, D. B. *The Dawn of Belief*. University of Arizona Press, 1990.

Eiseley, Loren. "Neanderthal Man and the Dawn of Human Paleontology." *Quarterly Review of Biology*, 32, no. 4, 1957.

Falk, D. *Braindance*. Henry Holt, 1992.

Frison, G. C. "Modern People in the New World," in G. Burenhult, ed., *The First Humans: Human Origins and History to 10,000 B.C.* HarperCollins, 1993.

Glover, I. C. "Tools and Cultures in Late Paleolithic Southeast Asia," in G. Burenhult, ed., *The First Humans: Human Origins and History to 10,000 B.C.* HarperCollins, 1993.

Gould, S. J. *The Mismeasure of Man*. W. W. Norton, 1981.

——. "Human Equality Is a Contingent Fact of History." *Natural History*, 93, 1984.

Hooton, E. A. *Up from the Ape*. Macmillan, 1946.

Howell, F. Clark. "European and Northwest African Middle Pleistocene Hominids." *Current Anthropology*, 1, 1960.

——. "Recent Advances in Human Evolutionary Studies." *Quarterly Review of Biology*, 42, 1967.

Howells, W. "The Dispersion of Modern Humans," in S. Jones, R. Martin, and D. Pilbeam, eds., *The Cambridge Encyclopedia of Human Evolution*. Cambridge University Press, 1992.

——. *Getting Here*. Compass Press, 1993.

Jones, S. "The Evolutionary Future of Humankind," in S. Jones, R. Martin, and D. Pilbeam, eds., *The Cambridge Encyclopedia of Human Evolution*. Cambridge University Press, 1992.

Klein, Richard G. *Man and Culture in the Late Pleistocene*. Chandler, 1969.

——. "The Archeology of Modern Human Origins." *Evolutionary Anthropology*, 1, 1992.

——. *The Human Career*. University of Chicago Press, 1989.

Kranzberg, Melvin, and Carroll W. Pursell, Jr., eds. *Technology in Western Civilization*, vol. 1. Oxford University Press, 1967.

Kurtén, Björn. *The Ice Age*. Putnam's, 1972.

——. *The Cave Bear Story*. Pantheon, 1977.

Lahr, M. M. "The Multiregional Model of Modern Human Origins: A Reassessment of Its Morphological Basis." *Journal of Human Evolution*, 26, 1994.

Laming, Annette. *Lascaux*. Penguin, 1959.

Lee, Richard B. *Studies of the !Kung San and Their Neighbors*. Harvard University Press, 1976.

——, and Irven DeVore, eds. *Man the Hunter*. Aldine, 1968.

Leroi-Gourhan, André. *Treasures of Prehistoric Art*. Abrams, 1967.

Levin, J., and D. Suzuki. *The Secret of Life*. WGBH Boston, 1993.

Lewontin, R. *Human Diversity*. Scientific American Library, 1982.

Littlefield, A., L. Lieberman, and L. T. Reynolds. "Redefining Race: The Potential Demise of a Concept in Physical Anthropology." *Current Anthropology*, 23, 1982.

Maringer, Johannes. *The Gods of Prehistoric Man*. Knopf, 1960.

——, and Hans-Georg Bandi. *Art in the Ice Age*. Praeger, 1953.

Marks, J. "Black, White, Other." *Natural History*, 103, 1994.

Marshack, Alexander. *The Roots of Civilization*. McGraw-Hill, 1972.

Mellars P., and C. Stringer, eds. *The Human Revolution*. Edinburgh University Press, 1989.

Meltzer, D. J. "Pleistocene Peopling of the Americas." *Evolutionary Anthropology*, 1, 1993.

Molnar, S. *Human Variation*, 3rd ed. Prentice Hall, 1992.

Mulvaney, D. J., and J. Gordon. *Aboriginal Man and Environment in Australia*. Australian National University Press, 1971.

Oakley, Kenneth P., Bernard G. Campbell, and Theya I. Mollison. *Catalogue of Fossil Hominids*, 3 vols. Trustees of the British Museum (Natural History), 1967–1977.

Osborn, H. F. *Men of the Old Stone Age*. Scribner's, 1915.

Ovey, C. D., ed. "The Swanscombe Skull." *Occasional Papers of the Royal Anthropological Institute*, 20. London, 1964.

Roberts, M. B., C. B. Stringer, and S. A. Parfitt "A Hominid Tibia from Middle Pleistocene Sediments at Boxgrove, UK." *Nature*, 369, 1994.

Robins, A. H. *Biological Perspectives on Human Pigmentation*. Cambridge University Press, 1991.

Schepartz, L. A. "Language and Modern Human Origins." *Yearbook of Physical Anthropology*, 36, 1993.

Semenov, S. A. *Prehistoric Technology*. Cory, Adams & Mackay, 1964.

Shanklin, E. *Anthropology and Race*. Wadsworth, 1994.

Smith, G. Elliot. "Neanderthal Man Not Our Ancestor." *Scientific American*, August 1928.

Sohn, S., and M. H. Wolpoff. "Zuttiyeh Face: A View from the East." *American Journal of Physical Anthropology*, 91, 1993.

Solecki, Ralph S. *Shanidar: The First Flower People*. Knopf, 1971.

Stoneking, M. "DNA and Recent Human Evolution." *Evolutionary Anthropology*, 2, 1993.

Stringer, C. "New Views on Modern Human Origins," in D. T. Rasmussen, ed., *The Origin and Evolution of Humans and Humanness*. Jones & Bartlett, 1993.

———, and C. Gamble. *In Search of the Neandertals*. Thames & Hudson, 1993.

———, and P. Andrews. "Genetic and Fossil Evidence for the Origin of Modern Humans." *Science*, 239, 1988.

Tattersall, I. *The Human Odyssey*. Prentice Hall, 1993.

Trinkaus, E., and P. Shipman. *The Neandertals*. Knopf, 1993.

Trinkaus, Erik, and William W. Howells. "The Neanderthals." *Scientific American*, 241, no. 6, 1979.

Ucko, Peter J., and André Rosenfeld. *Palaeolithic Cave Art*. McGraw-Hill, 1967.

Villa, P. "Cannibalism in Prehistoric Europe." *Evolutionary Anthropology*, 1, 1992.

Waddle, D. M. "Matrix Correlation Tests Support a Single Origin for Modern Humans." *Nature*, 368, 1994.

Wells, H. G. "The Grisly Folk." Original 1921, reprinted in Wells's *Selected Short Stories*. Penguin, 1958.

White, J. P. "The Settlement of Ancient Australia," in G. Burenhult, ed., *The First Humans: Human Origins and History to 10,000 B.C.* HarperCollins, 1993.

White, T. D. *Prehistoric Cannibalism at Mancos 5MTUMR-2346*. Princeton University Press, 1992.

Acknowledgments

The authors acknowledge permission to use material from the following sources:

Introduction to Physical Anthropology, second edition, by Frederick S. Hulse. Copyright © 1963, 1971 by Random House, Inc. Adapted by permission of Random House, Inc.

Part I

Page 1 © 1991 by Murray Alcosser. Used by permission of Nevraumont Publishing Company.

Chapter 1

Page 2 Mary Evans Picture Library. *Figure 1–1* The Bettmann Archive. *Figure 1–2* Buckland, *Reliquiae Diluvianae*. *Figure 1–6* The Bettmann Archive. *Figure 1–7* The Bettmann Archive. *Figure 1–8* Reprinted by permission of the publishers from *One Long Argument: Charles Darwin and the Genesis of Modern Evolutionary Thought* by Ernst Mayr, Cambridge, Mass.: Harvard University Press. Copyright © 1991 by Ernst Mayr. *Figure 1–9* Mary Evans Picture Library. *Figure 1–10* T. H. Huxley, *Evidence as to Man's Place in Nature*, frontispiece, London, 1863. *Figure 1–11* Lennart Nilsson, *A Child Is Born*. *Figure 1–12* Hugo van Lawick/National Geographic Image Sales. *Figure 1–18 top,* adapted from B. Wood, in *Nature*, Vol. 371, 1994.

Chapter 2

Page 35 © 1989 Mugshots/Gabe Palmer/The Stock Market. *Figure 2–1* The Bettmann Archive. *Figure 2–9* Brown Bros. *Figure 2–10* Photo by Jules Kirschner, courtesy Department Library Services, American Museum of Natural History.

Chapter 3

Page 52 Oscar Miller/SPL/Photo Researchers. *Figures 3–1* and *3–2* Adapted from *Genes and Genomes*, by M. Singer and P. Berg, Sausalito, Calif.: University Science Books, 1991. *Figure 3–3* Biophoto Associates, Photo Researchers. *Figure 3–4* © Biophoto/Photo Researchers. *Figures 3–6, 3–7, 3–8, 3–9, 3–10,* and *3–11* Adapted from *Genes and Genomes*, by M. Singer and P. Berg, Sausalito, Calif.: University Science Books, 1991. *Figure 3–14* Data used with permission of W. H. Freeman, from *The Genetics of Human Populations*, by L. L. Cavalli-Sforza and W. F. Bodmer, San Francisco, W. H. Freeman, 1971. *Figure 3–15* Photo Researchers. *Figure 3–17* Data from *The Human Species: An*

Part II

Page 85 © J. M. Labat/AUSCAPE International.

Chapter 4

Page 86 © 1984 Gregory G. Dimijian/Photo Researchers. *Figure 4–2* Map adapted by permission from *A Handbook of Living Primates*, J. Napier, P. Napier, London: Academic Press. Copyright © 1967. *Figure 4–3* Map adapted by permission from *A Handbook of Living Primates*, J. Napier, P. Napier, London: Academic Press. Copyright © 1967. *Figure 4–4* Sarah Blaffer Hrdy/Anthro-Photo. *Figure 4–5* © David Haring. *Figure 4–6* © Wildlife Conservation Society. *Figure 4–7* A. W. Ambler/ National Audubon Society/Photo Researchers. *Figure 4–8* A. W. Ambler/National Audubon Society/Photo Researchers. *Figure 4–9* Reprinted from *Primate Evolution* by Glenn C. Conroy, with the permission of W. W. Norton & Co., Inc. Copyright © 1990 by W. W. Norton & Co., Inc. *Figure 4–10* Figure adapted from *The Cambridge Encyclopedia of Human Evolution*, Jones, Martin, Pilbeam, eds., Cambridge University Press, 1992. *Figure 4–11* Figure adapted from *The Cambridge Encyclopedia of Human Evolution*, Jones, Martin, Pilbeam, eds., Cambridge University Press, 1992. *Figure 4–13 top left/bottom right*, D. J. Chivers/Anthro-Photo; *top right/bottom left*, Werner H. Muller/Peter Arnold. *Figure 4–14 top left*, Michael Rougier/The Primates; *top right*, Ralph Morse/*Time* Magazine © Time Warner; *bottom left*, © Wildlife Conservation Society; *bottom right*, Richard Wrangham/Anthro-Photo. *Figure 4–15* Figure adapted from *The Cambridge Encyclopedia of Human Evolution*, Jones, Martin, Pilbeam, eds., Cambridge University Press, 1992. *Figure 4–17 bottom*, Fritz Goro. *Figure 4–18* Ralph Morse/*Life* Magazine. *Figure 4–19* Dr. Geza Teleki/Committee for Conservation and Care of Chimpanzees. *Figure 4–20* Gibbs Gately. *Figure 4–22* Julie O'Neil. *Figure 4–23 left*, Laima Druskis/Photo Researchers; *right*, Roberta Hershenson/Photo Researchers. *Figure 4–24 right*, J. R. Napier and P. H. Napier, *A Handbook of Living Primates*, Academic Press, Inc. (London, Ltd.). *Figure 4–25 (photo)* Lester Bergman & Associates, Inc.

Chapter 5

Page 123 © 1979 Tom McHugh/Photo Researchers. *Figure 5–1* © Wildlife Conservation Society. *Figure 5–2* Richard Wrangham/Anthro-Photo. *Figure 5–3 left,* Sarah Blaffer Hrdy/Anthro-Photo; *right,* Anthro-Photo. *Figure 5–4* Anthro-Photo. *Figure 5–5* Irven DeVore/Anthro-Photo. *Figure 5–6* Joseph Popp/Anthro-Photo. *Figure 5–7* Irven DeVore/Anthro-Photo. *Figure 5–9* Anthro-Photo. *Figure 5–10* David Chivers/Anthro-Photo. *Figure 5–11* DeVore/Anthro-Photo. *Figure 5–12* Robert M. Campbell/National Geographic Society. *Figure 5–13* Terrence Spencer/Paul Popper, Ltd., *The Primates. Figure 5–14* Sarah Blaffer Hrdy/Anthro-Photo. *Figure 5–15* Hugo Van Lawick/National Geographic Image Sales. *Figure 5–17* Dr. Geza Teleki/Committee for Conservation and Care of Chimpanzees. *Figure 5–18* DeVore/Anthro-Photo. *Figure 5–19* Allison Hannah. *Figures 5–20* and *5–21* From de Waal (1989) *Peacemaking among Primates.*

Chapter 6

Page 170 C. Chesek (1994) Department Library Services, American Museum of Natural History. *Figure 6–3* Reprinted from *Primate Evolution* by Glenn C. Conroy, with the permission of W. W. Norton & Co., Inc. Copyright © 1990 by W. W. Norton & Co., Inc. *Figure 6–4* San Diego Zoological Society. *Figure 6–6* Figure adapted from *The Cambridge Encyclopedia of Human Evolution,* Jones, Martin, Pilbeam, eds., Cambridge University Press, 1992. *Figure 6–7* D. Rasmussen. *Figures 6–8, 6–10* and *6–11* Dr. E. L. Simons/Duke University Primate Center. *Figure 6–13* Figure adapted from *The Cambridge Encyclopedia of Human Evolution,* Jones, Martin, Pilbeam, eds., Cambridge University Press, 1992. *Figure 6–14* The Natural History Museum, London. *Figure 6–15* Figure adapted with permission from *Primate Adaptation and Evolution,* J. G. Fleagle, Academic Press, 1988. *Figure 6–16* Figure adapted from *The Cambridge Encyclopedia of Human Evolution,* Jones, Martin, Pilbeam, eds., Cambridge University Press, 1992. *Figure 6–17* William Sacco/Anthro-Photo File. *Figure 6–18* Figure adapted with permission from *Primate Adaptation and Evolution,* J. G. Fleagle, Academic Press, 1988. *Figure 6–22* Compiled/adapted with permission from *Introduction to Human Evolutionary Anatomy,* by C. Dean and L. Aiello, San Diego, Calif.: Academic Press, copyright © 1990, and from *The Life of Primates,* by A. H. Schultz, Universe Books, 1969. *Figure 6–23* Adapted with permission from *The Antecedents of Man* by W. Le Gros Clark, Edinburgh University Press, 1962. *Figure 6–24* Reprinted with permission from *Introduction to Human Evolutionary Anatomy* by C. Dean and L. Aiello, San Diego, Calif.: Academic Press. Copyright © 1990. *Figure 6–25* Compiled/adapted with permission from *Introduction to Human Evolutionary Anatomy* by C. Dean and L. Aiello, San Diego, Calif.: Academic Press, copyright © 1990, and from *Ascent of Man* by D. Pilbeam, Macmillan, 1972. *Figure 6–26* Compiled/adapted with permission from *Introduction to Human Evolutionary Anatomy,* by C. Dean and L. Aiello, San Diego, Calif.: Academic Press, copyright © 1990, and from *Ascent of Man* by D. Pilbeam, Macmillan, 1972.

Chapter 7

Page 197 © 1985 David L. Brill\Atlanta. *Figure 7–2* Ernest Shirley. *Figure 7–4* William B. Terry, *Early Man. Figure 7–6* Glenn Conroy, Washington University Medical School, St. Louis. *Figure 7–7* Transvaal Museum, D. C. Panagos. *Figure 7–8* Transvaal Museum. *Figure 7–10* Transvaal Museum, D. C. Panagos. *Figure 7–11* Transvaal Museum, D. C. Panagos. *Figure 7–12* Transvaal Museum, D. C. Panagos. *Figure 7–13* Figure adapted with permission from *Early Hominid Posture and Locomotion* by John Robinson. Copyright © 1972 John Robinson. *Figure 7–14* Ken MacLeish, *Early Man. Figure 7–15* Redrawn from the *South African Archaeological Bulletin,* Vol. 17, No. 66 (June 1962), p. 111.

Chapter 8

Page 221 © Des Bartlett/Photo Researchers. *Figure 8–2* Donald Johanson/Institute of Human Origins. *Figure 8–3* Bob Campbell © National Geographic Society. *Figure 8–4* Gordon Gahan/National Geographic Image Sales. *Figure 8–5* Des Bartlett/Photo Researchers. *Figure 8–7* F. Clark Howell. *Figure 8–8* John Reader, *Life* Magazine © 1969. *Figure 8–9* National Museums of Kenya. *Figure 8–10* Alan Walker © National Museums of Kenya. *Figure 8–11* © 1994 David L. Brill\Atlanta. *Figure 8–12* Redrawn from D. Johanson and J. Shreeve, *Lucy's Child.* Morrow, 1989. *Figure 8–13 top left,* Don Johanson/Institute of Human Origins; *bottom left,* Institute of Human Origins; *bottom center,* Nanci Kahn/Institute of Human Origins; *bottom right,* © David L. Brill\Atlanta. *Figure 8–14 top,* Don Johanson/Institute of Human Origins. *Figure 8–15* Bobbie Brown. *Figure 8–16* © 1993 David L. Brill\Atlanta. *Figure 8–17* Institute of Human Origins. *Figure 8–18* Redrawn from original drawings by Luba Dmytryk Gudz from *Lucy: The Beginnings of Humankind* by Donald C. Johanson and Maitland Edey, 1981, Simon & Schuster. *Figure 8–19* From *Olduvai Gorge,* vol. III, © 1971 by Mary Leakey and Cambridge University Press. Reprinted with permission of the publisher. *Figure 8–20* Peter Jones. *Figure 8–21* © 1994 Tim White\Brill\Atlanta.

Chapter 9

Page 264 © John Reader/SPL/Photo Researchers. *Figure 9–1* Figure adapted with permission of Pete Wheeler from *Natural History,* 102, 993, p. 66. *Figure 9–3* Adapted from *Evolution of Human Walking,* by C. Owen Lovejoy. Copyright © November 1988, by *Scientific American.* All rights reserved. *Figure 9–5* National Museums of Kenya. *Figure 9–6* R. Potts. *Figure 9–7* Kathy D. Schick and Nicholas Toth, CRAFT Research Center, Indiana University (from Schick and Toth 1993, p. 163). *Figure 9–8* Kathy D. Schick and Nicholas Toth, CRAFT Research Center, Indiana University (from Schick and Toth 1993, p. 171). *Figures 9–9, 9–10,* and *9–11* From *Olduvai Gorge,* Vol. III, © 1971 by Mary Leakey and Cambridge University Press. Reprinted with permission of the publisher.

Part III

Page 289 Dr. Donald C. Johanson, Institute of Human Origins.

Chapter 10

Page 290 Courtesy Department Library Services, American Museum of Natural History. *Figure 10–1* From an unpublished manuscript: *Trinil, A Biography of Professor Dr. Eugene Dubois, the Discoverer of Pithecanthropus Erectus,* by Dubois's son, Jean M. F.

Dubois. *Figure 10–2* Culver Pictures. *Figure 10–4* Photo by Dr. von Koenigswald, courtesy Department Library Services, American Museum of Natural History. *Figure 10–5* Courtesy of the Rijksmuseum van Natuurlijke Historie, Leiden. *Figures 10–6 and 10–7* From an unpublished manuscript: *Trinil, A Biography of Professor Dr. Eugene Dubois, the Discoverer of Pithecanthropus Erectus,* by Dubois's son, Jean M. F. Dubois. *Figure 10–8* Copied by J. Coxe, Courtesy Department Library Services, American Museum of Natural History. *Figure 10–9* Courtesy Department Library Services, American Museum of Natural History. *Figure 10–10* The Bettmann Archive. *Figure 10–11* Redrawn with permission from original drawings by Janis Cirulis from *Mankind in the Making* by William Howells © 1959, 1967. *Figure 10–12* Peabody Museum, Harvard University. *Figure 10–13* Bettmann Archive. *Figure 10–14* Courtesy Department Library Services, American Museum of Natural History. *Figure 10–16* National Museums of Kenya. *Figure 10–17* David L. Brill. *Figure 10–18 left/center,* figure adapted with permission from *Introduction to Human Evolutionary Anatomy,* by C. Dean and L. Aiello, San Diego, Calif.: Academic Press, copyright © 1990; *right,* figure adapted from *The Cambridge Encyclopedia of Human Evolution,* Jones, Martin, Pilbeam, eds., Cambridge University Press, 1992. *Figure 10–19* Figure adapted with permission from "The Endocast" by David Begun and A. Walker in *The Nariokotome Homo Erectus Skeleton,* Harvard University Press, 1993. Copyright © 1993 David Begun. *Figure 10–20 left,* figure adapted from *Gray's Anatomy,* 29th edition, Lea & Febiger, 1973, copyright © Lea & Febiger; *center* and *right,* chart data used with permission of Anne MacLarnon, from *The Nariokotome Homo Erectus Skeleton,* Harvard University Press, 1993. *Figure 10–22* The Natural History Museum, London.

Chapter 11

Page 324 Kathy D. Schick and Nicholas Toth, CRAFT Research Center, Indiana University (from Schick and Toth 1993, p. 236). *Figure 11–2* Figure adapted from *The Cambridge Encyclopedia of Human Evolution,* Jones, Martin, Pilbeam, eds., Cambridge University Press, 1992. *Figure 11–3* Figure adapted with permission from *Making Silent Stones Speak,* by Schick and Toth, Simon & Schuster, 1993. *Figure 11–4* M. Riboud/Magnum Photos. *Figure 11–5* Redrawn by permission from *The Old Stone Age,* by Frances Bordes © 1968 by Frances Bordes, Weidenfeld & Nicolson, publishers. *Figure 11–6* M. Riboud/Magnum Photos. *Figure 11–7* Kathy D. Schick and Nicholas Toth, CRAFT Research Center, Indiana University (from Schick and Toth 1993, p. 245). *Figure 11–8 top,* compiled and adapted from *The Cambridge Encyclopedia of Human Evolution,* Jones, Martin, Pilbeam, eds., Cambridge University Press, 1992 and with permission by Joe Le Monnier, from *Natural History,* October 1989, p. 50; *bottom,* adapted with permission from *Making Silent Stones Speak,* by Schick and Toth, Simon & Schuster, 1993. *Figure 11–9* Nicholas Toth, CRAFT Research Center, Indiana University, and Giancarlo Ligabue from Ligabue missions 1986–1990 (from Schick and Toth 1993, p. 277). *Figure 11–10 left,* DeVore/Anthro-Photo. *Figure 11–11* Courtesy of Henry de Lumley. *Figure 11–12* The British Museum (Natural History). *Figure 11–13* Figure adapted from *The Cambridge Encyclopedia of Human Evolution,* Jones, Martin, Pilbeam, eds., Cambridge University Press, 1992. *Figure 11–14* Figure adapted from *The Cambridge Encyclopedia of Human Evolution,* Jones, Martin, Pilbeam, eds., Cambridge University Press, 1992.

Chapter 12

Page 347 © Kenneth Good. *Figure 12–2* F. Clark Howell. *Figure 12–3* Shostak/Anthro-Photo. *Figure 12–4* Figure adapted from *The Cambridge Encyclopedia of Human Evolution,* Jones, Martin, Pilbeam, eds., Cambridge University Press, 1992. *Figure 12–5* Irven DeVore/Anthro-Photo. *Figure 12–6* From G. H. R. Koenigswald, *Begegnung mit dem Vormenschen,* © 1956, Eugen Diederichs Verlag, Köln.

Chapter 13

Page 366 John Reader/SPL/Photo Researchers. *Figure 13–1 top,* Irven DeVore, Richard Wrangham, Irven DeVore/all Anthro-Photo; *bottom left* and *right,* Barton Silverman/Leo de Wys, Inc; *bottom center,* Alex Bordulin. *Figure 13–2* From *In the Shadow of Man* by Jane van Lawick-Goodall, © 1971 by Hugo and Jane van Lawick-Goodall. Reprinted by permission of Houghton Mifflin Company and Hugo van Lawick. *Figure 13–3* Richard Wrangham/Anthro-Photo. *Figure 13–4* Richard Wrangham/Anthro-Photo. *Figure 13–5* H. S. Terrace/Anthro-Photo. *Figure 13–8* From Daniel E. Sheer, ed., *Electrical Stimulation of the Brain,* © 1961 by permission of The University of Texas Press. *Figure 13–9* Pictor Uniphoto. *Figure 13–14* Figure adapted with permission from *Braindance* by Dean Falk (right figure modified with Glenn Conroy in *Nature,* 306, 1983), New York: Henry Holt. Copyright © 1992 by Dean Falk.

Part IV

Page 395 © Kenneth Good.

Chapter 14

Page 396 © Eric Trinkaus. *Figure 14–1* Rheinisches Landesmuseum Bonn. *Figure 14–2* Photo J. Kirschner, courtesy Department Library, American Museum of Natural History. *Figure 14–3* Musée de l'Homme. *Figure 14–4* Musée de l'Homme. *Figure 14–5* Courtesy Masson S. A. Editeur, Paris; from Boule and Vallois, *Les Hommes Fossilés,* 1952. *Figure 14–8* Courtesy of the Trustees of The British Museum (Natural History). *Figure 14–9* Peabody Museum, Harvard University, photograph by Hillel Burger. *Figure 14–10* Redrawn with permission from original drawings by Janis Cirulis from *Mankind in the Making* by William Howells © 1959, 1967. *Figure 14–11* Javier Trueba/Madrid Scientific Films. *Figure 14–12* David L. Brill. *Figure 14–15 left,* Peabody Museum, Harvard University, photograph by Hillel Burger; *right,* Musée de l'Homme. *Figure 14–16* Redrawn with permission from original drawings by Janis Cirulis from *Mankind in the Making* by William Howells © 1959, 1967.

Chapter 15

Page 424 Ron Testa © The Field Museum. *Figure 15–2* Redrawn from "The Earth's Orbit and the Ice Ages," by Curt Covey, *Scientific American* 250:2. Copyright © 1984 Scientific American, Inc. *Figure 15–5* The Field Museum, Chicago, IL. *Figure 15–6* Lee Boltin. *Figure 15–9* Redrawn from R. Klein, 1989, *The Human Career,* University of Chicago Press. *Figure 15–10* Redrawn by permission from *The Old Stone Age* by Frances Bordes. © 1968 by

Frances Bordes. Published by Weidenfeld & Nicolson. *Figure 15–11* Redrawn by permission from *The Gods of Prehistoric Man* by Johannes Maringer, edited and translated from the German by Mary Ilford, © 1960 by Alfred A. Knopf, Inc. *Figure 15–12* Used by permission from *The Old Stone Age* by Frances Bordes. © 1968 by Frances Bordes. Published by Weidenfeld & Nicolson. *Figures 15–14* and *15–15* Ralph S. Solecki, Columbia University. *Figure 15–16* Musée de l'Homme. *Figure 15–17* Redrawn with permission from *The Cambridge Encyclopedia of Human Evolution*, Jones, Martin, Pilbeam, eds., Cambridge University Press, 1992.

Chapter 16

Page 454 © Ian Tattersall. *Figure 16–3* Peabody Museum, Harvard University, photograph by H. Movius. *Figure 16–4* Courtesy of the Trustees of the British Museum (Natural History). *Figures 16–5* and *16–6* Redrawn by permission from *The Old Stone Age* by Frances Bordes. © 1968 by Frances Bordes. Published by Weidenfeld & Nicolson. *Figure 16–7* Redrawn from "The Neandertals," by Erik Trinkaus and William W. Howells, *Scientific American* 241:6. Copyright © 1979 by Scientific American, Inc. *Figure 16–9* K. Porter/Photo Researchers. *Figure 16–11* Redrawn by permission of Allan Wilson. *Figure 16–13 top*, Musée de l'Homme; *bottom left*, photograph courtesy of the Peabody Museum, Harvard University; *bottom right*, photograph by Julius Kirschner, courtesy Department Library Services, American Museum of Natural History.

Chapter 17

Page 486 © Jean Clottes/Ministère de la Culture/Sygma. *Figure 17–1* Patrimoine de l'Institut Royal des Sciences Naturelles de Belgique. *Figure 17–2* Otto van Eersel, *Early Man*. *Figure 17–3* Pierre Boulat/Cosmos. *Figure 17–4* Richard Jeffery, courtesy of J. Tixier. *Figure 17–5* Pierre Boulat/Cosmos. *Figure 17–6* Axel Poignant Archive. *Figure 17–7* Photograph by J. Kirschner, courtesy Department Library Services, American Museum of Natural History. *Figure 17–8* Axel Poignant Archive. *Figure 17–9* © 1985 David L. Brill\Atlanta. *Figure 17–10* Photograph by H. S. Rice, courtesy Department of Library Services, American Museum of Natural History. *Figure 17–11* Alexander Marshack. *Figure 17–12* Ralph Morse, *Early Man*. *Figure 17–13 left*, Alexander Marshack. *Figure 17–14* Photograph by Jim Coxe, courtesy Department Library Services, American Museum of Natural History. *Figure 17–15* Gordon Tenney. *Figure 17–16* Photograph by Lee Boltin, courtesy Department Library Services, American Museum of Natural History. *Figure 17–17* G. Shlionsky/Sovfoto/Eastfoto. *Figure 17–18* Novosti Press Agency, London, England.

Chapter 18

Page 515 Jeff Dunn/Stock Boston. *Figure 18–4* David Rubinger, Israel. *Figure 18–6* Figure adapted from Robins, *Biological Perspectives on Human Pigmentation*, Cambridge University Press, 1991. *Figure 18–7 left*, Smucker/Anthro-Photo; *right*, Arktisk Institut. *Figure 18–8* Map adapted with permission of The Free Press, a division of Simon & Schuster, Inc., from *The Concept of Race* edited by Ashley Montagu. Copyright © 1964 by Ashley Montagu. *Figure 18–9* From Mark L. Weiss and Alan E. Mann, *Human Biology and Behavior: An Anthropological Perspective*, 3rd ed., p. 241. Copyright © 1981 by Mark L. Weiss and Alan E. Mann. Redrawn by permission of the publisher, Scott, Foresman and Co. *Figure 18–10* Map adapted with permission of The Free Press, a division of Simon & Schuster, Inc., from *The Concept of Race* edited by Ashley Montagu. Copyright © 1964 by Ashley Montagu. *Figure 18–11* From *The Living Races of Man*, by Carleton S. Coon, with Edward E. Hunt Jr. Copyright © 1965 by Carleton S. Coon. Reprinted by permission of Alfred A. Knopf, Inc. *Figure 18–12* Adapted from *The Human Species: An Introduction to Physical Anthropology*, second edition, by Frederick S. Hulse. Copyright © 1963, 1971, by Random House, Inc. Adapted by permission of Random House, Inc. *Figure 18–13* Figure adapted from *The Cambridge Encyclopedia of Human Evolution*, Jones, Martin, Pilbeam, eds., Cambridge University Press, 1992. *Figure 18–14* Figure adapted from *The Cambridge Encyclopedia of Human Evolution*, Jones, Martin, Pilbeam, eds., Cambridge University Press, 1992. *Figure 18–15* From *Human Diversity* by R. Lewontin. Copyright © 1982 by Scientific American Books. Used with permission of W. H. Freeman Books. *Figure 18–16 left*, © Betty Press, Woodfin Camp; *center* and *right*, E. A. Hooten, *Up from the Ape*, Macmillan, New York, 1946. *Figures 18–17* and *18–18* E. A. Hooten, *Up from the Ape*, Macmillan, New York, 1946.

Photo Essays

The Living Apes

1. Painting "Darwin and Friends" by Stephen D. Nash. Reproduced with permission of the Department of Physical Anthropology, University College, London. 2. © Tom McHugh, Photo Researchers. 3. © Tom McHugh, Photo Researchers. 4. © Michael Nichols/Magnum. 5. © Michael Nichols/Magnum. 6. 1979 Tom McHugh/Photo Researchers. 7 and 8. Robert Hynes, © Cartographic Division, National Geographic Society.

Fossil Hominids

1. Don Johanson/Institute of Human Origins. 2. © 1985 David L. Brill\Atlanta. 3. D. Finnin/C. Chesek/American Museum of Natural History. 4. © 1985 David L. Brill. 5. © 1993 John Reader. 6. © 1985 David L. Brill. 7. From Ian Tattersall, *The Human Odyssey*, Prentice Hall, 1993. Photo of casts by Willard Whitson. 8. Alan Walker © National Museums of Kenya. 9. From Ian Tattersall, *The Human Odyssey*, Prentice Hall, 1993. Photo of casts by Willard Whitson. 10. (*top left*) © 1985 David L. Brill\Atlanta; (*top right*) Israel Antiquities Authority; (*bottom*) © 1993 David L. Brill\Atlanta. 11. From Ian Tattersall, *The Human Odyssey*, Prentice Hall, 1993. Photo of casts by Willard Whitson.

Index

Abell, Paul, 250
Aborigines, 72, 465
  ancestors of, 478–479
  weapons of, 494
Absolute dating methods, 25–31
Abstract thought, 116, 119
Acheulean industry, 276, 328–336, 412,
  426–427, 431, 437, 460, 462
Adapidae, 175–176, 177
Adaptation
  arboreal, 107–110
  of archaic *H. sapiens*, 426
  cultural, 119
  environmental, 71–72, 517
  of Neandertals, 437–440
Adenine, 59
Adrar Mgorn site, 175
Aegyptopithecus, 178–181, 194
Africa. *See also specific regions, countries,*
  and sites
  archaic *H. sapiens* in, 406–407, 425, 437,
    463
  chimpanzee species in, 153–154
  early *Homo* in, 227–230, 237–240, 260
  fossil dating in, 28
  H. erectus in, 312–314, 318–320, 325
  human origins in, 17, 18, 182, 468,
    470–472, 517, 542
  modern humans in, 465–466, 468–472
  in Paleocene epoch, 174, 175
  in Pleistocene glaciation, 429–430
  primate studies in, 127
  prosimians in, 94
  robust australopithecine lineage in,
    465–466
  savanna in. *See* Savannas
  tools found in, 331, 332–335, 428, 460
African Eve, 468, 470–472
African hares, 352–353
Aged, care of, 447–448
Agglutination, 532
Aggression
  in archaic *H. sapiens*, 448
  in chimpanzees, 160–161

dominance hierarchy and, 133
  in gorillas, 151–152
  in *H. erectus*, 361–363
  sexuality and status in, 134–135
Agriculture, 521–524, 543
AIDS (acquired immune deficiency
  syndrome), 51
Aiello, Leslie, 219
Ainu people, 441–442
Alarm calls, 370–372, 373
Alexander, Richard, 139
Algeria, 175, 176–177
Algeripithecus, 177
Alice Boer site, 478
Alleles, 58, 534
  in genetic drift, 69
  Hardy-Weinberg theorem, 77
Allen, J. A., 527–528
Allia Bay site, 247, 250, 262
Allison, A. C., 74
Allomothering, 131
Allopatric speciation, 66, 67, 420, 467
Alpha males, 134, 154
Altiatlasius, 175–176
Altriciality, 355
Altruism, 80–81, 518–520
  care of old and handicapped, 447–448
  reciprocal, 141, 373, 519–520
Ambrona site, 338, 340, 343, 353
Ambush, 353–354
American Indians. *See* Native Americans
American Sign Language (ASL), 119, 375
Americas, 478. *See also* North America;
  South America
Amino acids, 29, 31, 59–62
Amniocentesis, 546
Amniotic fluid, 19, 546
Amphipithecus, 177
Amud site, 409, 411
Anasazi people, 452
Andersson, John Gunnar, 302
Andrews, Roy Chapman, 303–304
Anemia. *See* Sickle-cell anemia
Angular gyrus, 379–381

Animal husbandry, 521–522, 543
Animal sculpture, 503
Anopheles mosquito, 74
Antecedents of Man, The (Le Gros Clark), 90
Antelope, 250, 286, 296, 353
Anterior inferior iliac spine, 189, 192
Anthropoids, 101–119
Anthropomorpha, 88
Anthropopithecus erectus.
  See Pithecanthropus erectus
Antigens, 532
Antler tools
  of *Sinanthropus*, 307
  of Upper Paleolithic, 460, 488, 492
Apes. *See also specific types*
  A. afarensis compared with, 247
  ancestors of, 94, 165–166, 176–182,
    194–195
  arboreal adaptation in, 107–110
  brain of, 379, 385–386, 387
  classification of, 88–89, 183
  common ancestors with humans,
    165–166
  communication in, 368–370, 374–377
  as endangered group, 121
  grooming and, 139–141
  hands of, 115–116
  hominid evolution from, 255
  hominids compared with, 265–266
  Huxley's view of, 17
  incest taboo in, 358, 359
  limbic system of, 379–380
  locomotion of, 103–113, 188–192,
    194–195, 198
  Miocene, 182–187, 194–195
  morphology of, 181
  sexual selection in, 138
  socioecological characteristics of, 129
  studies of, 124, 125–126
  Taung skull compared with, 200, 204
  taxonomy of, 89–90
  threat gestures of, 274
  tool use by, 266
Aphasia, 378–379

Apidium, 178
Arabia, 475
Arago, 412
Arambourg, Camille, 231, 232
Aramis fossils, 251–255
Arboreality, 97–100, 146
    by earliest primates, 107–110, 176
    hominid descent from, 265–266
Arboreal theory, 96–100
Archaeology, 20, 168
Archaic *Homo sapiens*, 406–421, 425–452
    aggression in, 448
    art of, 442–443
    assessment of, 413–421
    brain of, 422
    burial rites of, 440, 443–447
    cannibalism in, 448–450, 451–452
    care for aged and handicapped by,
        447–448
    classification of, 418–420
    defined, 397
    environmental adaptations of, 437–440,
        517
    fate of, 459–472, 483–484
    glaciation cycles and, 428–433
    major characteristics of, 415
    modern humans compared with,
        463–464
    range and adaptations of, 425–428
    rituals of, 440–447
    skin adaptation of, 433–435
    species model and, 418–420
    tools used by, 402, 426–428, 435–437,
        459–462, 492
Arctic Ocean, 432
Arcy-sur-Cure cave, 443, 461, 462
Ardipithecus, 254. *See also Australopithecus
    ramidus*
Ardrey, Robert, 361
Arens, W., 452
Argon–argon dating techniques, 26, 29,
    319
Aridos site, 353, 355
Arnhem Land, 479
Arrowheads, 478
Art. *See also specific types*
    of archaic *H. sapiens*, 442–443
    of Upper Paleolithic, 498–506, 521
Articulation, 383
Artificial selection, 546
Asexual reproduction, 66
Asfaw, Berhane, 251–253
Asia. *See also specific countries, regions, and sites*
    archaic *H. sapiens* in, 408–409, 445
    fossil dating in, 25
    H. erectus in, 319–320, 325, 332–333
    modern humans in, 475, 478
    Neandertal burial rites, 445
    prosimians in, 94
    tools found in, 335, 460

types of apes in, 146–148
Asses, 68
Association, 379
Atapuerca, Sierra de, 413
Aterian industry, 437
Atlatl, 494
Atomic physics, in fossil dating, 19, 25–31
Attractiveness, 137
Auditory bulla, 174–175
Aurignacian industry, 461–462
Auroch, 494
Australia, 459, 460, 463, 465, 467, 468,
    478–480, 498. *See also Aborigines;
    specific sites*
Australopithecus (genus). *See also specific
    types*
    artifacts of, 214–218, 248
    bipedalism of, 250–251, 355
    classification of, 198, 218–219
    coexistence with other hominids, 230
    communication in, 382–383
    dentition of, 517
    environmental adaptation of, 517
    life expectancy of, 544
    skin color of, 433–434
Australopithecus aethiopicus, 232–233,
    236–238
Australopithecus afarensis, 233, 248–251
    bipedalism of, 243–245, 251, 267, 321
    brain of, 229–230
    characteristics of, 243–248, 267
    evolutionary relationships of, 259, 262,
        292
    lifestyles of, 257–258
    "Lucy" as, 243
Australopithecus africanus, 205–206, 222.
    See also Taung skull
    A. afarensis compared with, 247
    age of, 209–210, 227
    assessment of, 213–214
    bipedalism of, 321
    brain of, 321–322
    dentition of, 204–205, 207, 322
    discovery of, 200–205
    evolutionary relationships of, 259–260,
        292
    H. habilis compared with, 228–229
    lifestyles of, 257–258
    "Lucy" compared with, 243
    major characteristics of, 211
    tools used by, 214–217
Australopithecus anamensis, 262
Australopithecus ramidus, 222, 251–255.
    See also Ardipithecus
    dentition of, 252–253, 273, 517
    discovery of, 251–253
    evaluation of, 253–255
    evolutionary relationships of, 254–255,
        259, 260, 262, 292
    major characteristics of, 253

new information on, 255
as provisional species, 254
Aye-ayes, 93, 97, 121
Aztecs, 494

Baboons. *See also specific types*
    childhood learning in, 128, 130
    communication in, 370, 372
    dentition of, 273
    dominance hierarchy of, 133
    feeding strategies of, 145
    grooming behavior and, 139–140
    sexuality and status in, 134–135
    sexual physiology of, 136
    sexual selection in, 78, 138–139
    social interaction in, 140–141
    socioecological characteristics of, 129,
        144–145
    studies of, 124, 125, 127
    Taung find compared with, 204
    territory and ecology of, 143–145
Bächler, Emil, 441
Bacteria, 51
Badgers, 307
Bahn, Paul, 452
Balanced polymorphism, 74, 76, 531
Balzac, Honoré de, 9
Bateson, William, 54
Bear cult, 441–442
Bears, 9, 307. *See also Cave bears*
Begun, David, 317
Beijing fossils, 302–304, 309–311. *See also
    Peking man*
Belgium, 6, 399, 401–402. *See also specific
    sites*
Bellomo, Randy, 337–338
Bergmann, Carl, 527–528
Beringia, 477
Bering Sea, 477
Bering Strait, 478
Bible, xvii, 3–5, 7, 398–399
Bilophodonty, 103
Bilzingsleben, 412
Binford, Lewis, 281–282, 284, 307,
    338–339, 340, 343, 348, 362–363
Bingham, Harold, 125
Bioaltruism, 81, 141, 519–520
Biochemistry, in fossil dating, 21
Bioethicists, 84
Biological anthropology, 20
Biomes, 517
Bipedalism, 548
    in *A. afarensis*, 243–245, 251, 267, 321
    in *A. anamensis*, 262
    ape versus human, 188–193
    in *Australopithecus*, 250–251, 262, 355
    body temperature and, 268–269, 351,
        390–391
    brain evolution and, 390–391

in chimpanzees, 115, 164
defined, 108
of early hominids, 254–255, 257, 262, 266–274
energy efficiency and, 267–268
facultative versus obligatory, 251
first appearance of, 198
of "Lucy," 243
of *Pithecanthropus*, 321
Taung discovery and, 200
tool use and, 266–267
Birds
bioaltruism in, 519
natural selection in, 70–71
speciation in, 417–418
Birth canal, 271–272
Bison, 307, 458, 493, 502
Black, Davidson, 301–305, 306, 308
Black skull, 236–237. *See also Paranthropus aethiopicus*
Blade tools
of archaic *H. sapiens*, 437, 460–461
of modern humans, 490–491, 498
Blending inheritance, 36, 44, 51
Blood groups, 72, 79, 531–534, 537
Body build, 527–528
Body hair, 269, 350–351. *See also* Hair form
Body language, 369, 370, 373, 380
Body temperature, 268–269, 351, 390–391, 475
Boesch, Christophe, 157, 159
Boesch-Acherman, Hedwige, 157, 159
Böhlin, Birgir, 302–303
Boise, Charles, 226
Bolas, 344–345
Bone, as fuel, 489
Bone analysis, in fossil dating, 24
Bone tools
of archaic *H. sapiens*, 439
of *Sinanthropus*, 307
of Upper Paleolithic, 460, 488, 492
Bonobos (pygmy chimpanzees), 162–165, 376
environmental adaptation of, 146
evolutionary history of, 187
herbalism of, 157
major characteristics of, 166
politics among, 162
socioecological characteristics of, 129
studies of, 124
Border Cave, 466
Bordes, François, 436
Borneo, 127, 293–294, 463
Boucher de Perthes, Jacques, 6
Boule, Marcellin, 402–406, 415, 416, 452
Bouyssonie, Abbé Jean, 445
Boveri, Theodor, 54
Bovids, 286
Bow and arrow, 496

Bowcock, A. M., 468
Bow-wow hypothesis, 368, 373
Boxgrove tibia, 412
Brace, C. Loring, 431, 473
Brachiation, 106–107
Braidwood, Robert, 523
Brain
of *A. afarensis*, 229–230
of *A. africanus*, 321–322
of apes, 379, 385–386, 387
of archaic *H. sapiens*, 422
bipedalism and, 390–391
body weight ratio and, 386–387, 391
in communication process, 317, 373, 378, 379
of dolphins, 386
of elephants, 229, 386
environmental adaptation and, 517
of *H. erectus*, 314–318, 326, 352, 355–356, 384, 391
of *H. habilis*, 229–230, 239, 391
of *H. rudolfensis*, 239, 391
of *H. sapiens*, 229, 385
of hominids, 266, 280, 385
Homo (genus), 261–262, 390–391
human. *See* Human brain
of jackals, 386
of monkeys, 379, 385–386
of Neandertals, 399–400, 403–404, 414, 419
of *P. boisei*, 226
of *Pithecanthropus*, 300, 309, 321
of porpoises, 386
of prosimians, 97
of *Sinanthropus*, 304, 306–307, 309
tool use and, 280
of whales, 229, 306–307, 386
Brain, C. K., 213, 217
Branisella, 182
Brazil, 478
Breccia, 204
Breuil, Abbé Henri, 307, 499–500
British Association for the Advancement of Science, 400
Broca's area, 317, 378–379, 381
Brongniart, Alexandre, 9
Broom, Robert, 203, 205–214, 217, 219, 227, 248
Brown, Frank, 25
Brünn Society for the Study of Natural Science, 44
Buckland, William, 6
Buffalo, 307, 493
Buffon, Comte de, 7, 10
Burghers' Zoo (Holland), 161–162
Burial rites
of archaic *H. sapiens*, 440, 443–447
of modern humans, 457
of Neandertals, 443–447, 509
in Upper Paleolithic, 509–511

Burins
of archaic *H. sapiens*, 460
of Upper Paleolithic, 491–492
Burma, 177
Bush, Mike, 243
Bush babies, 92, 93, 102
Butchery
by early hominids, 277–278
by *H. erectus*, 331–332, 340–341, 349, 353, 354, 357
Butterflies, 48

Cache sites, 282–284
Cambrian period, 25
Cannibalism
among archaic *H. sapiens*, 448–450, 451–452
among *H. erectus*, 361–363
Cap Blanc cave, Le, 506
Carbon 14 dating, 26–27, 28, 479
Carpenter, C. R., 125
Cartmill, Matt, 97–100, 364–365
Catarrhines, 102–103. *See also* Old World monkeys
Catastrophism, 9–10
Catopithecus, 177–178
Cattle, 502, 521, 543
Cave, A. J. E., 415–416
Cave art, 442–443, 498–506, 513, 521
Cave bears, 5, 304, 429, 441–442
Cave dwellings, 22
of archaic *H. sapiens*, 410–411, 433
of *H. erectus*, 363
shelters inside of, 430
Cave of Witches, 440–441
Ceboidea. *See* New World monkeys
Cell proteins, 124
Central Africa, 127, 152, 153, 162
Central America, 127, 478
Central Europe
archaic *H. sapiens* in, 439
in Pleistocene glaciations, 429
tools found in, 490
in Upper Paleolithic, 488–489, 490
Cephalic index (CI), 535–538
Ceramics, 506–509
Cercopithecoidea. *See* Old World monkeys
Cercopithecus aethiops. *See* Vervet monkeys
Cerebrum, 116, 118
Chacma baboons, 125
Chain of Being, 398–399
Chapelle-aux-Saints, La, 402, 415–416, 443–444, 447, 463, 464
Chatelperronian tools, 461, 462
Cheney, Dorothy, 117–118, 373
Chert, 280
Chiasmata, 65
Childbirth, bipedalism and, 271–273
Childhood learning, in primates, 128–132
Chile, 478

Chimpanzee Material Culture (McGrew), 159–160, 168
Chimpanzee Politics (de Waal), 161
Chimpanzees. *See also specific types*
  A. afarensis compared with, 247
  aggression of, 160–161
  altruism in, 519
  bipedalism of, 115, 164
  childhood learning in, 128–130
  chromosomes of, 54
  classification of, 89
  communication in, 119, 369–370, 372–373, 374–376, 383
  culture among, 159–160, 168–169
  dentition of, 273
  evolutionary history of, 187
  extinct, 296
  feeding strategies of, 145, 156, 157
  gibbons compared with, 146
  in Gombe reserve. *See* Gombe chimpanzees
  gorillas compared with, 219
  hands of, 110, 115
  herbalism in, 157
  humans compared with, 30, 31
  hunting by, 156–157
  Huxley's view of, 17
  incest taboo in, 359
  limbic system of, 380
  locomotion of, 107–108
  of Mahale mountains, 154–155
  major characteristics of, 166
  manual dexterity of, 110, 111
  meat eating in, 141, 156–157
  politics in, 161–162
  sexuality and status in, 134
  social interaction in, 140–141
  socioecological characteristics of, 129
  species divergence in, 266
  studies of, 124, 125–126, 127
  territory and ecology of, 142
  tool use by, 158–160, 266, 267, 274
  weapon use by, 158–160
Chimpanzees of Gombe, The (Goodall), 153
China. *See also specific sites*
  archaic *H. sapiens* in, 409, 425, 463
  domestication of animals and plants in, 521
  Homo erectus in, 301–311, 338–340, 361–363
  modern humans in, 459, 477
  Proconsul in, 183
  search for evidence of early humans in, 301–308
Chins, of modern humans, 474–475
Chisels, 491–492. *See also* Burins
Choppers
  of hominids, 276–278
  of *Sinanthropus*, 307
Chromatids, 54, 65
Chromosomes, 53–54

abnormalities of, 74–76
  defined, 53
  replication of, 65
Chronometric dating methods, 25–31
Chronospecies, 467
Cities, 524–525
Civilization development, 523–526
Clacton-on-Sea, 426
Clades, 88
Cladistic classification, 88–89
Classification
  of apes, 88–89, 183
  of *H. habilis*, 228–229, 238–240
  of *H. rudolfensis*, 238–240
  of *H. sapiens*, 87–88
  lumpers in, 218–219, 235–236
  of Neandertals, 399–401, 405–406
  splitters in, 218–219, 235–236
Cleavers, of *H. erectus*, 331–332
Climate, 426
  glacial cycles, 327–328, 428–433
  grass spread and, 222
  hunting and, 350
  ice ages, 293, 295, 327–328, 428–433
  in Miocene epoch, 187
  in Paleocene epoch, 174
  and turnover pulse hypothesis of speciation, 286–287
  in Upper Paleolithic, 488
Close-knee stance, 192–193, 242, 245
Clothing
  of archaic *H. sapiens*, 401, 426, 433, 434, 439
  of *H. erectus*, 354, 428
  of Upper Paleolithic, 497–498, 508–509
Clovis points, 478
Co-dominant genes, 78
Codons, 59, 62
Collagen, 24, 59
Collective phenotypes, 68
Colobine monkeys, 145
Colombière cave, La, 496
Color vision, 114–115, 353
Colugos, 175
Combarelles cave, Les, 501
Combe Grenal site, 340
Communication. *See also* Language; Speech
  in apes, 368–370, 374–377
  in australopithecines, 382–383
  in baboons, 370, 372
  in chimpanzees, 119, 369–370, 372–373, 374–376, 383
  in monkeys, 141, 368, 369–371, 374–376
  nonlimbic, 372–374
  nonverbal, 369, 370, 380, 393
  in orangutans, 375
Composite tools, of Upper Paleolithic, 491–493
Computed tomography (CT), 251
Congo forests, 430, 437–438

Conkey, Margaret, 502, 505
Consortship, 134
Conspecifics, 15
Continental drift, 23, 173
Continuous evolution, 47–48
Cooking, by modern humans, 473
Coon, Carlton, 535
Coppens, Yves, 231, 232, 240, 243
Core area, 142
Core tools, of *H. erectus*, 329–336
Correns, Karl, 47
Cortex, 116–118
  in communication process, 378–379
  in language, 317, 373, 378–379, 381
Cotte de St. Brelade, La, 353
Courtship patterns, 68
Creationism, xvi–xvii, 34
Creation science, 34
Crelin, Edmund S., 382–383
Crick, F. H. C., 57, 58
Cro-Magnons. *See also* Modern humans
  archaic *H. sapiens* compared with, 463–464
  art of, 442
  diet of, 481
  discovery of, 457
  emergence of, 468
  Neandertals compared with, 405, 463–464
  tools used by, 405, 460, 462
Crossbreeding, 39–45
Crossing-over, 63–65
CT. *See* Computed tomography (CT)
Cultural adaptation, 119
Cultural anthropology, 167–168
Cultural differences, 141
Cultural history, 520–521
Culture
  among chimpanzees, 159–160, 168–169
  components of, 520
  defined, 119, 167, 168
  of *Homo* (genus), 262
  at Zhoukoudian, 307–308
Curtis, Garniss, 319
Cuvier, Georges, 9–10, 18
Cytoplasm, 54
Cytosine, 59
Czech Republic, 463, 465, 493, 506

Dali skull, 409
Dart, Raymond, 198–205, 209, 213–214, 215, 219, 307, 321–322
Darwin, Charles, xvi–xvii, 3, 10, 11–14, 19, 32, 53, 70–71, 78, 138, 139, 151, 266, 286, 293, 305–306, 368, 393, 398, 399–401, 402, 451–452, 518, 545
  early life of, 11
  interest in heredity, 36–37, 42, 45, 50–51
  theory formulated by, 14–18
Dawson, Charles, 321, 402
Dean, Christopher, 219

Débitage, 278
Decay process, in fossil dating, 25–31, 28–29
Decay rate, 25
Deep time, 7, 10
Deer, 307, 353, 441, 492, 493, 502
Deevey, Edward S., 542–543
Deforestation, 121, 525, 543–544
de la Mettrie, Julien Offroy, 374
de la Peyrère, Isaac, 5
Delibrias, Georgette, 478
de Lumley, Henry, 336–337, 412, 430
de Lumley, Marie-Antoinette, 412, 430
Denmark, 496
Dental apes, 182, 194–195
Dentition
  of *A. afarensis*, 246–247
  of *A. africanus*, 204–205, 207, 322
  of *A. ramidus*, 252–253, 273, 517
  of anthropoids, 103, 109
  bipedalism and, 273–274
  of chimpanzees, 273
  diet and, 273–274, 286–287
  of early *Homo*, 239
  of first higher primates, 179
  of *H. erectus*, 273
  of hominoids, 103, 109, 171
  of Koobi Fora hominids, 234
  of modern humans, 473–475, 530
  of monkeys, 179
  of Neandertals, 473
  of Omo fossils, 232–233
  of *P. boisei*, 226
  of *P. robustus*, 206, 207, 217
  of *Pithecanthropus*, 322
  of prosimians, 94, 101
  of *Sinanthropus*, 306
  stone tools and, 473
  of Taung skull, 203–205
Descent of Man, The (Darwin), 17, 266
DeVore, Irven, 360
De Vries, Hugo, 45–47
de Waal, Frans, 161–162
Dickson, D. Bruce, 511, 513
Diet. *See also* Meat eating; Vegetarianism
  of archaic *H. sapiens*, 426
  of chimpanzees, 156–157
  Cro-Magnon, 481
  dentition effect of, 273–274, 286–287
  of early hominids, 277–278, 281–284
  feeding strategies and, 145–146
  of gorillas, 148–149
  of *H. erectus*, 332, 339–341, 350, 357
  of modern humans, 473, 480–481, 494
  vitamins and, 434–435, 494, 527
Differential reproductive rate, 68
Dinosaurs, 16, 22, 82
Diploid numbers, 53–54, 80
Directional natural selection, 69
Discontinuous evolution, 47–48

Diseases, 63, 530–531
  blood groups and, 534
  genetic, 74–78, 530, 534, 546
  viral, 51
Diurnal pattern, 93
Diurnal vision, 101
Dmanisi site, 314, 318, 319
DNA (deoxyribonucleic acid), 21, 58–63, 124
  mitochondrial, 468–472, 478
  replication of, 59
  species divergence and, 31
Dobzhansky, Theodosius, 18
Dogs, 115, 368, 521
Dolni Vestonice site, 506
Dolphins, 386
Domestication of plants and animals, 521–523, 543
Dominance hierarchy, 131, 132–133, 134, 154, 369
  baboon, 133
  bonobo, 163
  chimpanzee, 161–162, 163
  gorilla, 132, 149–150, 151
Dominant characteristics, 40, 42
Donkeys, 410
Donner Party, 71
Dordogne region, 455–458, 481, 497, 498, 504
Double helix, 58–59
Down's syndrome, 74
Drachenloch cave, 441
Dragon bones, 296, 301–302
Dubois, Eugene, 291, 293–301, 308–309, 321–322, 322, 402
Duchin, Linda, 383
Dunker sect, 72

Earth
  age of, 7–8, 15, 16–17, 18, 23–25
  magnetic field of, 28
East Africa, 182, 312, 437. *See also specific sites*
  baboon territory and ecology in, 144–145
  chimpanzee studies in, 155, 156–157
  fossil dating in, 19, 25, 28
  grass spread in, 222
East Asia, 466–467
Eastern Europe. *See also specific sites*
  archaic/modern relationship in, 465
  tools found in, 461
Ecology, of primates, 141–146
Ecotones, 266
Egg cells, 54, 65
Egypt, 175, 367–368, 480
Elandsfontein site, 437, 466, 467
El Cedral site, 478
Electron spin resonance, 410

Elephants, 9, 229, 250, 255, 286, 307, 353, 386, 443
Encephalization Quotient (EQ), 385–386, 391
Endocasts, 199
England, 5–6, 7, 9, 411, 412, 426, 429
Environmental adaptation, 71–72, 517
Eocene epoch, 174–177
Eosimias, 177
Epicanthic folds, 529, 530
Eskimos, 72, 431, 475, 494, 498
Esper, Johann Friedrich, 5
Essay (Darwin), 14
Essay on the Principle of Population (Malthus), 14
Estrus, 134, 137, 152, 162, 269
Ethiopia, 26, 231–233, 312–313
  baboon territory and ecology in, 144
  grass spread in, 222
Ethnic cleansing, 541, 548
Ethnic groups, 541, 548
Ethology, 21
Eukaryotes, 51
Eurasia, 509
  archaic *H. sapiens* in, 466–467
  domestication of animals and plants in, 521
Europe. *See also specific countries and sites*
  archaic *H. sapiens* in, 400, 409, 411–413, 462–463
  female figurines in, 506–509
  first evidence of humans in, 301
  fossil dating in, 25
  fossils from, 314
  H. erectus in, 314, 318, 319
  Neandertals in, 397–406, 431–432, 437, 459, 460, 461
  in Paleocene epoch, 174
  in Pleistocene glaciations, 428–429, 430
  tools found in, 329, 331, 332, 431, 460, 461–462
  in Upper Paleolithic, 493, 497
Eve (mitochondrial), 468, 470–472. *See also* Mitochondrial (mt DNA)
Evening primrose studies, 46–47
Evolution
  continuous versus discontinuous, 47–48
  of early hominids, 259–260
  genetic mechanisms of. *See* Genes
  heredity in. *See* Heredity
  of hominids. *See* Hominids
  modern day, 545–546
  Neandertals in, 397–398
  of population and species, 66–82
  of speech, 381–384
  and turnover pulse hypothesis of speciation, 286–287
Evolutionary biology, 516–517
Evolutionary success, 542–543

Evolutionary theory, xvi-xvii, 14–18, 32, 348, 401, 402
  classification systems and, 88–89
  continental drift in, 23, 173
  early naturalists' influence on, 10
  heredity in, 37, 45
  on language, 367–368
  natural selection in. *See* Natural selection
  premises of, 14–15
  stumbling blocks in, 393
Exogamy, 80, 360, 475
Exons, 59
Extinction, 22, 81–82, 250
  of *A. africanus*, 209
  of archaic *H. sapiens*, 459
  of Neandertals, 459
  proof of, 9–10
  and turnover pulse hypothesis of speciation, 286
Eyelid form, 529, 530
Eyes. *See* Vision

Facial expressions, 369, 370, 380
Falk, Dean, 379, 390, 422
Family
  defined, 358
  food sharing and, 269–274, 355–358
  in *H. erectus*, 355–361
Famine, 71, 544
Faunal correlation, 24
Fayum Depression, 177
Feedback system
  civilization development and, 520–521, 525, 544–545
  in language development, 382
Feeding strategies, of primates, 145–146
Fejej site, 247, 250
Female figurines, 506–509
Females
  childbirth and bipedalism, 271–273
  dominance and mating patterns of, 135–136
  sexual selection by, 139
Femur, 189
Ferrassie site, La, 402, 444–445
Fertility art, 502–505, 509
Fibrinopeptides, 31
Fight-or-flight reaction, 361
Finches, 70–71
Fire
  archaic *H. sapiens* use of, 426, 433
  H. erectus use of, 337–339, 343, 360, 428
  Sinanthropus use of, 307
  in Upper Paleolithic, 488–489
Fisher, Ronald Aylmer, 48–50, 66
Fishing, in Upper Paleolithic, 496–497
Fission-track dating methods, 27, 28, 243, 255
Fitness, 80–81

Flake tools
  of archaic *H. sapiens*, 427–428, 435–437, 460–461
  disk-core technique in, 435–437
  of *H. erectus*, 329–336
  of hominids, 276–280
Flint, 328–329
Fluorine, in fossil dating, 24
Fontbrégoua cave, 452
Font-de-Gaume cave, 457, 500
Food. *See* Diet
Food gathering. *See* Hunting-and-gathering
Food sharing
  in chimpanzees, 156, 157
  family development and, 269–274, 355–358
Food supply
  primate behavior and, 142–143
  territory and ecology in, 144, 145
Foramen magnum, 200
Forest monkeys, 127
Fossey, Dian, 127, 148–153
Fossil dating, 19, 23–31, 209. *See also specific methods*
Fossil magnetism, 28, 243
Fossils. *See also specific fossils and sites*
  clues to archaic *H. sapiens* fate in, 462–463
  dating of. *See* Fossil dating
  defined, 21–22
  of earliest primates, 171–176
  early naturalists' interpretation of, 5–14
  of first higher primates, 171, 176–178
  hominid, 187–193
  limitations of, 124
  marine, 22
  nineteenth century view of, 17–18
  of prosimians, 93
  sale of, 296, 301–302
  scarcity of human, 21–22
  sites of, 22–23
Founder effect, 69–73, 476
Founder population, 69
Foxes, 307
France. *See also specific sites*
  archaic *H. sapiens* in, 430, 442–443, 463
  cannibalism evidence in, 449, 452
  cave art in, 498–506
  modern humans in, 455–458
  Neandertals in, 443–445
  in Paleocene epoch, 174
  tools found in, 5, 6, 461–462, 490
  in Upper Paleolithic, 493–494, 494, 496, 497
  weapons found in, 496
Frankfort plane, 464
Frere, John, 5–6
Fruit flies, experiments on, 55–57, 72
Fuegian Indians, 452
Fuhlrott, J. K., 398

Fusion-fission communities, 153–154, 165–166

Gabunia, L., 318
Galápagos finches, 11–12, 70–71
Galdikas, Biruté, 127
Galileo, 5
Gamble, Clive, 422, 447
Gametes, 43, 53
Gardner, Beatrice, 375
Gardner, Robert, 375
Garn, Stanley, 535
Gazelles, 353
Gelada baboons, 144, 340, 349
Gene flow, 66–73, 83
  in modern humans, 466–467, 476
Gene frequencies, 68
Gene pools
  advantages of large, 49, 476
  of archaic *H. sapiens*, 419
  defined, 63
  genotypes and, 66
  of modern humans, 476
  speciation and, 416–418
Genera, defined, 9
Generalist-opportunist feeding strategy, 145, 153
Gene replication, 59
Genes, 43, 51, 57–84
  discovery of, 56
  DNA in. *See* DNA
  Hardy-Weinberg theorem in, 76–78
  inclusive fitness and, 80–81
  mitochondrial, 58, 468–472
  recessive. *See* Recessive genes
  RNA in, 59–61
  sexual selection and, 78–80
Genetical Theory of Natural Selection, The (Fisher), 50
Genetic diseases, 530–531. *See also specific diseases*
Genetic drift, 69–73, 83
Genetic engineering, 83, 546
Genetic load, 73–76
Genomes, 83
Genotypes, 40–41, 42, 66, 77
Geochemistry, 20
Geographical isolation, 66–68, 72–73, 80, 467
Geologic time scales, 172
Geology, 20, 23
Georgia, Republic of, 314, 318
Germany, 5, 398, 400, 411, 412
  in Paleocene epoch, 174
  sculpture in, 503
  in Upper Paleolithic, 496
  weapons found in, 496
Gestures, 369, 382
Getting Here (Howells), 484
Gibbons, 31, 293–294

arboreal specialization of, 146
characteristics of, 146–148
classification of, 90
dominance hierarchy of, 146–147
environmental adaptation of, 146–148
group dependence of, 128
Huxley's view of, 17
locomotion of, 103–106
sexual selection among, 147
socioecological characteristics of, 129
studies of, 124, 125, 127, 128
territory and ecology of, 143
Gibraltar, 399, 400
Gibson, Kathleen, 376, 379
Gigantopithecus, 183–186
Giraffes, 68, 69, 250
Glaciation, 327–328, 428–433
Glib Zegdou site, 176–177
Gluteus medius, 192
Gluteus minimus, 192
Goats, 521, 525, 543
Gombe chimpanzees, 153–154
aggression in, 160–161
politics in, 161–162
social interaction in, 135, 140–141
tool and weapon use in, 158–160,
208, 266–267, 274
Goodall, Jane, 110, 111, 127, 135, 153–161
Gorillas, 121, 148–153. *See also specific types*
arboreal adaptations of, 148–149
chimpanzees compared with, 219
classification of, 89
communication in, 119
dentition of, 273
dominance hierarchy of, 132, 149–150, 151
evolutionary history of, 187
Fossey's research on, 127, 148–153
gibbons compared with, 146
herbalism of, 157
humans compared with, 30, 31
Huxley's view of, 17
locomotion of, 107–108
P. robustus compared with, 207
sexual dimorphism in, 151, 152
sexual selection in, 151, 152
Sinanthropus compared with, 306
social interaction in, 141
socioecological characteristics of, 129
studies of, 124, 127
territory and ecology of, 142
Gould, Stephen Jay, 393
Gouzoules, Harold, 371
Gouzoules, Sarah, 371
Grasses, spread of, 222. *See also* Savannas
Gravettian, 507–508
Gray, Tom, 243
Gray squirrels, 99, 102
Great apes. *See* Bonobos; Chimpanzees;
Gorillas; Orangutans
Greece, 412. *See also specific sites*

Greenfield, Leonard, 273–274
Grine, F. E., 219, 237
Grooming, 139–141
Grotte Chauvet, La, 505–506
Grotto della Basua (Cave of Witches),
440–441
Group selection, 518–519
Guanine, 59
Guidon, Niede, 478

Haberer, K. A., 301–302
Hadar fossils, 240–248, 249, 251, 255, 257,
278, 390
Haeckel, Ernst Heinrich, 293, 294, 299
Hair form, 475, 528–529. *See also* Body hair
Haldane, J. B. S., 48, 49, 518
Hamadryas baboons, 125, 132, 144
Hamilton, W. D., 80, 519
Hammers, 345
of *H. erectus*, 329, 330–331
Hamstring muscles, 190
Hand axes, 520
of archaic *H. sapiens*, 402, 426–427, 437
of *H. erectus*, 328–336, 349
of Neandertals, 431, 432
Handicapped, care of, 447–448
Handprints, 513
Hands, 115–116. *See also* Manual dexterity
of apes, 115–116
of chimpanzees, 110, 115
of earliest primates, 175
of gibbons, 147
of gorillas, 147
human, 115–116, 117
of monkeys, 115–116
opposable thumbs and, 89, 115, 217, 244
of orangutans, 147
of prosimians, 96–97
Hapacoya site, 478
Haploid numbers, 54, 63–65
Hardy, G. H., 77–78
Hardy-Weinberg theorem, 76–78
Harem polygyny, 150
Harlow, Harry, 126
Harlow, Margaret, 126
Harris, Jack, 255
Hartebeest, 493
Hartwig-Scherer, Sigrid, 249
Hausfater, Glenn, 134
Headhunters, 362
Hearths, 489, 498
Heidelberg fossils, 301, 412
Hemispheres of brain, language and,
378–379
Hemispherical asymmetry, 317
Hemoglobin, 31, 59, 69, 124
Henslow, J. S., 11
Herbalism, 157
Herder, Johann Gottfried, 368
Hereditary disorders, 530–531

Heredity, 36–51
De Vries's work in, 45–47
Mendel's work in. *See* Mendel, Gregor
units of, 53–65
Heritability, 65
Heterodent dentition, 90
Heterozygotes, 58
genetic load and, 73–76
Hardy-Weinberg theorem and, 77
Mendel's work on, 41, 43
Heuristic devices, 168
Hill, Andrew, 247, 254
Hippopotamus, 296
HIV. *See* Human immunodeficiency
virus
Ho, C. K., 307
Holloway, Ralph, 229, 387
Home base concept, 281, 360–361
Home range, 141–142
Hominidae. *See* Hominids
Hominids, 110–119, 198, 232–233, 265–287
bipedalism of, 254–255, 257, 262, 266–274
brain of, 266, 280, 385
classification of, 207, 236
evolutionary relationships among,
259–260, 262, 292–293
fossil record of, 187–193
lifestyles of early, 256–258, 281–284
locomotion of, 265–274
oldest, 251–255
technology of, 254, 274–284
tools used by, 257, 266–267, 274–284
Hominoidea (superfamily), 90, 91, 171,
182, 183
Hominoids, 102
African origin of, 182
monkeys compared with, 103–108
Homo (genus), 198, 207, 257, 259, 516. *See
also specific species*
brain size, 221–222, 272–273
coexistence with other hominids, 230
Homo erectus, 291–322, 325–345, 348–365,
470–472
in Africa, 312–314
aggression in, 361–363
anatomy of, 314–318
archaic *H. sapiens* compared with, 406,
409
brain of, 314–318, 326, 352, 355–356,
384, 391
butchery by, 331–332, 340–341, 349, 353,
354, 357
cannibalism of, 361–363
as chronospecies, 467
coexistence with other hominids, 230
culture of, 262
diet of, 332, 339–341, 350, 357
Dubois's work on, 293–301
environmental adaptation of, 517
exogamy in, 360

Homo erectus (Continued)
  family development in, 355–361
  home base concept in, 360–361
  hunting-and-gathering of, 339–341, 355
  hunting by, 348–354
  incest taboo in, 359
  language in, 317–318, 383–384
  life expectancy of, 360–361, 544
  major characteristics of, 316
  migrations of, 318–320, 326–328, 355
  modern humans compared with,
    472–473
  Neandertals and, 418–420
  shelters of, 336–337, 360, 428, 430
  social interaction in, 355–361
  speech of, 317–318
  at Terra Amata site. *See* Terra Amata site
  tools used by, 328–336, 349, 353, 491, 492
Homo ergaster, 314
Homo habilis, 238, 292, 341
  Australopithecus compared with,
    228–229
  brain of, 229–230, 391
  classification of, 228–229
  coexistence with other hominids, 230
  discovery of, 227–228
  environmental adaptation of, 517
  H. rudolfensis compared with, 238–240
  lifestyles of, 257–258
  major characteristics of, 239
  social interdependence in, 355
  tools used by, 8, 168, 222, 256, 280, 281
  and turnover pulse hypothesis, 287
Homo neanderthalensis, 399–401, 405–406.
  See also Neandertals
Homo rudolfensis, 292, 341, 391
  H. habilis compared with, 238–240
  lifestyles of, 257–258
  major characteristics of, 239
  social interdependence in, 355
  stone tools and, 256
  and turnover pulse hypothesis, 287
Homo sapiens, 310. *See also* Humans;
  Modern humans
  archaic. *See* Archaic *Homo sapiens*
  brain of, 229, 385
  as chronospecies, 467
  classification of, 87–88
  first appearance of, 463
  ongoing evolution of, 545–546
  sexual dimorphism in, 355–358
  taxonomy of, 89–90
  tools used by, 412
Homo sapiens, 455, 516. *See also* Modern
  humans
Homozygotes, 58, 531
  genetic load in, 73–76
  Hardy-Weinberg theorem and, 77
  Mendel's work on, 41, 43
Hooton, Earnest, 535

Horses, 23–24, 68, 114, 286, 410, 458, 493,
  502, 503–504
Hortus cave, 449
Housing. *See* Shelters
Howell, F. Clark, 231, 232
Howells, William, 219, 336, 484
Howler monkeys, 141, 145
How Monkeys See the World (Cheney and
  Seyfarth), 117–118
Hrdlicka, Alés, 300
Hughes, Alun, 215–216
Hulse, Frederick, 79
Human brain, 116–118. *See also* Brain;
  specific areas of brain
  in language, 118–119, 317, 373, 378–379,
    381, 382, 385–391
  Sinanthropus brain compared with,
    306–307
  vision and, 110, 114–115
Human immunodeficiency virus (HIV), 51
Human Nature (Wilson), 519–520
Human origins, xvi, 3–34
  Africa as site of, 17, 18, 182, 468,
    470–472, 542
  early naturalists' search for, 5–14
  evolution theory in. *See* Evolutionary
    theory
  modern excavations and, 31–32
  modern studies of, 19–21
  paleoanthropology in study of. *See*
    Paleoanthropology
Humans. *See also Homo sapiens*; Modern
  humans
  ancestors of, 187–193
  blood groups among, 72
  brain of. *See* Human brain
  characteristics of. *See under specific
    characteristics*
  chromosomes of, 54
  common ancestors with apes, 165–166
  locomotion of, 198
  major characteristics of, 166
  nonhuman primate similarity to,
    124–125, 146, 164–165
  origins of. *See* Human origins
  sexual physiology of, 137
  sexual selection among, 78–80
  species divergence in, 31
  status in, 137
Hungary, 412, 442–443, 459, 463. *See also
  specific sites*
Hunting. *See also* Hunting-and-gathering
  animal domestication and, 522
  by archaic *H. sapiens*, 440–441
  beginnings of, 352–354
  brain development and, 352
  by chimpanzees, 156–157
  diet and, 350
  be early *Homo*, 280–285
  by *H. erectus*, 348–354

  home base concept and, 360–361
  by modern humans, 481
  skin adaptation and, 351
  specialization in, 440–441
  in Upper Paleolithic, 493–496
Hunting-and-gathering. *See also* Hunting
  analogue models of, 343–345
  by archaic *H. sapiens*, 428
  by *H. erectus*, 339–341, 355
  sex roles in, 355–358, 364–365
Hunting rites
  of archaic *H. sapiens*, 440–442
  of modern humans, 457
  of Upper Paleolithic, 499–502
Hutton, James, xvi, 7–8, 15, 32
Huxley, Thomas H., 17–18, 90, 112,
  305–306, 400
Hybridization, 38–45, 46–47, 66. *See also*
  Interbreeding
Hyenas, 305, 307, 339, 363, 449–450
Hylobates. See Gibbons
Hyoid, 414
Hypotheses, defined, 314

Ibex, 502
Ice ages, 293, 295, 327–328, 428–433.
  See also specific epochs
Iliac blades, 189, 192, 244
Iliofemoral ligament, 192
Ilium, 112
Inbreeding, 80, 359
Incest taboo, 80, 358, 359
Inclusive fitness, 80–81
Independent assortment principle, 43–45, 57
India, 498
  archaic *H. sapiens* in, 409
  modern humans in, 475
  primate studies in, 127, 131
Indian Ocean, 26
Indians, American. *See* Native Americans
Industrial age, 543–544
Infanticide, in langurs, 151–152
Infants
  of *H. erectus*, 355–356
  language development and, 367–368,
    377, 384
  maternal bond with, 126
Inheritance, 10, 51, 57
Insects
  Anopheles mosquito, 74
  bioaltruism in, 519
  communication in, 368
  fruit fly experiments, 55–57, 72
Intelligence
  of archaic *H. sapiens*, 430–431
  ethnic group and, 541
  of *H. erectus*, 352
  hunting and, 352
Interbreeding, 68, 417, 418, 476. *See also*
  Hybridization

Intergenerational drift, 72
Introns, 59
IQ tests, 541
Iraq, 425. *See also specific sites*
Iron pyrite, as fire starter, 488–489
Isaac, Glynn, 233, 281, 349
Ischial shaft, 244–245
Ischium, 189, 192–193
Israel, 409–411, 437, 440, 465. *See also specific sites*
Italy, 440–441, 449–450
Itani, Junichiro, 154–155
Ivory tools, of Upper Paleolithic, 460, 488, 492

Jackals, 386
James IV, of Scotland, 368
Japan, 126–127, 441–442, 506
Japanese macaques, 126–127, 129, 132
    incest taboo in, 359
    sexuality and status in, 135
    sexual physiology of, 136–137
Java fossils, 26, 32, 295–301, 408–409, 425, 465. *See also Pithecanthropus erectus*
    controversy over, 299–301
    discovery of, 296–299
    fate of, 309–311
Jaws, of modern humans, 472–475
Jebel Irhoud site, 468
Jelinek, A. J., 336
Jeñyü, Wang, 125
Jericho, 524–525
Jerison, Harry, 385–386, 391
Jewish community, 72, 77–78
Jingniushan site, 409
Johannsen, W., 56
Johanson, Donald C., 228, 240–247, 249–250
Jolly, Clifford, 273–274
Jones, F. Wood, 97
Jones, Steve, 545–546
Judeo-Christian religious beliefs, xvi–xvii, 34. *See also* Bible

Kabwe skull, 406–408, 412, 422, 466, 468
Kanapoi site, 262
Kangaroos, 111
Kangatukuseo site, 236
Kanzi (bonobo), 376
Kattwinkel, Wilhelm, 223
Kebara site, 409–410
Keith, Arthur, 229
Kenya, 26, 134–135, 349, 521. *See also specific sites*
Keratin, 59
Khoisan site, 529
Kiik-Koba site, 445
Kimeu, Kamoya, 313–314
King, William, 400, 405–406
Kin selection, 81, 269, 373

Kinship, 358, 359
Klasies River Mouth site, 437, 466, 467
Klein, Richard, 336, 337, 340, 353, 442, 462
Klinefelter's syndrome, 74–76
Knuckle walking, 112, 115, 165
Köhler, Ilse, 525
Köhler, Wolfgang, 125–126
Kohl-Larsen, L., 248–249
Kohts, Nadie, 126
Koko (gorilla), 375–376
Koman, Jeremy, 159
Koobi Fora site, 233–236, 237–240, 255, 313, 337–338
Kortland, Adrian, 127
Krantz, Grover S., 353, 383–384
Krapina site, 448–449
Kromdraai site, 206–207, 217, 219, 248

Laboratories of Primate Biology, Florida, 125
Laetoli site, 222, 248–251, 257
Lahr, Marta Mirazon, 468
Lamarck, Chevalier de, 10
Lana (chimpanzee), 375–376
Lancaster, Jane, 380
Landsteiner, Karl, 532
Language, 118–119, 367–393. *See also* Communication; Speech
    animal communication compared with, 368–372, 374–376. *See also under specific animals*
    of archaic *H. sapiens*, 422
    brain in, 118–119, 317, 373, 378–379, 381, 382, 385–391. *See also under specific areas of brain*
    cultural adaptation and, 119
    defined, 367
    early theories on, 367–368
    evolution of, 381–384
    in early *Homo*, 258, 391–392
    in first humans, 384
    in *H. erectus*, 317–318, 383–384
    limbic system in, 372–374, 379–381, 383–384
    in modern humans, 459
    nature of, 374
    Neandertal potential for, 383, 431
    pharynx in, 376–377, 382, 383, 473–475
Langurs, 127, 129, 131, 132, 142, 151–152
Larynx, 382, 383, 473
Lascaux cave, 500
Laughlin, William, 72
Lazaret site, 430
Leakey, Jonathan, 227
Leakey, Louis, 153, 223–230, 248, 275, 280, 312, 314, 352, 410
Leakey, Mary, 223, 224–225, 227, 248, 249, 275–276, 280, 281
Leakey, Richard, 232, 233, 234, 236

Leakey family, 229, 280, 349
Lebanon, 441
Le Gros Clark, Wilfrid, 90, 213, 229, 309
Leisters, 496
Lemurs, 93, 96, 121, 176
Leopards, 307
Leroi-Gourhan, André, 502–503
Leroi-Gourhan, Arlette, 445–446
Leukocytes, 532
Levallois technique, 427–428, 435, 437
Levant, 525
Levine, Joseph, 546
Lewis-Williams, David, 501–502
Lewontin, R. C., 538
Lexigrams, 376
Libby, Willard, 26
Lieberman, Philip, 382–383
Life expectancy
    of *Australopithecus*, 544
    of *H. erectus*, 360–361, 544
    of modern humans, 487, 544
    in Upper Paleolithic, 467
Lightfoot, James, 4
Limbic system, in language, 372–374, 379–381, 383–384
Linnaean Society, 15–16
Linnaeus, Carl, 9, 87–90, 90
Lippmann, F., 57
Lithic technology, 328
Liujiang site, 463, 468
Locomotion, 198. *See also* Arboreality; Bipedalism; Quadrupedalism
    of apes, 103–113, 188–192, 194–195, 198
    energy efficiency of, 267–268
    hominid, evolution of, 265–274
    human, 198
    of monkeys, 198
Locus, 58
Lomekwi site, 236
Lorenz, Konrad, 361
Lorises, 93, 98, 102, 176
Lovejoy, Owen, 269–271, 358
Lower Paleolithic, 460
Lucy (skeleton), 243. *See also Australopithecus afarensis*
Lukenya Hill site, 521
Lumbar curve, 192
Lumpers, 218–219, 235–236
Lyell, Charles, 10, 11, 15, 23, 82, 286

Maba site, 409
Macaques. *See also specific types*
    brain of, 386
    childhood learning in, 131–132
    as endangered group, 121
    feeding strategies of, 145
    sexual physiology of, 137
    social interaction in, 140–141
    territory and ecology of, 142
MacEnery, J., 6

McGrew, W. C., 159–160, 168
McHenry, H. M., 260
Machiavelli, Niccolò, 161
McKenna, James, 139
Madagascar, 94, 96, 121
Magdalenian culture, 495, 498, 502
Magnetic field of earth, 28, 243
Makapansgat site, 214, 219, 248, 307
Maka site, 250
Malakunanja site, 479
Malaria, 74–76, 534
Males
  dominance hierarchy and, 133–134
  mating patterns of, 134–135
  paternal attention of, 132, 269–271
Malthus, Thomas R., 14, 543
Mammoths, 5, 6, 9, 432, 434, 492, 493, 500, 502
Mandibular symphysis, 474–475
Man-Eating Myth, The (Arens), 452
Mangabeys, 145
Manual dexterity, 147, 266. See also Hands
Manuports, 278
Marine fossils, 22
Maringer, Johannes, 499, 508
Marks, Jonathan, 539
Marler, Peter, 371
Marmosets, 101, 143
Marsh, O. C., 299
Marshack, Alexander, 503–505
Martin, William Charles, 125
Mason, Revil, 215–216
Material culture, 168
Matrilineal kinship, 128, 129–136
Mauer jaw, 301, 412
Mayr, Ernst, 14, 15
Meat eating
  in archaic H. sapiens, 426
  butchery and, 277–278, 331–332, 340–341, 349, 353, 354, 357
  in chimpanzees, 141, 156–157
  in early Homo, 257–258, 278–285
  and H. erectus, 331–332, 350, 355, 357
Mediterranean region. See also specific countries and sites
  environmental problems in, 525
  in Pleistocene glaciations, 429, 430
Meganthropus africanus, 249
Meiosis, 54, 57, 63–65, 66
Melanesians, 479
Melanin, 433, 526
Melka Kunteré, 312–313
Memory, 116, 352, 379
Mendel, Anton, 38
Mendel, Gregor, 37–45, 49, 50–51, 53, 54, 57
  Hardy-Weinberg Law and, 77
  rediscovery of work of, 45–47
Men of the Old Stone Age (Osborn), 483–484

Menstrual cycle, 137. See also Estrus
Messenger RNA, 59, 60
Metabolic rate, 530
Mexico, 478, 521
Microwear, 277
Middle East, 409–411, 425, 459, 460–461, 465, 468. See also specific countries and sites
  domestication of animals and plants in, 521, 523
  tools found in, 331, 332
Middle Paleolithic, 437–440, 460–461, 511
Miescher, Friedrich, 58
Migration, 318–320, 326–328, 355, 477–481
Mimicry, 47–48
Mind, 117–118
Miocene epoch, 171, 188
  apes of, 182–187, 194–195
  grass spread during, 222
Missing link, 18
  Dubois's search for, 293–296, 298–299, 301
  Neandertals as, 293, 398–399
  Taung skull as, 200–201, 203
Mr. Worzle (chimpanzee), 158–159
Mitochondria, 58
Mitochondrial DNA (mtDNA), 468–472, 478
Mitosis, 54
Mivart, George, 90, 93
Mladec site, 465
Modern humans, 455–548. See also Humans
  archaic H. sapiens compared with, 463–464
  biological and cultural transitions of, 472–475
  brain of. See Human brain
  characteristics of, 110–119, 458–459
  dentition of, 473–475, 530
  diet of, 473, 480–481, 494
  endangerment of nonhuman primates, 121–122
  environmental adaptation of, 71–72
  first appearance of, 455–459
  future prospects of, 545–546
  major characteristics of, 482
  migration of, 477–481
  origin of, 464–472
  in Upper Paleolithic. See Upper Paleolithic
Molecular clocks, 29–31
Monkeys, 307. See also specific types
  A. afarensis compared with, 248
  abnormal adaptation in, 103–108
  ancestors of, 90, 93–100, 178–182
  apes compared with, 103–108
  brain of, 379, 385–386
  childhood learning in, 131–132

  classification of, 90
  communication in, 141, 368, 369–371, 374–376
  dentition of, 179
  as endangered group, 121
  feeding strategies of, 145
  grooming and, 139
  hands of, 115–116
  hominid similarity to, 266
  incest taboo in, 358, 359
  limbic system of, 379–380
  locomotion of, 198
  mind and, 117–118
  morphology of, 181
  sexual physiology of, 136–137
  studies of, 124, 125
Monogamy, 78
Monogyny, 138–139, 143, 146, 271, 358
Monomorphic traits, 146–147
Montagna, William, 351
Monte Circeo cave, 449–450
Monte Verde site, 478
Morgan, Thomas Hunt, 55–56, 57
Morocco, 175, 312, 468
Morphological patterns, 181, 188–193
Motor output, 373
Mountain gorillas, 148–153
Mount Carmel sites, 409–411, 416
Mousterian industry, 435–437, 440, 460–461
Mousterian of Acheulean Tradition (MAT), 462
Mousterians. See also Neandertals
  art of, 444–445
  burial rites of, 444–445
  cannibalism in, 448–450, 451–452
  fate of, 459
  modern humans compared with, 463–464
Moustier cave, Le, 402
Movius, Hallam, 332–333
Movius line, 333, 334
mtDNA. See Mitochondrial DNA
Mules, 68, 410
Muller, H. J., 57, 63
Multimale-multifemale communities, 154, 163, 165, 257
Murder, among chimpanzees, 160–161
Muriqui monkeys, 121
Mutations, 45–50, 51, 83
  DNA replication and, 63
  gene flow and, 66
  genetic drift and, 69–73
  genetic load and, 74
  Hardy-Weinberg theorem and, 77
  mtDNA and, 469–470
  natural selection and, 47–50, 63, 66
  point, 63
  x-rays and, 63
Myers, Ronald, 373

Namibia, 498
Napier, John, 112, 115
Nariokotome boy, 292, 313–314, 317, 355, 356, 528. *See also* Homo erectus
Native Americans, 78, 452, 494, 529
Natural History (Buffon), 7
Naturalists, early, 5–14. *See also specific individuals*
Natural selection, xvi, 14, 36, 45, 68–69, 83, 393, 517
  altruism and, 518–520
  directional, 69
  examples of, 70–72
  feeding strategies and, 145–146
  gene selection and, 77
  H. erectus and, 355
  Hardy-Weinberg theorem and, 77
  in humans, 71
  mutations and, 47–50, 63, 66
  in phenotypes, 74
  and phyletic transformation, 81
  in population genetics, 53, 76–78
  premises of, 14–15
  sexual selection vs., 78–80
  stabilizing, 69
  variability and, 74
Nature magazine, 200, 203, 252, 260
Navigation, 480
Neandertals, 19, 22, 200, 397–411, 472. *See also* Archaic *Homo sapiens*
  art of, 442–443
  assessment of, 413–421
  brain of, 399–400, 403–404, 414, 419
  burial rites of, 443–447, 509
  Chapelle-aux-Saints, La, discoveries and. *See* Chapelle-aux-Saints, La
  classification of, 399–401, 405–406
  Cro-Magnons compared with, 405, 463–464
  dentition of, 473
  evolutionary role of, 397–398
  expansion and adaptations of, 437–440
  fate of, 459, 466, 483–484
  first views of, 397–406
  hunting rite of, 440–442
  intelligence of, 430–431
  language potential of, 383, 431
  major characteristics of, 415
  as "missing link," 293, 398–399
  modern humans compared with, 473
  reconstruction of, 402–406
  tools used by, 431, 432, 435–437, 460–462, 491
  violence among, 448
Neander Valley, 398–401, 443
Needles, 498, 508–509
Neocortex, 386–387
Neurons, 116, 387, 388
New South Wales, 479
Newton, Isaac, 5

New World monkeys, 31, 101–102, 127, 181–182, 386
Ngaloba site, 466, 468
Niah Cave, 468
Nishida, Toshisada, 127, 154–155, 156, 157
Nissen, Henry, 125
Nitrogen, in fossil dating, 24
Nocturnal pattern, 93
Nonlimbic communication, 372–374
Nonverbal communication, 369, 370, 373, 380
North Africa, 459, 468
North America
  early primates in, 175
  grass spread in, 222
  modern humans in, 459, 478
  in Paleocene epoch, 174
Northern Europe, 428–429
Nose shape, 529
Nucleotides, 59, 63

Occipital condyles, 253
Occipital torus, 314, 315
Occupation levels. *See also* Shelters
  at Olduvai Gorge, 280–284
  at Terra Amata, 336–337
Oldowan choppers, 329–330
Oldowan tool industry, 168, 224, 255, 262, 275–284, 320, 328, 329–330, 460, 543
Olduvai Gorge, 222–233, 238, 248–249, 255, 275–284, 312, 314, 349, 355
  fossil dating in, 28
  occupation levels at, 280–284
Old World monkeys, 31, 101–102, 194–195
  dentition of, 109
  hands of, 115
  socioecological characteristics of, 129
Olfactory sense, of prosimians, 97, 100
Oligocene epoch, 176, 178–181
Oligopithecines, 177–178
Olorgesailie site, 349
Omomyidae, 176, 177
Omo site, 231–233, 247, 255, 313–314, 466, 467
One-male groups, 358. *See also* Polygyny
On the Origin of Species by Means of Natural Selection (Darwin), xvii, 12, 14, 15–16, 17, 286, 398, 399, 401
Open words, 384
Opossum, 102
Opportunistic mating, 134
Opposable thumbs, 89, 115, 217, 244
Opposable toes, 217, 244
Orangutans, 294, 296
  arboreal specialization of, 146
  characteristics of, 147–148
  classification of, 89
  communication in, 375

environmental adaptation of, 147–148
  evolutionary history of, 187
  Huxley's view of, 17
  locomotion of, 107
  socioecological characteristics of, 129
  studies of, 124, 127
  territory and ecology of, 142
  tool use and, 147
Oreopithecus, 186
Organic evolution, xvi, 10
Osborn, Henry Fairfield, 300, 483–484
Osteodontokeratic culture, 214, 307
Ostriches, 111
Otavipithecus namibiensis, 183
Otters, 307
Ouch-ouch hypothesis, 368, 373
Ouranopithecus, 188
Outbreeding, 80, 360, 475
Ova, 43

Pair bonding, 270–271
Pakistan, 331
Paleoanthropology, 20, 21–32, 516–517
  dating methods in. *See* Fossil dating
  defined, 19
  modern excavations, 29–32
Paleocene epoch, 171, 172–175
Paleolithic, 543. *See also* Lower Paleolithic; Middle Paleolithic; Upper Paleolithic
Paleomagnetism, 28, 243
Paleontology, 20, 23
Palynology, 20
Pangaea II, 173
Panidae, 107–108
Pan paniscus. See Bonobos (pygmy chimpanzees)
Pan troglodytes. See Chimpanzees
Paranthropus (genus), 198, 218–219
  brain of, 390
  and turnover pulse hypothesis, 287
Paranthropus aethiopicus. See also Black skull
  lifestyles of, 257
  major characteristics of, 235
  stone tools and, 256
Paranthropus boisei, 233, 234–236
  age of, 226–227
  coexistence with other hominids, 230
  dentition of, 226
  discovery of, 224–226
  lifestyles of, 257
  major characteristics of, 235
  at Olduvai Gorge, 281
  stone tools and, 226, 256
Paranthropus robustus, 206–207
  assessment of, 213–214
  coexistence with other hominids, 230
  dentition of, 206, 207, 217
  discovery of, 206–207

Paranthropus robustus (Continued)
  lifestyles of, 257
  major characteristics of, 211
  P. boisei compared with, 226, 234–235
  tools used by, 217–218
Parapithecus, 178
Particulate inheritance, 51, 57
Passingham, Richard, 387
Patterson, Penny, 375
Pavlov site, 465, 493
Pebble tools, 18, 215–217, 223–224, 276.
  See also Choppers; Stone tools
Pêch de l'Azé cave, 442
Pech-Merle cave, 503
Pedology, 20
Pedra Furada site, 478
Peking man, 301, 303–308, 338. *See also*
  Beijing fossils
Penicillin, 51
Perforators, of Upper Paleolithic, 491
Perigordian industry, 507–508
Persistence hunting, 353
Perspiration. *See* Sweating, development of
Peru, 478, 521
PET. See Positron emission tomography
Petitto, Laura, 375
Petralona skull, 412
Petrology, 20
Pharynx, 376–377, 382, 383, 473–475
Phenetic classification, 88, 89
Phenotypes, 41, 66, 74
  collective, 68
  Hardy-Weinberg theorem and, 77–78
  sexual selection and, 78–80
Phenotypic divergence, 66
Phenylketonuria (PKU), 531
Phonation, 382–383
Phyletic transformation, 81, 467
Phylogenetic classification, 89
Physical anthropology, 20
Picks, 437, 439
Pigment recipes, 441, 502, 509, 512
Pigs, 286, 307, 493
Pikimachay site, 478
Pilbeam, David, 473–474
Piltdown hoax, 202, 210, 301, 321
Pithecanthropus erectus, 321–322, 402. *See*
  also Java fossils
  brain of, 300, 309, 321
  controversy over, 299–301
  discovery of, 296–299
  Sinanthropus and, 308–309
Pithecanthropus pekinensis, 310
Pivot words, 384
Placard cave, La, 494
Plasmids, 51
Platycephalic traits, 315
Platyrrhines, 102–103. *See also* New
  World monkeys
Pleistocene epoch, 299, 409, 428–433

Middle, 301, 412
Plesiadapiformes, 174–175
Pliocene epoch, 187, 266, 298
  A. africanus in, 209
  monkeys of, 248
Plio-Pleistocene epochs, 222, 327, 340
Point mutations, 63
Poison, in hunting, 353
Poland, 463
Pollen, in graves, 445–446, 502
Polygamy, 78
Polygenic traits, 56
Polygyny, 138–139, 144, 257, 271, 358. *See*
  also One-male groups
  harem, 150
Polymorphism, 73–76
Pondaungia, 177
Pongo. See Orangutans
Pope, Geoffrey, 335
Population
  evolutionary success and, 542–543
  genes in, 66–82
  primate, 121–122
Population genetics, 53, 76–78
Population growth, 543–545
Porpoises, 386
Positive feedback systems, 274
Positron emission tomography (PET),
  378–379
Postcranial anatomy, 103
Postorbital bar, 96
Potassium-argon (K/Ar) dating, 25–26,
  27, 243
  of *P. boisei*, 227
  of stone tools, 255
Potts, Richard, 282–284
Pounding slabs, of Upper Paleolithic, 491
Power grip, 115
Precision grip, 115–116, 217
Předmost site, 465
Prehensile tails, 102
Premack, David, 389
Primary sites, 349
Primates, 87–122, 124–169. *See also specific*
  types
  anthropoids, 90, 101–119
  brains of, 386–388
  childhood learning in, 128–132
  classification of, 87–90
  communication in nonhuman. *See*
    Communication
  dominance hierarchy of. *See*
    Dominance hierarchy
  earliest fossils of, 171–176
  earliest types of, 90–110
  feeding strategies of, 145–146
  first higher types, 176–178
  global emergency and, 121–122
  grooming in, 139–141
Hominidae, 104

Hominoidea, 104
  living genera of, 95
  major characteristics of, 92, 104
  prosimians, 90, 93–100, 104
  sexual physiology of, 136–138
  sexual selection in, 78, 138–139
  social interaction in, 140–141
  status among, 134–136
  studies of, 124–127
  territory and ecology of, 141–146
Principles of Geology (Lyell), 10, 11
Proceptivity, 137
Proconsul, 182–183, 184, 185, 194–195
Prognathic cranium, 236
Propliopithecus, 178–181
Prolonged dependence period, 128–132
Promiscuous mating system, 147
Prosimians, 104, 121
  adaptations of, 93–100
  earliest primates as, 175–176
  EQs of, 385–386
  species divergence in, 31
Protein immunology, 31
Proteins, defined, 59
Protein synthesis, 59
Proteopithecus, 177, 178
Protoculture, 168
Psammetichus (pharaoh), 367–368
Punctuated equilibrium, 287
Punnett, R. C., 54
Punnett squares, 43
Pygmies, 229–230, 353
Pygmy chimpanzees. *See* Bonobos
  (pygmy chimpanzees)
Pyrenees, 412

Qafzeh cave, 409–411, 461, 465, 468
Quadrupedalism, 88, 102–103, 107–108
Quina site, La, 402
Quinault Indians, 78

Races
  biological, 535–540
  blood groups of. *See* Blood groups
  defined, 535
  ethnic groups, 541, 548
  physical variability and, 526–540
Racism, 541
Radioactive dating methods, 19, 25–31,
  478
Radium, 25
Ramapithecus, 187
Random mating, 77
Rapid-replacement hypothesis, 467–472
Raup, D. M., 82
Ray, John, 5
Reasoned behavior, 116, 117
Receptivity, 137
Recessive genes, 40, 73–76, 80
Reciprocal altruism, 141, 373, 519–520

Reck, Hans, 223
Reconciliation, 162
Rectus femoris, 244
Red blood cells, 532
Red deer, 493, 502
Red ocher, 441, 509
Regional-continuity hypothesis, 464–467, 468
Regourdou site, 441
Reindeer, 432, 458, 466, 481, 502
Relative dating methods, 23–25
Religion, of Upper Paleolithic, 511–512. *See also* Rituals
Reproductive isolation, 66–68, 72–73, 467
Reproductive strategies, 152
    behavior and, 136–138
    bipedalism and, 269–271
    gorilla, 151, 152
    physiology and, 136–138
    sexual dimorphism and, 138–139
    status and, 134–136
Retroviruses, 51
Reynolds, Frances, 127
Reynolds, Vernon, 127
Rhesus monkeys, 126, 127
    communication in, 371, 372
    humans compared with, 30
    incest taboo in, 359
    sexuality and status in, 135
    sexual physiology of, 137
    territory and ecology of, 142
Rhesus (Rh) system, 532
Rhinarium, 101
Rhinoceroses, 5, 6, 250, 286, 307, 354, 429, 432, 434, 502
Rhodesian Man. *See* Kabwe skull
Rickets, 400, 435
Rifkin, Jeremy, 546
Rift Valley, 187, 222, 231, 255
Rightmire, G. Philip, 238, 314–315
Rituals. *See also specific rituals*
    of archaic *H. sapiens*, 440–443
    of Upper Paleolithic, 498–512
RNA (ribonucleic acid), 59–61
Robinson, J. T., 213, 215–216
Roche, Helene, 255
Rockefeller Foundation, 301, 302, 305
Rock painting, 478
Rollefson, Gary, 525
Rousseau, Jean-Jacques, 368
Rudapithecus, 186
Ruff, Christopher, 356
Russia, 432, 459, 489, 498. *See also specific sites*
Rwanda, 148–153, 548

Saber-toothed cats, 5, 232, 250
Sacrum, 189, 192
Sagittal crest, 207
Sagittal keel, 315–316

Sagittal suture, 226
St. Césaire site, 461, 462, 463
Salawuzu site, 463
Sangoan industry, 437, 439, 460
Sarah (chimpanzee), 375
Sarawak, 468
Sarich, Vincent, 30
Satellite DNA, 61
Savage-Rumbaugh, Sue, 376
Savanna baboons, 139, 142, 143–145
Savannas, 222–262, 517. *See also specific sites*
    defined, 112
    food supply in, 350
    locomotion evolution and, 112, 254–255, 268–269
    tools found in, 222–224, 255–256
Saws, of Upper Paleolithic, 491
Scavenging, 340
    daytime versus nighttime, 351
    by early *Homo*, 280–285
    by *H. erectus*, 348, 350, 351
    by hominids, 274–275, 280, 281–282
Schaffhausen, Hermann, 398
Schaller, George, 127
Schepartz, Lynn, 422
Schick, Kathy, 277–278, 331–332, 335, 340, 345
Schlosser, Max, 302
Schmerling, P. C., 6
Sciatic notch, 190–192
Scrapers
    of archaic *H. sapiens*, 437, 439
    of Upper Paleolithic, 491
Sculpture, in Upper Paleolithic, 506–509
Secondary altriciality, 355–356
Secondary sites, 349
Secret of Life, The (Levine and Suzuki), 546
Sedentism, 487–498
Seed-eating hypothesis, 273
Segregation principle, 43–45
Semicircular canal, 251
Sex chromosomes, 56, 57
Sex-linked traits, 55–56
Sex roles
    in chimpanzees, 159–160
    in *H. erectus*, 355–358, 364–365
    in hunting-and-gathering societies, 355–358, 364–365
Sex swellings, 137
Sexual behavior, 136–138
    bonobo, 164–165
    early primate studies of, 125
    estrus and, 134, 137, 152, 162, 269
    incest taboo, 80, 358–359
Sexual dimorphism
    in *A. afarensis*, 243, 246
    in primates, 138–139, 143, 151–152
Sexuality
    physiology and, 136–138

sexual selection and, 78–80, 138–139, 151–152
    status and, 134–136
Sexual physiology, 136–138
Sexual reproduction, 66
Sexual selection, 78–80, 138–139, 151–152
Seyfarth, Robert, 117–118, 373
Shanghuang, China, 177
Shanidar cave, 445–446, 448
Sheep, 307, 521, 543
Shelters. *See also* Cave dwellings; Occupation levels
    of archaic *H. sapiens*, 426, 433
    of *H. erectus*, 336–337, 360, 428, 430
    of Upper Paleolithic, 488–489, 498
Shipman, Pat, 281, 353
Siamangs, 103–106, 128, 143. *See also* Gibbons
Siberia, 441, 477, 507
Sickle-cell anemia, 74–76, 530, 534
Sidi Abderrahman site, 312
Signal systems, 370
Sign language, 374, 375–376
Silverback gorillas, 149–151
Sinanthropus pekinensis, 301, 303–308, 338
    assessment of, 306–307
    brain of, 304, 306–307, 309
    culture of, 307–308
    dentition of, 306
    discovery of, 302–304
Sinanthropus pekinensis
    Pithecanthropus and, 308–309
Singa site, 468
Sipka site, 465
Sister groups, 90
Sivapithecus, 186, 187
Skelton, R. R., 260
Skhūl site (Cave of the Kids), 409, 411, 448, 461, 465, 468
Skin adaptation
    in archaic *H. sapiens*, 433–435
    in *H. erectus*, 350–352
    sunlight and, 433–435, 526–527
Skin color
    of *Australopithecus*, 433–434
    as identifying feature, 526–527
Sloths, 88
Slovenia, 448–449
Small, Meredith, 139
Smith, B. Holly, 219
Smith, Grafton Elliot, 97, 296, 321
Smith, William, 9
Social interaction, 139–141
    chimpanzee, 135, 140–141
    in *H. erectus*, 355–361
Socioecology
    of apes, 129, 144–145
    defined, 144
    of Old World monkeys, 129
Solecki, Ralph, 441, 445–446

Soleihac site, 336
Solo man, 408–409
Solo River, 465
Solutrean laurel-leaf tools, 490–491, 498
Solutré site, 490–491, 493–494
Sonakia, Arun, 409
Song sparrows, speciation in, 417–418
South Africa, 125, 312, 437, 461, 466, 529.
    See also specific sites
    archaic *H. sapiens* in, 408
    modern humans in, 459
    in Upper Paleolithic, 497
South America, 121, 143. *See also specific
    countries and sites*
    domestication of animals and plants in,
    521
    modern humans in, 459, 478
    primate studies in, 127
Southeast Asia, 127, 143, 319, 333,
    466–467. *See also specific sites*
    H. erectus in, 325
    modern humans in, 459, 460, 465,
    478–480
Southern Asia, 438
South Korea, 333
Spain, 338, 413, 461–463. *See also specific
    sites*
Spears
    of archaic *H. sapiens*, 437, 448
    of *H. erectus*, 353
    of modern humans, 478
    of Upper Paleolithic, 492, 494–495, 496
Spear throwers, of Upper Paleolithic,
    494–495, 496
Specialist feeding strategy, 145–146
Speciation, 66–68
    allopatric, 66, 67, 420, 467
    archaic *Homo sapiens* and, 418–420
    described, 416–418
Species, defined, 9
Species divergence, 66–68
Species evolution, 66–82
Speech, 118–119. *See also*
    Communication; Language
    of archaic *H. sapiens*, 422
    defined, 368
    in early *Homo*, 258, 391–392
    early theories on, 368
    evolution of, 381–384
    of *H. erectus*, 317–318
    in modern humans, 473–474
    vocal apparatus for, 374–381
Sperm cells, 43, 54, 65
Spindles, 54
Splicing, 60
Splitters, 218–219, 235–236
Spy fossils, 401–402, 443, 445
Stabilizing natural selection, 69
Status, 134–136
Stegodons, 296

Steinheim fossils, 411–412, 422, 464
Steppe, 429
Stereoscopic vision, 97–98, 114–115, 266
Sterkfontein fossils, 205–206, 207,
    210–213, 215–217, 219, 248
Stewart, T. Dale, 448
Stillbirths, 74
Stone Age. *See also* Paleolithic
    clothing in, 498
    tools of, 492
Stoneking, Mark, 472
Stone knapping, 256, 257, 427, 437
Stone tools, 5–6, 168, 222, 228, 257, 267.
    See also Pebble tools; *specific types*
    of archaic *H. sapiens*, 426–427, 435–437
    of chimpanzees, 159
    of Cro-Magnons, 405, 460, 462
    disk-core technique in, 435–437
    early types of, 255–256
    of *H. erectus*, 328–336, 349, 353
    of hominids, 275–284
    Levallois technique, 427–428, 435, 437
    materials and techniques used in,
    276–280, 328–336
    Mousterian industry, 435–437, 440,
    460–461
    of Neandertals, 431, 432, 435–437
    significance of, 542–543
    of *Sinanthropus*, 307
    Solutrean laurel-leaf, 490–491, 498
    of Upper Paleolithic, 488, 490–493
Strata, 6, 7–9, 23–24
Stratigraphy, 23
Strauss, William, 415–416
Stringer, Christopher, 219, 253–254,
    405–406, 422, 447
Strum, Shirley, 134–135, 374
Successive creation doctrines, 10
Sugiyama, Yukimaru, 151, 159
Sumatra, 293–295
Sungir site, 509–510
Sunlight, skin adaptation and, 433–435,
    526–527
Suprainiac fossa, 414
Susman, Randall, 217, 219
Sussman, Robert, 100
Sutton, Walter, 54
Suwa, Gen, 251–253
Suzuki, David, 546
Swanscombe skull, 411–412, 464
Swartkrans cave, 207, 217–218, 219, 230,
    248, 312
Sweating, development of, 269, 350–352,
    432–433
Swisher, Carl, 319
Symons, Donald, 271
Sympathetic hunting magic, 499–500
Syntax, 376
Systema Naturae (Linnaeus), 87–88
Système des Animaux (Lamarck), 10

Szalatavus, 182

Tabūn site (Cave of the Oven), 409–411,
    437, 461
Taieb, Maurice, 240
Taiga site, 517
Tamarins, 101–102, 121
Tanzania, 127, 153, 155, 223, 408, 466. *See
    also specific sites*
Taphonomy, 20, 214
Tarahumara Indians, 353
Tarsiers, 93, 96, 99, 176, 177
Taung skull, 198–205, 219, 248, 301. *See
    also Australopithecus africanus*
Taxonomy, 89–90
Tay-Sachs disease, 77–78
Technology, 274–284, 520–521. *See also*
    Tools
Teeth. *See* Dentition
Teilhard de Chardin, 322
Temperature
    body, 268–269, 350–352, 390–391,
    432–433, 475
    climatic. *See* Climate
Terra Amata site, 336–337, 339, 354, 355,
    360, 426
Terrace, Herbert, 375
Territory, of primates, 141–146
Teshik-Tash site, 409, 445
Tetrads, 65
Thalassemia, 531
Theories, defined, 314
Theory of the Earth (Hutton), 7–8
Therianthropes, 501–502
Thermoluminescence dating, 27, 410, 479
Theropithecus oswaldi, 349
Thorium, in fossil dating, 27
Thymine, 59
Timor Trough, 478
Titi monkeys, 143
Tobias, Phillip, 215–216, 229, 238
Tools, 5–6, 165–166. *See also specific types*
    of *A. africanus*, 214–217
    antler, 307, 460, 488, 492
    of archaic *H. sapiens*, 402, 426–428,
    435–437, 459–462, 492
    bipedalism and, 266–267
    bone, 307, 439, 460, 488, 492
    brain development and, 280
    chimpanzee use of, 158–160, 266, 267, 274
    composite, 491–493
    of Cro-Magnons, 405, 460, 462
    of *H. erectus*, 328–336, 349, 353, 491, 492
    of *H. habilis*, 168, 228, 256, 280, 281
    hands and, 115
    of hominids, 257, 266–267, 274–284
    ivory, 460, 488, 492
    modern excavations of, 32
    of Neandertals, 431, 432, 435–437,
    460–462, 491

in occupation levels, 280–284
of *P. boisei*, 226, 256
of *P. robustus*, 217–218
of *Sinanthropus*, 307–308
specialization in, 491–493
stone. *See* Stone tools
of Upper Paleolithic, 460–462, 488, 490–493, 498
wooden, 275, 426
Toothcomb, 94
Torralba site, 338, 340, 343, 353
Toth, Nicholas, 277–278, 331–332, 335, 340, 345
Tracks, 27
Trade, 524–525
Transferrins, 31
Transfer RNA, 60–61
Transvaal hominid, 198–205, 223
artifacts of, 214–218
Broom's discoveries on, 205–214
Dart's discoveries on, 198–205
Tree dwelling. *See* Arboreality
Trevathan, Wenda, 271
Trivers, Robert, 519
True breeding, 38
Tschermak, Erick, 47
Tuffs, 25–26, 255
Tundra, 426, 429, 431–432, 437–440
Tunisia, 175
Turkana Lake, 231, 233–236, 237–240, 313–314. *See also* Koobi Fora site
Turner's syndrome, 74
Turnover pulse hypothesis, 286–287
Tylor, E. B., 167
Type specimens, 249

Uganda, 127
Ukraine, 507
Ultraviolet (UV) radiation, 526–527
Unearned resources, 481
Uniformitarianism, 10, 15
Upper Paleolithic, 437, 457, 463, 464, 481, 487–513
art and rituals of, 498–512
burial rites of, 509–511
fire mastery in, 488–489
fishing in, 496–497
hunting in, 493–496
sedentary lifestyle of. *See* Sedentism
shift from Middle Paleolithic, 460–461
tools of. *See under* Tools; *specific types*
weapons of, 494–496
Upper Perigordian, 507–508
Upright posture, 110–113. *See also* Bipedalism
in chimpanzees, 115
hand development and, 115
Uranium, in fossil dating, 24, 27, 410
Ussher, James (Archbishop of Armagh), 4, 15

Uzbekistan, 409, 445

Variability
factors affecting, 72–73
heredity and, 36–37, 45, 49
human, 526–540
in modern humans, 475
natural selection and, 74
outbreeding and, 80
Vegetarianism
in *P. robustus*, 207
in Transvaal hominid, 207
Velika Pečina site, 463
Venua, A., 318
Venus of Willendorf, 507, 509
Vértesszöllös, 412
Vervet monkeys, 142, 370–371, 373
Victoriapithecinae, 182
View to a Death in the Morning, A (Cartmill), 364–365
Viki (chimpanzee), 374–375, 376
Violence. *See* Aggression
Virchow, Rudolf, 400–401, 406
Viruses, 51
Vision, 113–115
color, 114–115, 353
diurnal, 101
human, 110, 114–115
of prosimians, 96–100
stereoscopic, 97–98, 114–115, 266
Visual predation theory, 99–100
Vitamin C, 494
Vitamin D, 434–435, 527
Vocalizations, 368–369, 370–371, 374. *See also* Speech
chimpanzee, 141, 383
Volcanic ash dating, 25, 27, 28–29, 227, 231, 232, 249, 250
von Koenigswald, G. H. R., 22, 308–309, 362
Vrba, Elisabeth, 214, 217, 286–287
Vygotskii, L., 389

Waddle, Diane, 468
Waddle and teeter bipedalism, 190
Walker, Alan, 236, 317, 318, 340, 356
Wallace, Alfred Russel, xvi, 3, 12–14, 15–16, 293–294, 393
Warfare, 160–161, 363
Washburn, Sherwood, 266–267, 273, 360, 374
Washoe (chimpanzee), 375–376
Watercraft, 480
Water supply, population growth and, 543
Watson, James D., 57, 58
Weapons. *See also* Tools; *specific weapons*
bipedalism and, 266

chimpanzee use of, 158–160
of modern humans, 478
of Upper Paleolithic, 494–496
Weidenreich, Franz, 305–309, 310
Weinberg, W., 77–78
Weirs, 497
Wells, H. G., 484
Wenzhong, Pei, 303
Wernicke's area, 317, 379, 381
West Africa, 127, 153, 155, 156–157, 159
Western Europe
archaic *H. sapiens* in, 463
cave art in, 521
Neandertals in, 397–406, 430–431, 460–461, 464
in Pleistocene glaciations, 430–431
tools found in, 490
in Upper Paleolithic, 490
in Upper Perigordian, 507–508
Whales, 229, 306–307, 386
Wheeler, Pete, 268–269
Whistle-and-grunt hypothesis, 368
White, Tim, 228, 243, 247–254, 273, 452
White blood cells, 532
Wide-knee stance, 188–189
Wilson, Allan, 30, 468–472
Wilson, Edward O., 519–520
Wolpoff, Milford, 317
Wolves, 9, 307, 368
Wood, Bernard, 219, 237, 238, 253, 260, 262
Woodruff, G., 389
Wood tools, 275, 426
Woodward, Arthur Smith, 321
Woolly rhinoceros, 432, 434
Wrangham, Richard, 157
Wright, Sewall, 48
Wynne-Edwards, V. C., 518

Xenophobia, 541
X-rays, genes and, 63
Xujiayao site, 409

Yerkes, Robert, 125
Yerkes Regional Primate Research Center, 125
Y–5 pattern (teeth), 103, 109

Zambia, 406, 466
Zebras, 307, 351, 493
Zhoukoudian site, 301–310, 322, 338, 340, 343, 355, 360–361, 362
Zinjanthropus boisei. *See Paranthropus boisei*
Zoological Evidences as to Man's Place in Nature (Huxley), 17
Zoos, as abnormal environments, 126
Zuckerman, Solly, 125, 136